IRISH HOTELS FEDERATION

Be Our Gu[illegible] Ir[illegible] 2010

Featuring almost 1,000 Hotels & Guesthouses

as well as details on Golfing,
Angling, Conferences & Meetings, Spa & Leisure
Facilities and extensive Touring Maps

IRISH HOTELS FEDERATION
13 Northbrook Road, Dublin 6, Ireland
Telephone +353 1 497 6459 Fax: +353 1 497 4613

When phoning Ireland from abroad, please use the following codes:
Republic of Ireland: 00 353 + local code (drop the 0). Northern Ireland: 00 44 + local code (drop the 0).
If dialling Northern Ireland directly from the Republic of Ireland replace the prefix code 028 with the code 048.
Please Contact Directory Enquiries in case of difficulty.

The Irish Hotels Federation does not accept any responsibility for errors, omissions or any information whatsoever in the Guide and members and users of the Guide are requested to consult page 11 hereof for further information.

Cover image - Curving mountain road following the rocky coastline on the Dingle Peninsula.

Design & Database published by NeoGen, www.neogen.ie - First Print.

CONTENTS

Contents

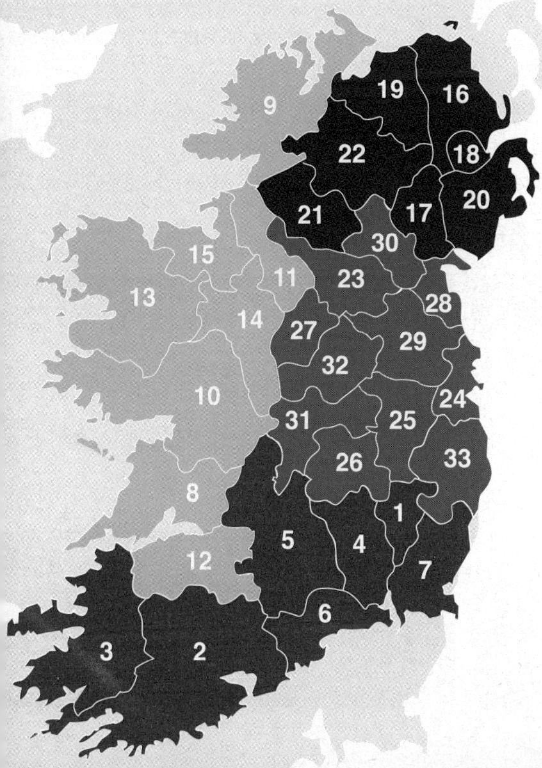

Regions

Begin by selecting the **Region(s)** you wish to visit. This guide divides into **4 separate Regions – Ireland South, Ireland West, Northern Ireland, Dublin & Ireland East** – and they are represented in that order.

Counties

Within each Region, Counties are presented alphabetically.

Locations – Cities, Towns, Villages

Within Counties, Locations are also presented alphabetically, see **Index to Locations** on Pages **14** & **15**.

Hotels & Guesthouses

Within Locations, Hotels and Guesthouses are also presented in alphabetical order, see **Index of Hotels and Guesthouses** on Pages **381** to **407**.

For further details on any of these symbols please contact the premises

- Total Number of Bedrooms, All En Suite unless otherwise stated
- Total Number of Bedrooms Without Bath/Shower & Toilet
- Lift/Elevator
- Can be Booked Through Travel Agent / Tourist Office and Commission Paid
- Child Friendly
- Garden for Visitors' Use
- Leisure Facilities
- Horse Riding/Pony Trekking on Site or Nearby
- Golf Course on Site
- Angling on Site or Nearby
- Car Parking
- Facilities for Pets
- Price Reduction for Senior Citizens excl. July/August and Subject to Availability
- Tea/Coffee Making Facilities in Bedroom
- Restaurant
- Wine Licence
- Licensed to Sell All Alcoholic Drink
- Internet Access
- Air Conditioning (Other than Conference Area)
- Guide Dogs Welcome

Food for Kids **Healthy Food For Kids**
See page 12 for details

Les Clefs d'Or Ireland
See page 13 for details

Eco Label Flower
European standard recognising exceptional environmental managment and performance

ACTIVITY SECTIONS

Green symbols Illustrated below denote that the hotel o guesthouse is included in a particular Activity Section. Detailed information on these Activities is shown on pages: 311 to 36

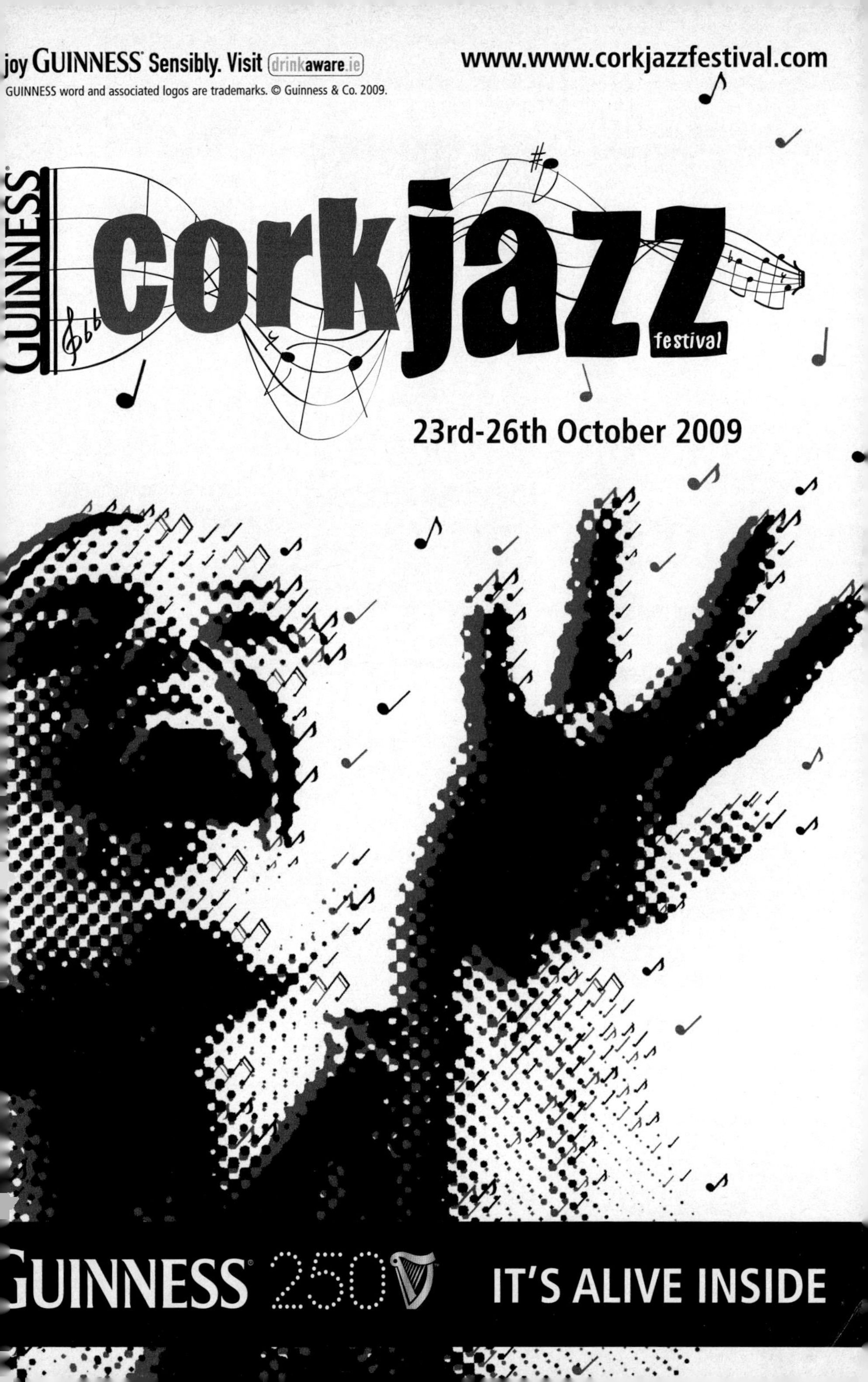
joy GUINNESS Sensibly. Visit drinkaware.ie
GUINNESS word and associated logos are trademarks. © Guinness & Co. 2009.
www.www.corkjazzfestival.com
GUINNESS
corkjazz
festival
23rd-26th October 2009
GUINNESS 250
IT'S ALIVE INSIDE

Guinness

SAMPLE ENTRY

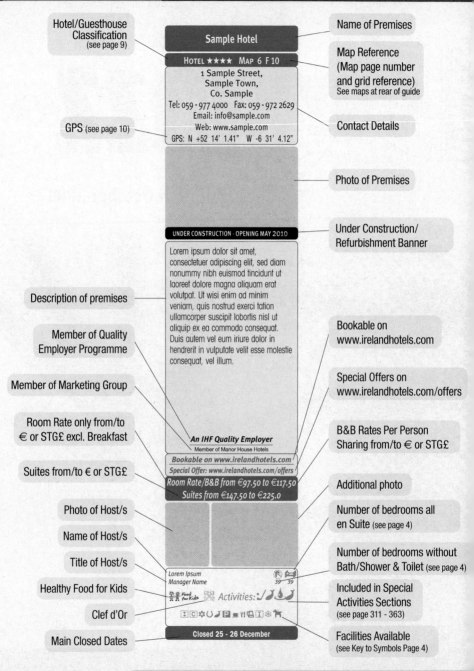

Hotel/Guesthouse Classification (see page 9)

Name of Premises

Map Reference (Map page number and grid reference) See maps at rear of guide

GPS (see page 10)

Contact Details

Sample Hotel

HOTEL ★★★★ MAP 6 F 10

1 Sample Street,
Sample Town,
Co. Sample
Tel: 059 - 977 4000 Fax: 059 - 972 2629
Email: info@sample.com
Web: www.sample.com
GPS: N +52 14' 1.41" W -6 31' 4.12"

Photo of Premises

UNDER CONSTRUCTION - OPENING MAY 2010

Under Construction/ Refurbishment Banner

Description of premises

Lorem ipsum dolor sit amet, consectetuer adipiscing elit, sed diam nonummy nibh euismod tincidunt ut laoreet dolore magna aliquam erat volutpat. Ut wisi enim ad minim veniam, quis nostrud exerci tation ullamcorper suscipit lobortis nisl ut aliquip ex ea commodo consequat. Duis autem vel eum iriure dolor in hendrerit in vulputate velit esse molestie consequat, vel illum.

Member of Quality Employer Programme

Member of Marketing Group

Bookable on www.irelandhotels.com

Special Offers on www.irelandhotels.com/offers

An IHF Quality Employer

Member of Manor House Hotels

Bookable on www.irelandhotels.com

Special Offer: www.irelandhotels.com/offers

Room Rate only from/to € or STG£ excl. Breakfast

B&B Rates Per Person Sharing from/to € or STG£

Suites from/to € or STG£

Room Rate/B&B from €97.50 to €117.50

Suites from €147.50 to €225.0

Photo of Host/s

Additional photo

Name of Host/s

Number of bedrooms all en Suite (see page 4)

Title of Host/s

Number of bedrooms without Bath/Shower & Toilet (see page 4)

Lorem Ipsum
Manager Name

39 39

Healthy Food for Kids

Food for Kids

Activities:

Included in Special Activities Sections (see page 311 - 363)

Clef d'Or

Facilities Available (see Key to Symbols Page 4)

Main Closed Dates

Closed 25 - 26 December

It is essential that when booking your accommodation you request the "Be Our Guest 2010" Rate

Our Guide features a broad selection of Irish Hotels and Guesthouses, from ultra modern buildings to stately Country Houses, luxurious Castles and old-world Inns. The majority of these Hotels and Guesthouses are members of the Irish Hotels Federation or the Northern Ireland Hotels Federation and we hope that the illustrations and descriptions of these premises and the amenities they offer will help you to choose the most suitable premises for your holiday.

All of the Hotels and Guesthouses featured in the Guide at the time of going to print (9th October 2009) have been registered, or are in the process of applying for registration by Fáilte Ireland or by the Northern Ireland Tourist Board, in accordance with the Statutory Registration Regulations which they administer.

B&B, ROOM AND SUITE RATES*

The only rates featured in this publication relate to either **a Bed & Breakfast Per Person Sharing, a Room Rate only or a Suite Rate.** These are **Guideline Rates**, please ensure that you contact the premises to verify the rates applicable to your reservation. **Supplements may be payable for suites* (see below) or superior/de luxe rooms. Also, where single or double/twin bedded rooms are occupied by one person, a supplement may be payable. Correspondingly, if more than two persons share a family room, special reduced rates may be arranged.**

***The definition of a Suite or Half Suite, broadly speaking, is:** The bedroom area must be either separate from the living area or clearly defined by an obvious divide i.e. a door or arch or different floor coverings e.g. carpet, tiles or wooden flooring. Please contact each premises to ascertain the exact definition of their suite(s).

Per Person Sharing: relates to the cost of Bed & Full Breakfast per Person per Night, on the basis of two persons occupying a Standard Double/Twin Bedded Room, most having private bath/shower.

Room Rate: relates to the cost of a Standard Room per Night. There may be a restriction on the number of persons allowed to share the room. It is advisable to check this when making your reservation.

Suites: relates to the cost of a Suite per Night. There may be a restriction on the number of persons allowed to share the suite. It is advisable to check this when making your reservation.

The rates range from minimum to maximum and are those generally in operation throughout the year, but may not apply during special occasions such as Public Holiday Weekends, Christmas and New Year, International Events, Major Festivals and Sporting Fixtures, or on such other occasions as individual premises may decide.

Rates are inclusive of Value Added Taxes at current (2009) rates and Services Charges (if any).
In the case of Hotels and Guesthouses in the Republic of Ireland, rates are quoted in **€ (Euro)**, whereas in Northern Ireland rates are quoted in **STG£**.

Special Offers: Many of the Hotels & Guesthouses featured in this guide offer great special offers. For more information visit **www.irelandhotels.com/offers.**

OPENING DATES FOR PREMISES UNDER CONSTRUCTION OR REFURBISHMENT

Some of the premises featured in the guide were not open at the guide print date (9th October 2009). The planned date of opening as supplied by these premises is displayed on the premises photograph.

EXPLANATION OF CLASSIFICATION (STAR RATING) SCHEME

Republic of Ireland

A mandatory **Hotel and Guesthouse Classification Scheme**, which was introduced during 2007, has been developed by Fáilte Ireland, in conjunction with the Irish Hotels Federation (IHF). This new classification scheme has been in place since 2009.

Hotels are rated from 1 Star to 5 Stars and Guesthouses are rated from 1 Star to 4 Stars. The stars are indicated on each entry under the Name of the Hotel or Guesthouse.

If the star rating is not shown, this means that the premises is perhaps undergoing a period of renovation or refurbishment and is awaiting its assessment for grading or, it was a late addition to the guide and missed the deadline for the inspection process. Where this is the case, the premises should be contacted directly for a classification update.

"Built to a 1/2/3/4/5 star specification": This is shown in the first line of description where premises are Under Construction and not yet opened at the time of going to print, but are due to open during 2010

or

where premises have not yet been registered by Fáilte Ireland

or

where premises have been registered prior to printing this guide, but have not yet been classified. This means that, although not yet formally inspected for their star grading, the premises has been built to the standards set out in the classification criteria and it is expected to reach this standard during the inspection visit.

As the new classification system is mandatory for all premises in the Republic of Ireland, their classification details must be displayed as outlined above.

The new classification criteria for each grade can be viewed and downloaded from **http://www.failteireland.ie/developing-enterprises/quality---standards/classification-scheme.aspx**

Please refer to Page 4 for the Explanation of Facilities/Key to Symbols shown at the end of each entry in order to review the services and facilities offered by individual premises. Further details of facilities and services available in each premises can be viewed on **www.discoverireland.ie**

Northern Ireland

All premises listed in the Northern Ireland section of this guide have been inspected and classified by Northern Ireland Tourist Board. Some premises are not currently classified. Please see page 29 for contact details.

GLOBAL POSITIONING SYSTEM

GPS in the **Be Our Guest Guide** is measured in Degrees Minutes and Seconds. An example of this would be:

N -53 17' 14.59" W -6 21' 58.97"

where N=North and W=West

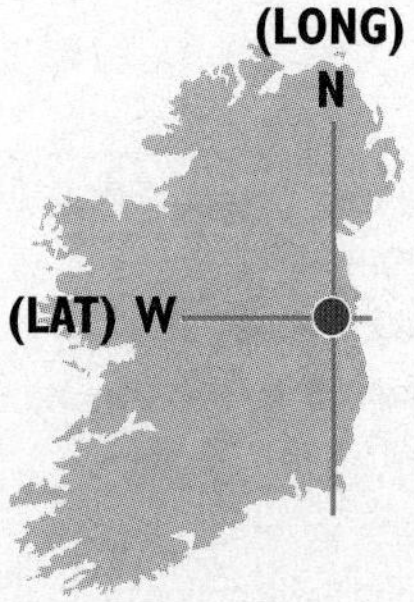

Input the co-ordinates shown for any hotel or guesthouse within the guide (shown above photo) into your SATNAV (satellite navigation system) to locate that property.

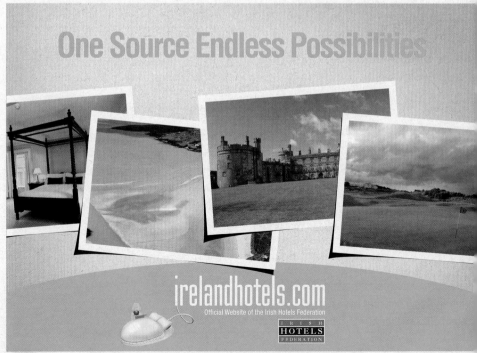

Reservations

Courtesy Onward Reservations

If you are moving around the country, the premises in which you are staying will be delighted to help you select your next accommodation from the Be Our Guest Guide and make your reservation.

The following are other ways in which a booking can be made:

1 Advance enquiries and reservations may be made directly to the premises by phone, fax, e-mail or letter and details of the reservation should be confirmed by both parties. A deposit should be forwarded if requested.

2 Book your accommodation online at:

irelandhotels.com
Official Website of the Irish Hotels Federation
One source
Endless possibilities
IRISH HOTELS FEDERATION

Irelandhotels.com features all premises listed in the Be Our Guest Guide.

www.irelandhotels.com

3 Some of the hotels and guesthouses in the Guide participate in a Central Reservations System which may be indicated in their entry.

4 Travel Agent - your travel agent will normally make a booking on your behalf without extra charge where the premises pays travel agents' commission (this is indicated by the symbol T in the Guide). In other cases, agents will usually charge a small fee to cover the cost of telephone calls and administration.

5 Some local tourist information offices listed in this guide (see pages 26-28) operate an enquiry and booking service and will make an accommodation reservation on your behalf.

Complaints

Should there be cause for complaint, the matter should be brought to the notice of the Management of the premises in the first instance. Failing satisfaction, the matter should be referred to the Tourist Information Office concerned (see list on pages 26-28) or Fáilte Ireland, Amiens Street, Dublin 1. In the case of Northern Ireland premises, complaints should be addressed to the Customer Relations Section, Northern Ireland Tourist Board, 59 North Street, Belfast BT1 1NB.

Errors And Omissions

The information contained in the accommodation section has been supplied by individual premises. While reasonable care has been taken in compiling the information supplied and ensuring its accuracy and compliance with consumer protection laws, the Irish Hotels Federation cannot accept any responsibility for any errors, omissions or misinformation regarding accommodation, facilities, prices, services, classification or any other information whatsoever in the Guide and shall have no liability whatsoever and howsoever arising to any person for any loss, whether direct, indirect, economic or consequential, or damages, actions, proceedings, costs, claims, expenses or demands arising therefrom. The listing of any premises in this guide is not and should not be taken as a recommendation from the IHF or a representation that the premises will be suitable for your purposes.

Think About Insurance

We strongly advise you to take out an insurance policy against accidents, cancellations, delays, loss of property and medical expenses. Such travel and holiday insurance policies are available quite cheaply and are worth every penny for peace of mind alone.

Cancellations

Should it be necessary to amend or cancel your reservation, please advise the premises immediately, as there may be a cancellation penalty. Please establish, when making a reservation, what cancellation policy applies.

Healthy Food For Kids Initiative

The Irish Hotels Federation's Healthy Food for Kids initiative was developed to guide and encourage hotels and guesthouses to provide healthier menu options for young diners. The initiative was launched in March 2008 by the IHF President, Matthew Ryan, and has generated great interest and support from the Irish Hotels Federation members. In excess of 260 establishments have committed to the programme and customer feedback has been excellent.

According to Matthew Ryan, everyone has a role to play in encouraging the promotion of healthy food to young people to assist in reducing the prevalence of obesity. This has been the first national hospitality programme of its kind which has aimed to constructively highlight the problems of childhood obesity. Feedback has been very positive and parents are enjoying the experience of seeing their children eating a tasty and healthy meal when dining in participating hotels and guesthouses.

The guidelines, which were compiled in conjunction with a prominent dietician, contain the correct balance of proteins and carbohydrates as deemed appropriate for an optimum healthy children's meal. The IHF guidelines also recommend cooking methods to ensure that whilst the food is nutritious, it remains tasty, attractive and fun for children.

Hotels and Guesthouses which are taking part in the programme are identifiable in the Be Our Guest Guide with the following logo

If you would like further details log on to **www.ihf.ie**

Spa Categories - www.discoverireland.ie/wellness

New Health & Wellness categorisation system launched by Failte Ireland. It is designed to help customers to better understand the variety of health and wellness offerings available to them.

Destination Spas - Set in an environment that is specifically devoted to health and wellness, their sole purpose is to offer a comprehensive full service wellness spa experience for overnight or day guests. On offer - private spa pool facilities, thermal wet spa experiences, weight loss, detox, a complete range of spa treatments and rituals.

Resort Spas - Offer a wide range of on-site leisure activities to enjoy along with a comprehensive range of spa treatments and rituals set in a hotel resort environment. Spa treatments, workshops and fitness facilities represent just some of the main activities on offer. Other on-site activities will typically include golf, equestrian and guided walking.

Hotel Spas - Offer a dedicated full service spa facility within the Hotel. The hotel spa is further sub divided into four categories; **Comprehensive, Extensive, Selective, Leisure Club. Specialised Retreats also feature.**

Hotel with Comprehensive Spa - This spa will be self-contained with a water immersion pool exclusive to spa guests only. Also on offer are thermal and wet spa experiences, relaxation room providing a complete range of spa facilities, treatments and spa rituals.

Hotel with Extensive Spa - Offers guests a carefully selected menu of spa services and treatments in a spa environment that is part of a wider hotel offering.

Hotel with Selective Spa - Offers guests a small but carefully selected variety of spa services and treatments in a spa environment.

Hotel with Leisure Club Spa - Offers guests carefully selected spa treatments. However, leisure pool, thermal and wet experiences may be shared with the leisure centre.

Specialised Retreats - Including **Thalassotherapy Resorts**, are dedicated to creating a well being experience.
Thalassotherapy Resort - Offers guests therapeutic marine based treatments using heated seawater, seaweed and mud. Guests visit for the sole purpose of enjoying therapeutic marine treatments and spa treatments.

Les Clefs d'Or Ireland - The Society of The Golden Keys of Ireland

Les Clefs d'Or is an international body of Professional Hotel Concierges. The Irish section was founded in 1957 and has been at the forefront of the international society ever since. Members of the society are distinguished by the golden crossed keys displayed on their lapels, a recognizable symbol held in the highest regard throughout the international hospitality industry. The organization welcomes those with the relevant experience to become members, however, a strict set of criteria are in place to ensure only the most dedicated Hotel Concierge may become a member of Les Clefs d'Or. Through the organization, members receive training and networking opportunities that would otherwise not be available to them. Combining a Les Clefs d'Or Concierge's wealth of knowledge with that of numerous colleagues - both at home and abroad - will impress the most discerning of guests. With a Les Clefs d'Or Concierge at the helm, hotel management can rest assured that guests are receiving the best possible care and attention. For further information on Les Clefs d'Or Ireland and information on how to apply for membership see **www.lesclefsdorireland.com**
In Service, through Friendship.

Matthew Ryan

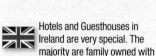

Matthew Ryan
President, Irish Hotels Federation

Ní haon ní coitianta é an Óstlann nó an Teach Lóistín in Éirinn. Is i seilbh teaghlaigh iad a bhformhór acu agus bíonn an t-úinéir agus baill den teaghlach romhat chun fáilte Uí Cheallaigh a chur romhat. Fiú nuair is le comhlacht iad, nó is cuid de ghrúpa iad, baineann meon agus atmaisféar áitreabh teaghlaigh leo – áiteanna ina gcuirfí fíorchaoin fáilte romhat.

Rud ar leith is ea an óstlann in Éirinn agus is dócha ná a mhalairt go bhfeidhmíonn sí mar lárionad sóisialta don phobal. Cuireann an óstlann i bhfad níos mó ná leaba agus béile ar fáil - is lárionad sóisialta,a siamsaíochta, gnó agus pobail ar fheabhas í chomh maith agus gach aon áis faoin spéir aici, a chuireann bia, lóistín, imeachtaí spóirt, áiseanna siamsíochta agus só agus tarraingtí nach iad ar fáil.

Agus tú ag taisteal timpeall na tíre gheobhaidh tú amach go mbeidh "**Bí i d'Aoi Againn**" an-áisiúil agus an chéad suíomh eile á roghnú agat. Is mian le hóstlannaithe agus le lucht tithe lóistín na hÉireann fáilte a chur romhat agus a bheith in ann a dheimhniú go mbainfidh tú sult as do sheal in Éirinn. Tá súil againn go bhfanfaidh tú linn agus go mbainfidh tú leas as an treoir seo chun do rogha óstlann nó teach lóistin a aimsiú, i dtreo is go mbeimid in ann a rá leat go pearsanta -

Be Our Guest

Hotels and Guesthouses in Ireland are very special. The majority are family owned with the proprietor and members of the family there to welcome guests and to extend to them renowned Irish hospitality. Even when they are owned by a company, or are part of a group, they still retain the character and ambience of a family premises - a place where you will be truly welcome.

The Irish hotel is unique, in that more often than not, it acts as a social centre for the community. Hotels offer a lot more than just a bed and a meal - they are fully fledged social, leisure, business and community centres with every imaginable facility and amenity, providing food, accommodation, sports, leisure facilities, entertainment and other attractions.

If you are moving around the country, you'll find that the "**Be Our Guest**" guide is an invaluable help in choosing your next location.

Ireland's hoteliers and guesthouse owners want to welcome you and want to play their part in ensuring that your stay in Ireland is a happy one. We hope that you will stay with us and that you will use this guide to select the hotel or guesthouse of your choice, so that we can personally invite you to -

Be Our Guest

Les hôtels et les pensions en Irlande sont d'un caractère particulier. Ils sont très souvent gérés par le propriétaire et des membres de sa famille, présents pour accueillir les visiteurs et leur faire découvrir la célèbre hospitalité irlandaise. Même s'ils appartiennent à une entreprise ou font partie d'un groupe de sociétés, ils possèdent toujours ce caractère et cette ambiance des lieux familiaux - un endroit où vous serez sincèrement bien accueillis.

L'hôtel irlandais est unique en ce qu'il joue très souvent le rôle de centre social pour la communauté. Les hôtels offrent beaucoup plus qu'un lit et un repas - ce sont, pour la communauté, de véritables centres sociaux, de loisirs et d'affaires, équipés de toutes les infrastructures et installations imaginables. Ils vous proposent le gîte et le couvert, mais aussi activités sportives et de loisir, divertissements et autres attractions.

Si vous voyagez dans le pays, vous trouverez que le guide "**Be Our Guest**" est d'une aide précieuse pour vous aider à choisir votre prochaine destination.

Les hôteliers et les propriétaires de pensions irlandais veulent vous accueillir et être là pour vous assurer un séjour agréable en Irlande. Nous espérons que vous resterez avec nous et que vous utiliserez ce guide pour sélectionner l'hôtel ou la pension de votre choix, afin que nous ayons le plaisir de vous compter parmi nos visiteurs -

Be Our Guest

Die Hotels und Pensionen in Irland sind von ganz besonderer Art. Zum größten eil handelt es sich dabei um private amilienbetriebe, in denen der Besitzer nd die Familienmitglieder ihre Gäste nit der vielgerühmten irischen astfreundschaft willkommen heißen. ber auch wenn sich diese Häuser in nternehmensbesitz befinden oder einer ette angehören, strahlen sie dennoch en Charakter und die Atmosphäre von amilienbetrieben aus - ein Ort, an dem ie immer herzlich willkommen sind.

otels in Irland sind einzig in ihrer Art nd dienen oftmals als Mittelpunkt eselliger Treffen. Hotels haben viel ehr zu bieten als nur ein Bett und eine ahlzeit - sie sind Gesellschafts-, eizeit-, Geschäfts- und öffentlicher effpunkt mit allen nur erdenklichen nrichtungen und Annehmlichkeiten, ngefangen bei Essen, Unterkunft, port und Freizeitmöglichkeiten s zur Unterhaltung und anderen nziehungspunkten.

uf Ihren Reisen im Land werden Sie ststellen, daß Ihnen der "**Be Our uest**"-Führer eine wertvolle Hilfe bei er Suche nach der nächstgelegenen nterkunft leistet.

ands Hotel und Pensionsbesitzer eißen Sie gerne willkommen und öchten ihren Anteil dazu beitragen, aß Ihnen Ihr Aufenthalt in Irland in ngenehmer Erinnerung bleibt. Wir offen, daß Sie uns besuchen werden d diesen Führer bei der Auswahl Ihres otels oder Ihrer Pension zu Rate ehen, so daß wir Sie persönlich llkommen heißen können -

Be Our Guest

Los hoteles y las pensiones en Irlanda son muy especiales. La mayoría son propiedades familiares habitadas por el mismo propietario junto a los miembros de su familia que se encuentran predispuestos a dar la bienvenida a los huéspedes y, de este modo, contribuir a ampliar su reconocida hospitalidad irlandesa. Incluso si pertecen a una compañía o forman parte de un grupo, siempre mantendrán el carácter y ambiente de las propiedades familiares, un lugar donde siempre serás bienvenido de corazón.

El hotel irlandés es único y se comporta bastante a menudo como el mismo centro social de la comunidad. Estos hoteles ofrecen algo más que una cama y comida, rebozan de centros sociales comunitarios de ocio y negocios con una amplia gama de servicios inimaginables. Ofrece comida, alojamiento, deportes, actividades de ocio, entretenimiento y todo tipo de atracciones.

Si te encuentras viajando por nuestro país, te darás cuenta que la ayuda que te ofrece "**Be Our Guest**", a la hora de elegir tu próximo destino, no tiene precio. Los hoteleros y propietarios de pensiones de Irlanda quieren darte la bienvenida y quieren contribuir a que tu estancia en Irlanda sea una estancia feliz. Esperamos que te quedes con nosotros y que utilices esta guía para elegir el hotel o pensión que tú elijas y para que nosotros podamos invitarte personalmente a ser nuestro invitado, el invitado de -

Be Our Guest

Gli hotel e le pensioni in Irlanda sono davvero speciali. Molti sono a conduzione familiare, e gli ospiti vengono accolti dai proprietari e le loro famiglie secondo le famose tradizioni di ospitalità irlandesi. Il calore e l'ambiente intimo e accogliente si ritrovano persino negli hotel delle grandi compagnie e catene alberghiere: avrete sempre la sensazione di essere ospiti graditi.

Una caratteristica unica degli hotel irlandesi è che, molto spesso, fungono anche da centro di aggregazione della comunità. Gli alberghi offrono molto di più di un letto e dei pasti: sono centri per socializzare, divertirsi, fare affari e vivere la dimensione locale. Qui si può trovare ogni attrezzatura e comfort immaginabile: ristoranti, alloggi, impianti sportivi, attività ricreative, divertimento e tante altre attrazioni.

Se prevedete molti spostamenti, scoprirete in "**Be Our Guest**" uno strumento di valore inestimabile per la scelta delle prossime mete. Gli albergatori e i proprietari delle pensioni irlandesi vi aspettano per darvi il benvenuto e fare la loro parte per rendere piacevole il vostro soggiorno in Irlanda. Ci auguriamo che vogliate viaggiare con noi, usando la nostra guida per scegliere un hotel o una pensione di vostro gusto, così da potervi invitare personalmente a -

Be Our Guest

Republic of Ireland

The **ABLE Tourism Awards scheme** has been developed by Rehab and EIQA in conjunction with Fáilte Ireland and ensures an accessible environment for customers and staff with disabilities.

Contact Details:

Rehab: Tel: 01 205 7315 **Email:** ableawards@rehab.ie **Web:** www.able.ie

Note: Many premises have the following at the end of their description: '**Please enquire about Facilities for Persons with Disabilities**'. This is an indication of some accessibility. However, it is essential to ascertain details from the premises.

Northern Ireland

No official approval system is currently in place. Therfore, we would advise that you contact the Hotel o Guesthouse directly in order to confirm the status of their accessibility for disabled persons.

Further information may also be available from:

Northern Ireland Tourist Board, 59 North Street, Belfast, BT1 1NB

Tel: +44 28 9023 1221 **Fax:** +44 28 9024 0960

or

Disability Action Northern Ireland

Tel: +44 28 9029 7880 **Fax:** +44 28 9029 7881 **Email:** hq@disabilityaction.org

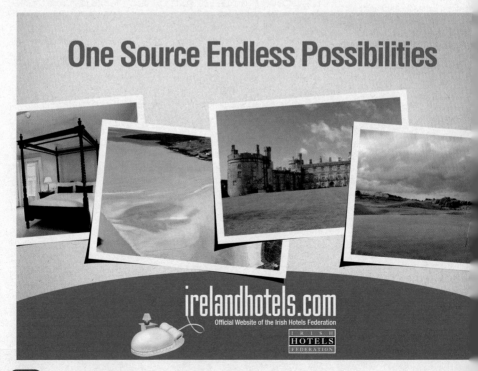

Language

Irish (Gaelic) and English are the two official languages of the Republic of Ireland and street and road signs are all bilingual. In Gaeltacht areas Irish is spoken daily, however English is spoken by everyone. In Northern Ireland, English is the official language. The Irish Language, Gaelic, is also taught in many schools, and summer schools. Ulster Scots, spoken in Northern Ireland, is on the increase and is being taught to those who are keen to explore another facet of their national identity.

Currency

The Euro is the local currency of the Republic of Ireland. One Euro consists of 100 cent. Notes are €5, €10, €20, €50, €100, €200 and €500. Coins are 1c, 2c, 5c, 10c, 20c, 50c, €1 and €2.

In Northern Ireland (as in the rest of the United Kingdom), Sterling is the local currency. Stg£1 consists of 100 pence. The notes consist of £5, £10, £20, £50 and £100. The coins are 1p, 2p, 5p, 10p, 20p, 50p, £1 & £2.

The Currencies of the Republic of Ireland and Northern Ireland are not interchangeable.

Regulations for under 21 year olds in bars

In the Republic of Ireland the Liquor Licensing Hours provide that persons under the age of 18 are not allowed in the bar areas of licensed premises (including hotels and guesthouses) after 9.00 p.m. (10.00 p.m. May to September). Persons aged 18 – 21 are required to produce evidence of age in order to be allowed enter or remain in the bar area of licensed premises (including hotels) after 9.00 pm. The acceptable evidence of age may be one of the following: Garda Age Card, a Passport or Identity Card of a EU Member State, a Driver's Licence.

Emergency numbers

In case of emergency, please ring 999 or 112.
The Irish Tourist Assistance Service (ITAS) is a free nationwide service offering support and assistance to tourists who are victims of crime while visiting the Republic of Ireland.
Website: www.itas.ie and email: info@itas.ie.
ITAS is also contactable via Garda (police) stations.

Prohibition on smoking

In order to combat the damage to health caused by tobacco smoke and to provide an environment of smoke free air, the Government of the Republic of Ireland introduced, early in 2004, a total ban on smoking in the workplace (indoors). This means that smoking is not permitted in all enclosed areas of hotels and guesthouses with the exception of hotel and guesthouse bedrooms. However the proprietor is not legally obliged to offer any smoking bedrooms and may choose to provide a totally smoke-free environment.

Driving

Visitors should be in possession of either; a valid full national driving licence, or an international driving permit issued abroad. These are readily available from motoring organisations in the country of origin. If planning to bring your car to Ireland, advise your insurance company before travelling.

Driving in Ireland is on the left and seat belts must be worn at all times in the front and the back of the vehicle; likewise, motorcyclists and their passengers must wear helmets. There are very strict laws on drinking and driving and the best advise is simply 'don't drink and drive'.

In both the Republic of Ireland and Northern Ireland, speed limits are 30-50kmph/20-30mph in built-up urban areas, 100kmph/60mph on the open road and 120kmph/75mph on the motorway.

In the Republic of Ireland, the majority of signposts denoting distance are now in kilometres and speed limits are denoted in kilometres per hour. All signposts and place names are displayed bilingually in both Irish (Gaelic) and English.

In Northern Ireland, all signposts and speed limits are in miles and place names are displayed in the English language.

Driving Association in Ireland:

The Automobile Association (AA), Tel: 01 617 9977 or visit www.aaireland.ie

KILLIMER**TARBERT**FERRY

From Killimer, Co. Clare *Sailing on the hour*

		First	Last
Apr to Sept	Monday–Saturday	07.00H	21.00H
	Sundays	09.00H	21.00H
Oct to Mar	Monday–Saturday	07.00H	19.00H
	Sundays	09.00H	19.00H

From Tarbert, Co. Kerry *Sailing on the half hour*

		First	Last
Apr to Sept	Monday–Saturday	07.30H	21.30H
	Sundays	09.30H	21.30H
Oct to Mar	Monday–Saturday	07.30H	19.30H
	Sundays	09.30H	19.30H

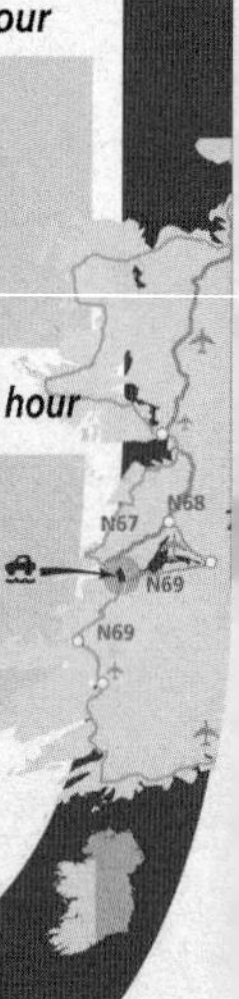

Bridging the best of Ireland's West

- Over 30 sailings a day
- Sailings everyday of the year except Christmas Day
- The direct route to and from Kerry and Clare
- Visitor Centre, Shop, Restaurant

June to September, Two ferries operate between 10.00 & 18.00 from Killimer and 10.30 & 18.30 from Tarbert, providing additional half-hourly service.

T 065-905 3124. F 065-905 3125. E enquiries@shannonferries.com www.shannonferries.com

SHANNON**FERRY** GROUP

One Source Endless Possibilities

irelandhotels.com

Official Website of the Irish Hotels Federation

IRISH HOTELS FEDERATION

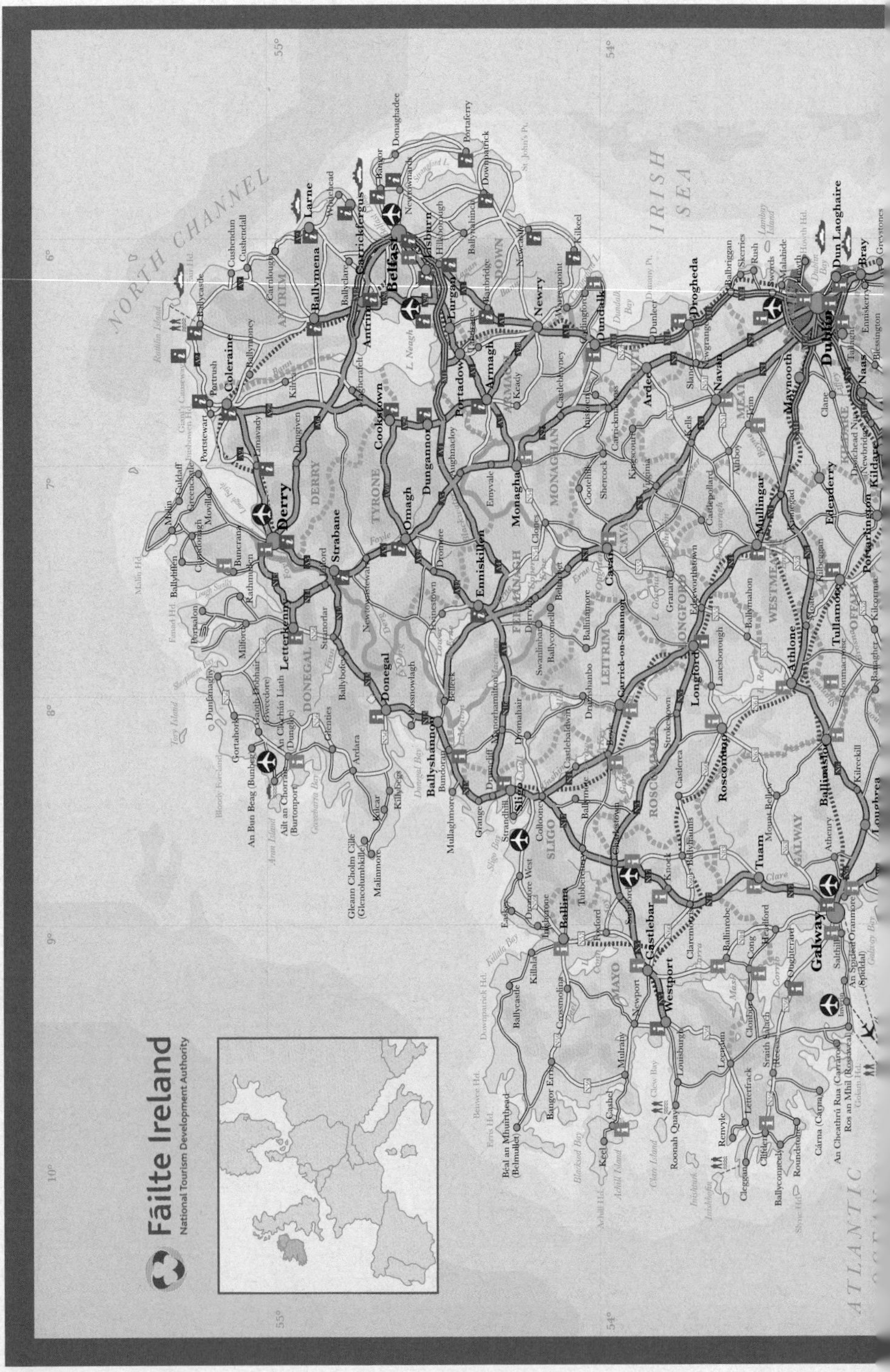
Fáilte Ireland
National Tourism Development Authority

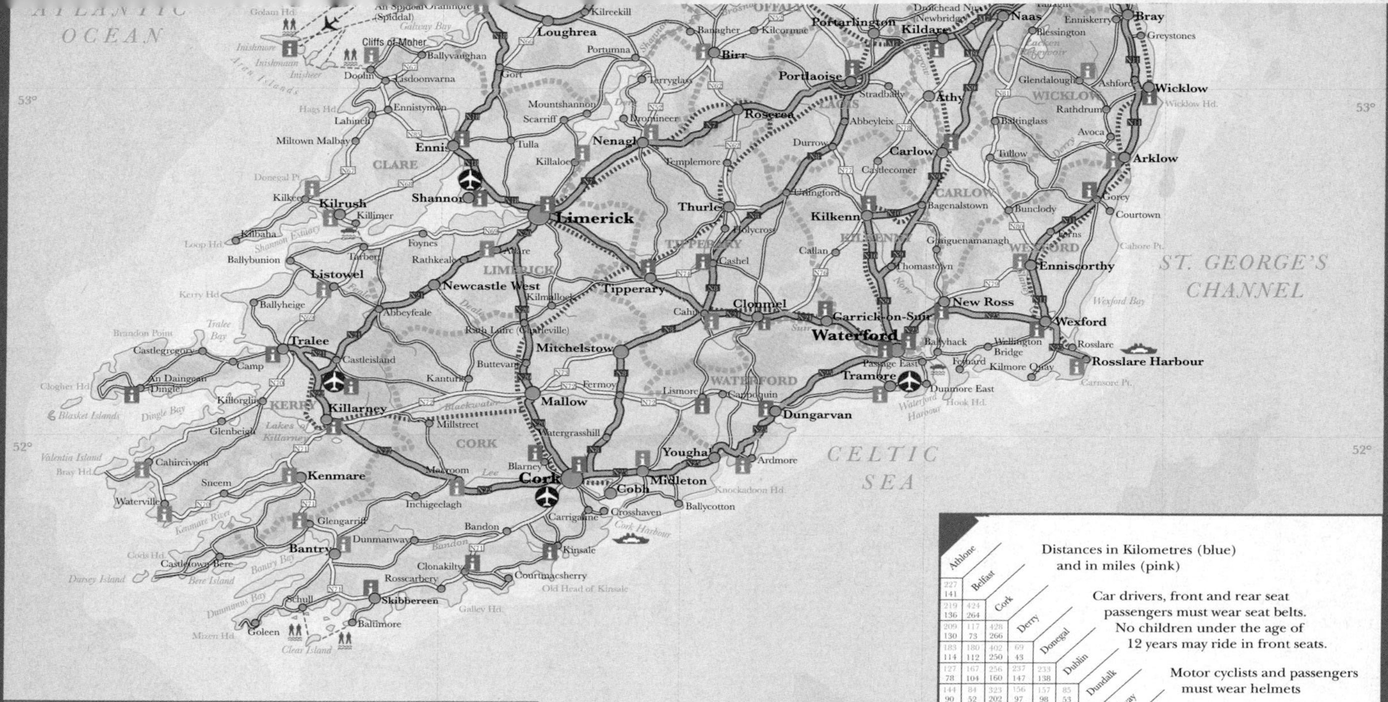

Motorways		Coastal Sandy Beach	
Motorways (under construction)		Airports	
National Primary Routes	N	International Car Ferry	
National Secondary Routes	N71	Local Car / Passenger Ferry	
Other Routes (selected)		Tourist Information Offices (all year)	
Railways		Tourist Information Offices (seasonal)	
County Boundary			
Northern Ireland Border			

KILOMETRES 0 20 40 60 80km

MILES 0 10 20 30 40 50mls

Whilst every care has been taken to ensure accuracy in the compilation of this map, Fáilte Ireland cannot accept responsibility for errors or omissions.

Because of the small scale of this map, not all holiday centres can be shown. The information on this map is correct at the time of going to press.

Distances in Kilometres (blue) and in miles (pink)

	Athlone	Belfast	Cork	Derry	Donegal	Dublin	Dundalk	Galway	Kilkenny	Killarney	Limerick	Roscommon	Rosslare Harbour	Shannon Airport	Sligo	Waterford
Belfast	227 / 141															
Cork	219 / 136	424 / 264														
Derry	209 / 130	117 / 73	428 / 266													
Donegal	183 / 114	180 / 112	402 / 250	69 / 43												
Dublin	127 / 78	167 / 104	256 / 160	237 / 147	233 / 138											
Dundalk	144 / 90	84 / 52	323 / 202	156 / 97	157 / 98	85 / 53										
Galway	93 / 58	306 / 190	209 / 130	272 / 169	204 / 127	212 / 136	237 / 148									
Kilkenny	116 / 78	284 / 177	148 / 92	335 / 208	309 / 192	114 / 73	197 / 123	172 / 107								
Killarney	232 / 144	436 / 271	87 / 54	441 / 274	407 / 253	304 / 192	350 / 219	193 / 120	198 / 123							
Limerick	121 / 75	323 / 201	105 / 65	328 / 204	296 / 184	193 / 123	242 / 150	104 / 65	113 / 70	111 / 69						
Roscommon	32 / 20	224 / 139	251 / 156	211 / 131	151 / 94	156 / 91	151 / 94	80 / 51	158 / 98	264 / 164	149 / 94					
Rosslare Harbour	201 / 130	330 / 205	208 / 129	397 / 247	391 / 243	153 / 101	245 / 153	274 / 170	98 / 62	275 / 171	211 / 131	241 / 150				
Shannon Airport	133 / 83	346 / 215	128 / 80	351 / 218	282 / 176	218 / 138	264 / 165	93 / 57	135 / 85	135 / 84	25 / 15	154 / 96	234 / 146			
Sligo	117 / 73	206 / 128	336 / 209	135 / 84	66 / 41	214 / 135	166 / 104	138 / 86	245 / 152	343 / 213	232 / 144	85 / 53	325 / 203	218 / 136		
Waterford	164 / 108	333 / 207	126 / 78	383 / 238	357 / 222	163 / 98	242 / 151	220 / 137	48 / 30	193 / 120	129 / 80	208 / 129	82 / 51	152 / 95	293 / 182	
Wexford	184 / 117	309 / 192	187 / 116	378 / 235	372 / 231	135 / 88	226 / 141	253 / 157	80 / 50	254 / 158	190 / 118	222 / 138	19 / 12	213 / 133	307 / 191	61 / 39

Car drivers, front and rear seat passengers must wear seat belts. No children under the age of 12 years may ride in front seats.

Motor cyclists and passengers must wear helmets

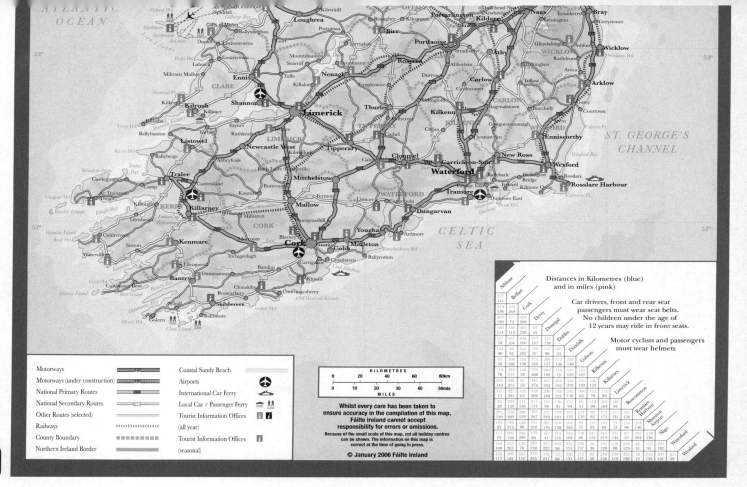

Adare
The Heritage Centre
Tel: 061 396255
Email:
touristofficeadare@shannondev.ie

Antrim
16 High Street
Tel: 028-9442 8331
Email: info@antrim.gov.uk

Aran Islands
Oifig Fáilte, Kilronan,
Inis Mór, Co. Na Gaillimhe
Tel: 099-61263
Fax: 099-61420
Email: aran@failteireland.ie

Armagh
40 English Street
Tel: 028-3752 1800
Email: tic@armagh.gov.uk

Ballycastle
7 Mary Street
Tel: 028-2076 2024
Email: tourism@moyle-council.org

Ballymena
The Braid, 1-29 Bridge Street,
Tel: 028-2565 7161
Email:
tourist.information@ballymena.gov.uk

Ballymoney
Ballymoney Town Hall,
1 Townhead Street, Ballymoney
Tel: 028-2766 0230
Email:
touristinfo@ballymoney.gov.uk

Banbridge
200 Newry Road
Tel: 028-4062 3322
Email: tic@banbridge.gov.uk

Bangor
34 Quay Street
Tel: 028-9127 0069
Email: tic@northdown.gov.uk

Belfast
47 Donegall Place
Tel: 028-9024 6609
Email:
welcomecentre@belfastvisitor.com
Also George Best, Belfast City Airport Arrivals Hall & **Belfast International Airport** Arrivals Hall

Bundoran
Main Street
Tel: 071-984 1350
Email: bundoran@failteireland.ie

Carlow
College Street
Tel: 059-913 1554
Fax: 059-917 0776
Email: carlow@failteireland.ie

Carrickfergus
Museum & Civic Centre,
Antrim Street
Tel: 028-9335 8049
Email: touristinfo@carrickfergus.org

Clonakilty
Ashe Street
Tel: 023-883 3226
Email: clonakiltytio@failteireland.ie

Coleraine
Railway Road
Tel: 028-7034 4723
Email: info@northcoastni.com

Cookstown
The Burnavon, Burn Road
Tel: 028-8676 9949
Email: tic@cookstown.gov.uk

Cork Airport
Arrivals Hall, Cork Airport, Co. Cork
Tel: 028-483 8018
Email: airporttio@failteireland.ie

Cork City
Grand Parade
Tel: 021-425 5100
Fax: 021-425 5199
Email: corkkerryinfo@failteireland.ie

Derry
44 Foyle Street
Tel: 028-7126 7284
Email: info@derryvisitor.com

Dingle
The Quay
Tel: 066-915 1188
Fax: 066-915 1270
Email: dingletio@failteireland.ie

Donegal Town
The Quay
Tel: 074-972 1148
Fax: 074-972 2762
Email: donegal@failteireland.ie

Downpatrick
St. Patrick's Centre,
53A Market Street
Tel: 028-4461 2233
Email:
downpatrick.tic@downdc.gov.uk

Dublin
Dublin City - Suffolk Street,
O'Connell Street
Dublin Airport - Arrivals Hall,
Dun Laoghaire - Ferry Terminal
For information and reservations please visit www.visitdublin.com or contact Dublin Reservations Freephone
Tel: 1850 230 330 / 1800 363 626

Dungannon / Killymaddy
190, Ballygawley Road (off A4)
Tel: 028-8776 7259
Email:
killymaddy.reception@dungannon.gov.uk

Dundalk
Jocelyn Street
Tel: 042-933 5484
Fax: 042-933 8070
Email: dundalk@failteireland.ie

Dungarvan
The Courthouse
Tel: 058-41741
Email: info@dungarvantourism.com

Ennis
Arthur's Row
Tel: 065 682 8366
Email:
touristofficeennis@shannondev.ie

Enniskillen
Wellington Road
Tel: 028-6632 3110
Email: tic@fermanagh.gov.uk

Galway
Aras Fáilte, Forster Street
Galway City
Tel: 091-537700
Fax: 091-537733
Email:
irelandwestinfo@failteireland.ie
www.discoverireland.ie/west

Giant's Causeway
Causeway Road, Bushmills
Tel: 028-2073 1855
Email:
info@giantscausewaycentre.com

Hillsborough
The Square
Tel: 028-9268 9717
Email:
tic.hillsborough@lisburn.gov.uk

Kildare Town
Heritage Centre
Tel: 045-521240

Kilkeel
The Nautilus Centre, Rooney Road
Tel: 028-4176 2525
Email: kdakilkeel@hotmail.com

Kilkenny
Shee Alms House
Tel: 056-775 1500
Fax: 056-776 3955
Email: kilkenny@failteireland.ie

Killarney
Beech Road
Tel: 064-663 1633
Fax: 064-663 4506
Email: killarneytio@failteireland.ie

Kinsale
Pier Road
Tel: 021-477 2234
Email: kinsaletio@failteireland.ie

Larne
Narrow Gauge Road
Tel: 028-2826 0088
Email:
larnetourism@btconnect.com

Letterkenny
Neil T Blaney Road
Tel: 074-912 1160
Fax: 074-912 5180
Email: letterkenny@failteireland.ie

Limavady
7 Connell Street
Tel: 028-7776 0307
Email: tourism@limavady.gov.uk

Limerick City
Arthur's Quay
Tel: 061 317 522
Email:
touristofficelimerick@shannondev.ie

Lisburn
Lisburn Square
Tel: 028-9266 0038
Email: tic.lisburn@lisburn.gov.uk

Magherafelt
The Bridwell, 6 Church Street
Tel: 028-7963 1510
Email:
thebridewell@magherafelt.gov.uk

Mullingar
Tel: 044-934 8650
Fax: 044-934 0413
Email: mullingar@failteireland.ie

Newcastle (Co. Down)
10-14 Central Promenade
Tel: 028-4372 2222
Email:
newcastle.tic@downdc.gov.uk

Newgrange
Bru na Boinne Tourist Office
Donore, Co. Meath
Tel: 041-988 0305
Email: brunaboinne@failteireland.ie

Newry City
Bagenal's Castle,
Castle Street, Newry
Tel: 028-3031 3170
Email:
newrytic@newryandmourne.gov.uk

Newtownards
31 Regent Street
Tel: 028-9182 6846
Email: tourism@ards-council.gov.uk

Omagh
Strale Arts Centre,
Townhall Square, Omagh
Tel: 028-8224 7831
Email: tourism@omagh.gov.uk

Oranmore
Co. Galway
Tel: 091 790811
Fax: 091 790187
Email: oranmore@iol.ie

Oughterard
Main Street, Oughterard, Co. Galway
Tel: 091 552808
Fax: 091 552811
Email: oughterardoffice@eircom.net
www.connemarabegins.com

Shannon Airport
Arrivals Hall
Tel: 061 471 664
Email:
touristofficeshannon@shannondev.ie

Skibbereen
North Street
Tel: 028-21766
Fax: 028-21353
Email: skibbereen@failteireland.ie

Sligo
Temple Street
Tel: 071-916 1201
Fax: 071-916 0360
Email: northwestinfo@failteireland.ie

Strabane
Alley Arts & Conference Centre,
1A Railway Street,
Strabane
Tel: 028-7138 4444
Email: tic@strabanedc.com

Tralee
Ashe Memorial Hall
Tel: 066-712 1288
Fax: 066-712 1700
Email: traleetio@failteireland.ie

Waterford City
The Quay
Tel: 051-875823
Fax: 051-876720
Email:
waterfordtouristoffice@failteireland.ie

Westport
James Street, Westport
Co. Mayo
Tel: 098-25711
Fax: 098-26709
Email: westport@failteireland.ie
www.discoverireland.ie/west

Wexford
The Quay Front
Tel: 053-9123111
Fax: 053-9141743
Email:
wexfordtouristoffice@failteireland.ie

Wicklow
Fitzwilliam Square
Tel: 0404-69117
Fax: 0404-69118
Email: wicklow@failteireland.ie

FÁILTE IRELAND
NATIONAL TOURISM DEVELOPMENT AUTHORITY

www.discoverireland.ie

IRELAND
Dublin
Fáilte Ireland,
Amiens Street, Dublin 1
Tel: 01 - 602 4000
Fax: 01 - 602 4100

NORTHERN IRELAND
Belfast
Fáilte Ireland,
53 Castle Street, Belfast BT1 1GH
Tel: 028 - 9026 5500
Email: infob@failteireland.ie

Derry
Fáilte Ireland,
44 Foyle Street, Derry BT48 6AT
Tel: 028 - 7136 9501
Email: failteireland@derryvisitor.com

**If dialling Northern Ireland directly from the Republic of Ireland the code 048 followed by the telephone number is sufficient.*

NORTHERN IRELAND TOURIST BOARD
www.discovernorthernireland.com

Belfast
Northern Ireland Tourist Board,
59 North Street, Belfast BT1 1NB
Tel: 028 - 9023 1221
Fax: 028 - 9024 0960

Dublin
Northern Ireland Tourist Board,
Tourist Information Centre,
Suffolk Steet, Dublin 2
Tel: 01 - 605 7732
Fax: 01 - 605 7725

TOURISM IRELAND – EUROPE
www.discoverireland.com

Austria
Simone Korb, Tourism Ireland,
Argentinierstr. 2/4, 1040 Wien, Austria
Tel: 581 89 22 70
Email: skorb@tourismireland.com
Web: www.discoverireland.com

Belgium/Luxembourg
Tourism Ireland,
Avenue Louise 66, Louizalaan,
1050 Brussels
Tel: 02 - 275 0171
Email: info.be@tourismireland.com
Web: www.ireland-tourism.be

Britain-London
Tourism Ireland, Nations House,
103 Wigmore Street, London WIU 1QS
Tel: 0808 234 2009 (Call Centre)
Email: info.gb@tourismireland.com
Web: www.discoverireland.com

Britain-Glasgow
Tourism Ireland,
James Miller House,
98 West George Street, (7th Floor),
Glasgow G2 1PJ
Tel: 0808 234 2009
Email: infoglasgow@tourismireland.com
Web: www.discoverireland.com

France
Tourisme Irlandais,
33 Rue de Miromesnil,
75008 Paris
Tel: 01 - 70 20 00 20
Email: info.fr@tourismireland.com
Web: www.irlande-tourisme.fr

Germany
Tourism Ireland,
Gutleutstrasse 32, D-60329
Frankfurt am Main
Tel: 069 668 00950
Email: info.de@tourismireland.com
Web: www.discoverireland.com/de

Italy
Turismo Irlandese,
Piazza Cantore 4,
20123 Milano
Tel: 02 - 4829 6060
Email:
informazioni@tourismireland.com
Web: www.discoverireland.com/it

The Netherlands
Tourism Ireland,
Spuistraat 104,
1012 VA Amsterdam
Tel: 020 - 504 0689
Email: info@ierland.nl
Web: www.ierland.nl

Nordic Region
Tourism Ireland,
Nyhavn 16, (3rd Floor),
DK 1051 Copenhagen K,
Denmark
Tel: 80 60 15 18
Email: info.nordic@tourismireland.com
Web: www.discoverireland.com

Finland Tel: 0800 41 969
Norway Tel: 800 35 018
Sweden Tel: 02 0015 9101

Spain
Tourism Ireland,
Paseo de la Castellana 46,
3a Planta, 28046
Madrid
Tel: 91-745 6420
Email: info.sp@tourismireland.com
Web: www.turismodeirlanda.com

Switzerland
Tourism Ireland, Badenerstrasse 15,
CH-8004, Zurich, Switzerland
Tel: 44 286 99 14
Fax: 44 286 99 37
Email: pdroz@tourismireland.com
Web: www.discoverireland.com

TOURISM IRELAND – REST OF THE WORLD
www.discoverireland.com

Australia
Tourism Ireland,
Level 5, 36 Carrington Street,
Sydney, NSW 2000
Tel: 02 - 9299 6177
Email: info@tourismireland.com.au
Web: www.discoverireland.com.au

New Zealand
Tourism Ireland,
Level 7, Citigroup Building,
23 Customs St. East, Auckland 1010
Tel: 09 - 977 2255
Fax: 09 - 977 2256
Email:
corporate.newzealand@tourismireland.com
Web: www.discoverireland.com/nz

Canada
Tourism Ireland,
2 Bloor St. West, Suite 3403
Toronto, M4W 3E2
Tel: 1800 - 7426 7625
Email: info.ca@tourismireland.com
Web: www.discoverireland.com

USA
Tourism Ireland,
345 Park Avenue, New York NY 10154
Tel: 1800 - 7426 7625
Email: info.us@tourismireland.com
Web: www.discoverireland.com

China
Tourism Ireland,
Suite 728, Shanghai Centre,
1376 Nanjing Road West,
Shanghai 200040
Tel: 021 6279 8788
Fax: 021 6279 8799
Email: sli@tourismireland.com
Web: www.discoverireland.com/cn

India
Tourism Ireland,
Beautiful Planet, Grants Building
Annexure, Office No. 46, 1st Floor,
Opposite Strand Cinema, Colaba,
Mumbai 400 005
Tel: 22 3096 1624
Fax: 22 2218 0489
Email: hfraser@tourismirelandindia.com
Web: www.discoverireland.com/in

Japan
Tourism Ireland,
International Place, 26-3, Sanei-cho,
Shinjuku-ku,
Tokyo 160-0008
Tel: 03 5367 6525
Email: corporate.japan@tourismireland.com
Web: www.discoverireland.com/jp

South Africa
Tourism Ireland,
c/o Development Promotions
62 Hume Road, Dunkeld,
P.O. Box 30615, Braamfontein 2017,
Johannesberg
Tel: 011 442 0824
Email: tourismireland@dpgsa.co.za
Web: www.discoverireland.com/za

The wonderful, diverse country of Ireland is divided into four regions each with its own charm, attractions and appealing characteristics. They are Ireland South, Ireland West, Northern Ireland and Dublin & Ireland East. Together, they form a very special island, full to bursting with dramatic landscapes, idyllic lakes, beaches, cosmopolitan towns and vibrant city life. Most of all, Ireland's regions are renowned for their rich cultural heritage, historical treasures and warm hospitality.

Discover a spectacular rural landscape of rich colour, an enchanted countryside dotted with reminders of a colourful past, a coastline etched out by the mighty Atlantic, great activities, ancient sites and city lights. Experience the renowned welcome for yourself.

Access has never been easier, either through the major ports or via airports. Many local airports offer an increasing range of flights from the UK, Europe and the USA, making it easier than ever to reach this wonderful island. Internal flights from Dublin make reaching other parts of the country straightforward.

Ireland South 31

Discover food as fresh as the air in picturesque Ireland South encompassing the South East with Cork and Kerry. From farmers markets and pub grub, to restaurants and fine dining, the South is fast acquiring a reputation as Ireland's gourmet region.

Northern Ireland 211

The six counties of Northern Ireland are just waiting to be explored, and welcome visitors with an enticing combination of history, culture, magnificent landscapes and vibrant festivals.

Ireland West 135

Ireland West covers the mighty Atlantic coastline from the northernmost tip of Donegal right down to Limerick, an unspoiled and pristine countryside proudly maintaining the traditions and cultures of yesteryear.

Dublin & Ireland East 227

Dublin & Ireland East incorporates the capital city as well as the East Coast and Midlands. Dublin itself is a fascinating city, energetic and youthful with a compelling mix of history, culture, architecture, pubs and shopping. The surrounding region offers so much for the visitor to see and do, all within easy reach.

...small enough for easy travelling, yet full of contrasts and contradictions, Ireland is waiting here for you

Ireland South

See page 365 for map with access points and driving distances

For Detailed Maps of this Region See Pages 365-380. Each Hotel or Guesthouse has a Map Reference to these detailed maps under their photograph.

Ireland South

Carlow, Cork, Kerry, Kilkenny, Tipperary, Waterford, Wexford

(see pages 2 & 3 for full County listing)

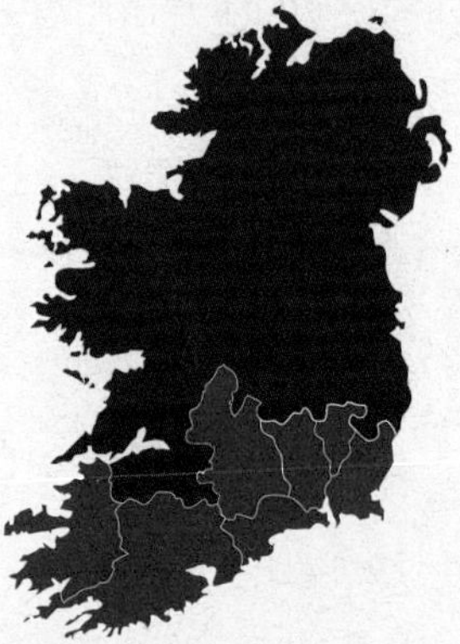

Welcome to Ireland South. Seven counties, like seven jewels adorning Ireland's golden southern shores.

Welcome to a land of unparalleled scenic beauty, a land of picturesque valleys and ancient roadways, vibrant streets and spectacular coastline. A land where the lilt of a fiddler's tune entwined with peat smoke and conversation in a city bar, is as eloquent an expression of its beauty as are the run of its waters, the vaunt of its peaks, or the glint of a leaping salmon in the fading evening light. Ireland South is special for so many reasons – the drama of its diverse yet spectacular landscapes, the naturally sculpted beauty of its award-winning beaches, the mystical charms of its ancient past, the quality and variety of its world-class visitor attractions, the unique personalities of its many famous cities, towns and villages and perhaps, most of all, the open warmth and creative spirit of its extraordinary people. All of this is waiting for you here, to explore, to discover, to fall in love with.

Carlow, framed by the River Barrow to the west and the River Slaney to the east, Carlow is a county defined by its rivers. The Barrow Navigation is hugely popular with tourists for pleasure boating, angling and walking, one of the best ways to get to know this beautiful river. Carlow is steeped in history and amoung its top visitor attractions are Altamont Gardens, Huntingdon Castle, Saint Lazerian's Cathedral, Duckett's Grove and Ballykeenan Pet Farm & Aviary.

Cork, perhaps no other corner of Ireland contains so much to see, do and experience as County Cork. Cork City is a thriving metropolis with a distinctively continental air. The east of the county is ripe with fertile farmlands, verdant river valleys and picturesque towns and villages while the west boasts a long, magnificent coastline, which stretches 200 miles from Youghal to Ardgroom on the Beara Peninsula.

This beautiful county is also brimming with must see visitor attractions, like the world famous island garden of Ilnacullin, Bantry House and Gardens, Blarney Castle, the Old Middleton Distillery, the Michael Collins Centre at Clonakilty and Fota Arboretum and Gardens.

Kerry, perhaps the most popular tourist destination in Ireland, Kerry is also considered by many to be the most beautiful. From the spectacular Ring of Kerry, to the extraordinary 25,000 acre Killarney National Park – home to Muckross House, to beauty spots like the Gap of Dunloe and Torc Waterfall, Kerry is replete in awe inspiring natural beauty. The county is rich in archaeological treasures too, none more famous or inspiring as the 6th century Skelligs UNESCO World Heritage Site, situated 12km off the southwest coast of Ireland. Among the many world class visitor attractions that have been developed in recent years, are The Geraldine Centre and the Kerry County Museum in Tralee, Derrynane House, Ardfert Cathedral, The Barracks Heritage Centre, Cahersiveen, the Skellig Experience and the Great Blasket Island Interpretative Centre.

Kilkenny, whether you're fishing for trout on the Nore, sinking a putt at Mount Juliet, or driving through pretty towns and villages like Thomastown and Inistioge, you'll be struck by the peaceful beauty of Kilkenny. The county has a wealth of fascinating visitor attractions, from the wonders of Dunmore Cave and Jerpoint Abbey, to the magnificently restored Kilkenny Castle or the many faceted Castlecomer Demesne. The ancient medieval city of Kilkenny itself is today a thriving, modern capital that has protected its precious heritage and crafts whilst evolving as one of Ireland's most vibrant and enjoyable cities in which to stay.

Tipperary, there's probably no livelier a collection of market towns in all Ireland than Carrick-on-Suir, Clonmel, Cahir, Tipperary and Cashel. Nor a more distinctive set of landmarks than Cahir Castle on its island in the middle of the River Suir and the great Rock of Cashel, rising like a sentinel above the Golden Vale and the Glen of Aherlow. Tipperary also has some fascinating visitor attractions, like Mitchelstown Cave, one of Europe's most spectacular, and the captivating Brú Ború Cultural Centre, commemorating Brian Boru, the Last of the High Kings, with a 'cultural village' dedicated to the study and celebration of native

Calendar of Events | GUINNESS

May
Carlsberg Kilkenny Rhythm, Kilkenny City

June
Cats Laugh Festival, Kilkenny City

July/August
Waterford Spraoi Festival, Waterford City

September
Listowel Racing Festival, Listowel, Co. Kerry

October/November
Guinness Jazz Festival, Cork City
Wexford Singing & Swinging Pubs, Wexford Town

A view to the Skelligs, Co. Kerry

Blarney Castle, Co. Cork

ish music, song, dance and theatre.

/aterford, famous the world over for the beauty and raftsmanship of its master glass cutters at the Waterford rystal Visitor Centre, Waterford offers visitors a choice etween a cosmopolitan vibrant city, charming seaside esorts with miles of sandy beaches and countryside etaway locations set against the backdrop of the omeragh Mountains. From the charm of rural towns and llages like Dungarvan, Lismore, Cappoquin and allyMcCarbry to the resort villages of Ardmore, Dunmore nd Tramore there is something to appeal to all tastes. here is an excellent choice of world-class visitor tractions to enjoy including The Museum of Treasures nd Edmund Rice Heritage Centre which are comple-nented by Jack Burtchaell Walking Tour all of which tell e story of Waterford - Ireland's oldest city. For families, e newly restored Waterford to Kilmeaden narrow gauge ilway is a fabulous way to take in the sweep of the Suir alley and to go back 450 million years you can take a tour the spectacular Copper Coast UNESCO Geopark.

/exford, located in the sunny South East of Ireland is fast ecoming the spa capital of Ireland. With new develop-ents such as the Monart destination spa and Seafield d Kelly's resort spas, Wexford is the ideal location for a stful and rejuvenating break. But long before the arrival 'spas', Wexford was famous for its rich history, the ory of which is told through the numerous visitor tractions in the county. The most fascinating include the markable Irish National Heritage Park at Wexford – hich will take you on a tour of how the Irish lived, worshipped and died from the stone age to the 12 Century; the Dunbrody Heritage Ship in New Ross - a replica of a 19th century famine ship that transported the Irish to the new world; the medieval Hook Lighthouse – where monks kept the fire alight as far back as the 5th Century; add to these the Irish Agricultural Museum at Johnstown Castle, the National 1798 Rebellion Centre in Enniscorthy, Ireland's premier wildfowl sanctuary, the Wexford Wildfowl Reserve and the JFK Arboretum and you get the finest array of quality visitor attractions in the country.

Heritage

With a rich cultural tapestry of towering castles, magnificent stately homes, ancient Celtic monuments, early Christian ecclesiastical sites, fascinating museums and intriguing city architecture, Ireland South boasts a wealth of world-class cultural and heritage visitor centres.

In every corner of these seven counties you'll find a thread of ancient times so alive it seems still woven to the present day; captivating history brought to life through enthralling tales, working museums, and state-of-the-art interpretative centres.

Discover the medieval splendour of the Rock of Cashel, boost your powers of eloquence by kissing the famous Blarney Stone at Blarney Castle, or take an easy wander round the magnificent Kilkenny Castle and Gardens overlooking the picturesque River Nore. There's also the fully restored elegance of Ross Castle in Kerry, and the fascinating war-entangled history of Charles Fort at Kinsale to explore.

Ireland South

10 Key Walks

1 Barrow Valley, Co. Carlow
2 Castlemorris, Co. Kilkenny
3 Glen of Aherlow, Co. Tipperary
4 Sheeps Head Peninsula, Co. Cork
5 Beara Peninsula, Co. Cork
6 Killarney National Park, Co. Kerry
7 Glenbeigh loops, Co. Kerry
8 Dingle Peninsula, Co. Kerry
9 Coastal walks, Co. Wexford
10 Comeragh Mountains, Co. Waterford

Maps for these walks and the other 200 looped walks across Ireland can be downloaded on *www.discoverireland.ie/walking*

Or why not try your hand at mountain biking in the Ballyhoura Mountains in East Limerick and North Cork?

Equestrian

Horse riding in Ireland is very popular and is an accessible pursuit for all ages, abilities and budgets. There are 11 tourism approved riding centres in the region that would be happy to provide you with anything from an hours riding, to trekking/trail riding or even beach riding. To find one near the hotel you are staying in, check out *www.discoverireland.ie/equestrian*
Or why not try your luck on the horses and spend a day at the races?

Top Attractions

1 Crawford Art Gallery, Cork
2 Lewis Glucksman Gallery, Cork
3 Cork City Gaol, Cork
4 Fota House & Gardens, Cork
5 Killarney National Park, Co. Kerry
6 Muckross House & Gardens, Killarney, Co. Kerry
7 Skelligs, Co. Kerry
8 Kilkenny Castle, Kilkenny
9 Dunbrody Famine Ship, New Ross, Co. Wexford
10 Altamont Gardens, Tullow, Co. Carlow
11 Rock of Cashel, Co. Tipperary
12 Waterford Museum of Treasures, Waterford

Angling

The coastal counties of Cork, Kerry, Waterford and Wexford offer spectacular deep sea fishing. There are numerous charter boat operators dotted along the coastline offering fishing over offshore wreck and reefs. The variety of species in Irish waters is impressive; turbot, gurnard, pollack, cod, tope, skate, bass, ling, bass and shark to name but a few. Serious anglers and the less experienced are always welcome. And don't worry if you don't have any equipment with you as tackle is available to hire on board.
For more information and the lists of towns that are part of our anglers welcome initiative visit *www.discoverireland.ie/angling*

Family Fun

Ireland South is ideal for families from Ballybunion all along the exquisite coast to North Wexford. There is loads to keep the family entertained endless water sports, horse riding, quad biking and fishing, or get involved or get involved in history and tradition at the many heritage sites and museums. Your biggest challenge will be deciding what to do.
For more information visit *www.discoverireland.ie/family*

Adventure

If you long for adventure and lots of it, let the Cork and Kerry region extend you a gilt-edged adrenalin-charged invitation. It is a paradise for sea kayakers, as well as windsurfers, kitesurfers and surfers who are hell bent on harnessing the swells that the North Atlantic sends pounding in, depending on her mood. The mountains too boast their own adventures. For some it will be riding a horse or a mountain bike through the rugged territory. For others, the mountaineering challenges of the MacGillycuddy's Reeks, home to Ireland's highest peak, Carrantouhill.
But don't let a lack of experience or skill put you off. If you like what you hear but don't know where to start, there are plenty of qualified instructors and guides ready to make your adrenalin dreams a reality - be they on land or sea.
For more information visit *www.discoverireland.ie/adventure*

Ireland's Islands

Visit the magnificent islands off the coast of West Cork. Take in a looped walk on Bere Island, experience the thrill of a journey in Ireland's only cable car across to Dursey Island, do some sailing on Heir Island or just get away from it all on Cape Clear.
For more information on Ireland's islands, including how to get there check out *www.discoverireland.ie*

Barrowville Town House

GUESTHOUSE ★★★ MAP 7 M 8

Kilkenny Road,
Carlow Town,
Co. Carlow
Tel: 059-914 3324 Fax: 059-914 1953
Email: barrowvilletownhouse@eircom.net
Web: www.barrowville.com
GPS: N +52° 49' 57.84" W -6° 56' 2.99"

Built over 200 years ago this beautiful Guesthouse and its owners offer a warm and friendly welcome. All bedrooms have en suite, tea/coffee and internet access. Breakfast menu available offering a variety of dishes with breakfast served in the conservatory overlooking the gardens. Relax in the sitting room containing beautiful antique furniture and fine art. Situated just a few minutes walk from the town centre. Ideal location for touring the South East and golf nearby.

B&B from €35.00 to €70.00

Anna & Dermot Smyth
Proprietors

7

Closed 24 - 28 December

Talbot Hotel Carlow

HOTEL ★★★★ MAP 7 M 8

Portlaoise Road,
Carlow Town,
Co. Carlow
Tel: 059-915 3000 Fax: 059-915 3001
Email: sales@talbothotelcarlow.ie
Web: www.talbotcarlow.ie
GPS: N +52° 50' 47.00" W -6° 56' 37.26"

Luxurious 4 star hotel situated off the N80 from Dublin & 2km walk into Carlow town centre. Facilities include 84 guestrooms, Liberty Tree 4th floor restaurant, Corries Bar & Bistro with live music every Fri & Sat night, conference & banqueting facilities, Inspirit Leisure Centre, Classic Beauty Salon, complimentary car parking. Located beside "The Dome" (Kids Entertainment Centre). Talbot Tigers Supervised Kids Program on weekends & holidays. The Talbot Group is renowned for impeccable service, mouth watering cuisine, great locations & the Talbot Carlow is no exception.

An IHF Quality Employer

Member of Talbot Hotel Group

Bookable on www.irelandhotels.com

Special Offer: www.irelandhotels.com/offers

B&B from €40.00 to €120.00
Suites from €140.00 to €290.00

Larry Bowe
General Manager

84

Food for Kids Activities:

Closed 24 - 26 December

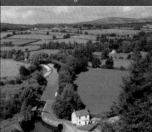

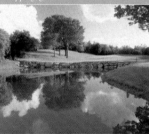

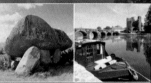

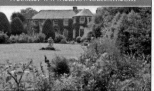

B&B Rates are per Person Sharing per Night incl. Breakfast.
or Room Rates are per Room per Night - See also Page 8

Leighlinbridge / Tullow / Allihies

Lord Bagenal Inn

HOTEL ★★★★ MAP 7 M 8

Main Street,
Leighlinbridge,
Co. Carlow
Tel: 059-977 4000 Fax: 059-972 2629
Email: info@lordbagenal.com
Web: www.lordbagenal.com
GPS: N +52° 44' 10.36" W -6° 58' 36.38"

Situated in the picturesque Heritage Village of Leighlinbridge along the River Barrow, with private marina & gardens, we are the perfect location to explore the South East. Our new en suite bedrooms are luxuriously furnished to the highest standards. Award-winning Lord Bagenal Restaurant is renowned for fine food & excellent wines. Locals & visitors frequent our bar & carvery daily. New Waterfront Restaurant overlooking the River Barrow, serving local organic & seasonal produce. Weddings, conferences, banquets catered for. Children welcome. Please enquire about Facilities for Persons with Disabilities.

B&B from €49.00 to €99.00
Suites from €120.00 to €240.00

James & Mary Kehoe

39

Activities:

Closed 25 - 26 December

Mount Wolseley Hotel Spa & Country Club

HOTEL ★★★★ MAP 8 N 8

Tullow,
Co. Carlow
Tel: 059-918 0100 Fax: 059-915 2123
Email: info@mountwolseley.ie
Web: www.mountwolseley.ie
GPS: N +52° 47' 27.67" W -6° 43' 53.05"

This charming and exclusive resort is an eclectic blend of contemporary design and lavish country house details. Featuring 143 bedrooms and conference facilities for up to 750 delegates. The hotel overlooks the 18th hole of the magnificent, Christy O'Connor designed, championship golf course. Other leisure facilities include a spa with 14 treatment rooms and a health club with 20 meter deck pool, sauna, steam bath, gym and aerobics studio. Tennis courts on site. Children's activity club. Please enquire about Facilities for Persons with Disabilities.

An IHF Quality Employer

Bookable on www.irelandhotels.com
Special Offer: www.irelandhotels.com/offers

B&B from €62.50 to €110.00
Suites from €200.00 to €295.00

Odhran Lawlor
General Manager

143

Food for Kids Activities:

Closed 25 - 27 December

Sea View Guest House

GUESTHOUSE ★★★ MAP 1 C 2

Cluin Village,
Allihies, Beara,
Co. Cork
Tel: 027-73004 Fax: 027-73211
Email: seaviewg@iol.ie
Web: www.allihiesseaview.com
GPS: N +51° 38' 26.44" W -10° 2' 38.51"

Sea View Guesthouse is a family-run concern in the remote and unspoilt Beara Peninsula. All bedrooms are en suite with TV and telephone. Situated in the village of Allihies, it is within walking distance of a beach, playground and tennis court. The nearby hills afford excellent opportunities for walking, offering breathtaking views. Traditional Irish music and a friendly welcome can be found in the village pubs.

B&B from €40.00 to €50.00

John & Mary O'Sullivan
Proprietors

10

Closed 31 October - 01 March

B&B Rates are per Person Sharing per Night incl. Breakfast. or Room Rates are per Room per Night - See also Page 8

Oriel House Hotel, Leisure Club & Spa

HOTEL ★★★★ MAP 2 H 3

Ballincollig,
Co. Cork

Tel: 021-420 8400 Fax: 021-487 5880
Email: info@orielhousehotel.ie
Web: www.orielhousehotel.ie
GPS: N +51° 53' 16.72" W -8° 36' 5.08"

The Oriel House Hotel Leisure Club & Spa is located on the west side of Cork city. Close proximity to Cork Airport, train station and gateway to Co. Kerry. The Oriel House is a listed building dating back to 1805, sits comfortably alongside the contemporary new building. Our facilities include 78 guest rooms, extensive conference and banqueting facilities, fully equipped business centre, bright and airy leisure Club and The Oriel Spa. The Oriel House Hotel is luxury and relaxation, pure and simple. Please enquire about Facilities for Persons with Disabilities.

An IHF Quality Employer

Member of Cork Luxury Hotel Group

Bookable on www.irelandhotels.com

Special Offer: www.irelandhotels.com/offers

Room Rate from €99.00 to €105.00
Suites from €130.00 to €180.00

Breda Keane Shortt
General Manager

78

Closed 24 - 28 December

Bayview Hotel

HOTEL ★★★★ MAP 3 J 3

Ballycotton,
Co. Cork

Tel: 021-464 6746 Fax: 021-464 6075
Email: res@thebayviewhotel.com
Web: www.thebayviewhotel.com
GPS: N +51° 49' 40.11" W -8° 0' 16.47"

Nestled in the unspoilt fishing village of Ballycotton, the Bayview Hotel directly overlooks miles of spectacular coastline. Embrace the invigorating sea air while relaxing in the original gardens. The Capricho Restaurant provides dishes with a balance of flavour, texture and presentation. Our chefs emphasise fish dishes caught literally on the doorstep. From the cold, crystal depths of the Atlantic Ocean to your plate in a matter of hours. A short distance away are Fota Wildlife Park, Heritage Centres, Trabolgan Holiday Village & an abundance of arts & crafts. Full use of sister property, Garryvoe Hotel, extensive leisure facilities for all.

Member of Manor House Hotels

Bookable on www.irelandhotels.com

Special Offer: www.irelandhotels.com/offers

B&B from €69.00 to €145.00
Suites from €220.00 to €300.00

Stephen Belton
General Manager

35

Activities:

Closed 1 November - 1 April

Seaview House Hotel

HOTEL ★★★★ MAP 2 E 2

Ballylickey,
Bantry,
Co. Cork

Tel: 027-50073 Fax: 027-51555
Email: info@seaviewhousehotel.com
Web: www.seaviewhousehotel.com
GPS: N +51° 43' 19.93" W -9° 26' 11.45"

Delightful country house hotel & restaurant, set back in extensive grounds on main Bantry/Glengarriff Road. All bedrooms en suite, D.D. telephone & colour TV. Ideal for touring West Cork & Kerry. 2 golf courses nearby. Recommended Egon Ronay, Good Hotel Guide etc. For the restaurant, AA Rosettes & Failte Ireland Awards of Excellence. Seafood a speciality. Member of Manor House Hotels. A wing of new superior rooms and a conservatory to the dining room was added in Winter 2000. Special midweek & weekend rates, subject to availability. Bookable on www.manorhousehotels.com

Member of Manor House Hotels

Bookable on www.irelandhotels.com

B&B from €65.00 to €85.00
Suites from €150.00 to €200.00

Kathleen O'Sullivan
Proprietor

25

Closed 15 November - 15 March

B&B Rates are per Person Sharing per Night incl. Breakfast.
or Room Rates are per Room per Night - **See also Page 8**

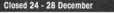

Ballyvourney / Baltimore

Abbey Hotel

HOTEL ★★★ MAP 2 F 3

Ballyvourney,
Macroom,
Co. Cork
Tel: 026-45324 Fax: 026-45830
Email: abbeyhotel@eircom.net
Web: www.theabbeyhotel.ie
GPS: N +51° 56' 22.03" W -9° 9' 28.74"

Family-run hotel nestles in the valley of the Sullane River among the Cork and Kerry Mountains on the N22. It combines a friendly atmosphere and excellent catering. An ideal base for touring Kerry and Cork. A wide range of activities is available to you at the hotel including fishing, mountaineering, nature walks and golfing. 39 bedrooms with private facilities, direct dial phone & colour TV. Within 20 minutes drive are two 18 hole golf courses and trout fishing on the Sullane River. Fully licensed function room for weddings, dinner dances and parties. Please enquire about Facilities for Persons with Disabilities.

B&B from €40.00 to €50.00

Cornelius Creedon
Proprietor
39

Activities:

Closed 30 October - 01 March

Casey's of Baltimore

HOTEL ★★★ MAP 2 E 1

Baltimore,
Co. Cork
Tel: 028-20197 Fax: 028-20509
Email: info@caseysofbaltimore.com
Web: www.caseysofbaltimore.com
GPS: N +51° 29' 4.81" W -9° 21' 44.99"

A warm welcome awaits you at Casey's of Baltimore. Situated at the entrance to Baltimore with its lovely views overlooking the bay, this superb family-run hotel is the perfect place to spend some time. All rooms feature en suite bathrooms, satellite TV, tea/coffee facility, direct dial phone, hairdryer and trouser press. The traditional pub and restaurant feature natural stone and wood décor, a spectacular view, extensive menu - seafood is our speciality. Activities can be arranged.

An IHF Quality Employer

Member of Irish Country Hotels

Bookable on www.irelandhotels.com
Special Offer: www.irelandhotels.com/offers

B&B from €79.00 to €91.00

Ann & Michael Casey
Owners
14

Closed 20 - 27 December

Waterfront (The)

GUESTHOUSE ★★★ MAP 2 E 1

The Square,
Baltimore,
Co. Cork
Tel: 028-20600 Fax: 028-20495
Email: res@waterfrontbaltimore.ie
Web: www.waterfrontbaltimore.ie
GPS: N +51° 28' 58.21" W -9° 22' 23.85"

Superbly appointed premises that recently added 5 generous en suite bedrooms, reception area, bar & restaurant on to 8 existing spacious rooms. Satellite TV, tea/coffee facilities and access to a comfortable residents' lounge. A family-run premises located on the square with stunning views of Baltimore Bay & The Islands. Convenient to its associated family pizza & grill, La Jolie Brise, The Lookout and the famous Chez Youen Seafood Restaurant. Please enquire about Facilities for Persons with Disabilities.

Bookable on www.irelandhotels.com

B&B from €40.00 to €60.00

Youen Jacob Snr.
Owner-Manager
13

Open All Year

B&B Rates are per Person Sharing per Night incl. Breakfast.
or Room Rates are per Room per Night - **See also Page 8**

Munster Arms Hotel

HOTEL ★★ MAP 2 G 2

Oliver Plunkett Street,
Bandon,
Co. Cork

Tel: 023-884 1562 Fax: 023-884 1562
Email: info@munsterarmshotel.com
Web: www.munsterarmshotel.com
GPS: N +51° 44' 42.64" W -8° 44' 3.24"

Set at the gateway to West Cork, 30 high quality en suite bedrooms with tea/coffee facilities, direct dial telephone, remote control TV and hairdryer. Set in beautiful scenic West Cork, accessible by the N71 route from Cork City. Renowned for its homely atmosphere and superb quality. Ideal touring base and easily accessible from Kinsale, Cork City, Blarney, Killarney and West Cork. The hotel is also home to the largest salmon ever cought in Bandon River, weighing in at an incredible 28lb 30oz.

B&B from €50.00 to €70.00

Don O'Sullivan
Owner

30

Activities:

Closed 25 - 27 December

Maritime Hotel (The)

HOTEL ★★★★ MAP 2 E 2

The Quay,
Bantry,
Co. Cork

Tel: 027-54700 Fax: 027-54701
Email: info@themaritime.ie
Web: www.themaritime.ie
GPS: N +51° 40' 48.15" W -9° 27' 25.61"

Overlooking Bantry Bay, The Maritime Hotel offers modern and contemporary 4**** standards in beautiful Bantry. Our one and two bedroomed suites are ideal for families, offering flexibility along the way with many of the comforts of home. The Club Maritime Leisure Centre, Ocean Resturant and Maritime Bar make the hotel a perfect venue for work or pleasure - and an ideal base for exploring the wonders of West Cork. Please enquire about Facilities for Persons with Disabilities.

Member of Best Loved Hotels

Bookable on www.irelandhotels.com

B&B from €65.00 to €130.00
Suites from €150.00 to €280.00

Simon Tiptaft
General Manager

117

Open All Year

Westlodge Hotel

HOTEL ★★★ MAP 2 E 2

Bantry,
Co. Cork

Tel: 027-50360 Fax: 027-50438
Email: reservations@westlodgehotel.ie
Web: www.westlodgehotel.ie
GPS: N +51° 40' 20.88" W -9° 28' 29.58"

3*** hotel situated in the scenic surroundings of Bantry Bay. Super health & leisure centre including indoor heated swimming pool, childrens' pool, toddlers' pool, sauna, steam room, jacuzzi, gym, aerobics, squash. Outdoor amenities include tennis, pitch & putt, woodland walks. The Westlodge specialises in family holidays with organised activities during Jul & Aug. A warm & friendly welcome awaits you at the Westlodge. Self-catering cottages available. Mighty Duck's Club opens during Jul & Aug. Guaranteed Tee Times at Bantry Bay Golf Club. Themed breaks now available: wellness, golf & walking.

An IHF Quality Employer

Member of Holiday Ireland Hotels

Bookable on www.irelandhotels.com

Special Offer: www.irelandhotels.com/offers

B&B from €55.00 to €70.00
Suites from €199.00 to €199.00

Eileen M O'Shea FIHI
General Manager

90

Food for Kids Activities:

Closed 21 - 28 December

B&B Rates are per Person Sharing per Night incl. Breakfast.
or Room Rates are per Room per Night - **See also Page 8**

Blarney

Ashlee Lodge

GUESTHOUSE ★★★★ MAP 2 H 3

Tower,
Blarney,
Co. Cork
Tel: 021-438 5346 Fax: 021-438 5726
Email: info@ashleelodge.com
Web: www.ashleelodge.com
GPS: N +51° 55' 27.58" W -8° 36' 44.04"

This charming 4* boutique style property is a rare find, striking the perfect balance between traditional comfort & a contemporary atmosphere. Offering peace & relaxation in a quiet suburb minutes from Blarney Village & Castle. Luxurious bedrooms & suites with all that one expects of a private hotel. Air-con, king sized beds, widescreen TV/CD units & sittingroom areas. Relax in our sauna & Canadian hot tub. A previous winner of AA Guest Accommodation of the Year, Sparkling Diamond Awards, Little Gem & Warm Welcome Awards. AA 5 Yellow Stars. Privately owned, personally managed.

Bookable on www.irelandhotels.com

Special Offer: www.irelandhotels.com/offers

B&B from €50.00 to €100.00
Suites from €160.00 to €290.00

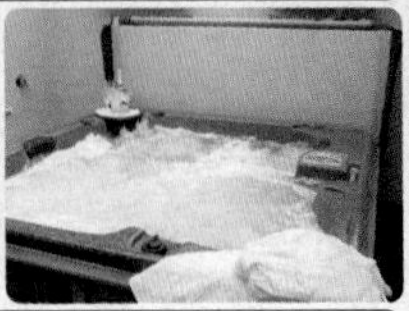

John O'Leary
Proprietor

10

Activities:

Closed 20 December - 20 January

Blarney Castle Hotel

HOTEL ★★★ MAP 2 H 3

Blarney,
Co. Cork
Tel: 021-438 5116 Fax: 021-438 5542
Email: info@blarneycastlehotel.com
Web: www.blarneycastlehotel.com
GPS: N +51° 55' 52.73" W -8° 34' 6.58"

Established in 1837, still run by the Forrest family. Picturesque inn on peaceful village green, 5 miles from Cork City. Tastefully appointed spacious bedrooms. Unspoilt traditional bar. Kitchen specialising in finest local produce. Killarney, Kenmare, Kinsale, Cobh, Waterford and numerous golf courses all an easy drive. Immediately to the left the magnificent grounds of Blarney Castle guarding that famous stone, to the right, Blarney Woollen Mills. Quality local entertainment regularly in bar. WiFi & safe in all bedrooms. Car park for hotel guests. Freshly cooked to order breakfasts served each morning until 11.00am.

Bookable on www.irelandhotels.com

B&B from €50.00 to €75.00

Ian Forrest / Una Forrest
Manager / Reservations

13

Activities:

Open All Year

Blarney Golf Resort

HOTEL ★★★★ MAP 2 H 3

Tower,
Blarney,
Co. Cork
Tel: 021-438 4477 Fax: 021-451 6453
Email: reservations@blarneygolfresort.com
Web: www.blarneygolfresort.com
GPS: N +51° 56' 16.41" W -8° 37' 45.00"

Set amongst 170 acres of the beautiful wooded Shournagh valley, Blarney Golf Resort has a lot to boast about. Its stunning location close to the historic town of Blarney in Co. Cork, steeped in history, legend & rugged natural beauty, would almost be reason enough to visit were it not for its many other attributes. The Resort's impressive signature championship golf course was co-designed by two-times Major winner, John Daly. The luxurious 4 star hotel has 62 stylishly designed bedrooms while the 56 beautifully appointed Golf Lodges offer a high level of comfort. Please enquire about Facilities for Persons with Disabilities.

Bookable on www.irelandhotels.com

Special Offer: www.irelandhotels.com/offers

B&B from €45.00 to €85.00
Suites from €115.00 to €150.00

Conor O'Toole
General Manager

62

Activities:

Open All Year

B&B Rates are per Person Sharing per Night incl. Breakfast.
or Room Rates are per Room per Night - See also Page 8

Blarney Woollen Mills Hotel

HOTEL ★★★ MAP 2 H 3

Blarney,
Co. Cork

Tel: 021-438 5011 Fax: 021-438 5350
Email: info@blarneywoollenmillshotel.com
Web: www.blarneywoollenmillshotel.com
GPS: N +51° 55' 59.65" W -8° 33' 54.95"

Blarney Woollen Mills 3*** Hotel with 48 beautifully appointed superior rooms including 3 executive suites. Many of the rooms have spectacular views of the famous Blarney Castle. All rooms have been tastefully decorated in the traditional style. All day dining in our Millroom Restaurant and evening dining in Christys Grill Bar. The hotel boasts one of the finest fitness centres in the area. Located within the old Mill buildings in the famous Blarney Woollen Mills complex where you can enjoy a relaxing drink and experience some Irish hospitality in Christy's Pub. Please enquire about Facilities for Persons with Disabilities.

Bookable on www.irelandhotels.com

B&B from €69.00 to €109.00

Dominic Heaney
General Manager

48

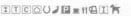

Closed 20 - 27 December

Muskerry Arms

GUESTHOUSE ★★★ MAP 2 H 3

The Square,
Blarney,
Co. Cork

Tel: 021-438 5200 Fax: 021-438 1013
Email: jerome@muskerryarms.com
Web: www.muskerryarms.com
GPS: N +51° 55' 59.35" W -8° 34' 4.05"

With all the attributes of a small hotel, the Muskerry Arms is ideally located for your stay in Blarney. Stylish, spacious guest rooms and family suites offer power showers and tea/coffee making facilities. Live music is a regular feature in the popular Muskerry Bar and two delicious menus are available in the bar and main restaurant. All within walking distance of Blarney Castle and Woollen Mills. Please enquire about Facilities for Persons with Disabilities.

Bookable on www.irelandhotels.com

B&B from €33.00 to €49.00

Nell O' Connor

11

Closed 25 December

Carrigaline Court Hotel & Leisure Centre

HOTEL ★★★★ MAP 3 H 3

Carrigaline,
Co. Cork

Tel: 021-485 2100 Fax: 021-437 1103
Email: reception@carrigcourt.com
Web: www.carrigcourt.com
GPS: N +51° 48' 58.06" W -8° 23' 31.69"

AA 4**** hotel, located just minutes from city centre, airport and ferry terminal. 91 spacious bedrooms with broadband internet access, satellite TV, tea/coffee facilities, in-room safe, trouser press & all modern comforts as standard. Superb contemporary restaurant with unique design features. Atmospheric & spacious bar. Exquisite leisure centre incl 20m pool, sauna, jacuzzi, steam room & gym. Golf arranged at Cork's best courses. Sailing, angling, horse riding & a host of other activities available in this beautiful area. Free kiddies' club, Camp Rock, available on certain dates. Optimus service award.

An IHF Quality Employer

Bookable on www.irelandhotels.com

Special Offer: www.irelandhotels.com/offers

B&B from €70.00 to €110.00
Suites from €200.00 to €300.00

Jerry Healy
General Manager

91

Closed 24 - 26 December

B&B Rates are per Person Sharing per Night incl. Breakfast.
or Room Rates are per Room per Night - See also Page 8

Carrigaline / Castlemartyr

Fernhill Hotel

HOTEL ★★ MAP 3 H 3

Fernhill,
Carrigaline,
Co. Cork
Tel: 021-437 2226 Fax: 021-437 1011
Email: info@fernhillgolfhotel.com
Web: www.fernhillgolfhotel.com
GPS: N +51° 49' 47.72" W -8° 22' 43.35"

Fernhill is a very pleasant and comfortable place to stay. We are 10 minutes from Cork City, 15 minutes from Cork Airport, 20 minutes from Kinsale and 30 minutes from West Cork. Facilities include a leisure centre, an 18 hole golf course, par 70 on site and also a tennis court.

B&B from €35.00 to €50.00

Alan Bowes
General Manager 38

Activities: ✓

Closed 25 - 26 December

Glenwood House

GUESTHOUSE ★★★★ MAP 3 H 3

Ballinrea Road,
Carrigaline,
Co. Cork
Tel: 021-437 3878 Fax: 021-437 3878
Email: info@glenwoodguesthouse.com
Web: www.glenwoodguesthouse.com
GPS: N +51° 49' 17.08" W -8° 23' 42.03"

Glenwood House is a purpose built, self contained guesthouse, designed with all guest requirements in mind. The rooms are large and spacious, offering similar facilities to those of quality hotels, firm orthopaedic beds, heated towel rails, complimentary beverages, trouser press, satellite TV, power shower, WiFi broadband communication and many more. Located close to Ringaskiddy Ferry Port (5mins), Cork City (7mins), Kinsale (15mins), Crosshaven (5mins), Airport (10mins). We offer secure car parking, and have facilities to look after disabled guests. All accommodation is of hotel quality.

Bookable on www.irelandhotels.com
Special Offer: www.irelandhotels.com/offers

B&B from €40.00 to €55.00

Adrian Sheedy
Proprietor 14

Closed 18 December - 10 January

Castlemartyr Resort

HOTEL ★★★★★ MAP 3 I 3

Castlemartyr,
Co. Cork
Tel: 021-4219000 Fax: 021-4623359
Email: reception@castlemartyrresort.ie
Web: www.castlemartyrresort.ie
GPS: N +51° 54' 40.59" W -8° 3' 45.06"

The Manor House has been restored and enhanced to offer 109 rooms and a luxury spa. The impeccably styled interiors incorporate original features that have been preserved and brought to life again. Fine linens and luxurious soft furnishings are the hallmark of each room where every modern comfort and convenience awaits you. A contemporary take on the best of local and seasonal produce offer a style of cooking that offers and experience worth travelling for. Please enquire about Facilities for Persons with Disabilities.

Member of Preferred Hotels & Resorts

Bookable on www.irelandhotels.com
Special Offer: www.irelandhotels.com/offers

B&B from €97.50 to €275.00
Suites from €375.00 to €3,250.00

Andrew Phelan
General Manager 109

Closed 25 December - 26 December

B&B Rates are per Person Sharing per Night incl. Breakfast.
or Room Rates are per Room per Night - **See also Page 8**

Castletownshend / Charleville / Clonakilty

Castle (The)

Guesthouse ★ Map 2 F 1

Castletownshend,
Near Skibbereen,
Co. Cork
Tel: 028-36100 Fax: 028-36166
Email: castle_townshend@hotmail.com
Web: www.castle-townshend.com
GPS: N +51° 31' 46.41" W -9° 10' 21.46"

18th century Townshend family home overlooking Castlehaven Harbour. Set in its own grounds at water's edge with access to small beach and woods. Most bedrooms en suite on second floor with excellent sea views. Panelled hall/sitting room with TV and open fire. Breakfast in elegant dining room. Mary Ann's Restaurant close by. Ideal for touring Cork and Kerry. Also self-catering apartments and cottages. Guided tours of The Castle in May, June & September & October by arrangement.
Website www.castle-townshend.com
Please enquire about Facilities for Persons with Disabilities.

B&B from €55.00 to €85.00

Anne & Malcolm Cochrane Townshend

7

Closed 15 December - 15 January

Charleville Park Hotel & Leisure Club

Hotel ★★★★ Map 2 G 5

Limerick Road,
Charleville,
Co. Cork
Tel: 063-33700 Fax: 063-30577
Email: info@charlevilleparkhotel.com
Web: www.charlevilleparkhotel.com
GPS: N +52° 21' 38.14" W -8° 40' 59.08"

The Charleville Park Hotel & Leisure Club boasts 91 bedrooms, conference facilities for 700 delegates, banqueting for up to 550 guests and full leisure club incl. 25m pool. This 4**** deluxe hotel offers the ultimate in luxury and relaxation. The Greenfinch Restaurant offers modern Irish food from ingredients sourced locally. Ed's Bar serves carvery lunch and bar food daily. Complimentary wireless internet access throughout the hotel. Only 5 minutes from train station. Please enquire about Facilities for Persons with Disabilities.

An IHF Quality Employer

Member of Cork Luxury Hotel Group

Bookable on www.irelandhotels.com

Special Offer: www.irelandhotels.com/offers

B&B from €60.00 to €115.00

Brendan Comerford
General Manager

91

Closed 24 - 26 December

Dunmore House Hotel

Hotel ★★★ Map 2 G 2

Muckross,
Clonakilty,
Co. Cork
Tel: 023-883 3352 Fax: 023-883 4686
Email: enq@dunmorehousehotel.ie
Web: www.dunmorehousehotel.ie
GPS: N +51° 35' 24.91" W -8° 52' 3.51"

Situated on the South West coast of Ireland, Dunmore House Hotel is family owned. Rooms are beautifully decorated, with spectacular views of the Atlantic Ocean. Sample a true taste of West Cork with our home-cooked local produce and seafood. Private foreshore available for sea angling. Green fees at the on-site golf club are free to residents. Horse riding available by arrangement. Interesting collection of local and modern Irish art. Please enquire about Facilities for Persons with Disabilities.

An IHF Quality Employer

B&B from €85.00 to €105.00

Derry & Mary O'Donovan
Proprietors

29

Activities:

Closed 10 January - 10 March

B&B Rates are per Person Sharing per Night incl. Breakfast.
or Room Rates are per Room per Night - See also Page 8

Clonakilty

Fernhill House Hotel

HOTEL ★★★ MAP 2 G 2

Clonakilty,
Co. Cork

Tel: 023-883 3258 Fax: 023-883 4003
Email: info@fernhillhousehotel.com
Web: www.fernhillhousehotel.com
GPS: N +51° 37' 36.19" W -8° 54' 28.40"

Fernhill House Hotel is a family-run Georgian style hotel located on picturesque grounds 0.8km from Clonakilty. Conference & function facilities available. Our hotel offers an intimate homely atmosphere, excellent food, fabulous gardens which features meandering pathways, a waterfall, geyser and marquee. Holiday with us and enjoy panoramic views of the rolling countryside. Please enquire about Facilities for Persons with Disabilities.

An IHF Quality Employer

B&B from €70.00 to €80.00

Michael & Teresa O'Neill
Proprietors

27

Activities:

Closed 23 December - 02 January

Inchydoney Island Lodge & Spa

HOTEL ★★★★ MAP 2 G 2

Clonakilty,
West Cork

Tel: 023-883 3143 Fax: 023-883 5229
Email: reservations@inchydoneyisland.com
Web: www.inchydoneyisland.com
GPS: N +51° 35' 50.55" W -8° 51' 44.20"

Situated on the idyllic island of Inchydoney, adjacent to a stunning EU Blue Flag beach, this luxurious hotel offers de luxe rooms, a fully equipped thalassotherapy (seawater) spa, award-winning restaurant, Dunes Pub and function and meeting facilities. Within a short distance guests can enjoy sailing, golf, riding and deep sea fishing, whale watching and surfing. The style of cooking in the Gulfstream Restaurant reflects the wide availability of fresh seafood and organically grown vegetables. Please enquire about Facilities for Persons with Disabilities.

An IHF Quality Employer

Bookable on www.irelandhotels.com
Special Offer: www.irelandhotels.com/offers

B&B from €85.00 to €130.00

The Team at Inchydoney Island Lodge & Spa

67

Activities:

Closed 23 - 27 December

O'Donovan's Hotel

HOTEL ★★ MAP 2 G 2

Pearse Street,
Clonakilty,
West Cork

Tel: 023-883 3250 Fax: 023-883 3250
Email: info@odonovanshotel.com
Web: www.odonovanshotel.com
GPS: N +51° 37' 22.74" W -8° 53' 23.83"

Charles Stewart Parnell, Marconi and Gen. Michael Collins found time to stop here. This fifth generation, family-run hotel is located in the heart of Clonakilty Town. Abounding in history, the old world charm has been retained whilst still providing the guest with facilities such as bath/shower en suite, TV, etc. Our restaurant provides snacks and full meals and is open to non-residents. Ideal for conferences, private functions, meetings, etc., with lock up car park.

An IHF Quality Employer

B&B from €45.00 to €60.00

O'Donovan Family
Proprietors

21

Closed 25 - 29 December

B&B Rates are per Person Sharing per Night incl. Breakfast.
or Room Rates are per Room per Night - See also Page 8

Commodore Hotel

HOTEL ★★ MAP 313

Westbourne Place,
Cobh,
Co. Cork
Tel: 021-481 1277 Fax: 021-481 1672
Email: commodorehotel@eircom.net
Web: www.commodorehotel.ie
GPS: N +51° 50' 59.46" W -8° 17' 46.59"

The Commodore Hotel, owned and managed by the O'Shea family, overlooks Cork Harbour. 25 minutes from Cork City centre - regular train service. Facilities: indoor swimming pool and sauna (seasonal) - weekend entertainment, free WiFi. Ideal location for visiting Fota Wildlife Park, Blarney, The Queenstown and Jamestown Heritage Centres. All 42 rooms have full facilities, (21 overlook Cork Harbour - supplement applies). Ringaskiddy Ferryport 15 minutes via river car ferry. Please enquire about Facilities for Persons with Disabilities.

An IHF Quality Employer

Bookable on www.irelandhotels.com
Special Offer: www.irelandhotels.com/offers

B&B from €45.00 to €85.00

Patrick O'Shea
General Manager
42

Food for Kids Activities:

Closed 24 - 25 December

WatersEdge Hotel

HOTEL ★★★ MAP 313

(Next To Cobh Heritage Centre),
Cobh,
Co. Cork
Tel: 021-481 5566 Fax: 021-481 2011
Email: info@watersedgehotel.ie
Web: www.watersedgehotel.ie
GPS: N +51° 50' 56.50" W -8° 17' 52.47"

Situated on the waterfront overlooking Cork Harbour. All rooms en suite with satellite TV, tea making facilities, direct dial phone, modem, hairdryer, trouser press. Our restaurant, Jacobs Ladder, is renowned for its seafood, steaks, ambience and friendly staff. Local activities and sightseeing include Cobh Heritage Centre (next door), Cathedral, Titanic Trail, Fota Wildlife Park, Fota House & Gardens, golf, sailing, angling, tennis, horse riding. Ideal touring base for Cork City, Kinsale & Blarney. Please enquire about Facilities for Persons with Disabilities.

Member of Cork Luxury Hotels

Bookable on www.irelandhotels.com
Special Offer: www.irelandhotels.com/offers

B&B from €50.00 to €150.00
Suites from €200.00 to €400.00

Paul Davidson
Manager
19

Activities:

Closed 24 - 26 December

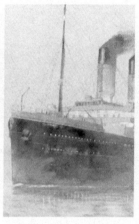

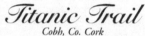

B&B Rates are per Person Sharing per Night incl. Breakfast.
or Room Rates are per Room per Night - **See also Page 8**

Cork Airport / Cork City

Cork International Airport Hotel

HOTEL ★★★★ MAP 2 H 3

Cork Airport,
Co. Cork

Tel: 021-454 9800 Fax: 021-454 9999
Email: reservations@corkairporthotel.com
Web: www.corkinternationalairporthotel.com
GPS: N +51° 51' 5.94" W -8° 29' 5.49"

In a break from what is regarded as the norm for airport hotels, this property offers the lucky guest a wide range of services. This 146 bedroomed hotel is located just a short walk from the airport terminal (a free shuttle bus service is also available) and just ten minutes from Cork City Centre. Cork International Airport Hotel is ideal for business or pleasure or that special occasion. Book online www.corkinternationalairporthotel.com Please enquire about Facilities for Persons with Disabilities.

Bookable on www.irelandhotels.com
Special Offer: www.irelandhotels.com/offers

B&B from €45.00 to €90.00

Aaron Mansworth
General Manager

146

Activities:

Closed 23 - 27 December

Radisson Blu Hotel Cork Airport

HOTEL ★★★★ MAP 2 H 3

Cork Airport,
Co. Cork

Tel: 021-494 7500 Fax: 021-494 7501
Email: reservations.airport.cork@radissonblu.com
Web: www.radissonblu.com
GPS: N +51° 50' 53.59" W -8° 29' 10.95"

The Radisson Blu Hotel Cork Airport is a stylish contemporary hotel conveniently located within walking distance to the terminal at Cork Airport. Complimentary shuttle to and from airport also provided. The Hotel offers its guests a leisure centre, business centre (internet access) and a wide range of meeting rooms. The Radisson Blu Hotel is the perfect base for business meetings or for early departure or late arrival flights into and out of Cork Airport. Bookable worldwide through Rezidor Hotel Reservations or in house reservations on 021-494 7500. Please enquire about Facilities for Persons with Disabilities.

An IHF Quality Employer

Member of Radisson Blu Hotels & Resorts

Bookable on www.irelandhotels.com
Special Offer: www.irelandhotels.com/offers

Room Rate from €59.00 to €155.00

Rose O'Donovan
General Manager

81

Open All Year

Achill House

GUESTHOUSE ★★★ MAP 2 H 3

Western Road,
Cork City

Tel: 021-427 9447 Fax: 021-427 8426
Email: info@achillhouse.com
Web: www.achillhouse.com
GPS: N +51° 53' 45.40" W -8° 29' 16.83"

The perfect balance of luxury style and location, Achill House is on of Cork's gems. A warm and relaxed welcome, whether on business or pleasure. Our individually styled bedrooms are decorated to the highest standards, with an optional jacuzzi. An extensive breakfast menu caters for all tastes, from hearty Irish breakfast to lighter options. An excellent base to explore Cork City & county. Complimentary internet access available. Please enquire about Facilities for Persons with Disabilities.

Bookable on www.irelandhotels.com
Special Offer: www.irelandhotels.com/offers

B&B from €40.00 to €55.00

Helena McSweeney
Manager

6

Closed 24 - 29 December

B&B Rates are per Person Sharing per Night incl. Breakfast.
or Room Rates are per Room per Night - **See also Page 8**

Ambassador Hotel & Health Club

HOTEL ★★★★ MAP 2 H 3

Military Hill,
St. Lukes,
Cork

Tel: 021-453 9000 Fax: 021-455 1997
Email: info@ambassadorhotel.ie
Web: www.ambassadorhotelcork.ie
GPS: N +51° 54' 18.49" W -8° 27' 33.83"

Located on a hilltop, the Ambassador Hotel commands spectacular views over Cork City and Harbour. 70 spacious bedrooms luxuriously decorated to the highest standards. A gourmet award-winning "Season's Restaurant", Cocktail Bar, Embassy Bar, Conference Centre and Banqueting facilities, all combine to ensure a memorable stay. Health Centre (gym, jacuzzi, sauna, steam room) allows guests to unwind at leisure. An excellent base to explore Cork City and county. Free wireless access in all bedrooms.

An IHF Quality Employer

Member of Cork Luxury Hotel Group

Bookable on www.irelandhotels.com

Special Offer: www.irelandhotels.com/offers

B&B from €62.50 to €92.50

Chris Crowley
Resident Manager

70

Closed 24 - 27 December

Ashley Hotel

HOTEL ★★ MAP 2 H 3

Coburg Street,
Cork City

Tel: 021-450 1518 Fax: 021-450 1178
Email: info@ashleyhotel.com
Web: www.ashleyhotel.com
GPS: N +51° 54' 7.03" W -8° 28' 14.93"

Within a wonderful mid – 19th century house, this charming hotel with its fashionable downtown location, close to bus and train stations, is offering free on-site parking with CCTV, locked at night and a 24hour front desk service. Well appointed bedrooms offering en suite bathrooms. Remote controlled television. Direct dial phone, complimentary tea and coffee tray. The main shopping centres and Cork's bustling St Patrick's Street is just around the corner. Local stouts and beers are served in the ground floor lounge bar, and enjoy our home-cooked food.

Bookable on www.irelandhotels.com

Special Offer: www.irelandhotels.com/offers

B&B from €55.00 to €100.00

Anita Coughlan

27

Open All Year

Blarney Stone

GUESTHOUSE ★★★ MAP 2 H 3

Western Road,
Cork City

Tel: 021-427 0083 Fax: 021-427 0471
Email: bsgh@eircom.net
Web: www.blarneystoneguesthouse.ie
GPS: N +51° 53' 45.36" W -8° 29' 17.14"

Our guesthouse is located five minutes from the city centre, opposite University College and close to a diverse range of restaurants, cocktail bars, traditional pubs and bustling nightlife. Close to train, bus, airport. All rooms en suite, newly decorated to highest standard - TV, DD phone, WiFi, Tea/Coffee facilities. We would like to share with you our luxurious accommodation. Our promise is to offer you a warm and friendly service in a relaxed atmosphere at moderate prices. Enjoy spending time with us. Bookable on www.blarneystoneguesthouse.ie. Please enquire about Facilities for Persons with Disabilities.

Bookable on www.irelandhotels.com

B&B from €39.50 to €59.50

Angela Hartnett
Proprietor

8

Open All Year

B&B Rates are per Person Sharing per Night incl. Breakfast.
or Room Rates are per Room per Night - **See also Page 8**

Cork City

Commons Inn

HOTEL ★★★ MAP 3 H 3

New Mallow Road,
Cork

Tel: 021-421 0300 Fax: 021-421 0333
Email: info@commonsinn.com
Web: www.commonsinn.com
GPS: N +51° 55' 18.65" W -8° 29' 15.43"

Close to Cork City, on the main Cork to Blarney road, this family-run hotel contains the popular Commons Bar, Baileys Restaurant and the Roebuck Room function centre. All rooms contain two queen sized beds and are priced per room. Enjoy carvery lunch in the bar or dinner in one of Cork's best restaurants. Whether you're in Cork on business or for pleasure, we are at your service. Please enquire about Facilities for Persons with Disabilities.

Room Rate from €80.00 to €110.00

Ashley Colson
Accommodation Manager 40

Activities:

Closed 24 - 27 December

Crawford Guesthouse

GUESTHOUSE ★★★ MAP 3 H 3

Western Road,
Cork

Tel: 021-427 9000 Fax: 021-427 9927
Email: info@crawfordhouse.ie
Web: www.crawfordhouse.ie
GPS: N +51° 53' 43.17" W -8° 29' 31.55"

One of Cork's finest guesthouses offering bed & breakfast in a contemporary setting. All the bedrooms provide comfort and luxury with oak-wood furniture and orthopaedic beds. De luxe en suites include jacuzzi baths and power showers. Fax/modem points in all rooms. Located directly across from University College Cork. 10 minutes walk to city centre. Private car park. AA 4 Yellow Stars & RAC ♦♦♦♦ and Sparkling Diamond Award. Recommended by Lonely Planet Guide, Time Out Guide, Bradt City Guide and Gourmet Magazine. Free Wi-Fi in reception.

Bookable on www.irelandhotels.com

B&B from €38.00 to €55.00

Cecilia O'Leary- Kareem
Manager 12

Closed 20 December - 10 January

Fitzgeralds Vienna Woods Hotel Cork

HOTEL ★★★ MAP 3 H 3

Glanmire,
Cork

Tel: 021-455 6800 Fax: 021-482 1120
Email: info@viennawoodshotel.com
Web: www.viennawoodshotel.com
GPS: N +51° 54' 43.11" W -8° 24' 10.74"

A country house hotel, set in 20 acres of woodlands, overlooking Cork Harbour. Excellent location, only 7 minutes from Cork city centre, and close to Fota Wildlife Park and Cork International Airport. An ideal base for touring the Cork region. Superb dining facilities serving à la carte, table d'hôte and snack menus. Excellent wedding and conference facilities with generous private car parking. Fitzgeralds Woodlands House Hotel and Spa is a sister hotel located in Adare, Co. Limerick. Please enquire about Facilities for Persons with Disabilities.

An IHF Quality Employer
Member of Irish Country Hotels

Bookable on www.irelandhotels.com
Special Offer: www.irelandhotels.com/offers

B&B from €40.00 to €90.00
Suites from €150.00 to €300.00

David Fitzgerald, Michael Magner
Proprietors 50

Closed 24 - 26 December

B&B Rates are per Person Sharing per Night incl. Breakfast.
or Room Rates are per Room per Night - See also Page 8

Garnish House

GUESTHOUSE ★★★ MAP 3 H 3

Western Road,
Cork

Tel: 021-427 5111 Fax: 021-427 3872
Email: garnish@iol.ie
Web: www.garnish.ie
GPS: N +51° 53' 45.23" W -8° 29' 18.50"

RAC 4♦♦♦♦ and AA 4*. Offers a homely atmosphere and personal attention normally reserved for old friends. Individually styled rooms, some with Jacuzzi baths, are tranquil and charming and our traditional welcome is more than mere words with tea, pastries and an award-winning gourmet breakfast as featured on national TV. 24/7 reception, central to the city and opposite Cork University. Awards: Sparkling Diamond, Bridgestone Chosen Place to Stay. 4**** studios/suites available. Free internet (wireless) access. Gulliver's Guest House Winner 2007.

Bookable on www.irelandhotels.com
Special Offer: www.irelandhotels.com/offers

B&B from €45.00 to €100.00
Suites from €100.00 to €200.00

Johanna Lucey
Manageress

21

Open All Year

Gresham Metropole

HOTEL ★★★ MAP 3 H 3

MacCurtain Street,
Cork

Tel: 021-464 3700 Fax: 021-450 6450
Email: info@gresham-metropolehotel.com
Web: www.gresham-hotels.com
GPS: N +51° 54' 4.52" W -8° 28' 3.97"

Situated in the heart of Cork City Centre, the Gresham Metropole Hotel is just a short stroll from the many excellent shops, boutiques, theatres, galleries & the business district of Cork. During your stay in this superb hotel in Cork City, you will be accommodated in one of 112 tastefully decorated bedrooms, equipped with all necessities to ensure a comfortable & relaxing stay. For those looking for that added bit of relaxation a visit to our leisure centre is a must.

An IHF Quality Employer
Member of Gresham Hotel Group

Bookable on www.irelandhotels.com
Special Offer: www.irelandhotels.com/offers

B&B from €45.00 to €130.00
Suites from €250.00 to €400.00

Roger Russell
General Manager

112

Activities:

Open All Year

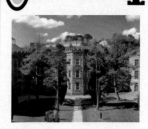

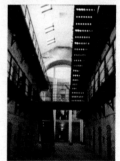

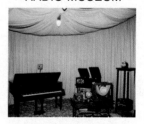

B&B Rates are per Person Sharing per Night incl. Breakfast.
or Room Rates are per Room per Night - **See also Page 8**

Cork City

Hayfield Manor Hotel

HOTEL ★★★★★ MAP 2 H 3

Perrott Avenue,
College Road,
Cork

Tel: 021-484 5900 Fax: 021-431 6839
Email: enquiries@hayfieldmanor.ie
Web: www.hayfieldmanor.ie
GPS: N +51° 53' 27.57" W -8° 29' 24.58"

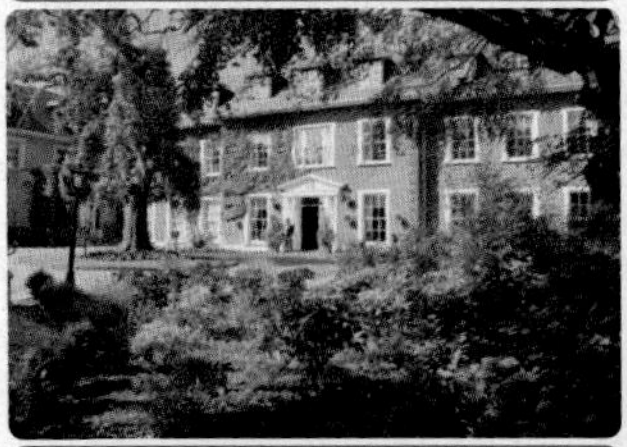

Hayfield Manor is a unique Irish experience with our staff dedicated to providing you with individual & memorable service. Our spacious rooms have been individually designed in classical style with elegant marble bathrooms. As a resident, you have exclusive access to The Beautique Spa. We offer two award-winning & distinctive restaurants, The Manor Bar & our renowned Afternoon Tea. Awarded IGTOA Hotel of the Year 2005, Georgina Campbell's Ireland Hotel of the Year 2006 & AA Irish Hotel of the Year 2003/2004. Hotel & Catering Review Gold Medal Awards 5* Hotel of the Year 2007. Condé Nast Gold List 2009.

An IHF Quality Employer

Member of Small Luxury Hotels of the World

Bookable on www.irelandhotels.com

B&B from €85.00 to €190.00
Suites from €390.00 to €1,031.00

Ettienne van Vrede
Managers
88

Open All Year

Hotel Isaacs

HOTEL ★★★ MAP 3 H 3

48 MacCurtain Street,
Cork

Tel: 021-450 0011 Fax: 021-450 6355
Email: cork@isaacs.ie
Web: www.isaacs.ie
GPS: N +51° 54' 5.75" W -8° 28' 5.13"

Unique Victorian Hotel tucked away underneath an archway in Cork's city centre. Minutes from bus and train stations. Beautifully furnished standard and air-conditioned superior rooms plus serviced holiday apartments. Facilities include television, phone, hospitality tray, hairdryer, ironing facilities and personal safe. Wi-Fi and broadband available throughout the hotel. Greenes Restaurant, overlooking the floodlit waterfall, offers modern creative cuisine. Dine al fresco all year in the heated courtyard garden. Limited free parking close to the hotel. Please enquire about Facilities for Persons with Disabilities.

Member of Isaacs Group

Bookable on www.irelandhotels.com
Special Offer: www.irelandhotels.com/offers

Room Rate from €50.00 to €200.00

Paula Lynch
General Manager
50

Activities:

Closed 23 - 27 December

Imperial Hotel with Escape Salon and Spa

HOTEL ★★★★ MAP 3 H 3

South Mall,
Cork

Tel: 021-427 4040 Fax: 021-427 5375
Email: reservations@imperialhotelcork.ie
Web: www.flynnhotels.com
GPS: N +51° 53' 49.80" W -8° 28' 12.66"

A national treasure built in 1813, the magnificently restored 4**** Imperial Hotel with Escape Salon & Spa, in the heart of Cork City. The Imperial's charm lies in its intimate atmosphere, stylish décor & personalised hospitality. You will find the staff warm & flexible with a spirit of unrivalled generosity. All rooms are individually designed and supremely comfortable. Enjoy a Guinness at South's Bar, dine at the Pembroke Restaurant which offers totally delicious food and treat yourself to an experience at Ireland's first Aveda Lifestyle Salon & Spa, Escape. Please enquire about Facilities for Persons with Disabilities.

Member of Flynn Hotels

Bookable on www.irelandhotels.com
Special Offer: www.irelandhotels.com/offers

Room Rate from €79.00 to €200.00
Suites from €250.00 to €950.00

Joe Kennedy
General Manager
130

Food for Kids

Closed 23 - 27 December

B&B Rates are per Person Sharing per Night incl. Breakfast.
or Room Rates are per Room per Night - **See also Page 8**

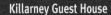

Jurys Cork Hotel

HOTEL ★★★★ MAP 2 H 3

Western Road,
Cork

Tel: 021-425 2700 Fax: 021-427 4477
Email: cork@doylecollection.com
Web: www.doylecollection.com
GPS: N +51° 53' 45.05" W -8° 29' 5.95"

Jurys Cork Hotel is steeped in luxury throughout - designed to delight the eye and capitalise on its commanding riverside location. With 182 stylish bedrooms and an entire floor dedicated to meeting rooms and a business centre, the hotel offers the perfect fusion of business and pleasure. Visitors can also enjoy the contemporary Weir Restaurant and Bar, luxurious Urban Escape Day Spa and a state-of-the-art leisure centre.

An IHF Quality Employer

Member of The Doyle Collection

Bookable on www.irelandhotels.com

Room Rate from €99.00 to €289.00

Ruairi O'Connor
General Manager

182

Food for Kids

Open All Year

Killarney Guest House

GUESTHOUSE ★★★ MAP 2 H 3

Western Road,
(Opp. UCC),
Cork City

Tel: 021-427 0290 Fax: 021-427 1010
Email: killarneyhouse@iol.ie
Web: www.killarneyguesthouse.com
GPS: N +51° 53' 43.27" W -8° 29' 30.71"

This charming, distinctive, delightful and different guesthouse is renowned for its unique blend of comfort, style and hospitality. Its sumptuous breakfast menu includes a buffet table laden with fresh produce and home baking. All rooms are en suite with optional jacuzzi bath. A close walk to the city centre and opposite the University College Cork. Large car park for your security. AA 4* Acclaimed and RAC ♦♦♦♦. Also available, superb self catering apartments.

Bookable on www.irelandhotels.com

Special Offer: www.irelandhotels.com/offers

B&B from €40.00 to €60.00

Margaret O'Leary
Manageress

19

Closed 24 - 27 December

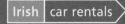

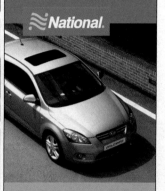

B&B Rates are per Person Sharing per Night incl. Breakfast.
or Room Rates are per Room per Night - **See also Page 8**

Cork City

Maldron Hotel Cork

HOTEL ★★★ MAP 2 H 3

John Redmond Street,
Shandon,
Cork
Tel: 021-452 9200 Fax: 021-452 9222
Email: info.cork@maldronhotels.com
Web: www.maldronhotels.com
GPS: N +51° 54' 9.93" W -8° 28' 28.56"

Nestled beneath the Shandon Bells, the Maldron Hotel Cork is conveniently located just a two minute walk from Patrick St, Cork's main vibrant thoroughfare. Facilities include 101 spacious guest rooms, Stir Restaurant and Bells Bar - a perfect place for a relaxing drink. Club Vitae Health and Fitness Club boasts a superb 20m pool, jacuzzi, steam room, sauna, treatment room and fully equipped gymnasium. Complimentary, but limited car parking. Free WiFi and Broadband internet access. Please enquire about Facilities for Persons with Disabilities.

An IHF Quality Employer

Member of Maldron Hotels

Bookable on www.irelandhotels.com

Special Offer: www.irelandhotels.com/offers

Room Rate from €69.00 to €139.00

Aidan Moynihan
General Manager

101

Food for Kids

Closed 23 - 27 December

Maryborough Hotel & Spa

HOTEL ★★★★ MAP 3 H 3

Maryborough Hill,
Douglas,
Cork
Tel: 021-436 5555 Fax: 021-436 5662
Email: info@maryborough.ie
Web: www.maryborough.com
GPS: N +51° 52' 25.68" W -8° 25' 13.02"

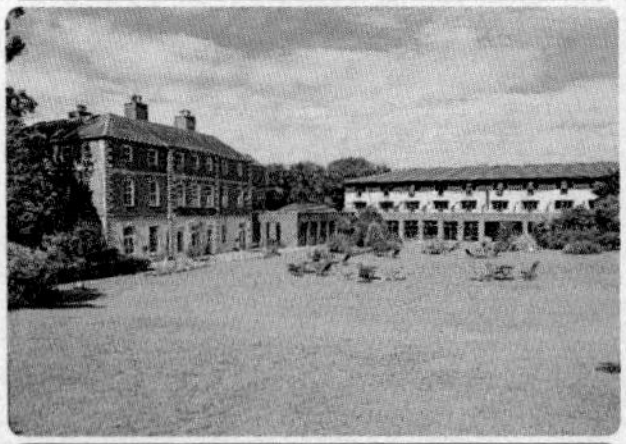

One of Cork's leading hotels, The Maryborough is a unique experience. This 4* de luxe hotel offers sophistication & luxury in an intimate atmosphere; an exclusive product with premier service, where customer service is the main focus & the perfect destination for business & pleasure. 93 executive rooms & suites, Zings Restaurant & Café Bar, 11 conference rooms, Maryborough Club & ESPA Spa. Impeccable hospitality, elegant & individual, you will enjoy the service excellence that we have to offer. EFQM Business Excellence. Please enquire about Facilities for Persons with Disabilities.

An IHF Quality Employer

Bookable on www.irelandhotels.com

Special Offer: www.irelandhotels.com/offers

B&B from €65.00 to €150.00

Justin McCarthy
General Manager

93

Food for Kids Activities:

Closed 24 - 26 December

Montenotte Hotel

HOTEL ★★★★ MAP 2 H 3

Middle Glanmire Road,
Montenotte,
Cork
Tel: 021-453 0050 Fax: 021-453 0060
Email: info@themontenottehotel.com
Web: www.themontenottehotel.com
GPS: N +51° 54' 16.39" W -8° 27' 7.86"

Superb four star hotel with spectacular views overlooking Cork City. Only minutes walk to the city centre, close to Cork's finest restaurants, including the famous Boardwalk Bar and Grill which is associated with this property, shopping and all that's required to enhance your 'Cork Experience'. Extensive free customer parking, leisure club complete with 20 metre pool , sauna, jacuzzi, steam room & gym, 19 self-catering apartments, fine food & wine. 'Cork's Best Hotel Address'.... Perfectly located for your convenience.

Member of Select Hotels

Bookable on www.irelandhotels.com

Special Offer: www.irelandhotels.com/offers

Room Rate from €59.00 to €179.00
Suites from €100.00 to €300.00

John Gately
MD / Proprietor

107

Activities:

Closed 23 - 27 December

B&B Rates are per Person Sharing per Night incl. Breakfast.
or Room Rates are per Room per Night - **See also Page 8**

Radisson Blu Hotel & Spa Cork

HOTEL ★★★★ MAP 2 H 3

Ditchley House,
Little Island,
Cork

Tel: 021-429 7000 Fax: 021-429 7101
Email: info.cork@radissonblu.com
Web: www.radissonblu.ie/hotel-cork
GPS: N +51° 54' 19.53" W -8° 21' 29.37"

Nestled on 9 acres of landscaped gardens, in close proximity to the city centre and Cork International Airport, the hotel is a fusion of old world charm and new world sophistication, offering 129 luxurious guest rooms and suites. The extravagant Retreat Spa & Fitness Centre includes 9 treatment rooms, state of the art gymnasium, Power Plates and a hydrotherapy treatment pool. Boasting extensive meeting and events facilities. Dining options include the chic "Island Grillroom" and the elegant "Banks Bar" for lighter meals and cocktails. Please enquire about Facilities for Persons with Disabilities.

Bookable on www.irelandhotels.com
Special Offer: www.irelandhotels.com/offers

B&B from €55.00 to €110.00
Suites from €208.00 to €340.00

Micheál Stapleton
General Manager

129

Closed 23 - 27 December

Silver Springs Moran Hotel

HOTEL ★★★★ MAP 3 H 3

Tivoli,
Cork

Tel: 021-450 7533 Fax: 021-450 7641
Email: silverspringsinfo@moranhotels.com
Web: www.moranhotels.com
GPS: N +51° 54' 15.19" W -8° 25' 24.39"

This 4**** hotel has been completely re-designed and re-furbished. All 109 bedrooms, including 5 de luxe suites, boast widescreen multi channel TV, fluffy duvets, hypoallergenic pillows, in room safe & high speed WiFi. Conveniently located only minutes from Cork City & 7 miles from Cork International Airport. Excellent base for touring Cork's many visitor attractions. Full leisure facilities available inc. 25m pool. Free parking. Please enquire about Facilities for Persons with Disabilities.

An IHF Quality Employer

Member of Moran Hotel Group

Bookable on www.irelandhotels.com
Special Offer: www.irelandhotels.com/offers

B&B from €50.00 to €150.00
Suites from €160.00 to €250.00

Tom Moran
Managing Director

109

Food for Kids *Activities:*

Closed 23 - 27 December

Courtmacsherry Hotel & Coastal Cottages

HOTEL ★★ MAP 2 G 2

Courtmacsherry,
Bandon,
Co. Cork

Tel: 023-884 6198 Fax: 023-884 6137
Email: courtmacsherryhotel@eircom.net
Web: www.courtmacsherryhotel.ie
GPS: N +51° 37' 57.87" W -8° 41' 55.94"

Courtmacsherry is an exquisite mansion located in west Cork. The hotel has a total of 10 rooms and has been recently refurbished. The rooms have been designed to add to the Victorian theme that is evident throughout every part of this unique hotel. All of these rooms are en suite with all of the basic commodoties. All of the front rooms have an exquisite view overlooking the bay, which is literally a stones throw away. Courtmacsherrys' award winning restaurant, The Cork Tree Restaurant, is well known all over West Cork. An ideal setting to unwind and enjoy the vast and diverse menu.

B&B from €45.00 to €55.00

Billy Adams

10

Closed 01 November - 10 March

B&B Rates are per Person Sharing per Night incl. Breakfast.
or Room Rates are per Room per Night - See also Page 8

Fota Island / Glengarriff

Fota Island Hotel & Spa

Hotel ★★★★★ Map 3 I 3

Fota Island Resort,
Fota Island,
Co. Cork
Tel: 021-467 3000 Fax: 021-467 3456
Email: reservations@fotaisland.ie
Web: www.fotaisland.ie
GPS: N +51° 54' 0.68" W -8° 17' 28.69"

Offering superb views of the surrounding championship golf courses and mature woodland, Fota Island Hotel & Spa has developed into one of Ireland's finest five star resort properties. Elegantly designed bedrooms and suites, world class spa facilities. Catering options ranging from informal to fine dining, three golf courses, a golf academy and all weather tennis courts are just some of the many services and facilities available to guests. Please enquire about Facilities for Persons with Disabilities.

Bookable on www.irelandhotels.com

Room Rate from €99.00 to €229.00
Suites from €164.00 to €554.00

John O'Flynn
General Manager

131

Activities:

Closed 20 - 27 December

Casey's Hotel

Hotel ★★ Map 1 D 2

Glengarriff,
Co. Cork

Tel: 027-63010 Fax: 027-63072
Email: info@caseyshotelglengarriff.ie
Web: www.caseyshotelglengarriff.com
GPS: N +51° 45' 0.06" W -9° 33' 3.86"

Casey's Hotel is owner managed by the Deasy family. Offering a personal, friendly service with old fashioned courtesy. All our rooms are en suite with telephone, TV and tea/coffee. Private off road car parking and gardens. The perfect base for day trips to Killarney, Sheep's Head and Gougane Barra. Come and discover the unspoilt beauty of the Beara Peninsula. Fine food assured in our bar and à la carte restaurant. Visit our website or phone for special offers.

B&B from €47.00 to €55.00

Donal & Eileen Deasy
Proprietors

19

Closed 15 November - 14 March

Glengarriff Eccles Hotel

Hotel ★★★ Map 2 D 2

Glengarriff,
Co. Cork

Tel: 027-63003 Fax: 027-63319
Email: info@eccleshotel.com
Web: www.eccleshotel.com
GPS: N +51° 45' 8.53" W -9° 32' 24.94"

Located opposite Garnish Island, in beautiful Bantry Bay. The Glengarriff Eccles Hotel is one of the oldest established hotels in Ireland (1745). Now fully restored, this family-run hotel boasts 66 en suite bedrooms, many with panoramic views, restaurant and bar. Ideally situated to explore the beauty of the Beara Peninsula. Golf (3 courses within 20 km), fishing, hill walking and sailing are all nearby. 17km from Bantry. Please enquire about Facilities for Persons with Disabilities.

An IHF Quality Employer

Bookable on www.irelandhotels.com

B&B from €50.00 to €150.00
Suites from €200.00 to €400.00

Willie Bucldey
Operations Manager

66

Activities:

Closed 01 January - 01 February

B&B Rates are per Person Sharing per Night incl. Breakfast.
or Room Rates are per Room per Night - See also Page 8

Glengarriff Park Hotel

HOTEL ★★★ MAP 1 D 2

The Village,
Glengarriff,
West Cork

Tel: 027-63000 Fax: 027-63526
Email: info@glengarriffpark.com
Web: www.glengarriffpark.com
GPS: N +51° 45' 1.29" W -9° 32' 58.74"

Located in the heart of the beautiful village of Glengarriff, at the entrance to the Blue Pool Park and Garnish island. Our hotel offers you the unique opportunity to relax and unwind, with a range of luxurious bedrooms and suites. Share a drink with the locals in our warm, friendly bar or enjoy superior dining in the Park Bistro. We are perfectly situated to tour the Beara Peninsula and the Ring of Kerry or take a walk through the 60 acres of parks, botanical gardens and nature reserve right on our doorstep. Please enquire about Facilities for Persons with Disabilities.

Bookable on www.irelandhotels.com

B&B from €49.00 to €79.00
Suites from €170.00 to €240.00

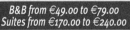

Maureen MacCarthy
Proprietor

26

Open All Year

Gougane Barra Hotel

HOTEL ★★★ MAP 2 E 3

Gougane Barra,
Ballingeary,
Co. Cork

Tel: 026-47069 Fax: 026-47226
Email: gouganebarrahotel@eircom.net
Web: www.gouganebarrahotel.com
GPS: N +51° 50' 19.99" W -9° 19' 0.94"

Our family-run hotel hotel is nestled in one of the most scenic & romantic glens in the south west of Ireland, at the source of the River Lee, overlooking Gougane Barra Lake and St. Finbarr's sixth century hermitage. A favourite place for visitors, this small imtimate hotel is renowned for its fine food, comfort, relaxed atmosphere, warm welcome and splendid views of the lake, the glen and hills beyond.

Member of Irish Country Hotels

Bookable on www.irelandhotels.com

B&B from €55.00 to €75.00

Katy & Neil Lucey

26

Closed 17 October - 01 April

Innishannon House Hotel

HOTEL ★★★ MAP 2 G 2

Innishannon,
Co. Cork

Tel: 021-477 5121 Fax: 021-477 5609
Email: info@innishannon-hotel.ie
Web: www.innishannon-hotel.ie
GPS: N +51° 45' 34.71" W -8° 38' 53.55"

The most romantic hotel in Ireland built in 1720 in the Petit Château style on the banks of the River Bandon, close to Kinsale. All rooms are en suite with TV, DD phone, radio, etc. Award-winning restaurant (RAC, Egon Ronay) serving fresh fish. Superb wine cellar, stunning views, free salmon and trout fishing from the grounds. Horse riding and golf nearby. GDS code: UI Toll Free 1-800-44 UTELL.

Room Rate from €50.00 to €130.00

David Roche
General Manager

12

Closed 30 January - 28 February

B&B Rates are per Person Sharing per Night incl. Breakfast.
or Room Rates are per Room per Night - **See also Page 8**

Kinsale

Actons Hotel

HOTEL ★★★ MAP 2 H 2

Pier Road,
Kinsale,
Co. Cork

Tel: 021-477 9900 Fax: 021-477 2231
Email: res@actonshotelkinsale.com
Web: www.actonshotelkinsale.com
GPS: N +51° 42' 11.95" W -8° 31' 16.31"

Superior 3 star hotel located in landscaped gardens overlooking Kinsale's beautiful harbour. Renowned for its welcoming and friendly atmosphere, Actons also features an award-winning restaurant (Kinsale Good Food Circle Member), bar/bistro, and health & fitness club with new lobby, lounges and gardens. Conference and banqueting facilities available. Located in the historic town of Kinsale with restaurants, pubs, cafés, art and craft shops. Activities nearby: golfing, fishing, sailing, walking, historical sites.

An IHF Quality Employer

Member of Select Hotels of Ireland

Bookable on www.irelandhotels.com

B&B from €50.00 to €75.00

Jack Walsh
General Manager

73

Activities:

Open All Year

Blue Haven Kinsale (The)

HOTEL ★★★ MAP 2 H 3

3-4 Pearse Street,
Kinsale,
Co. Cork

Tel: 021-477 2209 Fax: 021-477 4268
Email: info@bluehavenkinsale.com
Web: www.bluehavenkinsale.com
GPS: N +51° 42' 23.15" W -8° 31' 22.53"

One of Ireland's best known hotels, The Blue Haven graciously combines the charm of yesterday with the luxuries of today. Each room is individually furnished with exquisite furniture, the ultimate in luxury pocket sprung beds, plasma TVs and finer touches to make each room unique. The Blue Haven is famous for its fine cuisine and service excellence, whether it's in our luxurious Restaurant blu, our newly refurbished Bar or our stylish café, Café Blue.

An IHF Quality Employer

Member of The Blue Haven Collection

Bookable on www.irelandhotels.com

B&B from €60.00 to €115.00

Declan Delaney / Loretto Kiernan
Managers

17

Food for Kids *Activities:*

Closed 24 - 26 December

Carlton Hotel & C-Spa Kinsale

HOTEL ★★★★ MAP 2 H 2

Rathmore Road,
Kinsale,
Co. Cork

Tel: 021-470 6000 Fax: 021-470 6001
Email: info@carltonkinsalehotel.com
Web: www.carlton.ie/kinsale
GPS: N +51° 41' 56.62" W -8° 27' 52.86"

Situated on 90 acres of mature wooded parkland, the Carlton Kinsale Hotel & C-Spa is committed to providing the highest of standards. 90 luxury bedrooms and garden suites, most with views overlooking Oysterhaven Bay. Our restaurant offers superb cuisine with fine menus & spectacular views. Captain's Bar serves food all day. Conference & banqueting facilities are magnificent. Guests can enjoy our luxury leisure club & indulge in the C-Spa. 5 mins. from Kinsale Town & 20 mins. from Cork City. Complimentary parking & shuttle bus to Kinsale for all our guests. Room Reservations LoCall 1890 288 288.

An IHF Quality Employer

Member of Carlton Hotel Group

Bookable on www.irelandhotels.com

Special Offer: www.irelandhotels.com/offers

B&B from €49.00 to €129.00
Suites from €258.00 to €420.00

John McGrath
General Manager

90

Closed 24 - 27 December

B&B Rates are per Person Sharing per Night incl. Breakfast.
or Room Rates are per Room per Night - See also Page 8

Friar's Lodge

GUESTHOUSE ★★★★ MAP 2 H 2

Friar's Street,
Kinsale,
Co. Cork
Tel: 021-477 7384 Fax: 021-477 4363
Email: mtierney@indigo.ie
Web: www.friars-lodge.com
GPS: N +51° 42' 25.74" W -8° 31' 36.31"

Welcome! Friar's Lodge is situated in the heart of beautiful, award-winning, historical Kinsale. An ideal base for exploring the wonders of West Cork. All the rooms are luxurious, offering our guest every facility. A short stroll to the world famous restaurants and lively bars. Golfers welcomed, tee times can be arranged and we have a golf club drying room. Secure off street car park. RAC ♦♦♦♦♦, AA 5*. iPod stations in most rooms. Please enquire about Facilities for Persons with Disabilities.

Bookable on www.irelandhotels.com

B&B from €45.00 to €75.00
Suites from €120.00 to €170.00

Maureen Tierney
Owner

18

Closed 22 - 27 December

Jim Edwards

GUESTHOUSE ★★ MAP 2 H 2

Market Quay,
Kinsale,
Co. Cork
Tel: 021-477 2541 Fax: 021-477 3228
Email: info@jimedwardskinsale.com
Web: www.jimedwardskinsale.com
GPS: N +51° 42' 21.04" W -8° 31' 22.77"

Family-run since 1971, Jim Edwards has a tradition of a warm, friendly welcome. All rooms are en suite and tastefully decorated with TV, telephone, tea/coffee making facilities. The guesthouse boasts an excellent seafood restaurant (fully licensed) which is a member of Kinsale Good Food Circle. The bar with its nautical theme throughout serves bar food all day. Being situated in the heart of the town means easy access to all the lively bars and entertainment. Local amenities include golf, deep sea angling, sailing, horse riding.

B&B from €35.00 to €45.00

Jim Edwards

7

Open All Year

Kilcaw Guesthouse

GUESTHOUSE ★★★ MAP 2 H 2

Kinsale,
Situated On R600,
Co. Cork
Tel: 021-477 4155 Fax: 021-477 4755
Email: info@kilcawhouse.com
Web: www.kilcawhouse.com
GPS: N +51° 42' 35.54" W -8° 30' 1.85"

A family-run guesthouse, just north of Kinsale Town centre, with safe off the road parking and beautifully landscaped gardens. The guesthouse is built with a traditional flair yet is modern and luxurious. The bedrooms are spacious, furnished in antique pine and are en suite with TV, phone and tea/coffee making facilities. Just a 20 minute drive from Cork Airport and ferry. An ideal base for touring Blarney, Cobh, West Cork and Old Head of Kinsale. We welcome you to experience the warmth and hospitality of our home. Mobile: 087 7971752

B&B from €32.00 to €55.00

Henry & Christina Mitchell
Owners

7

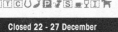

Open All Year

B&B Rates are per Person Sharing per Night incl. Breakfast.
or Room Rates are per Room per Night - **See also Page 8**

Kinsale

Old Bank House (The)

GUESTHOUSE ★★★★ MAP 2 H 2

11 Pearse Street,
Kinsale,
Co. Cork
Tel: 021-477 4075 Fax: 021-477 4296
Email: info@oldbankhousekinsale.com
Web: www.oldbankhousekinsale.com
GPS: N +51° 42' 21.55" W -8° 31' 18.82"

Located in the heart of Kinsale, this magnificent building is the perfect blend of Georgian splendour and modern comfort. Many rooms enjoy views of the harbour town of Kinsale & full gourmet Irish breakfast is included in the rate. The new 'Collection Suite' is an exclusive suite with an elegant finish, AV entertainment and jacuzzi bath. Cafe No. 11, Gourmet Burger Bar, Boutique Bakery & Food Store are all new additions to the Old Bank House that offer a wide variety of innovative & exciting homemade produce, available to dine in or take away.

B&B from €60.00 to €115.00
Suites from €190.00 to €350.00

Ciaran Fitzgerald
Managing Director

17

Activities:

Closed 24 - 26 December

Tierney's Guest House

GUESTHOUSE ★★ MAP 2 H 2

70 Main Street,
Kinsale,
Co. Cork
Tel: 021-477 2205
Email: info@tierneys-kinsale.com
Web: www.tierneys-kinsale.com
GPS: N +51° 42' 19.90" W -8° 31' 26.14"

Tierney's Guesthouse is a well established guesthouse situated in the heart of award-winning Kinsale. We offer TV, hairdryer, tea/coffee in each room, all of which are en suite and have been newly refurbished to a high standard. Enjoy breakfast in our beautiful Courtyard Conservatory Café. WiFi zone available. A warm welcome is guaranteed and we will be only too happy to direct you to the many activities available and places to visit in Kinsale.

Bookable on www.irelandhotels.com

B&B from €35.00 to €45.00

Fiona O'Mahony
Owner

9

Closed 23 - 27 December

Trident Hotel

HOTEL ★★★★ MAP 2 H 2

World's End,
Kinsale,
Co. Cork
Tel: 021-477 9300 Fax: 021-477 4173
Email: info@tridenthotel.com
Web: www.tridenthotel.com
GPS: N +51° 42' 3.48" W -8° 31' 7.10"

The Trident has a spectacular setting on the water's edge in Kinsale. A 4**** hotel, it has 75 bedrooms and luxury suites. There are magnificent views from almost every vantage point in the hotel, particularly from the Schooner Lounge and the 'Pier One' Restaurant, where local seafood is a speciality. The cosy Wharf Tavern serves excellent bar food and has a lovely sheltered terrace overlooking the hotel's marina. Guests of the Trident Hotel can avail of full leisure centre, pool and outdoor hot tub at nearby Actons Hotel (just 5 minutes walk). Please enquire about Facilities for Persons with Disabilities.

An IHF Quality Employer

Bookable on www.irelandhotels.com

B&B from €40.00 to €85.00
Suites from €100.00 to €500.00

Hal McElroy
Managing Director

75

Activities:

Closed 24 - 26 December

B&B Rates are per Person Sharing per Night incl. Breakfast.
or Room Rates are per Room per Night - **See also Page 8**

White House

GUESTHOUSE ★★★ MAP 2 H 2

Pearse St. & The Glen,
Kinsale,
Co. Cork
Tel: 021-477 2125 Fax: 021-477 2045
Email: whitehse@indigo.ie
Web: www.whitehouse-kinsale.ie
GPS: N +51° 42' 23.79" W -8° 31' 24.05"

The White House epitomises Kinsale hospitality with 3*** accommodation, Le Restaurant d'Antibes and a thoroughly modern bar and bistro where all the old values of guest satisfaction, comfort and value for money prevail. We have welcomed both visitors and locals since the 1850s and from its earliest days it has enjoyed a reputation for fine food, drinks of good cheer and indulgent service. Today we pride ourselves on enhancing that tradition. A member of Kinsale's Good Food Circle, West Cork Fuschia branding and Féile Bia Charter.

An IHF Quality Employer

Member of Premier Guesthouses

Bookable on www.irelandhotels.com

B&B from €55.00 to €100.00

Rose & Michael Frawley
Proprietors

10

Activities:

Closed 24 - 26 December

Coolcower House

GUESTHOUSE ★★ MAP 2 F 3

Coolcower,
Macroom,
Co. Cork
Tel: 026-41695
Email: info@coolcowerhouse.ie
Web: www.coolcowerhouse.ie
GPS: N +51° 53' 14.97" W -8° 56' 33.11"

Coolcower House is a large country residence on picturesque grounds. The house is ideally located within easy driving distance of all the tourist attractions in the Cork-Kerry region including Killarney, Kenmare, Kinsale, Blarney, Bantry, Cobh and Midleton. Located on the edge of the River Lee for coarse fishing and boating. Our bedrooms offer TVs, tea/coffee making facilities, DD telephones and hairdryers. Fully licensed bar and home cooked meals available. Outdoor tennis court for residents use. We look forward to welcoming you to Coolcower House.

Bookable on www.irelandhotels.com

Special Offer: www.irelandhotels.com/offers

B&B from €40.00 to €48.00

Evelyn Casey
Proprietor

12

Activities:

Closed 30 November - 14 March

Riverside Park Hotel (The)

HOTEL ★★★ MAP 2 F 3

Killarney Road,
Macroom,
Co. Cork
Tel: 026-20090 Fax: 026-20093
Email: info@riversideparkhotel.ie
Web: www.riversideparkhotel.ie
GPS: N +51° 54' 16.80" W -8° 59' 7.56"

Nestled on the banks of the River Sullane, we are on the main Cork to Killarney road on the outskirts of Macroom. With Macroom's old town charm, a golf club adjacent to the hotel, game and coarse angling nearby, we are ideally situated for those looking for the perfect break. Ideal for weddings (up to 250) and boasting 33 luxurious rooms, some with beautiful river views. Please enquire about Facilities for Persons with Disabilities.

Member of The Mulcahy Hotel Group

B&B from €45.00 to €55.00
Suites from €120.00 to €160.00

Gerry Lavin
General Manager

33

Closed 24 - 27 December

B&B Rates are per Person Sharing per Night incl. Breakfast.
or Room Rates are per Room per Night - **See also Page 8**

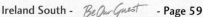

Mallow / Mitchelstown / Rosscarbery

Springfort Hall Hotel

HOTEL ★★★ MAP 2 G 4

Mallow,
Co. Cork

Tel: 022-21278 Fax: 022-21557
Email: stay@springfort-hall.com
Web: www.springfort-hall.com
GPS: N +52° 11' 7.20" W -8° 39' 24.72"

This magical, elegant country house hotel is located just outside Mallow, North Cork. Hidden away amidst tranquil ancient woodlands, Springfort Hall evokes memories of a bygone era full of gentility, charm, great country cooking and sincere customer service. Located in the heart of the Blackwater Valley just 30 minutes from Cork City, Springfort Hall is the perfect base for exploring Cork, its history, its beauty and its unique charm. The Walsh family and their team of professionals invite you to join them at their elegant and magical 18th century country manor. Please enquire about Facilities for Persons with Disabilities.

An IHF Quality Employer

Bookable on www.irelandhotels.com

B&B from €59.00 to €79.00

Walsh Family
Proprietors

49

Activities:

Closed 23 - 27 December

Fir Grove Hotel

HOTEL ★★ MAP 3 I 5

Cahir Hill,
Mitchelstown,
Co. Cork

Tel: 025-24111 Fax: 025-84541
Email: info@firgrovehotel.com
Web: www.firgrovehotel.com
GPS: N +52° 16' 27.72" W -8° 16' 20.02"

The Fir Grove Hotel is a modern newly renovated hotel, set in its own grounds in the shadow of the Galtee Mountains. Situated on the N8, main Cork/Dublin route, we are the ideal base for touring Munster. Our Mulberry Restaurant and Gradoge Bar serve good local food at affordable prices. All bedrooms are en suite with multi channel TV. Local facilities include golf, fishing, hill walks, pony-trekking and Mitchelstown Caves. From Cork/Dublin M8 - come off at exit 12 or 13 and hotel is situated on Limerick road roundabout. From Limerick - 2nd exit on roundabout. From Mitchelstown - 4th exit on roundabout.

B&B from €55.00 to €65.00

Brenda & Pat Tangney
Proprietors

14

Closed 23 - 26 December

Celtic Ross Hotel Conference & Leisure Centre

HOTEL ★★★ MAP 2 F 1

Rosscarbery,
West Cork

Tel: 023-884 8722 Fax: 023-884 8723
Email: info@celticrosshotel.com
Web: www.celticrosshotel.com
GPS: N +51° 34' 33.18" W -9° 1' 44.17"

West Cork is an area of outstanding beauty; the Celtic Ross Hotel, nestled in Rosscarbery Bay, is at the heart of this charming and historical region - the ideal base for touring West Cork and the islands. Superior 3 star hotel with 66 well appointed rooms, many with sea views. Druids Restaurant offers table d'hôte & à la carte menu, our Kingfisher Bar and Lounge offers high quality meals all day. Conference and banqueting facilities for up to 250 people. Leisure centre: 15m heated pool, bubble pool, baby pool, steam room, sauna and gym. Beauty and massage therapies in our Holistic Suite!

An IHF Quality Employer

Member of Select Hotels

Bookable on www.irelandhotels.com

Special Offer: www.irelandhotels.com/offers

B&B from €45.00 to €100.00

Christopher Byrnes
General Manager

66

Activities:

Closed 09 January - 12 February

B&B Rates are per Person Sharing per Night incl. Breakfast.
or Room Rates are per Room per Night - **See also Page 8**

Corthna-Lodge Guesthouse

GUESTHOUSE ★★★ MAP 1 D 1

Airhill,
Schull,
Co. Cork
Tel: 028-28517
Email: info@corthna-lodge.net
Web: www.corthna-lodge.net
GPS: N +51° 31' 32.61" W -9° 33' 37.27"

Charming high standard Guesthouse in a quiet setting, within walking distance of lovely Schull Village and harbour. Ideally positioned for touring in West Cork, golfing in Bantry or walking on the nice beaches of Barley Cove, boat trips to Cape Clear, etc. Our beautifully landscaped gardens, with an outdoor Hot Tub and a Sauna House, are the perfect place to relax and dream. All our nicely decorated bedrooms are en suite with TV, phone and hairdryer. Free use of our gym and BBQ area. Our guests have a separate Lounge with Tea/Coffee facilities and Wireless Internet access.

Room Rate from €80.00 to €90.00

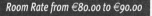

Andrea & Martin Mueller
Owners

6

Closed 30 September - 01 May

Harbour View Hotel

HOTEL ★★★ MAP 1 D 1

East End,
Schull,
Co. Cork
Tel: 028-28101 Fax: 028-27557
Email: info@harbourviewhotelschull.com
Web: www.harbourviewhotelschull.com
GPS: N +51° 31' 38.45" W -9° 32' 37.24"

This newly opened hotel overlooks Schull Harbour. The 30 bedrooms are finished to the highest standard and offer many breathtaking views of the harbour. The leisure centre includes 16 metre pool, steam room, sauna, hydrotherapy pool, gym and two treatment rooms. Lunch served daily from 12.30 - 3pm. Comprehensive bar menu from 12.30 - 9.30pm, Restaurant from 6.00pm - 9.30pm offering à la carte and table d'hôte menus. All functions catered for up to 200 people. We also have 8 apartments next to the hotel, all with sea views and with full use of leisure facilities within the hotel.

B&B from €45.00 to €80.00

Shane Nallan
General Manager

30

Closed 25 - 27 December

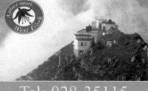

Shanagarry / Skibbereen / Youghal

Garryvoe Hotel

HOTEL ★★★★ MAP 3 J 3

Ballycotton Bay,
Shanagarry,
Co. Cork
Tel: 021-464 6718 Fax: 021-464 6824
Email: res@garryvoehotel.com
Web: www.garryvoehotel.com
GPS: N +51° 51' 33.90" W -8° 0' 13.97"

The coastal location of Garryvoe Hotel directly overlooking 5 kms of one of Ireland's finest beaches, is an ideal holiday destination. The hotel provides the holidaymakers with a warm and friendly feeling which will be long remembered. This beautiful area of Cork has an abundance of sporting and leisure pursuits. Combined with the above and only 30 minutes drive from Cork City, Garryvoe Hotel's new bedrooms enhance the spectacular views from the hotel. Extensive leisure facility added Winter 2009. Please enquire about Facilities for Persons with Disabilities.

Member of Irish Country Hotels

Bookable on www.irelandhotels.com
Special Offer: www.irelandhotels.com/offers

Room Rate from €69.00 to €145.00
Suites from €220.00 to €300.00

Stephen Belton
General Manager

60

Activities:

Closed 24 - 26 December

West Cork Hotel

HOTEL ★★★ MAP 2 E 1

Ilen Street,
Skibbereen,
Co. Cork
Tel: 028-21277 Fax: 028-22333
Email: info@westcorkhotel.com
Web: www.westcorkhotel.com
GPS: N +51° 33' 2.89" W -9° 16' 13.97"

The West Cork Hotel offers one of the warmest welcomes you will find in Ireland, and combines old-fashioned courtesy with the comfort of tastefully decorated and well-equipped accommodation. Guests can enjoy the friendly bar atmosphere or dine in the elegant restaurant. However long your stay, the West Cork Hotel is the perfect base from which to discover and explore the glorious surroundings and activities available in West Cork.

Bookable on www.irelandhotels.com
Special Offer: www.irelandhotels.com/offers

B&B from €40.00 to €75.00

Charlie Costelloe
General Manager

30

Activities:

Closed 23 - 28 December

Quality Hotel & Leisure Centre Youghal

HOTEL ★★★ MAP 3 J 3

Redbarn Beach,
Youghal,
Co. Cork
Tel: 024-93050 Fax: 024-20699
Email: info.youghal@qualityhotels.ie
Web: www.qualityhotelyoughal.com
GPS: N +51° 55' 29.99" W -7° 52' 21.51"

Superb beachside location. Facilities include Club Vitae Health & Fitness Club incorporating swimming pool, sauna, steam room, jacuzzi, children's pool, 4 treatment and therapy suites, 2 outdoor sports pitches, children's crèche, playground, movie room, games room, along with Lannigan's Restaurant and Coast Bar, which are both ocean facing. Our accommodation offering includes both standard and family guest rooms, 2 bedroom apartments and 3 & 4 bedroom holiday homes. Please enquire about Facilities for Persons with Disabilities.

Member of Maldron Hotels - Partner Hotel

Bookable on www.irelandhotels.com
Special Offer: www.irelandhotels.com/offers

Room Rate from €39.00 to €109.00
Suites from €79.00 to €199.00

Allen McEnery
General Manager

25

Food for Kids

Closed 15 - 27 December

B&B Rates are per Person Sharing per Night incl. Breakfast.
or Room Rates are per Room per Night - See also Page 8

Walter Raleigh Hotel

HOTEL ★★★ MAP 3 J 3

O'Brien Place,
Youghal,
Co. Cork
Tel: 024-92011 Fax: 024-93560
Email: info@walterraleighhotel.com
Web: www.walterraleighhotel.com
GPS: N +51° 56' 48.33" W -7° 50' 36.74"

Wake up to spectacular sea views, enjoy our friendly atmosphere and value orientated offerings. Ideal base to explore the sunny southeast and Youghal's pristine Blue Flag beaches - we can tailor any type of holiday on your request. Experience real Irish hospitality from our local staff members and soak up the quiet and relaxed ambience, leaving you fresh for the night's activities. Angling, golf and group packages our speciality. Pet friendly rooms available on request. Please enquire about Facilities for Persons with Disabilities.

Bookable on www.irelandhotels.com
Special Offer: www.irelandhotels.com/offers

Room Rate from €59.00 to €99.00
Suites from €129.00 to €159.00

Michael Davitt
General Manager

40

Activities:

Closed 25 December

B&B Rates are per Person Sharing per Night incl. Breakfast.
or Room Rates are per Room per Night - See also Page 8

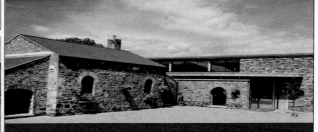

Ballybunion / Caragh Lake

Eagle Lodge

GUESTHOUSE ★ MAP 5 D 6

Town Centre,
Ballybunion,
Co. Kerry
Tel: 068-27224

GPS: N +52° 30' 42.08" W -9° 40' 20.62"

Owner managed, delightful guesthouse situated in town centre. All bedrooms with bathrooms and central heating throughout. A beautiful lounge and private car park for guests. Local amenities include two championship golf courses, sea fishing, tennis, pitch and putt, swimming and boating. Extra value reduced green fees at Ballybunion Golf Club. Cliff walks and wind surfing also available. Ballybunion Health & Leisure Centre nearby.

B&B from €40.00 to €60.00

Mildred Gleasure

8

Open All Year

Ard-Na-Sidhe Country House

HOTEL ★★★★ MAP 1 D 4

Caragh Lake,
Killorglin,
Co. Kerry
Tel: 066-976 9105 Fax: 066-976 9282
Email: reservations@ardnasidhe.com
Web: www.ardnasidhe.com

GPS: N +52° 3' 36.87" W -9° 50' 28.80"

18 bedroomed 4**** de luxe Victorian mansion delightfully located in its own park on Caragh Lake. Tastefully furnished with antiques and open fireplaces. Luxurious lounges and restaurant. Free boating, fishing and facilities of sister hotels - The Europe Hotel Resort and Hotel Dunloe Castle - available to guests. 10 major golf courses nearby. Special green fees. Please enquire about Facilities for Persons with Disabilities.

Member of Killarney Hotels Ltd

Bookable on www.irelandhotels.com

B&B from €85.00 to €150.00

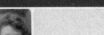

Michael W. Brennan
Group Manager

18

Activities:

Closed 15 October - 01 May

Carrig Country House

GUESTHOUSE ★★★★ MAP 1 D 4

Caragh Lake,
Killorglin,
Co. Kerry
Tel: 066-976 9100
Email: info@carrighouse.com
Web: www.carrighouse.com

GPS: N +52° 4' 26.23" W -9° 51' 0.58"

Charming Victorian Manor on acres of lakeside woodlands & gardens (935 plant species). Furnished in period style with antique furniture. Central to 12 superb golf courses, fishing, shooting, hill walking or just lazing by the fireside with a good book. Award-winning restaurant (open to non residents). Ideal for touring the Ring of Kerry, Dingle & Killarney. Recommended by Bridgestone Guide, 100 Best Places to Stay in Ireland, The Good Hotel Guide, an AA "Country House of the Year 2003/4" & Best Loved Hotels, The Michelin Guide. AA Rosette Restaurant. Georgina Campbells "Hideaway of the Year '09".

Member of Private Ireland Collection

Bookable on www.irelandhotels.com
Special Offer: www.irelandhotels.com/offers

B&B from €75.00 to €125.00

Frank & Mary Slattery
Hosts / Proprietors

17

Activities:

Closed 01 December - 01 March

B&B Rates are per Person Sharing per Night incl. Breakfast
or Room Rates are per Room per Night - See also Page 8

Harbour House & Leisure Centre

GUESTHOUSE ★★★ MAP 1 C 5

Scraggane Pier,
Castlegregory,
Co. Kerry

Tel: 066-713 9292 Fax: 066-713 9557
Email: stay@iol.ie
Web: www.maharees.ie
GPS: N +52° 18' 54. 40" W -10° 2' 18.00"

The family-run Harbour House is superbly located on the tip of the Maharees Peninsula and has its own indoor heated swimming pool, sauna and gym. Fitz Old World Bar offers an excellent Bar menu all day. Its Islands Restaurant has panoramic views of the breathtaking scenery of the Maharees Islands and offers an excellent range of locally caught seafood, prime steak, meat and vegetarian dishes. If you want tranquillity, serenity, charm and true Irish hospitality, this is the place for you. Local amenities include golf, walking, scuba diving, windsurfing, surfing, fishing, horse riding, cycling etc.

Bookable on www.irelandhotels.com

B&B from €35.00 to €47.50

Pat & Ronnie Fitzgibbon

8

Activities:

Closed 16 December - 03 January

Old Ship Inn

GUESTHOUSE ★★★ MAP 1 C 5

West Main Street,
Castlegregory,
Co. Kerry

Tel: 066-713 9927 Fax: 066-713 9935
Email: oldshipinn1@gmail.com
Web: www.oldshipinn.ie
GPS: N +52° 15' 18.27'' W -10° 1' 20.90''

The Old Ship Inn is a charming guesthouse, dating back to 1881. idyllically situated in the heart of Castlegrogory Village, affording our guests the perfect base to explore and enjoy the innumerable activities locally both on land & sea! A family-run business, which has luxurious bedrooms, with tea/coffee making facilities and all rooms are en suite with power showers. A restaurant on the ground level serves seafood, meat & vegetarian dishes. Have a camera ready because this area is one of the most picturesque in Ireland & pictures taken here will be a memory for a life time.

Bookable on www.irelandhotels.com
Special Offer: www.irelandhotels.com/offers

B&B from €35.00 to €47.50

Phillip Fitzgibbon

8

Closed 22 - 28 December

O'Connor's Guesthouse

GUESTHOUSE ★★ MAP 1 B 5

Cloghane,
Dingle Peninsula,
Co. Kerry

Tel: 066-713 8113 Fax: 066-713 8270
Email: oconnorsguesthouse@eircom.net
Web: www.cloghane.com
GPS: N +52° 14' 4.86" W -10° 10' 56.38"

A long established, spacious country home with spectacular views of sea and mountains, overlooking Brandon Bay and within easy reach of Dingle on the Dingle Way. Private car park, guest lounge, open fire, home cooked meals, restaurant, pub and a warm welcome are just some of the things awaiting our guests. Ideal area for walking, fishing, cycling, pony trekking, swimming, birdwatching or just relaxing.

B&B from €35.00 to €60.00

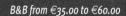

Micheal & Elizabeth O'Dowd
Owners

9

Closed 01 November - 28 February

B&B Rates are per Person Sharing per Night incl. Breakfast.
or Room Rates are per Room per Night - **See also Page 8**

Dingle (An Daingean)

Alpine House

GUESTHOUSE ★★★ MAP 1 B 4

Mail Road,
Dingle,
Co. Kerry
Tel: 066-915 1250 Fax: 066-915 1966
Email: alpinedingle@eircom.net
Web: www.alpineguesthouse.com
GPS: N +52° 8' 15.13" W -10° 16' 8.57"

Run by the O'Shea Family who enjoy conversation with their guests. Highly acclaimed & recommended guesthouse. Bright & spacious double, twin & family ensuite bedrooms, with TV, telephone, hairdryers, central heating & Tea/Coffee facilities. Breakfast is a choice of hot menu & buffet. Relaxing lounge. Two minute stroll to town centre, harbour, restaurants & bus stop. No need for car or taxis. Restaurants & activity reservations made. Drying facilities for walkers & cyclists. Packed lunches. Luggage transfers arranged. Member of 'Get out There' adventure holidays. Non-smoking. eBrochure: http://alpinedingle-ebrochure.com

Member of www.dingleway.com

B&B from €35.00 to €60.00

Paul O'Shea
Proprietor

10

Closed 11 - 25 January

An Bothar Pub

GUESTHOUSE ★★★ MAP 1 B 5

Cuas, Ballydavid,
Dingle, Tralee,
Co. Kerry
Tel: 066-915 5342
Email: botharpub@eircom.net
Web: www.botharpub.com
GPS: N +52° 13' 35.16" W -10° 18' 26.29"

An Bóthar Guesthouse, Restaurant and Bar is a family-run guesthouse and pub situated at the foot of Mount Brandon just 6 miles from Dingle. Where the Dingle Way Walk passes the door at the start of the next day's stage. An ideal base for a walking holiday close to beaches, fishing & golf. In the heart of the Gaeltacht, Gaelic is the first language of the house. À la carte menu and bar menu available during season, March - September. Meals arranged by request out of season. Home-baking & local produce on menu. Additional Tel No's: 066-915 5519 & 087 236 5608

B&B from €40.00 to €40.00

Maurice Walsh
Owners

7

Closed 24 - 25 December

An Portán

GUESTHOUSE ★★ MAP 1 B 4

Dunquin,
Co. Kerry
Tel: 066-915 6212 Fax: 066-915 6222
Email: donn@eircom.net
Web: www.anportan.com
GPS: N +52° 8' 4.19" W -10° 27' 8.30"

Located in Dún Chaoin, the most westerly village in Ireland, opposite Blasket Islands. 15 - 20 minute drive from An Daingean / Dingle. Ferry to the Blasket Islands, 1km, 18 hole golf links 4 km, horse riding 4.5 km, shore angling. Award-winning restaurant fully licensed, small conference room, 14 bedrooms each with separate entrance in secluded setting. Private car park. Please enquire about Facilities for Persons with Disabilities.

B&B from €40.00 to €45.00

Rónán O'Donnchadha

14

Closed 01 October - 01 April

B&B Rates are per Person Sharing per Night incl. Breakfast. or Room Rates are per Room per Night - See also Page 8

Dingle (An Daingean)

Bambury's Guest House

GUESTHOUSE ★★★ MAP 1 B 4

Mail Road,
Dingle,
Co. Kerry
Tel: 066-915 1244 Fax: 066-915 1786
Email: info@bamburysguesthouse.com
Web: www.bamburysguesthouse.com
GPS: N +52° 8' 11.84" W -10° 16' 9.45"

New house, excellent location, 2 minutes walk to town centre. Offering peaceful accommodation in spacious, double, twin or triple rooms all en suite with direct dial telephone and satellite TV. Attractive guest lounge to relax in. Private car parking, choice of breakfast in spacious dining room. Local attractions: Dingle Peninsula, horse riding, angling and golf on local 18 hole golf links. Reduced green fees can be arranged. Listed in all leading guides. Please enquire about Facilities for Persons with Disabilities.

B&B from €35.00 to €60.00

Bernie Bambury
Proprietor

12

Open All Year

Barr na Sraide Inn

GUESTHOUSE ★★★ MAP 1 B 4

Upper Main Street,
Dingle,
Co. Kerry
Tel: 066-915 1331 Fax: 066-915 1446
Email: info@barrnasraide.ie
Web: www.barrnasraide.ie
GPS: N +52° 8' 34.33" W -10° 16' 14.28"

Family-run guesthouse and bar. Located in the town centre. The Barr na Sraide Inn has been recently refurbished to a very high standard. An extensive menu awaits our guests for breakfast. End each day with a relaxing drink in our comfortable bar amongst the locals. Private enclosed car park. Ideal base for your stay in the South West. Golf, fishing, sailing, cycling, horse riding and trips to Fungi the dolphin available nearby. Please enquire about Facilities for Persons with Disabilities.

Member of VFI

Bookable on www.irelandhotels.com

B&B from €35.00 to €55.00

Patricia Geaney

26

Activities:

Closed 18 - 26 December

Boland's Guesthouse

GUESTHOUSE ★★ MAP 1 B 4

Goar Street (Upper Main Street),
Dingle,
Co. Kerry
Tel: 066-915 1426
Email: bolanddingle@eircom.net
Web: www.bolandsdingle.com
GPS: N +52° 8' 37.20" W -10° 16' 23.11"

Boland's Guesthouse is situated in Dingle Town, at the top of Main Street overlooking Dingle Bay. Ideal base for touring Slea Head drive. Minutes walk to restaurants, pubs, entertainment, fishing, golfing, horse riding. Hill walking and sea trips to Fungi the Dingle Dolphin and the Blasket Islands. Our rooms are bright and spacious with modern amenities, some with views of Dingle Bay. We have a full breakfast menu served in our conservatory dining room. Can also be contacted by 085 714 2297. Please enquire about Facilities for Persons with Disabilities.

Member of B&B Network Worldwide

Bookable on www.irelandhotels.com

B&B from €30.00 to €60.00

Breda Boland
Owner

8

Closed 1 - 26 December

B&B Rates are per Person Sharing per Night incl. Breakfast.
or Room Rates are per Room per Night - **See also Page 8**

Dingle (An Daingean)

Castlewood House

GUESTHOUSE ★★★★ MAP 1 B 4

The Wood,
Dingle,
Co. Kerry
Tel: 066-915 2788
Email: castlewoodhouse@eircom.net
Web: www.castlewooddingle.com
GPS: N +52° 8' 28.72" W -10° 17' 10.11"

At Castlewood House a warm welcome awaits you. Luxurious 4 Star, AA 5 Star property located on the shores of Dingle Bay. All rooms are large and well appointed to a very high standard. most with bay views. Facilities include en suite bathrooms with Jacuzi, bath, seperate power shower, TV, DVD, bathrobes & hospitality tray. Free internet access, elevator, non-smoking premises. Winner 2009 Trip Advisor Awards - Hidden Gem Europe & Best Bargain World 2009. AA Breakfast award. Michelin approved. Please enquire about Facilities for Persons with Disabilities.

Bookable on www.irelandhotels.com

B&B from €45.00 to €85.00

Helen Woods Heaton &
Brian Heaton

12

Closed 05 January -10 February

Coastline Guesthouse

GUESTHOUSE ★★★ MAP 1 B 4

The Wood,
Dingle,
Co. Kerry
Tel: 066-915 2494 Fax: 066-915 2493
Email: coastlinedingle@eircom.net
Web: www.coastlinedingle.com
GPS: N +52° 8' 26.89" W -10° 17' 4.39"

Beautiful seafront guesthouse on the water's edge of Dingle Harbour. All rooms are en suite with direct dial phone, TV, hairdryer, tea/coffee facilities and most have panoramic views of the harbour. Ground floor rooms available. Enjoy our excellent breakfast. Relax in our guest lounge or garden and watch the local fishing fleet return with their catch. Private car parking. 5 minute walk to town centre. Ideal base to enjoy all Dingle has to offer - excellent restaurants and pubs. WiFi. Please enquire about Facilities for Persons with Disabilities.

B&B from €35.00 to €55.00

Vivienne O'Shea
Proprietor

8

Closed 15 November - 10 February

Dingle Bay Hotel

HOTEL ★★★ MAP 1 B 4

Strand Street,
Dingle,
Co. Kerry
Tel: 066-915 1231 Fax: 066-915 2740
Email: info@dinglebayhotel.com
Web: www.dinglebayhotel.com
GPS: N +52° 8' 22.30" W -10° 16' 26.03"

Dingle's newest hotel, located by the pier and marina in Dingle Town. The hotel has been designed to the highest standards throughout. Unwind and relax in the very stylish Paudie's Bar and sample the renowned food - seafood is a specialty. The hotel offers regular live entertainment. Guest receive reduced green fees at Dingle Golf Links. Please enquire about Facilities for Persons with Disabilities.

B&B from €45.00 to €110.00

Kathleen Sheehy
General Manager

25

Closed 13 - 26 December

B&B Rates are per Person Sharing per Night incl. Breakfast.
or Room Rates are per Room per Night - **See also Page 8**

Dingle (An Daingean)

Dingle Benners Hotel

HOTEL ★★★ MAP 1 B 4

Main Street,
Dingle,
Co. Kerry
Tel: 066-915 1638 Fax: 066-915 1412
Email: info@dinglebenners.com
Web: www.dinglebenners.com
GPS: N +52° 8' 28.90" W -10° 16' 6.01"

Located in the heart of Dingle Town, the hotel is favoured for its old world charm and style. Luxuriously appointed bedrooms provide an intimate cosy atmosphere complemented by authentic Irish antique furnishings. Mrs. Benner's Bar & Lounges will captivate you on arrival, have a warm friendly welcome and will fill you with a sense of yesteryear. Special weekend and midweek packages available. Please enquire about Facilities for Persons with Disabilities.

An IHF Quality Employer

Member of Manor House Hotels

Bookable on www.irelandhotels.com

B&B from €60.00 to €105.00

Muireann Nic Giolla Ruaidh
General Manager

51

Closed 18 - 27 December

Dingle Skellig Hotel & Peninsula Spa

HOTEL ★★★★ MAP 1 B 4

Dingle,
Co. Kerry
Tel: 066-915 0200 Fax: 066-915 1501
Email: reservations@dingleskellig.com
Web: www.dingleskellig.com
GPS: N +52° 8' 1.90" W -10° 16' 9.90"

Renowned hotel situated on the shores of Dingle Bay with luxurious leisure club & pool. Fungi Kid's Club & Crèche open on weekends & holidays (crèche daily April - October). Excellent cuisine in the Coastguard Restaurant. Established conference and banqueting centre with stunning views. The Peninsula Spa features hydrotherapy, signature treatments plus Yon-Ka face and body treatments, relaxation suite and outdoor hot tub overlooking Dingle Bay. Please enquire about Facilities for Persons with Disabilities.

Bookable on www.irelandhotels.com

B&B from €60.00 to €135.00

Graham Fitzgerald
General Manager

113

Food for Kids *Activities:*

Closed 21 - 27 December

Gorman's Clifftop House and Restaurant

GUESTHOUSE ★★★★ MAP 1 B 5

Glaise Bheag, Ballydavid,
Dingle Peninsula, Tralee,
Co. Kerry
Tel: 066-915 5162 Fax: 066-915 5003
Email: info@gormans-clifftophouse.com
Web: www.gormans-clifftophouse.com
GPS: N +52° 12' 21.88" W -10° 21' 36.94"

A welcoming cliff-top refuge on the western edge of the Dingle Peninsula. All rooms pay homage to the landscape, offering breathtaking views. Our emphasis is on comfort, mini suites boasting king sized beds and jacuzzi baths. Downstairs guests can gather around the fire to read or chat, dine in our fully licensed restaurant. AA 5* Premier Select. Les Routiers "Hidden Gem Ireland" 2001 & "Hotel of the Year" 2001. Georgina Campbell 'Guesthouse of the Year' 2002 (Jameson Guide). Good Food Ireland. Guesthouse and Restaurant of the Year 2006.

Member of Good Food Ireland

Bookable on www.irelandhotels.com
Special Offer: www.irelandhotels.com/offers

B&B from €55.00 to €85.00

Vincent & Sile O'Gormain
Proprietors

9

Closed 24 - 27 December

B&B Rates are per Person Sharing per Night incl. Breakfast.
or Room Rates are per Room per Night - **See also Page 8**

Dingle (An Daingean)

Greenmount House

Guesthouse ★★★★ Map 1 B 4

Upper John Street,
Dingle,
Co. Kerry
Tel: 066-915 1414 Fax: 066-915 1974
Email: info@greenmounthouse.ie
Web: www.greenmounthouse.ie
GPS: N +52° 8' 17.88" W -10° 15' 46.47"

Greenmount House is the proud recipient of several awards for its accommodations & breakfasts. A charming 4**** country house yet centrally located. Spacious lounges to relax in and take advantage of its magnificent scenic location overlooking Dingle Town and harbour. All bedrooms have private bathroom, TV/ radio, direct dial phone & WiFi. Breakfast is served in a conservatory. This year all rooms have been upgraded & a hot tub has been installed in the garden. Wine Bar also new to premises. Recognised by all leading guides. Please enquire about Facilities for Persons with Disabilities.

B&B from €40.00 to €80.00

Maria Curran
Manager

14

Closed 20 - 27 December

Heaton's Guesthouse

Guesthouse ★★★★ Map 1 B 4

The Wood,
Dingle,
Co. Kerry
Tel: 066-915 2288 Fax: 066-915 2324
Email: heatons@iol.ie
Web: www.heatonsdingle.com
GPS: N +52° 8' 26.14" W -10° 16' 51.52"

Heaton's House is a 4**** family-run guesthouse situated on the shore of Dingle Bay with spectacular views, 5 minutes walk from the town. All rooms are en suite (pressure shower and bath), with TV, DD phone and tea/coffee welcome tray and internet access. Breakfast is our speciality. Luxury junior suites and deluxe rooms available. Local amenities include golf, sailing, fishing, surfing, cycling, walking and horse riding. Recognised by many leading guides. Please enquire about Facilities for Persons with Disabilities.

Bookable on www.irelandhotels.com

B&B from €39.00 to €69.00
Suites from €118.00 to €180.00

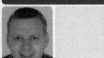

Nuala & Cameron Heaton
Proprietors

16

Closed 28 November - 27 December

Hillgrove (The)

Guesthouse ★ Map 1 B 4

Spa Road,
Dingle,
Co. Kerry
Tel: 066-915 1131 Fax: 066-915 1272
Email: info@hillgrovedingle.com
Web: www.hillgrovedingle.com
GPS: N +52° 8' 35.86" W -10° 15' 46.96"

From the moment you arrive at the Hillgrove, our friendly staff will help make you feel right at home. We pride ourselves in the care and courtesy that we pay to our guests, to ensure that your visit with us is as enjoyable as possible. Accommodation consists of a range of triple, double and twin rooms. Ideally located at the foot of the Conor Pass, just a three minute walk to Dingle town centre.

Bookable on www.irelandhotels.com

B&B from €45.00 to €70.00

Kieran Ashe
Proprietor

12

Open All Year

B&B Rates are per Person Sharing per Night incl. Breakfast. or Room Rates are per Room per Night - See also Page 8

Hillville Manor

HOTEL ★★ MAP 1 C 5

Conor Pass Road,
Dingle Peninsula,
Co. Kerry
Tel: 066-713 8118 Fax: 066-713 8159
Email: bookings@dinglemanorhouse.com
Web: www.dinglemanorhouse.com
GPS: N +52° 14' 14.79" W -10° 6' 48.89"

Hillville Manor built in 1833 is situated off the Conor Pass Road overlooking Brandon Bay. Formerly home to the Hickson family, Captain Paget, Le Marchant, Lord Harrington & Crutchs. This delightful residence owned & managed by the MacDonnell family. Bedrooms are tastefully decorated, some with sea views, 4 poster beds, spacious bathrooms. Traditional home cooking using local fresh produce. Cosy bar with open fireplace. Local activities: golf, walks, river & sea fishing, surfing & dive schools, pony trekking, bird watching & island trips. Location 4km west of Stradbally Village on the Conor Pass Road.

Bookable on www.irelandhotels.com

B&B from €40.00 to €65.00
Suites from €100.00 to €150.00

Ron & Sandra
Proprietors

10

Closed 04 November - 27 December

Milltown House

GUESTHOUSE ★★★★ MAP 1 B 4

Dingle,
Co. Kerry
Tel: 066-915 1372 Fax: 066-915 1095
Email: info@milltownhousedingle.com
Web: www.milltownhousedingle.com
GPS: N +52° 8' 24.22" W -10° 17' 20.30"

Award-winning family-run Milltown House is ideally located overlooking Dingle Bay and town from our private gardens. All rooms which retain the character of the 130 year old house, are en suite, have tea/coffee making facilities, direct dial phone, TV, trouser press, hairdryer and safety deposit box. The house was home to Robert Mitchum during the making of David Lean's epic movie "Ryan's Daughter". Assistance in planning your day. One of the most scenic and tranquil locations in the town area, less than 15 minutes walk or 2 minutes drive! Secure booking on www.milltownhouse.com.

Bookable on www.irelandhotels.com

B&B from €55.00 to €85.00

Tara Kerry

10

Closed 29 October - 06 May

Old Pier, Restaurant and Guesthouse

GUESTHOUSE ★★★ MAP 1 B 4

An Fheothanach,
Ballydavid, Dingle,
Co. Kerry
Tel: 066-915 5242
Email: info@oldpier.com
Web: www.oldpier.com
GPS: N +52° 12' 44.05" W -10° 21' 17.63"

Situated in the heart of the West Kerry Gaeltacht on the Dingle Peninsula overlooking beautiful Smerwick Harbour and the Atlantic Ocean. This family-run establishment offers 3*** accommodation with beautiful sea and mountain vistas. The Old Pier Restaurant offers a broad range of locally caught seafood, prime steak and meat dishes. Adjacent activities include 18 hole golf course, deep sea angling, mountain walking and archaeology sites. A warm welcome awaits you. Please enquire about Facilities for Persons with Disabilities.

B&B from €35.00 to €50.00

Padraig & Jacqui O'Connor

6

Closed 24 - 26 December

Dingle (An Daingean) / Kenmare

Pax House

GUESTHOUSE ★★★★ MAP 1 B 4

Upper John Street,
Dingle,
Co. Kerry
Tel: 066-915 1518 Fax: 066-915 0865
Email: paxhouse@iol.ie
Web: www.pax-house.com
GPS: N +52° 8' 1.77" W -10° 15' 26.14"

Voted one of the top ten places to stay in Ireland. Pax House has undeniably one of the most spectacular views in the peninsula - overlooking Dingle Bay, Ring of Kerry, Blaskets Islands and the entrance to the harbour. Sit back on the balcony and enjoy the activity in the bay and a sighting of Fungi the Dolphin, gulls diving and little fishing boats heading back with the daily catch. Only a 9 minute walk down to the town centre. Please enquire about Facilities for Persons with Disabilities.

Member of Premier Guesthouses

B&B from €45.00 to €65.00
Suites from €120.00 to €200.00

John O'Farrell

12

Closed 01 November - 01 March

Coachmans Townhouse

HOTEL ★★ MAP 1 D 3

8 Henry Street,
Kenmare,
Co. Kerry
Tel: 064-664 1311 Fax: 064-668 9193
Email: info@thecoachmans.com
Web: www.thecoachmans.com
GPS: N +51° 52' 46.05" W -9° 35' 1.25"

Kenmare's newest luxury hotel, the Coachmans offers state of the art accommodation in Kenmare Town Centre. Rooms & suites have AC, king sized beds, sofas, baths & power showers, plasma TVs, underfloor heating. We also offer a small local bar, an informal restaurant, an intimate live music venue & "Ireland's finest" pub courtyard. The Jones family have run the Coachmans for generations & offer a wealth of info. Check out our website for images & special offers. Good service & hospitality. Please enquire about Facilities for Persons with Disabilities.

B&B from €35.00 to €75.00
Suites from €160.00 to €260.00

Padraig Jones
Proprietor

10

Closed 24 - 26 December

Foleys Townhouse

GUESTHOUSE ★★★ MAP 1 D 3

Henry Street,
Kenmare,
Co. Kerry
Tel: 064-664 2162 Fax: 064-664 1799
Email: info@foleyskenmare.com
Web: www.foleyskenmare.com
GPS: N +51° 52' 45.78" W -9° 35' 0.20"

Foley's Townhouse is located in the idyllic village of Kenmare, in the heart of the Ring of Kerry & the Ring of Beara. Foley's is a well appointed & ideal guest house base in easy driving distance to all that picturesque southwest of Ireland has to offer. Foley's boasts an award-winning restaurant & pub with "live" traditional Irish music nightly & big screen televisions carrying all major sporting events. Our menu offers the finest Kerry beef & lamb as well as local produce. All our seafood and shellfish is from the Kenmare Bay. www.foleyskenmare.com for current rates, live secure booking & specials.

B&B from €39.00 to €65.00

Marion Foley
Owner / Manager

10

Open All Year

B&B Rates are per Person Sharing per Night incl. Breakfast. or Room Rates are per Room per Night - See also Page 8

Lansdowne Arms Hotel

HOTEL ★★★ MAP 1 D 3

Main Street,
Kenmare,
Co. Kerry
Tel: 064-664 1368 Fax: 064-664 1114
Email: info@lansdownearms.com
Web: www.lansdownearms.com
GPS: N +51° 52' 44.60" W -9° 34' 53.93"

Built in the 1790s and situated at the top of Kenmare Town. The Lansdowne Arms Hotel, now owned by the Quill family, has undergone extensive refurbishment throughout. Enjoy a relaxed atmosphere in front of the open fires and the hospitality from the warm and friendly staff. All of the 26 rooms and bathrooms have been redecorated and finished to a very high standard with king sized beds, safes, hairdryers, tea/coffee facility, telephone, TV and ironing presses. Private parking. Enjoy a pint in The Bold Thady Quills Traditional Irish Pub & Restaurant, or a relaxing afternoon tea in The Poets Bar.

Member of AA Hotels

Bookable on www.irelandhotels.com

B&B from €55.00 to €85.00

The Quill Family
Proprietors

26

Closed 24 - 25 December

O'Donnabhain's

GUESTHOUSE ★★★ MAP 1 D 3

Henry Street,
Kenmare,
Co. Kerry
Tel: 064-664 2106 Fax: 064-664 2321
Email: info@odonnabhain-kenmare.com
Web: www.odonnabhain-kenmare.com
GPS: N +51° 52' 45.50" W -9° 35' 1.28"

O'Donnabhain's Bar, Restaurant & Guesthouse provides a memorable & quality experience for food, drink and accommodation located in the centre of Kenmare. Rooms are spacious & have been completely redesigned in 09 with the comfort of the guest in mind including all en suite rooms, multi channel, WiFi, phone. Our rooms are located away from the street & bar area to ensure that you have a pleasant nights rest. We also have a car park to the back of the property. You are most welcome to experience the hospitality that our family have been giving to visitors, & locals alike. We look forward to greeting you. Jer & Vanessa.

Bookable on www.irelandhotels.com

B&B from €30.00 to €55.00

Jeremiah Foley
Owner

10

Activities:

Closed 05 December - 31 January

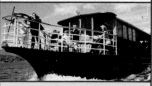

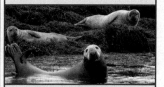

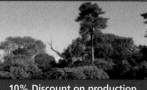

B&B Rates are per Person Sharing per Night incl. Breakfast.
or Room Rates are per Room per Night - See also Page 8

Kenmare

Park Hotel Kenmare

HOTEL ★★★★★ MAP 1 D 3

Shelbourne St,
Kenmare,
Co. Kerry
Tel: 064-664 1200 Fax: 064-664 1402
Email: info@parkkenmare.com
Web: www.parkkenmare.com
GPS: N +51° 52' 40.02" W -9° 34' 49.96"

Since 1897 travellers have enjoyed the gracious elegance of the Park Hotel Kenmare. In a heavenly location overlooking Kenmare Bay the hotel is renowned for its attentive service and international standards. In the deluxe Destination Spa SAMAS and 25 mt lap pool, guests can indulge in the ethos of a true spa to rejuvenate the body, mind & spirit. A host of classes & activities encompass the wonderful location of this special corner of Ireland. 18 hole golf course, tennis, 12 acres of gardens & 40 acre National Park adjoin the grounds. Enjoy one of Ireland's magnificent locations.

An IHF Quality Employer

Member of Small Luxury Hotels

Bookable on www.irelandhotels.com

Special Offer: www.irelandhotels.com/offers

B&B from €145.00 to €275.00
Suites from €696.00 to €846.00

Francis Brennan
Proprietor

46

Activities:

Closed 01 January - 02 April

Sea Shore Farm Guesthouse

GUESTHOUSE ★★★ MAP 1 D 3

Tubrid,
Kenmare,
Co. Kerry
Tel: 064-664 1270 Fax: 064-664 1270
Email: seashore@eircom.net
Web: www.seashorekenmare.com
GPS: N +51° 52' 38.61" W -9° 36' 0.69"

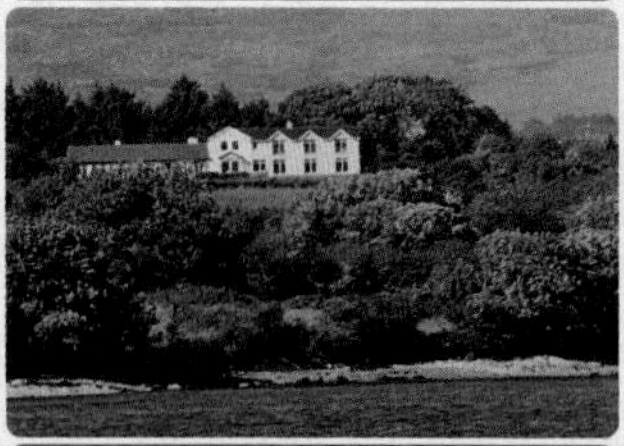

Our setting on the bay is uniquely peaceful and private yet only 1 mile from Kenmare Town, farm extends to the shore affording unspoilt walks in natural habitat with plentiful bird/wildlife. Large en suite rooms with panoramic seascapes, king beds, DD phone, tea facilities. AA 4* selected, Recommended Guide du Routard/Fodors/Karen Brown/ Dummies. Signposted on right - immediately out of Kenmare Town on Killarney Nat. Park Road [N71] [take left on to Tubbrid L5773 Rd] also signposted on N70 Sneem/Ring of Kerry Road - 1 mile from Kenmare Town.

B&B from €50.00 to €65.00

Mary Patricia O'Sullivan
Proprietor

6

Closed 01 November - 10 March

Sheen Falls Lodge

HOTEL ★★★★★ MAP 1 D 3

Kenmare,
Co. Kerry
Tel: 064-664 1600 Fax: 064-664 1386
Email: info@sheenfallslodge.ie
Web: www.sheenfallslodge.ie
GPS: N +51° 52' 27.45" W -9° 33' 48.56"

Uniquely set on the shores of Kenmare Bay & Sheen River, only 2km from the Heritage Town of Kenmare, on a 300 acre woodland estate. Our restaurant La Cascade, offers a distinctive fine dining experience overlooking the Sheen Waterfalls. We also offer casual dining in The Restaurant Lounge. Choose from an extensive array of estate activities from salmon fishing to clay pigeon shooting, or unwind with a visit to the Health Club. Dedicated staff uphold the most outstanding service to make your stay as unforgettable & unique as Ireland itself. Please enquire about Facilities for Persons with Disabilities.

An IHF Quality Employer

Member of Relais et Châteaux

Bookable on www.irelandhotels.com

Special Offer: www.irelandhotels.com/offers

Room Rate from €220.00 to €410.00
Suites from €340.00 to €1,310.00

Alan P Campbell
General Manager

66

Activities:

Closed 02 January - 06 February

B&B Rates are per Person Sharing per Night incl. Breakfast.
or Room Rates are per Room per Night - See also Page 8

19th Green (The)

GUESTHOUSE ★★★ MAP 2 E 4

Lackabane,
Fossa, Killarney,
Co. Kerry
Tel: 064-663 2868 Fax: 064-663 2637
Email: 19thgreen@eircom.net
Web: www.19thgreen-bb.com
GPS: N +52° 4' 7.89" W -9° 33' 41.66"

Comfortable, cosy and welcoming, we are the ideal location for visiting Killarney or the Kerry area, just 3km from Killarney and 500 metres from the beautiful Lakes. All our rooms are decorated to the highest standard with your comfort in mind. Where better to relax with a glass of wine than our sumptuous "Par 4" Lounge with its soft lighting and rich leather furniture.

Bookable on www.irelandhotels.com

B&B from €30.00 to €65.00

John & Freda Sheehan
Proprietors

13

Closed 01 November - 01 March

Abbey Lodge

GUESTHOUSE ★★★★ MAP 2 E 4

Muckross Road,
Killarney,
Co. Kerry
Tel: 064-663 4193 Fax: 064-663 5877
Email: abbeylodgekly@eircom.net
Web: www.abbey-lodge.com
GPS: N +52° 3' 19.02" W -9° 30' 24.02"

A genuine Irish welcome awaits you at Abbey Lodge. Our guesthouse is family-run and boasts 15 luxurious en suite rooms with TV, direct dial phone, power showers and central heating. We are conveniently located on the Muckross Road (N71) a mere three minute walk to the town centre. The house is tastefully decorated throughout and features many interesting antiques and art. With 30 years in the business - anywhere else is a compromise. Complimentary wirless internet in all bedrooms and also P.C available in lounge. Please enquire about Facilities for Persons with Disabilities.

Member of Premier Guesthouses

Bookable on www.irelandhotels.com

B&B from €45.00 to €85.00

John King
Host

15

Closed 20 - 28 December

B&B Rates are per Person Sharing per Night incl. Breakfast.
or Room Rates are per Room per Night - **See also Page 8**

Killarney

Aghadoe Heights Hotel & Spa

HOTEL ★★★★★ MAP 2 E 4

Lakes of Killarney,
Killarney,
Co. Kerry
Tel: 064-663 1766 Fax: 064-663 1345
Email: info@aghadoeheights.com
Web: www.aghadoeheights.com
GPS: N +52° 3' 33.18" W -9° 28' 45.14"

Located in Ireland's most spectacular natural setting Aghadoe Heights Hotel & Spa is the premier destination Spa resort in Ireland. Consistently recognised for its service, guest rooms, suites & penthouse Aghadoe is one of only 4 hotels in Ireland to have achieved five Red Stars from the Automobile Association. We invite you to visit with us and be inspired by the breathtaking views, spellbound by the myth and legend, soothed by our Spa and enchanted by our people.

An IHF Quality Employer

Member of Virtuoso & Ireland's Inspiring Spas

Bookable on www.irelandhotels.com

Special Offer: www.irelandhotels.com/offers

B&B from €75.00 to €185.00
Suites from €225.00 to €325.00

Marie & Pat Chawke
General Manager

74

Activities:

Open All Year

Arbutus Hotel

HOTEL ★★★★ MAP 2 E 4

College Street,
Killarney,
Co. Kerry
Tel: 064-663 1037 Fax: 064-663 4033
Email: stay@arbutuskillarney.com
Web: www.arbutuskillarney.com
GPS: N +52° 3' 34.44" W -9° 30' 21.92"

The Arbutus Hotel and the Buckley family - at the heart of Killarney hospitality since 1926. Generations of visitors have enjoyed their personal introduction to the many attractions of the area whilst enjoying the warmth of a townhouse hotel where loving attention to detail is evident in home-cooked food, the original Buckley's Bar and the marvellous Celtic Deco design throughout. A truly special hotel. Please enquire about Facilities for Persons with Disabilities.

Bookable on www.irelandhotels.com

Special Offer: www.irelandhotels.com/offers

B&B from €60.00 to €95.00

Seán Buckley
Proprietor

30

Closed 08 December - 10 February

Ashville House

GUESTHOUSE ★★★ MAP 2 E 4

Rock Road,
Killarney,
Co. Kerry
Tel: 064-663 6405 Fax: 064-663 6778
Email: info@ashvillekillarney.com
Web: www.ashvillekillarney.com
GPS: N +52° 3' 48.65" W -9° 30' 44.86"

Ashville is an award winning, family-run guesthouse, 2 mins walk from town centre, on main Tralee Road (N22). Private car park. Comfortably furnished en suite rooms include DD telephone, multi channel TV, hairdryer. Sample our varied breakfast menu. Convenient to Killarney National Park, pony trekking, golf & fishing. Ideal touring base for Ring of Kerry, Dingle & Beara. Declan & Elma assure you of a warm welcome at Ashville. Awarded AA 4*. Sparkling Diamond & Warm Welcome Awards. Ground floor rooms available. Complimentary WiFi access.

An IHF Quality Employer

Member of Premier Guesthouses

Bookable on www.irelandhotels.com

B&B from €30.00 to €55.00

Declan & Elma Walsh
Proprietors

12

Closed 01 November - 01 March

B&B Rates are per Person Sharing per Night incl. Breakfast.
or Room Rates are per Room per Night - **See also Page 8**

Best Western Eviston House Hotel

HOTEL ★★★ MAP 2 E 4

New Street,
Killarney,
Co. Kerry
Tel: 064-663 1640 Fax: 064-663 3685
Email: info@evistonhouse.com
Web: www.evistonhouse.com
GPS: N +52° 3' 31.71" W -9° 30' 38.31"

Located in Killarney Town centre, minutes from Killarneys famous beauty spots & championship golf. Our family-run hotel has 103 luxurious rooms; from excellent value standard rooms to superior rooms. For an extra special stay, try one of our luxurious deluxe rooms with king bed & whirlpool bath. Enjoy candllelit dinner in the Colleen Bawn Restaurant or dine in the famous pub "The Danny Mann", while enjoying lively traditional music. Health conscious guests will appreciate our fitness suite. Free WiFi available to all guests. Our reception staff will gladly book tours, golf and activities. A warm welcome is just the beginning!

An IHF Quality Employer

Member of Best Western Hotels

Bookable on www.irelandhotels.com

B&B from €39.00 to €79.00

Edward Eviston
Proprietor

103

Activities:

Closed 23 - 25 December

Brehon (The)

HOTEL ★★★★ MAP 2 E 4

Muckross Road,
Killarney,
Co. Kerry
Tel: 064-663 0700 Fax: 064-663 0701
Email: info@thebrehon.com
Web: www.thebrehon.com
GPS: N +52° 2' 45.30" W -9° 30' 16.02"

The Brehon & Angsana Spa, is a luxurious hotel of unique grace and elegance set amid Killarney's alluring landscape. Each guestroom and suite reflects a contemporary blend of beauty, style and space. Angsana Spa at the Brehon provides a sanctuary for the inner self. The experienced Thai therapists offer a range of holistic spa treatments and massages to refresh and revitalise the spirit, mind and physical being. Please enquire about Facilities for Persons with Disabilities.

An IHF Quality Employer

Member of Gleneagle Group

Bookable on www.irelandhotels.com

B&B from €75.00 to €160.00
Suites from €250.00 to €1,000.00

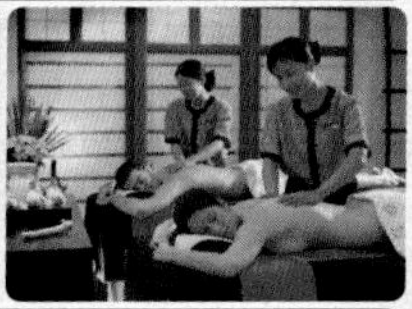

Seán O'Driscoll
General Manager

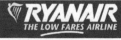

125

Activities:

Open All Year

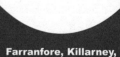

B&B Rates are per Person Sharing per Night incl. Breakfast.
or Room Rates are per Room per Night - **See also Page 8**

Killarney

Brook Lodge Hotel

HOTEL ★★★★ MAP 2 E 4

MSGR. O'Flaherty Road,
High Street, Killarney,
Co. Kerry
Tel: 064-663 1800 Fax: 064-663 5001
Email: brooklodgekillarney@eircom.net
Web: www.brooklodgekillarney.com
GPS: N +52° 3' 38.81" W -9° 30' 45.00"

De luxe family-run 4* hotel in Killarney Town centre off the street with private parking and landscaped gardens. Large bedrooms & junior suites include tea/coffee facilities, hairdryer, iron and ironing board, TV, elevator, wheelchair friendly. Free internet access available. Our hotel has justifiably earned an outstanding reputation for its friendly personal service and relaxed atmosphere. Please enquire about Facilities for Persons with Disabilities.

Bookable on www.irelandhotels.com

B&B from €50.00 to €90.00

Joan Counihan
Owner

24

Closed 01 November - 01 April

Cahernane House Hotel

HOTEL ★★★★ MAP 2 E 4

Muckross Road,
Killarney,
Co. Kerry
Tel: 064-663 1895 Fax: 064-663 4340
Email: reservations@cahernane.com
Web: www.cahernane.com
GPS: N +52° 2' 36.01" W -9° 30' 36.95"

Formerly the residence of the Herbert family, Earls of Pembroke, Cahernane House dates back to the 17th century. Cahernane House Hotel is situated on its own parklands on the edge of Killarney's National Park, an area of outstanding natural beauty with its untamed landscape of mountains, lakes and woodland walks and is only 10 minutes walk from Killarney Town. All of the 38 bedrooms are beautifully appointed, many with antique furniture, jacuzzis and private balconies. No pets allowed. Please enquire about Facilities for Persons with Disabilities.

Member of Manor House Hotels

Bookable on www.irelandhotels.com

B&B from €65.00 to €125.00
Suites from €290.00 to €320.00

Jimmy Browne
Proprietor

38

Closed 23 December - 01 March

Castle Lodge Guesthouse

GUESTHOUSE ★★ MAP 2 E 4

Muckross Road,
Killarney,
Co. Kerry
Tel: 064-663 1545 Fax: 064-663 2325
Email: castlelodge@eircom.net
Web: www.castlelodgekillarney.com
GPS: N +52° 3' 19.14" W -9° 30' 27.23"

Welcome to our family run guest house with a warm welcoming hospitality and family friendly atmosphere, ideally located in the hub of Killarney Town centre, beside the National Park Gates. Our rooms include newly refurbished ground floor and family bedrooms with fresh spacious surroundings and stylish finishing touches. Delicious Traditional Home Cooked Breakfasts set you up for the days activities and adventures ahead and our cosy TV Lounge has an outdoor terrace & gardens for you to relax in every evening. Please enquire about Facilities for Persons with Disabilities.

B&B from €35.00 to €60.00

Aoife & Clara O'Shea
Hosts

1 24

Closed 24 - 26 December

B&B Rates are per Person Sharing per Night incl. Breakfast.
or Room Rates are per Room per Night - **See also Page 8**

Castlerosse Hotel and Golf Resort

HOTEL ★★★ MAP 2 E 4

Lower Lake,
Killarney,
Co. Kerry

Tel: 064-663 1144 Fax: 064-663 1031
Email: res@castlerosse.ie
Web: www.castlerosse.ie
GPS: N +52° 3' 57.49" W -9° 32' 23.91"

The Castlerosse Hotel & Golf Resort located on the lakeside 2kms from Killarney Town with panoramic views of the lakes and mountains. It is flanked on one side by the National Park and on the other by Killarney Golf & Fishing Club. There is a choice of double, twin and family rooms, some with lake and mountain views. Leisure facilities: On-site: 9 hole golf course, health and leisure club with 20m pool, gym, jacuzzi, sauna and spa treatment rooms.

An IHF Quality Employer

Bookable on www.irelandhotels.com
Special Offer: www.irelandhotels.com/offers

B&B from €45.00 to €90.00

Danny Bowe
General Manager

120

Food for Kids *Activities:*

Closed 01 November - 29 March

Crystal Springs

GUESTHOUSE ★★★ MAP 2 E 4

Woodlawn Rd (Off N71),
Ballycasheen, Killarney,
Co. Kerry

Tel: 064-663 3272 Fax: 064-663 5518
Email: crystalsprings@eircom.net
Web: www.crystalspringsbb.com
GPS: N +52° 3' 10.47" W -9° 29' 15.77"

Located on the banks of the peaceful River Flesk offering fishing on location. Just off N22/Cork Road, only a short walk to town centre, where many traditional pubs and fine restaurants can be found. Close to lakes, National Park, Ring of Kerry and I.N.E.C. Spacious en suite rooms, AA**** award. TV, tea/coffee facilities, hairdryers, DD phones, trouser press and refrigerators. Extensive menus including vegetarian and home specialities. Ample safe parking. Fishing on location. Please enquire about Facilities for Persons with Disabilities.

Bookable on www.irelandhotels.com

B&B from €38.00 to €58.00

Eileen & Tim Brosnan

8

Closed 21 - 27 December

Killarney

Darby O'Gill's Country House Hotel

HOTEL ★★★ MAP 2 E 4

Mallow Road(N72),
Lissivigeen, Killarney,
Co. Kerry
Tel: 064-663 4168 Fax: 064-663 6794
Email: darbyogill@eircom.net
Web: www.darbyogillskillarney.com
GPS: N +52° 3' 8.24" W -9° 26' 55.20"

A charming, family-run hotel with mountain views, 5 minutes drive from Killarney Town. The hotel offers a lively lounge with entertainment 7 nights a week during peak season (inc. traditional Irish music). Guests can choose from an extensive Bar Food Menu or dine in Cluricaune's Restaurant. The Sports bar offers Sky and Setanta Sports channels, a pool table, darts, table football and Internet access. Guests can take advantage of free Wi-Fi Hotspots, gardens with outdoor seating & free onsite parking. Please enquire about Facilities for Persons with Disabilities.

An IHF Quality Employer

Bookable on www.irelandhotels.com

Special Offer: www.irelandhotels.com/offers

B&B from €35.00 to €70.00

Pat Gill
Managing Director

43

Closed 24 - 25 December

Dromhall Hotel

HOTEL ★★★★ MAP 2 E 4

Muckross Road,
Killarney,
Co. Kerry
Tel: 064-663 9300 Fax: 064-663 9301
Email: info@dromhall.com
Web: www.dromhall.com
GPS: N +52° 3' 11.92" W -9° 30' 22.63"

Killarney's famous mountain scenes provide a magnificent backdrop for the Dromhall Hotel. Located 5 minutes walk from town, the hotel offers the comfort and service one associates with a first class hotel while retaining the friendliness and welcome of a family-run hotel. From the moment you enter the elegant marbled lobby the scene is set for a special experience. Banquet and conference facilities for up to 300. Award-winning Kaynes Bistro. Club Santé leisure facilities are available to all guests. For sheer indulgence pay a visit to our Zen Day Spa. Please enquire about Facilities for Persons with Disabilities.

An IHF Quality Employer

Member of Randles Hotels

Bookable on www.irelandhotels.com

Special Offer: www.irelandhotels.com/offers

B&B from €55.00 to €119.00

Bernadette Randles
Managing Director

69

Closed 19 - 27 December

Earls Court House

HOTEL ★★★★ MAP 2 E 4

Woodlawn Junction,
Muckross Road, Killarney,
Co. Kerry
Tel: 064-663 4009 Fax: 064-663 4366
Email: info@killarney-earlscourt.ie
Web: www.killarney-earlscourt.ie
GPS: N +52° 3' 6.03" W -9° 30' 17.13"

Luxury 4 star hotel, family-run, offering peace & relaxation in a quiet suburb, only 7 mins walk to town centre. Winner of the "Romantic Elegance Award for Ireland" 2006 & "Ireland's Best Breakfast Award". Experience the elegance & charm of a country house, open fires, tea & home baking. Enjoy spacious rooms graced with antiques, king beds, full bathrooms, four poster suites some with jacuzzi. Wheelchair friendly, tea facilities, elevator & private parking, internet access. Tours & golf arranged. Lounge menu until 8pm. Wine licence. Please enquire about Facilities for Persons with Disabilities.

Bookable on www.irelandhotels.com

Special Offer: www.irelandhotels.com/offers

B&B from €55.00 to €70.00
Suites from €130.00 to €175.00

Emer & Ray Moynihan
Owners

30

Closed 15 November - 12 March

B&B Rates are per Person Sharing per Night incl. Breakfast.
or Room Rates are per Room per Night - **See also Page 8**

Europe Hotel Resort (The)

HOTEL ★★★★★ MAP 2 E 4

Killarney,
Co. Kerry

Tel: 064-667 1300 Fax: 064-663 7900
Email: reservations@theeurope.com
Web: www.theeurope.com
GPS: N +52° 4' 1.10" W -9° 34' 24.89"

Magnificent 5* resort in the most stunning of locations on the Lakes of Killarney & at the foot of the magnificent Kerry mountains. Welcoming guests for almost 50 years the hotel offers exceptional service & world class facilities with the most breathtaking views. All guests enjoy complimentary access to the ESPA at the Europe incl 20m lap pool, indoor & outdoor vitality pools, thermal suites, relaxation areas & techno-gym. Horse riding & indoor tennis also complimentary, boating & fishing can be arranged from hotel's private pier. Killarney Golf Club adjacent. Please enquire about Facilities for Persons with Disabilities.

Member of Killarney Hotels Ltd

Bookable on www.irelandhotels.com

Special Offer: www.irelandhotels.com/offers

B&B from €110.00 to €175.00
Suites from €400.00 to €1,500.00

Michael W. Brennan

187

Food for Kids *Activities:*

Closed 13 December - 05 February

Failte Hotel

HOTEL ★★ MAP 2 E 4

College Street,
Killarney,
Co. Kerry

Tel: 064-663 3404 Fax: 064-663 6599
Email: failtehotel@eircom.net
Web: www.failtehotelkillarney.com
GPS: N +52° 3' 33.86" W -9° 30' 24.58"

The Failte Hotel, furnished to a very high standard, is owned and managed by the O'Callaghan family. It is internationally known for its high standard of cuisine. Paudie supervises the award-winning bar. It is situated in the town centre, adjacent to railway station, new factory outlet, shopping complex. Also close by are many local cabarets and night clubs. Local amenities include golfing, fishing, walking.

Member of Killarney Chamber of Tourism

B&B from €45.00 to €75.00

Dermot & Eileen O'Callaghan
Proprietors

14

Closed 24 - 27 December

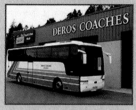

B&B Rates are per Person Sharing per Night incl. Breakfast.
or Room Rates are per Room per Night - **See also Page 8**

Killarney

Fairview Guesthouse

GUESTHOUSE ★★★★ MAP 2 E 4

Michael Collins Place,
College Street, Killarney,
Co. Kerry
Tel: 064-663 4164 Fax: 064-667 1777
Email: info@fairviewkillarney.com
Web: www.fairviewkillarney.com
GPS: N +52° 3' 35.95" W -9° 30' 23.18"

Superbly located in the heart of Killarney Town, yet out of noise's way, Fairview is a luxurious boutique style guesthouse that is unique in quality, location, service & elegance. Parking, spacious rooms with optional jacuzzi suites, all modern amenities including lift & wheelchair facilities, category 3 VAS. A de luxe base from which to tour, golf or socialise. Privately owned & managed. Awards: AA 5* and Sparkling Diamond & Warm Welcome Award, Killarney Best New Development & Guesthouse Awards & the prestigious Little Gem Awards. New Fifth Season Restaurant & optional executive rooms, mini suites & penthouse.

Bookable on www.irelandhotels.com

B&B from €38.00 to €69.00

James & Shelley O' Neill
Proprietors

29

Activities:

Closed 24 - 25 December

Foley's Townhouse & Restaurant

GUESTHOUSE ★★★★ MAP 2 E 4

23 High Street,
Killarney,
Co. Kerry
Tel: 064-663 1217 Fax: 064-663 4683
Email: info@foleystownhouse.com
Web: www.foleystownhouse.com
GPS: N +52° 3' 38.93" W -9° 30' 35.67"

Originally a 19th Century Coaching Inn, this beautiful, old house has hosted generations of travellers. Newly & lovingly refurbished, this is a 4* family run, town centre guesthouse. Luxury bedrooms designed for comfort with every modern amenity, antique furnishings and 12 rooms with jacuzzi baths, lift, wheelchair access & 2 de luxe suites. Downstairs is our award-winning restaurant. Chef/Owner, Carol, provides meals from fresh local produce. Extensive wine list of 300 wines. Personal supervision. Free private car park on premises. Awards: AA & RAC, 5*. A long, outstanding reputation for quality and service.

Member of Premier Guesthouses

Bookable on www.irelandhotels.com

B&B from €50.00 to €75.00
Suites from €200.00 to €300.00

Carol Hartnett
Proprietor

28

Activities:

Closed 01 December - 01 March

Friars Glen

GUESTHOUSE ★★★★ MAP 2 E 4

Mangerton Road,
Muckross, Killarney,
Co. Kerry
Tel: 064-663 7500 Fax: 064-663 7388
Email: friarsglen@eircom.net
Web: www.friarsglen.ie
GPS: N +52° 01' 14" W -9° 29' 21"

"Magnificent, extremely beautiful, delightful, absolutely wonderful, stunning, peaceful and tranquil, fantastic, charming, delicious, relaxing, gracious, comfortable, We'll be back!" Some of the words used by guests to describe Friars Glen in the guest book. Set in its own 28 acres within the world renowned Killarney National Park, Friars Glen is a 4**** country house that offers the highest standards of accommodation and service. The ideal base for exploring Killarney National Park and Ireland's Southwest. Please enquire about Facilities for Persons with Disabilities.

Bookable on www.irelandhotels.com

B&B from €50.00 to €65.00

Mary Fuller
Proprietor

10

Closed 24 October - 12 March

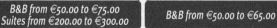

B&B Rates are per Person Sharing per Night incl. Breakfast or Room Rates are per Room per Night - **See also Page 8**

Fuchsia House

GUESTHOUSE ★★★★ MAP 2 E 4

Muckross Road,
Killarney,
Co. Kerry
Tel: 064-663 3743 Fax: 064-663 6588
Email: fuchsiahouse@eircom.net
Web: www.fuchsiahouse.com
GPS: N +52° 3' 2.83" W -9° 30' 27.05"

We invite you to enjoy the affordable luxury of Fuchsia House which is set well back from Muckross Road in mature leafy gardens. Only 7 minutes walk from Killarney Town centre. Purpose built to combine the amenities of a modern 4**** guesthouse with the elegance of an earlier age. We offer spacious rooms with orthopaedic beds, dressed in crisp cotton and linen, DD phone, private bath with power shower. Separate guest kitchen with tea/coffee making facilities. Spacious lounges & conservatory. Complimentary WiFi access throughout. Irish & vegetarian menus. Recommended by all leading guidebooks.

B&B from €40.00 to €60.00

Neil & Marie Burke
Proprietors/Managers

10

Activities:

Closed 01 November - 14 March

Gleann Fia Country House

GUESTHOUSE ★★★ MAP 2 E 4

Lower Coolcorcoran,
Kilcummin Road, Killarney,
Co. Kerry
Tel: 064-663 5035 Fax: 064-663 5000
Email: info@gleannfia.com
Web: www.gleannfia.com
GPS: N +52° 4' 30.14" W -9° 30' 23.43"

Gleann Fia Country House, open year round, is located 2km from Killarney Town. Situated on acres of gardens, river & woodland walks. Our location is perfect for touring scenic sights of Kerry, playing golf on world renowned championship parklands & links courses, fishing & hill walking. All bedrooms are tastefully decorated, some furnished with antiques & all rooms have pleasant views of the surrounding countryside. Breakfast is hot & cold buffet with fresh juices, breads, yogurts, cheese platters. Safe & secure parking. A professional & friendly home style service.

Member of Premier Collection

Bookable on www.irelandhotels.com

B&B from €30.00 to €65.00

Conor & Bridget O'Connell
Proprietors /Hosts

19

Activities:

Open All Year

B&B Rates are per Person Sharing per Night incl. Breakfast.
or Room Rates are per Room per Night - **See also Page 8**

Killarney

Gleneagle Hotel

HOTEL ★★★ MAP 2 E 4

Killarney,
Co. Kerry

Tel: 064-663 6000 Fax: 064-663 2646
Email: info@gleneaglehotel.com
Web: www.gleneaglehotel.com
GPS: N +52° 2' 39.79" W -9° 30' 7.28"

Ireland's leading leisure and conference/convention hotel, adjacent to Killarney's National Park with beautifully furnished rooms. Ireland's National Events Centre is ideally suited for conventions, conferences, exhibitions, sporting events, concerts and theatrical productions. Our award-winning chefs will delight you in both our restaurants. We have a great line-up of entertainment all year round. Relax and unwind using our indoor/outdoor leisure facilities. Please enquire about Facilities for Persons with Disabilities.

An IHF Quality Employer

Member of Gleneagle Group

Bookable on www.irelandhotels.com

B&B from €49.00 to €95.00
Suites from €150.00 to €300.00

John Dolan
General Manager

246

Activities:

Open All Year

Heights Hotel - Killarney (The)

HOTEL ★★★ MAP 2 E 4

Cork Road,
Killarney,
Co. Kerry

Tel: 064-663 1158 Fax: 064-663 5198
Email: info@killarneyheights.ie
Web: www.killarneyheights.ie
GPS: N +52° 3' 33.15" W -9° 28' 45.13"

Situated 1km from Killarney Town centre, this beautiful 71 bedroomed hotel overlooks the breathtaking Torc and Mangerton Mountains. Privately owned and family-run, the hotel offers unparalleled standards of service, luxury accommodation, fine dining and entertainment. The Heights Hotel Killarney is the perfect venue to begin your holiday or tour of our beautiful scenic countryside. Two conference rooms available, facilities include broadband and audio visual equipment. Please enquire about Facilities for Persons with Disabilities.

Bookable on www.irelandhotels.com

B&B from €40.00 to €80.00
Suites from €150.00 to €210.00

Tom O'Mahony
General Manager

71

Activities:

Closed 24 - 26 December

Holiday Inn Killarney

HOTEL ★★★ MAP 2 E 4

Muckross Road,
Killarney,
Co. Kerry

Tel: 064-663 3000 Fax: 064-663 3001
Email: info@holidayinnkillarney.com
Web: www.holidayinnkillarney.com
GPS: N +52° 2' 58.41" W -9° 30' 26.64"

Holiday Inn Killarney enjoys a quiet but central location close to Killarney Town centre. Its 100 spacious en suite guest rooms including 24 family suites, are tastefully decorated to the highest standards. Our fully equipped leisure centre is the perfect place to relax and unwind. Our Library Point Restaurant serves the finest of local cuisine while Saddlers Pub serves food daily and has a live entertainment programme. A haven for all seasons!

An IHF Quality Employer

Bookable on www.irelandhotels.com

Room Rate from €69.00 to €189.00
Suites from €99.00 to €219.00

Misja Herfurt
General Manager

100

Closed 24 - 25 December

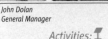

B&B Rates are per Person Sharing per Night incl. Breakfast
or Room Rates are per Room per Night - See also Page 8

Hotel Dunloe Castle

HOTEL ★★★★★ MAP 2 E 4

Killarney,
Co. Kerry

Tel: 064-664 4111 Fax: 064-664 4583
Email: reservations@thedunloe.com
Web: www.thedunloe.com
GPS: N +52° 3' 34.85" W -9° 37' 38.65"

The 5 star Hotel Dunloe Castle prides itself on the elegance, style & warmth of service it can offer. Its luxurious guestrooms make the most of the surrounding landscape offering breathtaking views of mountains or gardens. In this most beautiful natural setting the hotel restaurants offer dishes which showcase the finest local produce & herbs from the kitchen garden. Complimentary leisure facilities include fishing, horse riding, indoor tennis & 25m pool, not to mention the 64 acres of gardens. Space, grace and elegance on a grand scale. Please enquire about Facilities for Persons with Disabilities.

Member of Killarney Hotels Ltd

Bookable on www.irelandhotels.com

Special Offer: www.irelandhotels.com/offers

B&B from €95.00 to €145.00
Suites from €600.00 to €600.00

Jason Clifford
General Manager

98

Food for Kids *Activities:*

Closed 17 October - 03 April

International Hotel

HOTEL ★★★ MAP 2 E 4

Killarney,
Co. Kerry

Tel: 064-663 1816 Fax: 064-663 1837
Email: inter@iol.ie
Web: www.killarneyinternational.com
GPS: N +52° 3' 29.65" W -9° 30' 27.27"

Nestled in the heart of beautiful Killarney, blending the charm & intimacy of times past with contemporary elegance. Recently refurbished, boasting 90 luxurious guestrooms furnished to an exceptional standard. Executive rooms and suites available complete with Italian furniture & flatscreen TVs and an en suite jacuzzi to soothe those aching muscles. Relax in our fitness suite or play world famous courses on our 3D golf simulator. Facilities include Hannigan's award-winning traditional bar & restaurant, live music nightly, golfers drying room & snooker room. Killarney National Park opposite the hotel.

An IHF Quality Employer

Bookable on www.irelandhotels.com

B&B from €49.00 to €99.00
Suites from €150.00 to €250.00

Terence Mulcahy
General Manager

90

Activities:

Closed 22 - 26 December

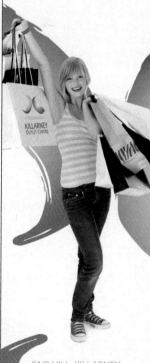

B&B Rates are per Person Sharing per Night incl. Breakfast.
or Room Rates are per Room per Night - See also Page 8

Killarney

Inveraray Farm Guesthouse

GUESTHOUSE ★★ MAP 2 E 4

Coolmagort,
Beaufort,
Killarney
Tel: 064-664 4224 Fax: 064-664 4775
Email: inver@indigo.ie
Web: www.inver-aray.com
GPS: N +52° 3' 52.76" W -9° 38' 5.19"

Welcoming, family friendly farm guesthouse in a quiet sylvan setting, view of Killarney lake, Gap of Dunloe & Carrantuohill, Ireland's highest mountain. We offer traditional hospitality, enjoy our mature gardens. Free Trout & Salmon fishing on River Laune. A walkers paradise, angling & golfing groups welcome. Tours arranged. Comfortable rooms (some with door to gardens). DD Phones, Wi-Fi, play ground, pony & dog for children. Singing pub locally. Home baking, dinner available with fresh garden produce. Le Guide du Routarde & Michelin 2009. We are 9 km west from Killarney, on the N72.

Bookable on www.irelandhotels.com

Special Offer: www.irelandhotels.com/offers

B&B from €35.00 to €45.00

Eileen & Noel Spillane
Proprietors

9

Activities:

Closed 20 November - 01 March

Kathleens Country House

HOTEL ★★★★ MAP 2 E 4

Tralee Road,
Killarney,
Co. Kerry
Tel: 064-663 2810 Fax: 064-663 2340
Email: info@kathleens.net
Web: www.kathleens.net
GPS: N +52° 4' 51.89" W -9° 31' 0.60"

Charming 4* residence immersed in luscious gardens at the edge of Killarney National Park in a peaceful tranquil location, private car park, 15 mins walk to town. Enjoy attentiveness, friendliness, traditional hospitality. AA 5 diamond. Elegant décor throughout. All bedrooms en suite with orthopaedic beds, tea/coffee facilities, hairdryer, telephone. Sumptuous breakfasts. Light snack menu, until 8pm. Wine licence. Internet access. WiFi. Customised itineraries & golfing tee times arranged. Ideal golfing & touring base for the Ring of Kerry & Dingle. Singles welcome. Non smoking. Easy to get to! Hard to Leave!

An IHF Quality Employer

Bookable on www.irelandhotels.com

B&B from €45.00 to €70.00

Kathleen O'Regan Sheppard
Proprietor

17

Closed 01 October - 21 April

Killarney Avenue Hotel

HOTEL ★★★★ MAP 2 E 4

Town Centre,
Killarney,
Co. Kerry
Tel: 064-663 2522 Fax: 064-663 3707
Email: info@killarneyavenue.com
Web: www.killarneyavenue.com
GPS: N +52° 3' 26.07" W -9° 30' 21.64"

This boutique 4**** hotel has an idyllic setting in the heart of Killarney. Well appointed air-conditioned guest rooms provide guests with every care and comfort. Druids Restaurant provides a perfect blend of local and classical cuisine. The Kenmare Rooms is a distinctly different hotel bar. Guests are welcome to use the leisure facilities of our sister hotel (Killarney Towers Hotel), 100m away. Underground garage parking available. Close to shopping, vistor attractions and Kerry's premier golf courses.

Bookable on www.irelandhotels.com

Special Offer: www.irelandhotels.com/offers

B&B from €49.00 to €89.00

Denis McCarthy
General Manager

66

Closed 24 - 28 December

B&B Rates are per Person Sharing per Night incl. Breakfast.
or Room Rates are per Room per Night - See also Page 8

Killarney Lodge

GUESTHOUSE ★★★★ MAP 2 E 4

Countess Road,
Killarney,
Co. Kerry
Tel: 064-663 6499 Fax: 064-663 1070
Email: klylodge@iol.ie
Web: www.killarneylodge.net
GPS: N +52° 3' 23.81" W -9° 30' 21.19"

Welcome to Killarney Lodge, a purpose built four star guesthouse set in private walled-in gardens, yet only 2 minutes walk from Killarney Town centre. The Lodge provides private parking, spacious en suite, air-conditioned bedrooms with all modern amenities. Guests can avail of internet access at the Lodge. Enjoy an extensive breakfast menu, relax in comfortable lounges with open fires where traditional home baking is served. The Lodge has justifiably earned an outstanding reputation for quality of service, relaxed atmosphere and friendliness. Please enquire about Facilities for Persons with Disabilities.

Bookable on www.irelandhotels.com

B&B from €50.00 to €70.00

Catherine Treacy
Owner

16

Activities:

Closed 01 November - 01 March

Killarney Park Hotel

HOTEL ★★★★★ MAP 2 E 4

Town Centre,
Killarney,
Co. Kerry
Tel: 064-663 5555 Fax: 064-663 5266
Email: info@killarneyparkhotel.ie
Web: www.killarneyparkhotel.ie
GPS: N +52° 3' 27.94" W -9° 30' 17.13"

Superbly located in the heart of Killarney Town on its own grounds, this family owned hotel is renowned as a place of elegance laced with warmth and hospitality. The hotel offers 68 beautifully appointed guest rooms and suites complemented by a luxurious full service spa. Other hotel features include a 20m swimming pool, outdoor hot-tub, jacuzzi, library, drawing room, billiards room, games room, golf locker, club drying room and putting green in the gardens. Conference facilities for up to 150 delegates. A warm welcome awaits you both here and across the road in our sister hotel The Ross.

An IHF Quality Employer

Member of Leading Small Hotels of the World

Bookable on www.irelandhotels.com

B&B from €135.00 to €200.00
Suites from €375.00 to €580.00

Niamh O'Shea
General Manager

68

Activities:

Closed 24 - 26 December

Killarney Plaza Hotel & Spa

HOTEL ★★★★ MAP 2 E 4

Town Centre,
Killarney,
Co. Kerry
Tel: 064-662 1100 Fax: 064-662 1190
Email: info@killarneyplaza.com
Web: www.killarneyplaza.com
GPS: N +52° 3' 27.75" W -9° 30' 31.93"

The Killarney Plaza successfully blends gracious hospitality, quality service and amenities in such a way that guests using the hotel for business or pleasure feel at ease. This elegant hotel enjoys a wonderful location in Killarney. The leisure area and Molton Brown Spa allow guests to unwind and relax in luxurious surroundings. All bedrooms and suites are luxuriously furnished and air-conditioned. The Killarney Plaza is a "must see, must stay" rendezvous.

Bookable on www.irelandhotels.com

B&B from €69.00 to €99.00
Suites from €240.00 to €500.00

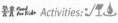

Edith Kirk
General Manager

198

Food for Kids Activities:

Closed 12 December - 01 February

B&B Rates are per Person Sharing per Night incl. Breakfast.
or Room Rates are per Room per Night - **See also Page 8**

Killarney

Killarney Royal Hotel

HOTEL ★★★★ MAP 2 E 4

College Street,
Killarney,
Co. Kerry
Tel: 064-663 1853 Fax: 064-663 4001
Email: reception@killarneyroyal.ie
Web: www.killarneyroyal.ie
GPS: N +52° 3' 36.18" W -9° 30' 20.14"

Family owned & run, located in the heart of Killarney Town, the Killarney Royal is the perfect base for walking, golfing and touring the South West of Ireland. Air-conditioned throughout, this 4* boutique property boasts 24 deluxe rooms and 5 junior suites tastefully designed by the proprietor who modestly uses a country, classical design. After three generations of ownership, the Scally's see excellence as the main ingredients for their reputation, an aim seen in their staff's genuine desire to please.

Bookable on www.irelandhotels.com

B&B from €55.00 to €160.00
Suites from €150.00 to €360.00

Noreen Cronin & Gillian O'Dea
Operations Managers

29

Activities:

Closed 23 - 27 December

Killarney Towers Hotel & Leisure Centre

HOTEL ★★★ MAP 2 E 4

Town Centre,
Killarney,
Co. Kerry
Tel: 064-663 1038 Fax: 064-663 1755
Email: info@killarneytowers.com
Web: www.killarneytowers.com
GPS: N +52° 3' 31.10'' W -9° 30' 25.48''

The Tower is a wonderfully located town centre hotel. Having undergone a €10 million refurbishment in 2008, our hotel provides guests with the very best in comfort & modern services. It's town centre location make it one of Killarney's most sought after hotels. Whether one is looking for a midweek or weekend getaway or flying into Kerry on business, the Killarney Towers is the perfect place to stay.

B&B from €49.00 to €89.00

Michael O'Donoghue
Owner

182

Closed 31 October - 01 February

Killeen House Hotel

HOTEL ★★★ MAP 2 E 4

Aghadoe,
Lakes Of Killarney,
Co. Kerry
Tel: 064-663 1711 Fax: 064-663 1811
Email: charming@indigo.ie
Web: www.killeenhousehotel.com
GPS: N +52° 4' 33.12" W -9° 34' 16.30"

The Killeen House is truly a charming little hotel. With only 23 rooms, 8 of them de luxe, it is the ideal base for touring 'God's own country', the magical Kingdom of Kerry. With our DIY Golf Pub and Rozzers elegant dining room you are assured of a memorable experience. Go on, do the smart thing and call us now! We look forward to extending the 'hostility of the house' to you! Please enquire about Facilities for Persons with Disabilities.

An IHF Quality Employer

Bookable on www.irelandhotels.com
Special Offer: www.irelandhotels.com/offers

B&B from €70.00 to €120.00

Geraldine & Michael Rosney
Owners

23

Closed 21 October - 20 April

B&B Rates are per Person Sharing per Night incl. Breakfast.
or Room Rates are per Room per Night - **See also Page 8**

Kingfisher Lodge Guesthouse

GUESTHOUSE ★★★ MAP 2 E 4

Lewis Road,
Killarney,
Co. Kerry
Tel: 064-663 7131 Fax: 064-663 9871
Email: info@kingfisherlodgekillarney.com
Web: www.kingfisherlodgekillarney.com
GPS: N +52° 3' 48.86" W -9° 30' 20.78"

Kingfisher Lodge is an award-winning family-run Fáilte Ireland approved and AA 4* registered guesthouse. Quietly located yet just 4 minutes walk from town centre pubs, restaurants, entertainment and shopping. Beautifully decorated spacious bedrooms with TV, phone, hairdryer, tea/coffee, WiFi, computer for guest use. Guest lounge with satellite TV, books, magazines. Varied breakfast menu. Private parking, large gardens. Tackle, drying rooms. Groups welcome. Tours, golfing, walking, angling arranged with Donal, a qualified guide. Non-smoking house.

Member of Insight Web Marketing

Bookable on www.irelandhotels.com

B&B from €32.00 to €55.00

Donal & Ann Carroll
Proprietors

11

Activities:

Closed 12 December - 13 February

Lake Hotel

HOTEL ★★★★ MAP 2 E 4

On Lake Shore,
Muckross Road, Killarney,
Co. Kerry
Tel: 064-663 1035 Fax: 064-663 1902
Email: info@lakehotel.com
Web: www.lakehotel.com
GPS: N +52° 3' 4.67" W -9° 30' 22.33"

The most beautiful location in Ireland, set on Killarney's lower lake. Open log fires, double height ceilings, relaxed & friendly atmosphere. Woodland view rooms, Superior & Deluxe lake view rooms with jacuzzi bath, balcony, some four poster beds and refrigerators, in room safes (laptop). Outdoor hot tub on the lakeside, sauna, steam room, gym, floodlit tennis court & treatment rooms, library, free Wi-Fi & 3 state of the art meeting rooms. Complimentary parking. Ideal for walking, cycling, boating, golfing, horse riding, touring. Top 1% online "Insiders" Award 2009, Failte Ireland Optimus "Irelands Best" Award 2008.

An IHF Quality Employer

Bookable on www.irelandhotels.com

Special Offer: www.irelandhotels.com/offers

B&B from €50.00 to €150.00

Niall Huggard
General Manager

131

Food for Kids Activities:

Closed 06 December - 02 January

Loch Lein Country House

HOTEL ★★★★ MAP 2 E 4

Old Golf Course Road,
Fossa, Killarney,
Co. Kerry
Tel: 064-663 1260 Fax: 064-663 6151
Email: stay@lochlein.com
Web: www.lochlein.com
GPS: N +52° 4' 7.16" W -9° 35' 12.46"

A secluded country house with magnificent uninterrupted views over Killarney's famous Lower Lake and the MacGillicuddy Reeks. The hotel's emphasis is on friendly personal service and high standards of food and accommodation. Spacious non-smoking bedrooms have many thoughtful touches to enhance a comfortable and relaxing stay. Ideally located on the Ring of Kerry/Dingle roads, near the Gap of Dunloe. Nearby four golf courses, fishing and horse riding. May we welcome you. Please enquire about Facilities for Persons with Disabilities.

Bookable on www.irelandhotels.com

B&B from €70.00 to €120.00

Paul & Annette Corridan
Hosts

25

Closed 01 November - 31 March

B&B Rates are per Person Sharing per Night incl. Breakfast.
or Room Rates are per Room per Night - **See also Page 8**

Killarney

Malton (The)

HOTEL ★★★★ MAP 2 E 4

Town Centre,
Killarney,
Co. Kerry
Tel: 064-663 8000 Fax: 064-663 1642
Email: res@themalton.com
Web: www.themalton.com
GPS: N +52° 3' 31.97" W -9° 30' 13.23"

The Malton is a stunning Victorian hotel and much-loved Irish landmark. Since opening our doors in 1854, this historic hotel has been a cherished destination, welcoming visitors from all over the world. Known for its distinctive architecture, effortless service and genuine hospitality the hotel is ideally located in the town centre, right beside the railway station, yet on it's own private grounds of six acres.

An IHF Quality Employer

Bookable on www.irelandhotels.com
Special Offer: www.irelandhotels.com/offers

B&B from €70.00 to €140.00
Suites from €300.00 to €500.00

Conor Hennigan
General Manager

172

Food for Kids Activities:

Open All Year

Muckross Park Hotel & Cloisters Spa

HOTEL ★★★★★ MAP 2 E 4

Lakes Of Killarney,
Killarney,
Co. Kerry
Tel: 064-662 3400 Fax: 064-663 1965
Email: info@muckrosspark.com
Web: www.muckrosspark.com
GPS: N +52° 1' 29.29" W -9° 29' 23.32"

Excellence surrounded by beauty - elegant, luxurious guest rooms and suites, award-winning bars & restaurants, superb business facilities and our world class Cloisters Spa ensure an enjoyable stay. Combine this with our unique location in Killarney National Park, surrounded by magnificent mountains, lakes and 7 championship golf courses and you will discover that The Muckross Park Hotel & Cloisters Spa is truly a unique hotel experience. Please enquire about Facilities for Persons with Disabilities.

Member of Preferred Hotel

Bookable on www.irelandhotels.com
Special Offer: www.irelandhotels.com/offers

Room Rate from €180.00 to €360.00
Suites from €250.00 to €1,000.00

Jackie Lavin
Proprietor

68

Activities:

Closed 12 January - 12 February

Murphys of Killarney

GUESTHOUSE ★★★ MAP 2 E 4

18 College Street,
Killarney,
Co. Kerry
Tel: 064-663 1294 Fax: 064-663 1294
Email: info@murphysofkillarney.com
Web: www.murphysofkillarney.com
GPS: N +52° 3' 34.05" W -9° 30' 22.32"

Murphy's of Killarney: a town centre family-run guesthouse with all rooms newly refurbished, adjacent to bus and rail stations. Incorporating Lord Kenmare's renowned restaurant, Murphy's Traditional Irish Bar, where you can enjoy live Irish music and the more contemporary Squires Bar. Sean, Maire & the staff will make sure that your visit to "Murphy's" is enjoyable and memorable. Amenities include: golf, fishing, horse riding, scenic walks and shopping. Local tours arranged. "Murphy's - a sense of Tradition". Please enquire about Facilities for Persons with Disabilities.

B&B from €40.00 to €70.00

Sean Murphy
Proprietor

20

Closed 21 - 28 December

B&B Rates are per Person Sharing per Night incl. Breakfast.
or Room Rates are per Room per Night - See also Page 8

Old Weir Lodge

GUESTHOUSE ★★★★ MAP 2 E 4

Muckross Road,
Killarney,
Co. Kerry

Tel: 064-663 5593 Fax: 064-663 5583
Email: oldweirlodge@eircom.net
Web: www.oldweirlodge.com
GPS: N +52° 3' 5.04" W -9° 30' 26.07"

A magnificent, luxurious, family-run 4* (AA 5*) guesthouse 5 mins. walk from town, on main road, towards National Park. Set in 3/4 acre landscaped gardens. 30 large bedrooms, some with king sized beds, bath, power showers, orthopaedic beds, telephone, multi-channel TV, tea/coffee facilities, ice & hairdryers. 2 lounges, fresh flowers, private parking, home baking, traditional, vegetarian, coeliac breakfasts. Friendly staff, ground floor bedrooms & elevator, drying room. Local advice offered, tours arranged. Non-smoking. Internet Facilities. Please enquire about Facilities for Persons with Disabilities.

Bookable on www.irelandhotels.com

B&B from €40.00 to €65.00

Maureen & Dermot O'Donoghue
Proprietors

30

Closed 20 December - 28 December

Randles Court Hotel

HOTEL ★★★★ MAP 2 E 4

Muckross Road,
Killarney,
Co. Kerry

Tel: 064-663 5333 Fax: 064-663 9301
Email: info@randlescourt.com
Web: www.randlescourt.com
GPS: N +52° 3' 14.17" W -9° 30' 23.23"

This AA/RAC 4**** hotel is one of Killarney's gems. Family owned and run, this de luxe hotel offers all the elegance and charm of a country house. Dating back to 1906, the hotel has been tastefully restored with beautiful furniture and open fires. Checker's Restaurant is truly a unique dining experience. Club Santé leisure facilities are available to all guests. For sheer indulgence, pay a visit to Zen Day Spa. The fully automated conference suite is ideal for all events and WiFi is available throughout the hotel. The perfect setting for a special wedding day and available for Civil Ceremonies.

An IHF Quality Employer

Member of Randles Hotels

Bookable on www.irelandhotels.com
Special Offer: www.irelandhotels.com/offers

B&B from €65.00 to €200.00
Suites from €180.00 to €450.00

Tom Randles
General Manager

68

Closed 19 - 27 December

Ross (The)

HOTEL ★★★★ MAP 2 E 4

Town Centre,
Killarney,
Co. Kerry

Tel: 064-663 1855 Fax: 064-662 7633
Email: info@theross.ie
Web: www.theross.ie
GPS: N +52° 3' 29.16" W -9° 30' 28.04"

The Ross, in the centre of Killarney Town, offers a seamless fusion of luxury and cool and provides the services and amenities of a luxury hotel within a stylish environment. Perfectly situated adjacent to our sister hotel, The Killarney Park Hotel, this 29 bedroom hotel is also home to our unique Cellar One Restaurant, lively Lane Café Bar, the chilled out Pink Lounge and Nespresso Bar. Just steps from the Killarney National Park, local bars, restaurants and great shopping. The Ross is simply the best address in town. Please enquire about Facilities for Persons with Disabilities.

Bookable on www.irelandhotels.com

B&B from €85.00 to €122.50

Padraig & Janet Treacy
Proprietors

29

Food for Kids

Closed 24 - 26 December

B&B Rates are per Person Sharing per Night incl. Breakfast.
or Room Rates are per Room per Night - **See also Page 8**

Killarney / Killorglin

Scotts Hotel Killarney

HOTEL ★★★ MAP 2 E 4

Scotts Street,
Killarney,
Co. Kerry
Tel: 064-663 1060 Fax: 064-663 6656
Email: info@scottshotelkillarney.com
Web: www.scottshotelkillarney.com
GPS: N +52° 3' 33.46" W -9° 30' 22.67"

Scotts Hotel Killarney is a family owned hotel run by the O'Donoghue family in Killarney Town centre. Originally built in 1930, the newly constructed hotel now boasts 120 guest bedrooms. With renovated bedrooms, additional de luxe suites, family rooms and plush apartments, guests are sure to indulge in cozy comfort during their stay in Scotts Hotel Killarney. Other feature includes a selection of bars, a modern contemporary restaurant known as The Courtyard Restaurant. Secure on site parking available to all guests. Please enquire about Facilities for Persons with Disabilities.

Member of The Gleneagle Group

Bookable on www.irelandhotels.com

Special Offer: www.irelandhotels.com/offers

B&B from €50.00 to €95.00
Suites from €130.00 to €240.00

Maurice Eoin O'Donoghue
Managing Director

120

Activities:

Closed 24 - 25 December

Victoria House Hotel

HOTEL ★★★ MAP 2 E 4

Muckross Road,
Killarney,
Co. Kerry
Tel: 064-663 5430 Fax: 064-663 5439
Email: info@victoriahousehotel.com
Web: www.victoriahousehotel.com
GPS: N +52° 2' 36.00" W -9° 30' 0.17"

Traditional family-run hospitality, overlooking Killarney National Park, our cosy and charming Boutique Hotel offers an exceptional warm welcome and personal service. Our Restaurant and Ivy Room Bar provides excellent choice of local produce with frequent live traditional entertainment. Newly refurbished elegant bedrooms now offer upgrades of De luxe and Superior rooms. Pampering within, and cycling, walking and National Park on our doorstep. Let us make your Killarney experience the most unique - your way! Member of www.irishfamilyrun.com and Best Loved Hotels.

Member of Best Loved Hotels

Bookable on www.irelandhotels.com

Special Offer: www.irelandhotels.com/offers

B&B from €50.00 to €110.00
Suites from €140.00 to €260.00

John Courtney
Proprietor

35

Closed 13 December - 01 February

Bianconi

GUESTHOUSE ★★★ MAP 1 D 4

Annadale Road,
Killorglin,
Co. Kerry
Tel: 066-976 1146 Fax: 066-976 1950
Email: bianconi@iol.ie
Web: www.bianconi.ie
GPS: N +52° 6' 21.82" W -9° 47' 5.45"

Family-run inn on The Ring of Kerry. Gateway to Dingle Peninsula, Killarney 18km. On the road to Glencar - famous for its scenery, lakes, hill walking and mountain climbing. Famous for its table. High standard of food in bar. Á la carte available. 50 minutes to Waterville, Tralee & Ballybunion golf courses. 15 minutes to Dooks & Beaufort courses. 5 minutes to Killorglin course. 15 mins to Killarney course. Private access to Caragh Lake. Mentioned by many guides. Broadband available throughout premises.

B&B from €45.00 to €60.00

Ray Sheehy
Owner

14

Activities:

Closed 23 - 29 December

B&B Rates are per Person Sharing per Night incl. Breakfast.
or Room Rates are per Room per Night - **See also Page 8**

Westfield House

GUESTHOUSE ★★★ MAP 1 D 4

Killorglin,
Co. Kerry

Tel: 066-976 1909 Fax: 066-976 1996
Email: westhse@iol.ie
Web: www.westfieldhse.com
GPS: N +52° 6' 9.97" W -9° 48' 1.36"

Westfield House is a family-run guesthouse. All rooms are bright and spacious en suite with orthopaedic beds, direct dial telephone, TV and tea/coffee maker. Extra large family room available. We are situated on the Ring of Kerry in a quiet peaceful location only 5 minutes walk from town with panoramic views of McGillycuddy Reeks. There are five 18 hole golf courses within 20 minutes drive. Recognised stop for many weary cyclists. Ideal location for the hill walker and climber.

Bookable on www.irelandhotels.com

Special Offer: www.irelandhotels.com/offers

B&B from €37.50 to €45.00

Marie & Leonard Clifford
Proprietors

10

Closed 01 November - 01 March

Moorings (The)

GUESTHOUSE ★★★ MAP 1 B 3

Portmagee,
Co. Kerry

Tel: 066-947 7108 Fax: 066-947 7220
Email: moorings@iol.ie
Web: www.moorings.ie
GPS: N +51° 53' 8.54" W -10° 21' 57.21"

The award-winning Moorings overlooks Portmagee Harbour and provides tasteful and spacious accommodation and a renowned dining experience. Winner of "Licensing World Tourist Bar of the Year" 2007, The Bridge Bar adjoining, hosts Irish set dancing and live music throughout the year. Our delightful new gift shop, Cois Cuain offers a selection of quality gifts, many with a nautical theme in keeping with the harbour-side location. Visit our updated website for details of our exciting new Skelligs Package. Please enquire about Facilities for Persons with Disabilities.

An IHF Quality Employer

B&B from €45.00 to €50.00
Suites from €120.00 to €140.00

Patricia & Gerard Kennedy
Proprietors

16

Closed 24 - 25 December

Parknasilla Resort

HOTEL ★★★★ MAP 1 C 3

Sneem,
Co. Kerry

Tel: 064-667 5600 Fax: 064-664 5323
Email: info@parknasillahotel.ie
Web: www.parknasillahotel.ie
GPS: N +51° 48' 56.44" W -9° 52' 29.25"

One of Ireland's finest resort hotels, 500 acres of on-site facilities; walks, tennis, golf, archery, swimming & clay pigeon shooting. Exceptional standards of service within plush surroundings and a warm Irish welcome. Standard rooms, superior rooms & suites with views over Kerry countryside. Try our 3 bed villas. Dine in style at the Pygmalion Restaurant and Doolittle Bar. Balmy subtropical vegetation, mountainous backdrop and tranquil waters - it is the perfect place to relax. Spa with swimming pool, 2 outdoor hot tubs and thermal suite. Book online parknasillahotel.ie.

An IHF Quality Employer

Bookable on www.irelandhotels.com

Special Offer: www.irelandhotels.com/offers

B&B from €95.00 to €170.00
Suites from €250.00 to €2,000.00

Jim Feeney
General Manager

83

Activities:

Closed 02 January - 02 April

Sneem / Tahilla / Tarbert

Sneem Hotel

HOTEL ★★★★ MAP 1 C 3

Goldens Cove,
Sneem,
Co. Kerry
Tel: 064-667 5100 Fax: 064-667 5199
Email: information@sneemhotel.com
Web: www.sneemhotel.com
GPS: N +51° 50' 17.40" W -9° 53' 57.45"

Newly opened in a quiet perfect cove Sneem Hotel is a 4* Hotel. Located on the Ring of Kerry & in the picturesque village of Sneem, this family-run hotel boasts a banqueting room for up to 300, a range of luxury accommodations which includes 69 bedrooms, 28 2/3 bedroomed self contained apartments & suites, many offering impressive sea views with premium rooms having sizeable balconies. This hidden gem on the Ring of Kerry is an ideal wedding & conference venue. It is within driving distance of Waterville, Ring of Kerry & killarney golf courses. Great location for trekking & exploring the Kerry Way.

Bookable on www.irelandhotels.com
Special Offer: www.irelandhotels.com/offers

B&B from €65.00 to €95.00
Suites from €190.00 to €250.00

Nicola Duggan
General Manager

69

Activities:

Closed 24 - 26 December

Tahilla Cove Country House

GUESTHOUSE ★★★ MAP 1 D 3

Tahilla,
Near Sneem,
Co. Kerry
Tel: 064-664 5204 Fax: 064-664 5104
Email: tahillacove@eircom.net
Web: www.tahillacove.com
GPS: N +51° 49' 50.78" W -9° 48' 19.89"

Travel writers have described this family-run, fully licensed seashore guesthouse as the most idyllic spot in Ireland - the haunt of Irish/British dignitaries. Located on The Ring of Kerry seashore. 14 acre estate boasts mature gardens and private pier. Ideal place for a relaxing holiday/touring centre. Each room has en suite facilities, phone, TV, radio, hairdryer, iron and tea/coffee facilities. Log fires, superb views, home cooking. Take Sneem Road from Kenmare (N70).

B&B from €50.00 to €75.00

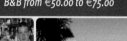

James / Deirdre / Chas Waterhouse
Owners

9

Closed 20 October - 01 April

Kirby's Lanterns Hotel

HOTEL ★★★ MAP 5 E 7

Glin / Tarbert Coast Road,
Tarbert,
Co. Kerry
Tel: 068-36210 Fax: 068-36553
Email: reservations@thelanternshotel.ie
Web: www.thelanternshotel.ie
GPS: N +52° 34' 4.45" W -9° 20' 45.79"

Kirby's Lanterns Hotel overlooking the majestic Shannon Estuary is an ideal tourist base for Kerry, Limerick & Clare. Central to world famous golf courses at Ballybunion, Tralee, Killarney, Adare, Doonbeg and Lahinch. Enjoy a day angling, horse riding or walking. Relax on golden beaches. Visit Kirby's Lanterns Hotel where a warm Kirby welcome awaits you. Superb accommodation, great food & friendly service. Food served from 7 am to 10 pm daily. Music sessions every weekend. Special mid-week and weekend breaks available year round.

Bookable on www.irelandhotels.com
Special Offer: www.irelandhotels.com/offers

B&B from €30.00 to €85.00

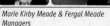

Marie Kirby Meade & Fergal Meade
Managers

22

Closed 25 December

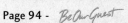

B&B Rates are per Person Sharing per Night incl. Breakfast.
or Room Rates are per Room per Night - See also Page 8

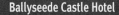

Ballygarry House Hotel & Spa

HOTEL ★★★★ MAP 1 D 5

Killarney Road,
Tralee,
Co. Kerry
Tel: 066-712 3322 Fax: 066-712 7630
Email: info@ballygarryhouse.com
Web: www.ballygarryhouse.com
GPS: N +52° 15' 39.92" W -9° 39' 35.65"

Set amidst six acres of mature landscaped gardens at the foot of the Kerry Mountains offering guests an inspiring mixture of mountain, lake woodland and sea. Ballygarry House offers you the complete country house experience where the warmest of welcomes awaits you. Luxurious guest rooms and suites, library, drawing room, Brooks Restaurant and 'Nádúr Spa' combine to create an atmosphere of unhurried tranquility. 1.5km from Tralee and 6km from Kerry Airport - perfect for golfing or touring the South West. Please enquire about Facilities for Persons with Disabilities.

An IHF Quality Employer

Bookable on www.irelandhotels.com

Special Offer: www.irelandhotels.com/offers

B&B from €65.00 to €95.00
Suites from €180.00 to €250.00

Padraig McGillicuddy
General Manager

64

Activities:

Closed 21 - 28 December

Ballyseede Castle Hotel

HOTEL ★★★★ MAP 1 D 5

Ballyseede,
Tralee,
Co. Kerry
Tel: 066-712 5799 Fax: 066-712 5287
Email: info@ballyseedecastle.com
Web: www.ballyseedecastle.com
GPS: N +52° 15' 23.51" W -9° 38' 48.06"

Ballyseede Castle is steeped in history. Be a king or queen for the night in our elegant bedrooms. Drink wine or chat with the locals in our cosy cocktail bar and enjoy the best of traditional and continental food in our elegant restaurant. Located on 30 acres of pasture and gardens off the main Tralee Killarney road (N21). We are ideally located for touring both the Ring of Kerry or the Dingle Peninsula and within reach of several championship golf courses.

Member of Manor House Hotels

Bookable on www.irelandhotels.com

B&B from €65.00 to €125.00
Suites from €190.00 to €270.00

Marnie Corscadden & Rory O'Sullivan

22

Closed 06 January - 10 March

Brook Manor Lodge

GUESTHOUSE ★★★★ MAP 1 D 5

Fenit Road,
Tralee,
Co. Kerry
Tel: 066-712 0406 Fax: 066-712 7552
Email: brookmanor@eircom.net
Web: www.brookmanorlodge.com
GPS: N +52° 17' 0.75" W -9° 44' 46.77"

Luxury 4 star guesthouse situated on the outskirts of Tralee Town. The Slieve Mish Mountains form an ever changing backdrop - a most wonderful scene to wake up to! Spacious bedrooms with en suite bathrooms. Tea/coffee making facilities, TV, DVD, WiFi, trouser press/iron, hairdryer. Guest lounge offers a tranquil space to read or browse the internet. Extensive breakfast menu to be enjoyed in our conservatory. Ideal base for golf or touring holidays. 4 Star tourist board approved, recommended by many leading guide books.

B&B from €50.00 to €75.00
Suites from €130.00 to €160.00

Sandra & Jerome Lordan
Owners

8

Closed 21 - 31 December

B&B Rates are per Person Sharing per Night incl. Breakfast.
or Room Rates are per Room per Night - See also Page 8

Tralee

Fels Point Hotel

HOTEL ★★★★ MAP 1 D 5

Fels Point,
Tralee,
Co. Kerry
Tel: 066-719 9100 Fax: 066-711 9987
Email: info@felspointhotel.ie
Web: www.felspointhotel.ie
GPS: N +52° 15' 49.06" W -9° 42' 2.43"

The 4 star Fels Point Hotel was opened in June 2007. This new stylish hotel has 165 air-conditioned guest rooms with internet access, a health & leisure suite, Clarets Bar and Morels Restaurant. Extensive conference and banqueting facilities. Parking provided on-site. Ideally located 5 minutes walk from Tralee Town centre and close to numerous golf courses and visitor attractions, Fels Point Hotel offers new standards in hospitality combining modern comfort with an excellent location. Please enquire about Facilities for Persons with Disabilities.

Bookable on www.irelandhotels.com
Special Offer: www.irelandhotels.com/offers

Room Rate from €79.00 to €200.00

Thys Vogels
General Manager
165

Food for Kids *Activities:*

Closed 23 - 26 December

Grand Hotel

HOTEL ★★★ MAP 1 D 5

Denny Street,
Tralee,
Co. Kerry
Tel: 066-712 1499 Fax: 066-712 2877
Email: info@grandhoteltralee.com
Web: www.grandhoteltralee.com
GPS: N +52° 16' 8.16" W -9° 42' 17.82"

The Grand Hotel is Tralee's most historic and centrally located hotel with its welcoming open fires in both reception and bar. It is well established as Tralee's No.1 meeting place. Our extensive bedroom refurbishment is of a very high standard and features all 21st century mod cons including WiFi access. Discount available on green fees at Dooks Golf Club. We are very popular with families, business people, etc. Limited car parking available for residents.

An IHF Quality Employer

Bookable on www.irelandhotels.com
Special Offer: www.irelandhotels.com/offers

B&B from €50.00 to €85.00

Dick Boyle
General Manager
44

Activities:

Open All Year

Hopper Inn

GUESTHOUSE MAP 1 D 5

Coast Road,
Clashmealcon, Causeway,
Tralee, Co. Kerry
Tel: 066-7148 641 Fax: 066-7148 641
Email: info@hopperinn.ie
Web: www.hopperinn.ie
GPS: N +52° 27' 24.57" W -9° 43' 47.06"

Built to a 3*** specification. The Hopper Inn is a spacious family-run bar and guesthouse, nestled on the Coast Road with some magnificent views of the River Shannon and beyond. The Hopper Inn is an ideal base to explore County Kerry.

B&B from €25.00 to €30.00

David Barron
10

Open All Year

B&B Rates are per Person Sharing per Night incl. Breakfast.
or Room Rates are per Room per Night - **See also Page 8**

Manor West Hotel, Spa & Leisure Club

HOTEL ★★★★ MAP 1 D 5

Manor West,
Tralee,
Co. Kerry
Tel: 066-719 4500 Fax: 066-719 4545
Email: info@manorwesthotel.ie
Web: www.manorwesthotel.ie
GPS: N +52° 15' 50.57" W -9° 40' 34.95"

Tralee's luxury destination with 75 bedrooms, the AA 4* Manor West Hotel is designed with the discerning guest in mind. Situated on the site of Kerry's largest shopping destination, Manor West Retail Park, the hotel's location in the heart of Kerry makes it the ideal base for exploring the jewels of the kingdom. The hotel provides all the facilities you would associate with a de luxe hotel including the AA Rosette award-winning Walnut Room Restaurant. The Harmony Leisure Club & Wellness Suites are a must for all guests. Situated on the main Limerick/Killarney Road, less than 20 mins from Kerry Intl. Airport.

Member of Select Hotels of Ireland

Bookable on www.irelandhotels.com
Special Offer: www.irelandhotels.com/offers

B&B from €69.00 to €99.00
Suites from €160.00 to €300.00

Hazel Boyle
General Manager
75

Activities:

Closed 25 - 26 December

Meadowlands Hotel

HOTEL ★★★★ MAP 1 D 5

Oakpark,
Tralee,
Co. Kerry
Tel: 066-718 0444 Fax: 066-718 0964
Email: info@meadowlands-hotel.com
Web: www.meadowlands-hotel.com
GPS: N +52° 16' 34.36" W -9° 41' 28.72"

A charming and intimate hotel, set in a tranquil corner of Tralee, on its own beautiful landscaped gardens. This luxurious hotel comprises 57 superbly appointed rooms, including suites. Our award-winning restaurant specialises in the freshest of locally caught seafood and shellfish cuisine. State of the art conference centre. Ideal base for golfing enthusiasts and touring the Dingle Peninsula and The Ring of Kerry. Experience an experience!

An IHF Quality Employer

Bookable on www.irelandhotels.com

B&B from €40.00 to €80.00
Suites from €200.00 to €350.00

Padraig & Peigi O'Mathuna
Owners
57

Activities:

Closed 24 - 28 December

Brookhaven Country House

GUESTHOUSE ★★★★ MAP 1 B 3

New Line Road,
Waterville,
Co. Kerry
Tel: 066-947 4431 Fax: 066-947 4724
Email: brookhaven@esatclear.ie
Web: www.brookhavenhouse.com
GPS: N +51° 50' 24.63" W -10° 10' 42.56"

Welcome to Brookhaven, a 4 star family-run, luxury guesthouse, on the Ring of Kerry. All our spacious en suite rooms have king beds, multi-channel TV, free internet access and tea and coffee making facilities. Rooms with views of the Atlantic Ocean and the Waterville Golf Course. Skelllig Bay Golf Course 2 mins drive. 10% discount offered. Centrally located to all amenities, golf, fishing lake and sea, beaches, surfing, horse riding, bird watching, historic Skellig Islands, walking, Kerry Way route, cycling and gourmet restaurants. Recommended by all leading guide books.

Member of Premier Collection Marketing Group

B&B from €45.00 to €60.00
Suites from €120.00 to €130.00

Mary Clifford
Proprietor
6

Activities:

Closed 15 November - 31 January

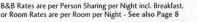

B&B Rates are per Person Sharing per Night incl. Breakfast.
or Room Rates are per Room per Night - **See also Page 8**

Waterville / Graiguenamanagh

Butler Arms Hotel

HOTEL ★★★★ MAP 1 B 3

Waterville,
Co. Kerry

Tel: 066-947 4144 Fax: 066-947 4520
Email: reservations@butlerarms.com
Web: www.butlerarms.com
GPS: N +51° 49' 39.97" W -10° 10' 20.29"

This charming hotel, on the scenic Ring of Kerry, has been run by 4 generations of the Huggard family. Tastefully furnished bedrooms, many with magnificent sea views, cosy lounges, award-winning restaurant specializing in local seafood and the Fishermens Bar with its cosmopolitan ambience. Only 1 mile from Waterville's Championship Golf Links. Renowned salmon and seatrout fishing, sandy beaches, horse riding, hill walking. Please enquire about Facilities for Persons with Disabilities.

An IHF Quality Employer

Member of Manor House Hotels

Bookable on www.irelandhotels.com

B&B from €60.00 to €100.00
Suites from €200.00 to €400.00

Louise & Paula Huggard
Proprietors 36

Food for Kids *Activities:*

Closed 31 October - 01 April

Smugglers Inn

GUESTHOUSE ★★★ MAP 1 B 3

Cliff Road,
Waterville,
Co. Kerry

Tel: 066-947 4330 Fax: 066-947 4422
Email: info@thesmugglersinn.ie
Web: www.thesmugglersinn.ie
GPS: N +51° 50' 13.73" W -10° 11' 41.89"

The Smugglers Inn, family-run, was a 180 year old farmhouse restored by the Hunt Family in 1980. Renowned world-wide for its warm welcome & super restaurant. Situated in a quiet location on a 2km sandy beach, adjacent to Waterville Golf Links, a haven for golfing, fishing, surfing, scuba diving, walking. Comfortable guest bedrooms, many with sea views. Helicopter landing. Panoramic views from our conservatory restaurant. Chef/proprietor Henry Hunt. Fully licenced bar serving bar food. It has been said "if our fish was any fresher it would have to be cooked underwater". Licensing World Bar Food Award Winner 2009.

Bookable on www.irelandhotels.com

B&B from €45.00 to €75.00

Henry Hunt
Proprietor 14

Activities:

Closed 01 November - 01 April

Waterside

GUESTHOUSE ★★★ MAP 7 M 7

The Quay,
Graiguenamanagh,
Co. Kilkenny

Tel: 059-972 4246 Fax: 059-972 4733
Email: info@watersideguesthouse.com
Web: www.watersideguesthouse.com
GPS: N +52° 32' 25.39" W -6° 57' 13.63"

A beautifully restored 19th century cornstore with feature wooden beams and imposing granite exterior. Riverside location, all rooms have a view of the River Barrow. Excellent base for boating, fishing, hill walking. 16km from Mount Juliet for golf. Nearby 13th century Duiske Abbey. 27km from historical Kilkenny. Superb restaurant features continental cuisine and international flavour wine list. Relaxed and friendly approach. Perfect for small groups. Graiguenamanagh hosts annual 'Town of Books' Festival.

B&B from €39.00 to €59.00

Brian & Brigid Roberts 10

Activities:

Closed 01 - 31 January

B&B Rates are per Person Sharing per Night incl. Breakfast.
or Room Rates are per Room per Night - See also Page 8

Berkeley House

GUESTHOUSE ★★★ MAP 7 L 7

5 Lower Patrick Street,
Kilkenny

Tel: 056-776 4848 Fax: 056-776 4829
Email: berkeleyhouse@eircom.net
Web: www.bookkilkenny.com
GPS: N +52° 39' 0.00" W -7° 15' 5.61"

A warm and genuine welcome awaits you here at this charming owner operated period residence, uniquely situated in the very heart of mediaeval Kilkenny City. Berkeley House boasts ample private car parking,10 spacious & tastefully decorated rooms, all en suite with multi channel TV, direct dial phone & tea/coffee facilities. We pride ourselves on a dedicated and professional team and ensure that every effort will be made to make your stay with us a most enjoyable one. Please enquire about Facilities for Persons with Disabilities.

B&B from €45.00 to €75.00

Trish Kiely
Manager

10

T C P

Closed 20 - 28 December

Bridge Court House

GUESTHOUSE ★★★ MAP 7 L 7

Greensbridge,
Kilkenny

Tel: 056-776 2998
Email: anegan@eircom.net
Web: www.kilkennybridgecourt.com
GPS: N +52° 39' 27.73" W -7° 15' 17.76"

Bridge Court House is a modern comfortable family run 3 star guesthouse which offers excellent value in a great city location. Located in a quiet side of the city but yet in walking distance of all major tourist attractions and shopping areas. We provide complimentary parking and free broadband access. A cosy guest tv room awaits where tea & coffee can be made.

B&B from €30.00 to €40.00

Don & Niamh Egan

9

P S I

Closed 24 - 26 December

Butler House

GUESTHOUSE ★★★★ MAP 7 L 7

Patrick Street,
Kilkenny

Tel: 056-776 5707 Fax: 056-776 5626
Email: res@butler.ie
Web: www.butler.ie
GPS: N +52° 38' 55.82" W -7° 15' 3.39"

Butler House is the magnificent Dower House of Kilkenny Castle, situated in Kilkenny City Centre. Sweeping staircases magnificent plastered ceilings and marble fireplaces are all features of this 16th century house. The house is a combination of contemporary furnishing and period elegance. The larger superior rooms and suite have graceful bow windows with lovely views of the Georgian garden and Kilkenny Castle. Private parking. Chairlift available.

Bookable on www.irelandhotels.com
Special Offer: www.irelandhotels.com/offers

B&B from €60.00 to €110.00
Suites from €150.00 to €300.00

Gabrielle Hickey
Manager

13

Activities:

T C P S I

Closed 23 - 29 December

B&B Rates are per Person Sharing per Night incl. Breakfast.
or Room Rates are per Room per Night - **See also Page 8**

Kilkenny City

Club House Hotel

HOTEL ★★ MAP 7 L 7

Patrick Street,
Kilkenny

Tel: 056-772 1994 Fax: 056-777 1920
Email: clubhse@iol.ie
Web: www.clubhousehotel.com
GPS: N +52° 38' 57.65" W -7° 15' 6.49"

Situated uniquely in a cultural & artistic centre and against the background of Kilkenny's mediaeval city, the magnificent 18th century Club House Hotel maintains a 200 year old tradition of effortless comfort, hospitality and efficiency. En suite rooms are decorated in both modern & period style with complimentary beverages, TV, hairdryer & phone. Food is locally sourced, cooked and presented to highest standards. Victors Bar has old world charm & luxury. Live music Saturday nights.

An IHF Quality Employer

Member of Countrywide Hotels - MinOtel Ireland

Bookable on www.irelandhotels.com

B&B from €45.00 to €125.00

James P. Brennan / Ian Brennan
Managing Director / General Manager 28

Food for Kids

Closed 24 - 29 December

Fanad House

GUESTHOUSE ★★★ MAP 7 L 7

Castle Road,
Kilkenny

Tel: 056-776 4126 Fax: 056-775 6001
Email: fanadhouse@hotmail.com
Web: www.fanadhouse.com
GPS: N +52° 38' 48.02" W -7° 14' 32.30"

Overlooking Kilkenny Castle Park, Fanad House is a five minute walk from the city centre. The newly built guesthouse offers all en suite rooms with complimentary beverages, multi-channel TV, hairdryer and direct dial phone. Extensive breakfast menu available. Private and secure parking provided. An ideal base for exploring the mediaeval city. We are adjacent to Kilkenny Tennis Club. Owner operated is your guarantee for an enjoyable stay. WiFi available. Please enquire about Facilities for Persons with Disabilities.

Member of Premier Guesthouses

Bookable on www.irelandhotels.com

B&B from €40.00 to €120.00

Pat Wallace
Proprietor 12

Open All Year

Glendine Inn

GUESTHOUSE ★★ MAP 7 L 7

Castlecomer Road,
Kilkenny

Tel: 056-772 1069 Fax: 056-777 0714
Email: info@glendineinn.com
Web: www.glendineinn.com
GPS: N +52° 40' 1.63" W -7° 15' 10.51"

The Glendine Inn has been a licensed tavern for over 200 years. It consists of 7 bedrooms (all en suite), a residents' lounge, residents' dining room, and public lounge and bars serving snack or bar lunches. We are ideally located for golf (course 200m away), the railway station and the historic city of Kilkenny are only 1.5km away. We assure you of a friendly welcome. Under new ownership of the Phelan family. Please enquire about Facilities for Persons with Disabilities.

Bookable on www.irelandhotels.com

B&B from €35.00 to €85.00

The Phelan Family
Proprietors 7

Closed 25 - 27 December

B&B Rates are per Person Sharing per Night incl. Breakfast.
or Room Rates are per Room per Night - **See also Page 8**

Hotel Kilkenny

HOTEL ★★★★ MAP 7 L 7

College Road,
Kilkenny

Tel: 056-776 2000 Fax: 056-776 5984
Email: experience@hotelkilkenny.ie
Web: www.hotelkilkenny.ie
GPS: N +52° 38' 35.22" W -7° 15' 40.65"

Hotel Kilkenny - the leading 4* hotel in Kilkenny, boasting 138 spacious guest bedrooms incorporating 36 exclusive de luxe rooms. Flat Screen TV and tea/coffee making facilities in all rooms. Pure Bar is home to the best drinks list in Kilkenny with Taste Restaurant serving fresh ingredients with a difference every evening. 10 min walk from the city centre. Large 20m pool with separate children's pool. Supervised Kids Club open every weekend. Onsite Beautician and Hairdressers. Extensive Conference Facilities also available from 2 - 750 people. Please enquire about Facilities for Persons with Disabilities.

An IHF Quality Employer

Bookable on www.irelandhotels.com

Special Offer: www.irelandhotels.com/offers

B&B from €65.00 to €135.00
Suites from €180.00 to €320.00

Michael Griffin
Director

138

Activities:

Open All Year

Kilford Arms Hotel

HOTEL ★★★ MAP 7 L 7

John Street,
Kilkenny

Tel: 056-776 1018 Fax: 056-776 1128
Email: info@kilfordarms.ie
Web: www.kilfordarmshotel.com
GPS: N +52° 39' 14.58" W -7° 14' 52.16"

This city centre hotel is just a few minutes walk from the rail and bus station, with all the services you would expect from a first class hotel e.g. 3 bars offering a full range of food menus, White Oak Restaurant, Nite Club (Fri/Sat only). O'Faolains Bar is Kilkenny's most vibrant with 3 levels of stunning architecture. The Kilford Hotel is perfectly located with all facilities and a fabulous atmosphere. Please enquire about Facilities for Persons with Disabilities.

Member of Kilkenny Tourism

Bookable on www.irelandhotels.com

Special Offer: www.irelandhotels.com/offers

B&B from €45.00 to €130.00

Pius Phelan
Owner

60

Activities:

Open All Year

Kilkenny House Hotel

HOTEL ★★★ MAP 7 L 7

Freshford Road,
Talbot's Inch,
Kilkenny

Tel: 056-777 0711 Fax: 056-777 0698
Email: kilkennyhouse@eircom.net
Web: www.kilkennyhousehotel.ie
GPS: N +52° 40' 2.23" W -7° 16' 0.09"

Enter the warmth and traditional style of Kilkenny House Hotel. Ideally located between St. Lukes and Aut Even Hospitals on the R693. A continuous room sale is available in 2010 for guests. The spacious and tastefully decorated bedrooms are real value. Dore's Public Bar serves bar food and beverages daily. The Talbot's Inch Suite caters for meetings and events (50 persons). Situated enviably on 2 acres with 100 car parking spaces. Owner operated guarantees Kilkenny's best value accommodation, with rest for the tired.

Bookable on www.irelandhotels.com

B&B from €25.00 to €75.00

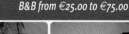

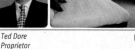

Ted Dore
Proprietor

30

Closed 20 December - 01 April

B&B Rates are per Person Sharing per Night incl. Breakfast.
or Room Rates are per Room per Night - **See also Page 8**

Kilkenny City

Kilkenny Ormonde Hotel

HOTEL ★★★★ MAP 7 L 7

Ormonde Street,
Kilkenny

Tel: 056-772 3900 Fax: 056-772 3977
Email: info@kilkennyormonde.com
Web: www.kilkennyormonde.com
GPS: N +52° 38' 58.56" W -7° 15' 11.69"

4* Kilkenny Ormonde Hotel is Kilkenny's most centrally located hotel. Fully refurbished in 2008, all 118 rooms are amongst the largest in the city centre. Enjoy formal dining at Savour, relaxed dining at O'Reilly's Steakhouse. Or sit back and enjoy comfort of the Ormonde Lounge. White Flag, award-winning Health Club and new KO Spa. 10 conference & event rooms with free parking for residents & hotel patrons. The perfect base to enjoy Kilkenny City and County. Please enquire about Facilities for Persons with Disabilities.

An IHF Quality Employer

Bookable on www.irelandhotels.com

Room Rate from €100.00 to €300.00
Suites from €162.00 to €392.00

Colin Ahern
General Manager

118

Food for Kids Activities:

Closed 24 - 27 December

Kilkenny River Court

HOTEL ★★★★ MAP 7 L 7

The Bridge,
John Street,
Kilkenny

Tel: 056-772 3388 Fax: 056-772 3389
Email: info@rivercourthotel.com
Web: www.rivercourthotel.com
GPS: N +52° 39' 5.55" W -7° 14' 57.37"

Award-winning newly refurbished RAC/AA 4**** hotel, leisure club and conference centre. City centre location, stunning views of Kilkenny Castle and the River Nore. Ideal as a conference venue or simply sheer relaxation. Offering 90 luxurious & spaciously appointed bedrooms. Leisure facilities include swimming pool, sauna, geyser pool, jacuzzi, fully equipped gymnasium and treatment rooms. Within easy access of Dublin, Waterford and Cork. Due to our prime city centre location, there is a car park fee of €2 for all guests. Please enquire about Facilities for Persons with Disabilities.

An IHF Quality Employer

Member of Spectra Group Hotels

Bookable on www.irelandhotels.com
Special Offer: www.irelandhotels.com/offers

B&B from €45.00 to €130.00
Suites from €180.00 to €400.00

Xavier McAuliffe
Proprietor

90

Food for Kids Activities:

Closed 23 - 27 December

Langton House Hotel

HOTEL ★★★ MAP 7 L 7

67-69 John Street,
Kilkenny

Tel: 056-776 5133 Fax: 056-776 3693
Email: reservations@langtons.ie
Web: www.langtons.ie
GPS: N +52° 39' 11.93" W -7° 14' 53.48"

This fabulous boutique style hotel is situated in the heart of Medieval Kilkenny City. Offering beautifully appointed guest rooms incorporating a collection of suites each opulently decorated with all modern conveniences. An award-winning restaurant in lavish surroundings with a selection of excellent bars offering guests a mixture of superb food & lively entertainment in a relaxed atmosphere. Renowned both locally & nationally for its impeccable customer service, good wholesome cuisine & genuine welcome. Please enquire about Facilities for Persons with Disabilities.

Bookable on www.irelandhotels.com
Special Offer: www.irelandhotels.com/offers

B&B from €44.50 to €75.00
Suites from €100.00 to €250.00

Sean Read
Manager

34

Activities:

Closed 25-26 December

B&B Rates are per Person Sharing per Night incl. Breakfast.
or Room Rates are per Room per Night - **See also Page 8**

Laragh Guest House

GUESTHOUSE ★★★★ MAP 7 L 7

Smithsland North,
Waterford Road,
Kilkenny City

Tel: 056-776 4674 Fax: 056-770 3605
Email: info@laraghhouse.com
Web: www.laraghhouse.com
GPS: N +52° 38' 22.69" W -7° 14' 58.21"

Laragh House is a modern 4 star, award-winning Guest House, within easy reach of the city centre. Reviewed as a good alternative to hotels, guests are assured of a friendly welcome, comfortable accommodation and an excellent breakfast menu. From all routes use bypass (N/10) as far as Waterford road roundabout then via R/910 toward city centre for 400 metres (on left). Guests enjoy free off street parking & broadband. Please enquire about Facilities for Persons with Disabilities.

B&B from €35.00 to €50.00

Helen Cooney
Manager

8

Open All Year

Laurels

GUESTHOUSE ★★★ MAP 7 L 7

College Road,
Kilkenny

Tel: 056-776 1501 Fax: 056-777 1334
Email: laurels@eircom.net
Web: www.thelaurelskilkenny.com
GPS: N +52° 38' 40.97" W -7° 15' 39.17"

Chosen as one of Kilkenny's Premier Guesthouses. Purpose built 9 bed-roomed en suite Bed & Breakfast 6-10 minutes walk from the city centre and main tourist attractions. Luxurious accommodation with selected number of superior rooms with the benefit of super king sized beds and whirlpool baths. All rooms include a hospitality tray and have a TV, hairdryer and wireless broadband. Secure private parking for all guests. "Best B&B we've visited in Ireland", "First class and recommendable" are some of the comments we have received.

Member of Premier Guesthouses

Bookable on www.irelandhotels.com
Special Offer: www.irelandhotels.com/offers

B&B from €30.00 to €50.00

Brian & Betty McHenry

9

Open All Year

Lyrath Estate Hotel, Spa & Convention Centre

HOTEL ★★★★★ MAP 7 L 7

Dublin Road,
Kilkenny

Tel: 056-776 0088 Fax: 056-776 0089
Email: info@lyrath.com
Web: www.lyrath.com
GPS: N +52° 38' 52.26" W -7° 11' 50.69"

Lyrath is delighted to welcome its guests to a place of contemporary elegance and sophistication, where we guarantee a memorable and unique hospitality experience. Situated on 170 acres, Lyrath's 17th century house plays an integral part in the overall development. At the Oasis Spa & the Oasis Health Club, with 17m infinity pool, we offer you a unique & exclusive opportunity to unwind & take time out just for you. With 3 resident golden retrievers to keep the children amused. Bring them for a stroll amid 170 acres, try boating on our lakes or cycling on the grounds. Please enquire about Facilities for Persons with Disabilities.

An IHF Quality Employer

Member of Spectra Group Hotels

Bookable on www.irelandhotels.com
Special Offer: www.irelandhotels.com/offers

B&B from €65.00 to €160.00
Suites from €230.00 to €999.00

Patrick Joyce
General Manager

137

Activities:

Closed 20 - 25 December

B&B Rates are per Person Sharing per Night incl. Breakfast.
or Room Rates are per Room per Night - **See also Page 8**

Kilkenny City

Newpark Hotel

HOTEL ★★★★ MAP 7 L 7

Castlecomer Road,
Kilkenny

Tel: 056-776 0500 Fax: 056-776 0555
Email: info@newparkhotel.com
Web: www.flynnhotels.com
GPS: N +52° 39' 51.71" W -7° 15' 1.69"

The newly refurbished 4**** Newpark Hotel, newest member of the Flynn Hotel Group, set in 20 acres of parkland, yet only a short stroll from the mediaeval city of Kilkenny. 129 superior rooms and suites. Additional facilities include Escape Health Club & Spa using Aveda Products, a fabulous Outdoor Infinity Pool. The Newpark offers a wide range of dining options including Dove Bistro with carvery lunch and evening menu.

An IHF Quality Employer

Member of Flynn Hotels

Bookable on www.irelandhotels.com
Special Offer: www.irelandhotels.com/offers

B&B from €55.00 to €95.00
Suites from €250.00 to €500.00

John & Allen Flynn
Proprietors
129

Activities:

Closed 24 - 25 December

Rosquil House

GUESTHOUSE ★★★★ MAP 7 L 7

Castlecomer Road,
Kilkenny

Tel: 056-772 1419 Fax: 056-775 0398
Email: info@rosquilhouse.com
Web: www.rosquilhouse.com
GPS: N +52° 39' 45.38" W -7° 15' 3.39"

Located a short walk from the centre of the medieval Kilkenny City, Rosquil House offers the ambience of a hotel with the best traditions of Irish hospitality. With seven luxury en suite bedrooms with all the facilities, a guest lounge to enjoy a glass of wine and breakfast a culinary treat, Rosquil House all adds up to an experience not to be missed. Extensive private parking. Please enquire about Facilities for Persons with Disabilities.

Bookable on www.irelandhotels.com

B&B from €45.00 to €60.00

Jenny Nolan
Manager
7

Closed 23 - 27 December

Springhill Court Hotel, Conference, Leisure & Spa Hotel

HOTEL ★★★ MAP 7 L 7

Waterford Road,
Kilkenny

Tel: 056-772 1122 Fax: 056-776 1600
Email: reservations@springhillcourt.com
Web: www.springhillcourt.com
GPS: N +52° 37' 55.91" W -7° 15' 4.78"

Located mins. from the bustling centre of "the Marble City". We boast one of Kilkenny's most modern leisure clubs. Facilities incl. a 19m deck level pool, sauna, jacuzzi, steam room & fully equipped gym. Unwind in "Lavendar Spa" offering 7 treatment rooms incl. floatation therapy. This compliments our superb restaurant, friendly bar, conference centre & 85 well appointed bedrooms. Sister Hotels: Arklow Bay Conference Leisure & Spa Hotel, Wicklow, Clonmel Park Conference Leisure & Spa Hotel, Tipperary, Bettystown Court Conference Leisure & Spa Hotel, Meath & Green Isle Conference & Leisure Hotel, Dublin.

An IHF Quality Employer

Member of Brennan Hotel Group

Bookable on www.irelandhotels.com
Special Offer: www.irelandhotels.com/offers

B&B from €45.00 to €100.00

Seamus O'Carroll
General Manager
85

Food for Kids

Open All Year

B&B Rates are per Person Sharing per Night incl. Breakfast.
or Room Rates are per Room per Night - **See also Page 8**

Knocktopher / Mullinavat / Thomastown

Carrolls Hotel

HOTEL ★★ MAP 7 L 6

Knocktopher,
Co. Kilkenny

Tel: 056-776 8082 Fax: 056-776 8290
Email: info@carrollsknocktopher.com
Web: www.carrollshotel.com
GPS: N +52° 29' 9.08" W -7° 13' 3.96"

Situated on the N10 between Kilkenny and Waterford. Enjoy the excellent service, warmth and luxury of our family-run hotel. All rooms are en suite with TV and direct dial phone. Our Sionnach Sioc Restaurant has an excellent reputation for good food. The hotel provides live music 2 nights a week. Golfing, karting, fishing, horse riding and shooting are available nearby.

B&B from €40.00 to €60.00

Padraig Carroll
General Manager

10

Closed 24 - 26 December

Rising Sun

GUESTHOUSE ★★★ MAP 4 L 6

Mullinavat,
Via Waterford,
Co. Kilkenny

Tel: 051-898173 Fax: 051-898435
Email: info@therisingsun.ie
Web: www.therisingsun.ie
GPS: N +52° 22' 15.02" W -7° 10' 18.81"

A family-run guesthouse, 14km from Waterford City on the Waterford to Dublin road, just off the M9 (Junction 11 Mullinavat) (R704). It has 10 luxurious bedrooms all en suite with D/D telephone, TV and tea/coffee making facilities. The Rising Sun Guesthouse is an ideal base for sports enthusiasts, surrounded by some beautiful golf courses within 15-30 minutes drive. The old world charm of stone and timberwork sets the tone of comfort and relaxation in the bar and lounge. Traditional home cooked lunches and bar food served daily. The Restaurant offers full à la carte menu and wine list.

B&B from €45.00 to €65.00

Kathrena O'Connor
General Manager

10

Activities:

Closed 23 - 29 December

Mount Juliet

HOTEL ★★★★ MAP 7 L 6

Thomastown,
Co. Kilkenny

Tel: 056-777 3000 Fax: 056-777 3019
Email: info@mountjuliet.ie
Web: www.mountjuliet.ie
GPS: N +52° 31' 45.84" W -7° 11' 16.73"

Sprawling countryside, lush gardens, luxurious accommodation and award-winning dining are just some of the pleasures awaiting guests who pass through the gates. Choose from the Georgian elegance of Mount Juliet House, the informal atmosphere of the Club Rooms in Hunters Yard or the spacious Rose Garden Lodges. Extensive range of activities throughout the 1,500 acre estate include an 18-hole championship golf course, state of the art equestrian facilities, angling, clay target shooting, archery, tennis, croquet, walking and cycling tours and a spa and leisure centre.

An IHF Quality Employer

Bookable on www.irelandhotels.com

B&B from €49.50 to €149.50

William Kirby
General Manager

57

Activities:

Open All Year

B&B Rates are per Person Sharing per Night incl. Breakfast.
or Room Rates are per Room per Night - **See also Page 8**

Cahir / Carrick-on-Suir

Cahir House Hotel

HOTEL ★★★ MAP 3 J 6

The Square,
Cahir,
Co. Tipperary
Tel: 052-744 3000 Fax: 052-744 2728
Email: info@cahirhousehotel.ie
Web: www.cahirhousehotel.ie
GPS: N +52° 22' 27.77" W -7° 55' 27.96"

Cahir House Hotel is dedicated to providing excellent service & facilities. Ideal location for touring. Situated in the historic town of Cahir & within walking distance of Cahir Castle & The Swiss Cottage. Also close to Mitchelstown Caves, the famous Rock of Cashel & within ten miles of 8 top Golf Courses. Golf breaks are a speciality. Bistro & bar open with good food served all day. Member of Féile Bia promotion of Irish food. Spa & Leisure facilities open - please book in advance to avoid disappointment. Parking to rear of hotel where guests may enjoy our beautifully landscaped courtyard with covered beer garden.

An IHF Quality Employer

Bookable on www.irelandhotels.com

B&B from €55.00 to €130.00

Robert Scannell
Director
40

Activities:

Closed 24 - 26 December

Kilcoran Lodge Hotel, Lodges & Leisure Centre

HOTEL ★★★ MAP 3 J 6

Cahir,
Co. Tipperary
Tel: 052-744 1288 Fax: 052-744 1994
Email: info@kilcoranlodgehotel.com
Web: www.kilcoranlodgehotel.com
GPS: N +52° 20' 52.09" W -8° 0' 55.49"

Kilcoran, a former hunting lodge, is set in 20 acres of manicured gardens overlooking beautiful countryside. An ideal holiday base located equal distance from Cork, Kilkenny, Limerick and Waterford. The hotel has the charm of bygone days yet all the modern facilities of a good 3*** hotel. Guests have free access to our leisure centre with indoor pool. There are also 17 luxury holiday lodges, self catering for up to 6 persons, ideal for golf, walking and fishing breaks. Special bed and breakfast rates available for lodges and mews. Please enquire about Facilities for Persons with Disabilities.

B&B from €50.00 to €65.00
Suites from €150.00 to €200.00

Jacqueline Mullen
General Manager
22

Activities:

Open All Year

Carraig Hotel

HOTEL ★★★ MAP 3 K 5

Main Street,
Carrick-on-Suir,
Co. Tipperary
Tel: 051-641455 Fax: 051-641604
Email: info@carraighotel.com
Web: www.carraighotel.com
GPS: N +52° 20' 43.96" W -7° 24' 45.10"

Located in the town centre of Carrick in the heart of the Suir Valley, close to Waterford, Kilkenny and the coast. Welcoming bar and restaurant with a great reputation for food. Excellent salmon & trout fishing on the Suir, golf on the local course with commanding views over the Suir Valley, or simply browse some great local shops, the farmer's market and the design centre. Visit The Ormonde Castle or simply enjoy Irish Hospitality at its best. Live music at weekends.

An IHF Quality Employer

Bookable on www.irelandhotels.com
Special Offer: www.irelandhotels.com/offers

B&B from €40.00 to €75.00

Paul Norris
General Manager
24

Closed 24 - 26 Dec & Good Friday

B&B Rates are per Person Sharing per Night incl. Breakfast.
or Room Rates are per Room per Night - **See also Page 8**

Baileys of Cashel

HOTEL ★★★★ MAP 3 J 6

Main Street,
Cashel,
Co. Tipperary
Tel: 062-61937 Fax: 062-63957
Email: info@baileys-ireland.com
Web: www.baileys-ireland.com
GPS: N +52° 30' 56.84" W -7° 53' 24.01"

Baileys is a beautifully restored listed Georgian house ideally situated in the town centre with private off-street parking. The fully licensed Cellar Bar serves food all day in a cosy environment, while at No. 42 superb bistro style food is served on five evenings. Elegant rooms provide DD phone, broadband internet & interactive TV with on-demand movies. New luxuriously appointed suite now available. Leisure facilities: 20m pool, fully equipped gym, sauna, steam room & jacuzzi. We offer old-world charm in a modern world.

B&B from €60.00 to €75.00
Suites from €180.00 to €220.00

Phil Delaney
Manager

20

Activities:

Closed 24 - 28 December

Cashel Palace Hotel

HOTEL ★★★★ MAP 3 J 6

Main Street,
Cashel,
Co. Tipperary
Tel: 062-62707 Fax: 062-61521
Email: reception@cashel-palace.ie
Web: www.cashel-palace.ie
GPS: N +52° 31' 2.46" W -7° 53' 21.29"

Built in 1730 as an Archbishop's Palace, the Cashel Palace is complemented by tranquil walled gardens and a private walk to the famous Rock of Cashel. Our 23 bedrooms are all en suite with TV, phone & trouser press. Our Bishop's Buttery Restaurant is open for lunch & dinner, while the Guinness Bar is open for light snacks daily. The hotel has recently been completely restored & guests can now enjoy the finest furnishings, fabrics, art & antiques in the most elegant surroundings. AA 4**** hotel. AA Rosette Award for Culinary Excellence 2007/2008.

Bookable on www.irelandhotels.com

B&B from €65.00 to €99.00
Suites from €199.00 to €300.00

Susan & Patrick Murphy
Proprietors

23

Food for Kids *Activities:*

Closed 23 - 27 December

Dundrum House Hotel, Golf & Leisure Resort

HOTEL ★★★ MAP 3 I 7

Dundrum,
Cashel,
Co. Tipperary
Tel: 062-71116 Fax: 062-71366
Email: reservations@dundrumhouse.ie
Web: www.dundrumhousehotel.com
GPS: N +52° 32' 58.97" W -8° 1' 47.27"

Escape on a country break at Dundrum House Hotel renowned as one of Ireland's best inland golf & leisure resorts surrounded by the manicured fairways of its own Philip Walton designed 18H C'Ship golf course, par 72, 7,200 yards. The Georgian Manor oozes old world charm & new 4* self-catering houses offer modern day comforts on 200 acres. Exquisite cuisine in the Rossmore Restaurant not to be missed. The Health & Wellness Centre: 21M pool, jacuzzi, sauna, steam & gym. Kids Club family season. Please enquire about Facilities for Persons with Disabilities.

Member of Manor House Hotels

Bookable on www.irelandhotels.com
Special Offer: www.irelandhotels.com/offers

B&B from €50.00 to €120.00

William Crowe
Director of Golf

65

Activities:

Closed 23 - 26 December

B&B Rates are per Person Sharing per Night incl. Breakfast.
or Room Rates are per Room per Night - **See also Page 8**

Clonmel

Brighton House

GUESTHOUSE ★★ MAP 3 K 5

1 Brighton Place,
Clonmel,
Co. Tipperary
Tel: 052-612 3665 Fax: 052-618 0209
Email: brighton@iol.ie
Web: www.brightonhouse.ie
GPS: N +52° 21' 22.75" W -7° 42' 10.34"

Family-run 3 storey Georgian guesthouse, with a hotel ambience and antique furnishings. Clonmel Town centre - the largest inland town in Ireland bridging Rosslare Harbour (132km) with Killarney (160km) and the South West. Host to Fleadh Cheoil na hEireann 2003/04. Visit the Rock of Cashel, Mitchelstown Caves, Cahir Castle etc. Golf, fishing and pony trekking arranged locally. All rooms have direct dial phones, TV, radio, hairdryer and tea/coffee making facilities. Situated opposite Dunnes Stores Oakville Shopping Centre. Private and secure parking.

B&B from €35.00 to €75.00

Bernie & Pat Morris
Proprietors

6

Closed 24 - 29 December

Clonmel Park Conference Leisure & Spa Hotel

HOTEL ★★★★ MAP 3 K 5

Cahir Road Roundabout,
Clonmel,
Co. Tipperary
Tel: 052-618 8700 Fax: 052-618 8766
Email: info@clonmelparkhotel.com
Web: www.clonmelparkhotel.com
GPS: N +52° 21' 23.67" W -7° 44' 19.63"

This luxury hotel offers 99 modern guestrooms and all you would expect of a modern 4 star standard hotel. Enjoy dinner in Howards followed by drinks in the lively Wheat Bar. Why not book a treatment at Eco Spa? Conference & Banqueting facilities for up to 500. A leisure centre and free parking completes a wonderful stay. Member of Brennan Hotels Dublin, Meath, Arklow, Kilkenny & Clonmel. Please enquire about Facilities for Persons with Disabilities.

An IHF Quality Employer

Member of Brennan Hotels

Bookable on www.irelandhotels.com

Special Offer: www.irelandhotels.com/offers

B&B from €50.00 to €110.00
Suites from €150.00 to €310.00

Michael Boyle
General Manager

99

Open All Year

Fennessy's Hotel

HOTEL ★★ MAP 3 K 5

Gladstone Street,
Clonmel,
Co. Tipperary
Tel: 052-612 3680 Fax: 052-612 3783
Email: info@fennessyshotel.com
Web: www.fennessyshotel.com
GPS: N +52° 21' 16.53" W -7° 42' 7.69"

This beautiful Georgian building is recently restored and refurbished. Right in the centre of Clonmel, it is centrally located opposite the town's main church. All bedrooms are en suite and have security safes, DD phone, multi channel TV, hairdryer, tea/coffee facilities, some with jacuzzis. Family-run hotel. Elegant ambience throughout. Main shopping area, swimming pool, leisure centre, riverside walks are a stone's throw from our front door. Golf, hill walking, fishing, pony trekking. After your visit, you will wish to return.

Bookable on www.irelandhotels.com

Special Offer: www.irelandhotels.com/offers

B&B from €40.00 to €80.00

Richard & Esther Fennessy
Proprietors

10

Open All Year

B&B Rates are per Person Sharing per Night incl. Breakfast.
or Room Rates are per Room per Night - **See also Page 8**

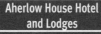

Hotel Minella & Leisure Club

HOTEL ★★★★ MAP 3 K 5

Clonmel Road,
Clonmel,
Co. Tipperary

Tel: 052-612 2388 Fax: 052-612 4381
Email: frontdesk@hotelminella.ie
Web: www.hotelminella.ie
GPS: N +52° 21' 10.30" W -7° 41' 12.15"

Hotel Minella is nestled between the Comeragh Mountains & the River Suir, a 5min drive from Clonmel town centre. The original Georgian house dates back to 1863, and opened as a hotel in 1963 by Mr & Mrs Jack Nallen. Minella offers 90 classic & contemporary rooms, incl 4 superior suites with balconies & 2 with outdoor hot tubs. The restaurant is renowned for its excellent quality food & warm personal service. Minella can host a wide range of events from weddings to conferences. Club Minella offers an extensive range of fitness equipment, a 20m pool, jacuzzi, steam & sauna room, outdoor hot tub & treatment rooms.

Member of Manor House Hotels

Bookable on www.irelandhotels.com

B&B from €75.00 to €150.00
Suites from €250.00 to €500.00

John Nallen
Managing Director

90

Activities:

Closed 22 - 30 December

Aherlow House Hotel and Lodges

HOTEL ★★★ MAP 3 I 6

Glen of Aherlow,
Co. Tipperary

Tel: 062-56153 Fax: 062-56212
Email: reservations@aherlowhouse.ie
Web: www.aherlowhouse.ie
GPS: N +52° 25' 28.78" W -8° 11' 32.19"

Aherlow House Hotel and 4**** de luxe lodges. The hotel & lodges are set in the middle of a coniferous forest just 4 miles from Tipperary Town. Originally a hunting lodge now converted into an exquisitely furnished hotel. Aherlow House welcomes you to its peaceful atmosphere, enhanced by a fine reputation for hospitality, excellent cuisine and unique wines. Aherlow House overlooks the Glen of Aherlow and has beautiful views of the Galtee Mountains. An ideal venue for the social or experienced walker. Activities can be arranged. Please enquire about Facilities for Persons with Disabilities.

Member of Premier Guesthouse

Bookable on www.irelandhotels.com

B&B from €69.50 to €79.50
Suites from €250.00 to €250.00

Ferghal & Helen Purcell
Owners

29

Open All Year

Horse and Jockey Hotel

HOTEL ★★★★ MAP 7 J 7

Horse and Jockey,
Co. Tipperary

Tel: 0504-44192 Fax: 0504-44747
Email: info@horseandjockeyhotel.com
Web: www.horseandjockeyhotel.com
GPS: N +52° 36' 56.19" W -7° 46' 32.64"

Suitably located on one of the major crossroads in Ireland, 200 metres from exit 6 on the M8. Owned and operated by the Egan family our facilities include the traditional Enclosure Bar, Silks Restaurant, 67 luxurious bedrooms, complimentary WiFi. State of the art conference centre comprising of 10 dedicated conference rooms and tiered auditorium (200 delegates). Leisure complex includes 21m pool, steam room, hydro-therapy area. The Elemis Spa is a haven of relaxation with 7 treatment rooms.

Bookable on www.irelandhotels.com
Special Offer: www.irelandhotels.com/offers

B&B from €75.00 to €90.00
Suites from €190.00 to €220.00

Tom Egan
Proprietor

67

Food for Kids

Closed 24 - 26 December

B&B Rates are per Person Sharing per Night incl. Breakfast.
or Room Rates are per Room per Night - See also Page 8

Nenagh / Templemore / Thurles

Abbey Court Hotel, Lodges & Trinity Leisure Spa

HOTEL ★★★ MAP 6 I 8

Dublin Road,
Nenagh,
Co. Tipperary

Tel: 067-41111 Fax: 067-41022
Email: info@abbeycourt.ie
Web: www.abbeycourt.ie
GPS: N +52° 51' 52.92" W -8° 11' 24.37"

The Abbey Court Hotel, Lodges & Trinity Leisure Spa is the mid-west of Irelands leading 3 star hotel easily accessed just off the N7 Dublin - Limerick road. With 82 elegant bedrooms, 24 4 star holiday homes, award winning restaurant, Abbots Bar, state of the art Leisure centre, extensive conference & Banqueting facilities, Rugrats kids club, crèche, Hair & Beauty suite and magnificent gardens. This beautifully designed hotel will offer you a most enjoyable stay. Please enquire about Facilities for Persons with Disabilities.

An IHF Quality Employer

Member of Select Hotels of Ireland

Bookable on www.irelandhotels.com

Special Offer: www.irelandhotels.com/offers

B&B from €75.00 to €140.00

Matthias Muller MIHI
General Manager

82

Food for Kids Activities:

Closed 25 - 26 December

Templemore Arms Hotel

HOTEL ★★ MAP 7 J 8

Main Street,
Templemore,
Co. Tipperary

Tel: 0504-31423 Fax: 0504-31343
Email: info@templemorearms.com
Web: www.templemorearms.com
GPS: N +52° 47' 50.21" W -7° 49' 59.93"

The Templemore Arms Hotel is located in the shadow of one of Ireland's most prominent landmarks, The Devil's Bit, in the centre of the town of Templemore. Recently rebuilt to match the demands of the most discerning guests, it boasts lounge bars, carvery, restaurant, banqueting suite and conference room, providing first class service. Visit the Templemore Arms Hotel and experience an enjoyable getaway.

B&B from €49.95 to €69.95
Suites from €145.00 to €165.00

Dan Ward

16

Activities:

Open All Year

Anner Hotel & Leisure Centre

HOTEL ★★★ MAP 7 J 7

Dublin Road,
Thurles,
Co. Tipperary

Tel: 0504-21799 Fax: 0504-22111
Email: info@annerhotel.ie
Web: www.theannerhotel.com
GPS: N +52° 40' 43.32" W -7° 47' 46.74"

The Anner Hotel is located on the outskirts of Thurles (home of the GAA), and set in its own magnificent landscaped gardens. The Hotel presents 64 tastefully decorated bedrooms featuring WiFi throughout. Exclusive Banqueting & conference facilities. We offer our guests a warm welcome, excellent food & a friendly service in comfortable surroundings. Superb leisure centre boasts 18m swimming pool, kiddies pool, jacuzzi, steam room, sauna & gym. 1 hours from all major cities and airports. Close to Holy Cross Abbey & the Rock of Cashel. Ideal base for touring, golf, walking and leisure breaks.

B&B from €60.00 to €95.00

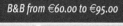

Michael Cleary
General Manager

64

Closed 25 - 27 December

B&B Rates are per Person Sharing per Night incl. Breakfast.
or Room Rates are per Room per Night - **See also Page 8**

Ach Na Sheen Guesthouse

GUESTHOUSE ★★ MAP 316

Clonmel Road,
Tipperary Town,
Co. Tipperary

Tel: 062-51298 Fax: 062-80467
Email: gernoonan@eircom.net
Web: www.achnasheen.ie
GPS: N +52° 28' 22.80" W -8° 9' 17.49"

Family-run guesthouse, 5 minutes walk from the town centre with a spacious sun lounge and dining room overlooking gardens and the beautiful Galtee Mountains. Our 8 rooms are all en suite, equipped with TV and tea/coffee making facilities. Ach-na-Sheen is adjacent to the picturesque Glen of Aherlow where fishing and hill walking can be arranged. Golf can be enjoyed at any number of nearby championship courses. Ger & Sylvia Noonan offer you the utmost in Irish hospitality.

B&B from €50.00 to €60.00

Sylvia & Ger Noonan
Proprietors

8

Activities:

Closed 11 December - 14 January

Ballyglass Country House

HOTEL ★★ MAP 316

Glen of Aherlow Road,
Ballyglass,
Tipperary Town

Tel: 062-52104 Fax: 062-52229
Email: info@ballyglasshouse.com
Web: www.ballyglasshouse.com
GPS: N +52° 26' 31.23" W -8° 9' 56.28"

Ballyglass Country House is an 18th century country residence set in its own grounds on the outskirts of Tipperary and just 2km from the beautiful Glen of Aherlow. Here at this family-run hotel you can enjoy the best of local produce in our "Colonel's Restaurant" and relax in front of a real coal fire in our "Forge Bar". Ballyglass Country House is perfectly situated for touring Munster. Golfing, fishing, hill walking and horse riding are all available locally.

B&B from €45.00 to €50.00

Joan & Bill Byrne
Proprietors

10

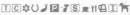

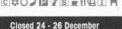

Closed 24 - 26 December

Ballykisteen Hotel & Golf Resort

HOTEL ★★★★ MAP 616

Limerick Junction,
Co. Tipperary

Tel: 062-33333 Fax: 062-31555
Email: info@ballykisteenhotel.com
Web: www.ballykisteenhotel.com
GPS: N +52° 30' 7.65" W -8° 13' 0.45"

Ballykisteen Hotel & Golf Resort is a relaxing country location set in the lea of the Galtee Mountains close to Limerick Junction railway station and Shannon Airport. The hotel offers a Des Smyth designed championship golf course, Serenity Day Spa, leisure facilities, Bally K Kids Club during bank holidays and school breaks and children's playroom. Situated amidst 170 acres of the former Ballykisteen Stud, there is an overwhelming sense of space, the perfect haven of peace and tranquility. Please enquire about Facilities for Persons with Disabilities.

Bookable on www.irelandhotels.com
Special Offer: www.irelandhotels.com/offers

B&B from €50.00 to €76.50
Suites from €125.00 to €178.00

ballyK kids club

Stephen O'Connor
General Manager

133

Food for Kids Activities:

Closed 25 - 26 December

B&B Rates are per Person Sharing per Night incl. Breakfast.
or Room Rates are per Room per Night - See also Page 8

Ardmore

Cliff House Hotel

HOTEL ★★★★★ MAP 3 K 3

Ardmore,
Co. Waterford

Tel: 024-87800 Fax: 024-87820
Email: info@thecliffhousehotel.com
Web: www.thecliffhousehotel.com
GPS: N +52° 9' 8.72" W -7° 9' 46.45"

One of Ireland's most intriguing hotels with a contemporary Irish design, literally built into the cliff, with all of its well appointed bedrooms (most with their own private terraces) and public rooms overlooking the glorious expanse of Ardmore Bay. The House Restaurant uses only locally sourced produce and offers exquisite food. Enjoy the bar and large outdoor terrace. The Well offers superb spa treatments, outdoor jacuzzi, pool and water sports. Please enquire about Facilities for Persons with Disabilities.

Member of Relais et Châteaux

Bookable on www.irelandhotels.com

Special Offer: www.irelandhotels.com/offers

B&B from €80.00 to €130.00
Suites from €295.00 to €500.00

Adriaan Bartels
General Manager

39

Closed 10 January - 05 February

Newtown Farm Guesthouse

GUESTHOUSE ★★★ MAP 3 K 3

Grange,
Ardmore, Via Youghal,
Co. Waterford

Tel: 024-94143 Fax: 024-94054
Email: newtownfarm@eircom.net
Web: www.newtownfarm.com
GPS: N +51° 59' 46.04" W -7° 43' 36.67"

This is a charming guesthouse set in its own lands. Located near the coastal resort of Ardmore. Our guest rooms offer a haven of relaxation and are tastefully furnished with a country house feel. A fully equipped sauna and a hard tennis court are extras we offer our guests. Breakfast is served overlooking the garden with a view of the Atlantic Ocean. The breakfast includes local ingredients. Situated on N25 halfway between Waterford and Cork. Rosslare 2 hours drive. Our guests have a separate lounge with wireless internet access. Please enquire about Facilities for Persons with Disabilities.

Member of Premier Guesthouses

Bookable on www.irelandhotels.com

B&B from €38.00 to €45.00

Teresa O'Connor
Proprietor

7

Closed 31 October - 01 March

Round Tower Hotel

HOTEL ★★ MAP 3 K 3

College Road,
Ardmore,
Co. Waterford

Tel: 024-94494 Fax: 024-94254
Email: rth@eircom.net
GPS: N +51° 57' 1.86" W -7° 43' 37.41"

Situated within walking distance of Ardmore's award-winning beach, the Round Tower Hotel offers 12 well appointed en suite bedrooms. Fresh local produce features prominently on both the bar and restaurant menus. The ancient monastic settlement of St. Declan & the Round Tower are situated behind the hotel. Ardmore also boasts some world famous cliff walks and breathtaking scenery. 21kms from Dungarvan and a 2 hour drive from the port of Rosslare on the Primary N25 route. Please enquire about Facilities for Persons with Disabilities.

Member of Irish Countrywide Hotels

Bookable on www.irelandhotels.com

Special Offer: www.irelandhotels.com/offers

B&B from €50.00 to €65.00

Patricia Quirke & Aidan Quirke M.I.H.C.I
Proprietors

12

Closed 23 - 29 December

B&B Rates are per Person Sharing per Night incl. Breakfast.
or Room Rates are per Room per Night - **See also Page 8**

Hanoras Cottage

Guesthouse ★★★★ Map 3 K 5

Nire Valley,
Ballymacarbry,
Co. Waterford

Tel: 052-613 6134 Fax: 052-613 6540
Email: hanorascottage@eircom.net
Web: www.hanorascottage.com
GPS: N +52° 16' 38.62" W -7° 38' 2.13"

A haven of peace and tranquillity in the Comeragh Mountains, Hanoras has everything for discerning guests. Relax in the sheer bliss of an adult only house with the soothing sounds of the Nire River rippling by. Luxurious rooms with jacuzzi tubs. Superior rooms for that special occasion! Our Ballymaloe School chefs are delighted to cater for any dietary requirements. AA ***** National winners of Georgina Campbell's Guesthouse & Breakfast of the Year Awards. Right next door to a lovely cut-stone church, we are perfect for small private weddings. The Wall Family Welcomes You. Mid-Week & Weekend special offers.

B&B from €70.00 to €100.00

The Wall Family
Proprietors

10

Closed 20 - 28 December

Richmond House

Guesthouse ★★★★ Map 3 J 4

Cappoquin,
Co. Waterford

Tel: 058-54278 Fax: 058-54988
Email: info@richmondhouse.net
Web: www.richmondhouse.net
GPS: N +52° 8' 21.34" W -7° 50' 48.15"

Delightful 18th century Georgian country house and fully licenced award-winning restaurant set in private grounds. Relax in total peace and tranquillity in front of log fires. Each room is a perfect blend of Georgian splendour combined with all modern comforts for the discerning guest. Recommended in the Bridgestone Guides; 100 Best Places to Stay, 100 Best Restaurants in Ireland and all leading guides. Ideal location for a short break. Georgina Campbell's Féile Bia Award 2006.

B&B from €60.00 to €120.00

Paul & Claire Deevy
Proprietors

9

Closed 23 December - 15 January

Barnawee Bridge Guesthouse

Guesthouse ★★★ Map 3 K 4

Kilminion,
Dungarvan,
Co. Waterford

Tel: 058-42074
Email: michelle@barnawee.com
Web: www.barnawee.com
GPS: N +52° 6' 2.19" W -7° 34' 59.01"

Our established guesthouse with fabulous sea and mountain views near all local amenities including three 18 hole golf courses, indoor swimming, sea angling, tennis, fishing and bird watching. Also various countryside walks. Food and drinks available locally, also a kitchennette for tea/coffee and snacks available for all our customers. All rooms are en suite and very spacious with colour TV, making for a very enjoyable stay. Mobile number: 087 262 0269.

B&B from €35.00 to €45.00

Michelle Dwane / Gary Treen
Proprietors

6

Open All Year

B&B Rates are per Person Sharing per Night incl. Breakfast.
or Room Rates are per Room per Night - **See also Page 8**

Dungarvan

Clonea Strand Hotel, Golf & Leisure

HOTEL ★★★ MAP 3 K 4

Clonea,
Dungarvan,
Co. Waterford
Tel: 058-45555 Fax: 058-42880
Email: info@clonea.com
Web: www.clonea.com
GPS: N +52° 5' 39.93" W -7° 32' 46.59"

Clonea Strand Hotel overlooking Clonea Beach. Family-run by John and Ann McGrath. All rooms en suite with tea/coffee making facilities, hairdryer and colour TV. Indoor leisure centre with heated pool, jacuzzi, sauna, Turkish bath, gymnasium and ten pin bowling alley. Situated close by is our 18 hole golf course bordering on the Atlantic Ocean with a scenic background of Dungarvan Bay and Comeragh Mountains. Our Bay Restaurant specialises in locally caught seafood. 1 thousand sq foot children's soft play facility. www.playloft.net.

Room Rate from €59.00 to €129.00

Mark Knowles
Resort Director

59

Closed 23 - 25 December

Lawlors Hotel

HOTEL ★★★ MAP 3 K 4

Bridge Street,
Dungarvan,
Co. Waterford
Tel: 058-41122 Fax: 058-41000
Email: info@lawlorshotel.com
Web: www.lawlorshotel.com
GPS: N +52° 5' 26.47" W -7° 37' 15.33"

Family-run and situated in the historic town of Dungarvan, close to all amenities. Accommodation in spacious en suite bedrooms. All rooms offer traditional comforts and modern facilities. Food is a speciality at "Lawlors" with a wide variety of menus, delicious locally sourced ingredients are at the heart of the hotel's restaurants. "Lawlors" and Dungarvan is the ideal choice for your stay in the beautiful west Waterford countryside. Please enquire about Facilities for Persons with Disabilities.

B&B from €49.00 to €75.00

Michael Burke
Proprietor

89

Closed 23 - 27 December

Park Hotel, Leisure Centre & Holiday Homes

HOTEL ★★★ MAP 3 K 4

Dungarvan,
Co. Waterford
Tel: 058-42899 Fax: 058-42969
Email: reservations@parkhoteldungarvan.com
Web: www.flynnhotels.com
GPS: N +52° 5' 40.52" W -7° 37' 24.51"

Overlooking the Colligan River Estuary, and minutes from beautiful beaches and Golf Courses, The Park Hotel provides the ideal setting for leisure or business. The hotel's 86 spacious rooms and suites are elegantly furnished with flair and imagination. The hotel has its Aqua & Fitness centre with swimming pool, sauna, steam room and gym. There are also 15 new self catering holiday homes on the grounds of the hotel.

Member of Flynn Hotels

Bookable on www.irelandhotels.com
Special Offer: www.irelandhotels.com/offers

B&B from €59.00 to €85.00
Suites from €190.00 to €280.00

Pierce Flynn
Manager

86

Food for Kids Activities:

Closed 24 - 26 December

B&B Rates are per Person Sharing per Night incl. Breakfast.
or Room Rates are per Room per Night - **See also Page 8**

Seaview

GUESTHOUSE ★★★ MAP 3 K 4

Windgap,
N25/Youghal Road, Dungarvan,
Co. Waterford
Tel: 058-41583 Fax: 058-41679
Email: info@seaviewdungarvan.com
Web: www.seaviewdungarvan.com
GPS: N +52° 2' 54.67" W -7° 39' 39.08"

Want your vacation to never stop being a vacation? Enjoy breakfast overlooking the sea? Play one of Dungarvan's three 18 hole golf courses. How about dinner, entertained by traditional Irish musicians, at the nearby Marine Bar? Make every ounce of your vacation count. Try Seaview on N25, 5km west of Dungarvan. Fax and e-mail facilities available. Continental and full Irish breakfast served. Laundry service available. Gulliver Ireland award-winner 2007. Please enquire about Facilities for Persons with Disabilities.

Bookable on www.irelandhotels.com
Special Offer: www.irelandhotels.com/offers

B&B from €35.00 to €45.00

Martin & Nora Fahey
Owners

8

T C U P S I

Closed 01 December - 31 January

Beach Guest House

GUESTHOUSE ★★★★ MAP 4 M 5

Lower Village,
Dunmore East,
Co. Waterford
Tel: 051-383316 Fax: 051-383319
Email: beachouse@eircom.net
Web: www.dunmorebeachguesthouse.com
GPS: N +52° 9' 18.98" W -6° 59' 42.52"

Newly built in a superb location overlooking Dunmore East Strand. The Beach Guest House provides luxury accommodation, stunning sea views and private parking. A central base from which to explore charming hidden coves, superb cliff walks and neat rows of pretty thatched cottages in this picturesque village 10 miles from Waterford, in the centre of Dunmore East with excellent restaurants and sporting amenities nearby including 4 championship golf courses within 10 miles. AA 4 Yellow Stars & RAC ♦♦♦♦. Disabled access room available. Please enquire about Facilities for Persons with Disabilities.

Member of Premier Guesthouses

Bookable on www.irelandhotels.com

B&B from €40.00 to €50.00

Breda Battles
Host

7

T P S I

Closed 01 November - 28 February

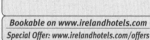

B&B Rates are per Person Sharing per Night incl. Breakfast.
or Room Rates are per Room per Night - **See also Page 8**

Dunmore East / Faithlegg / Lismore

Ocean Hotel

HOTEL ★★ MAP 4 M 5

Dunmore East,
Co. Waterford

Tel: 051-383136 Fax: 051-383576
Email: info@theoceanhotel.com
Web: www.theoceanhotel.com
GPS: N +52° 8' 52.67" W -6° 59' 37.96"

The Ocean Hotel is located in one of the most picturesque fishing villages in the county. Dunmore East, with its thatched cottages and stunning beaches, is located just 20kms from Waterford City. All 12 en suite rooms have been recently refurbished and have TV, tea/coffee making facilities and irons. The Alfred D Snow Bar offers an extensive and mouth watering bar menu featuring a wide range of hot & cold local seafood.

B&B from €35.00 to €60.00

Joe Fortune
Manager

12

Activities:

Open All Year

Faithlegg House Hotel

HOTEL ★★★★ MAP 4 M 5

Faithlegg,
Co. Waterford

Tel: 051-382000 Fax: 051-382010
Email: reservations@fhh.ie
Web: www.faithlegg.com
GPS: N +52° 15' 29.17" W -7° 1' 30.99"

An FBD Hotel - Faithlegg House Hotel is located on the already renowned 18 hole championship golf course, overlooking the estuary of the river Suir. This elegantly restored country house hotel incorporates 82 bedrooms, including 14 master rooms in the original house, a unique fitness, health and beauty club, featuring a 17m pool, plus comprehensive meeting, conference and event facilities. AA 4 star approved. Special offers available on www.fbdhotels.com. FBD Hotels - Optimus - Achieving Business Excellence. Please enquire about Facilities for Persons with Disabilities.

An IHF Quality Employer

Member of FBD Hotels

Bookable on www.irelandhotels.com

Special Offer: www.irelandhotels.com/offers

B&B from €79.00 to €109.00
Suites from €199.00 to €278.00

Alison Redmond
General Manager

82

Activities:

Closed 20 - 27 December

Lismore House Hotel

HOTEL MAP 3 J 4

Main Street,
Lismore,
Co. Waterford

Tel: 058-72966 Fax: 058-53068
Email: info@lismorehousehotel.com
Web: www.lismorehousehotel.com
GPS: N +52° 8' 15.03" W -7° 55' 57.37"

Built to a 4**** specification. Built in 1797 and located in the heart of Lismore, the hotel has been completely restored and refurbished to retain the glory of it's Georgian old world style and charm and reflect the heritage of Lismore Castle and surrounds. The team look forward to welcoming you in the true Traditional Irish style and to offering you the best in personal service. Lismore Castle, gardens, heritage centre and so much more, from our doorstep. Please enquire about Facilities for Persons with Disabilities.

Member of Isaacs Group

Bookable on www.irelandhotels.com

Room Rate from €30.00 to €180.00

John Hornby
General Manager

29

Activities:

Open All Year

B&B Rates are per Person Sharing per Night incl. Breakfast.
or Room Rates are per Room per Night - **See also Page 8**

Beach Haven House

GUESTHOUSE ★★★ MAP 4 L 5

Tivoli Terrace,
Tramore,
Co. Waterford
Tel: 051-390208 Fax: 051-330971
Email: beachhavenhouse@eircom.net
Web: www.beachhavenhouse.com
GPS: N +52° 9' 56.52" W -7° 8' 43.74"

This luxurious home in the heart of Tramore has a warm and friendly atmosphere. Finished to the highest standards and with your comfort in mind. We are located just a few minutes walk to the beach, town centre, Splashworld and the racecourse. Tramore has great restaurants and pubs and lots to do for the whole family. All rooms are en suite with TV, phone and coffee and tea making facilities. Extensive breakfast menu, family suites, comfy guest lounge, private parking.

Bookable on www.irelandhotels.com

B&B from €30.00 to €40.00

Avery & Niamh Coryell
Owners

8

Open All Year

Top Two Visitor Attractions
Lismore, Co. Waterford.

Lismore Castle Gardens & Gallery

Prince John first built a castle in Lismore in 1185, and a round tower, dating from the 13th century still stands today. Within the defensive walls of the castle, the gardens at Lismore provide spectacular views, and the herbaceous border gives an impressive show of colour throughout summer. There is also a fine selection of specimen magnolias, camellias, and rhododendrons, and a remarkable yew walk where Edmund Spenser is said to have written the 'Faerie Queen'. While wandering the gardens, visitors are invited to enjoy several pieces of contemporary sculpture, and encouraged to visit Lismore Castle Arts, which shows works by some of the worlds leading contemporary artists, providing a vibrant programme to be enjoyed by the local community and tourists alike. Visitors to the gardens are welcome to visit the gallery free of charge. Lismore Castle is the Irish home of the Duke of Devonshire and his family and, when not in residence, the castle may be rented, fully staffed, to guests.

Tel: 058 54424 Fax: 058 54896
E-mail: lismoreestates@eircom.net
Website: www.lismorecastle.com
www.lismorecastlearts.ie
Open Daily llam to 4.45pm from 17th March to 30th September 2010

Adult €8 Child €4 (under 16)
Family Ticket €20 (2 adults & 3 children & any additional children €4 each)
Friends €35, Friends Family ticket €60
Concessions 6 (pensioners and students)
Group rate (20+) €6 each (Group leader free)

Lismore Heritage Centre

Situated in the centre of the town, is a must for those who wish to experience the rich history of the town and its surroundings. Your host Brother Declan (alias Niall Toibin) will take you on a fascinating journey through time in "The Lismore Experience" – an exciting audio-visual presentation which tells the story of the town since St. Carthages arrival in 636AD. Also exhibition galleries on Monastic, Norman and Medieval Lismore and a science exhibition room on the life and works of Robert Boyle, 'the Father of Modern Chemistry' who was born at Lismore Castle. Guided tours of this monastic town leave the Heritage Centre at appointed times each day.

Open 9.30am – 5.30pm
Monday – Friday (year round)
10am – 5.30pm Saturday
(April – September)
12noon – 5.30pm Sunday
(April – September)

Admission charges €5.00 (adults)
Special rates for families and OAPs
Tel: 058 54975 Fax: 058 53009
e-mail: lismoreheritage@eircom.net

B&B Rates are per Person Sharing per Night incl. Breakfast.
or Room Rates are per Room per Night - **See also Page 8**

Tramore

Majestic Hotel

HOTEL ★★★ MAP 4 L 5

Tramore,
Co. Waterford

Tel: 051-381761 Fax: 051-381766
Email: info@majestic-hotel.ie
Web: www.majestic-hotel.ie
GPS: N +52° 9' 47.20" W -7° 8' 54.23"

A warm welcome awaits you at the award-winning Majestic Hotel, overlooking Tramore Bay and its famous 5km of sandy beach. Only 10km from Waterford City. 60 en suite bedrooms with TV, phone, WiFi, safe, hairdryer, and tea/coffee facilities. Family friendly hotel with leisure facilities available to guests at "Splashworld" opposite hotel. All our food is sourced from local Irish producers with healthy options menu for kids. Golf packages on South East sunshine circuit a speciality. Extensive free car-parking. Awards for outstanding quality, good food and warm hospitality.

An IHF Quality Employer

Bookable on www.irelandhotels.com

Room Rate from €79.00 to €99.00

Danny & Annette Devine
Proprietors

60

Activities:

Closed 24 - 25 December

O'Shea's Hotel

HOTEL ★★★ MAP 4 L 5

Strand Street,
Tramore,
Co. Waterford

Tel: 051-381246 Fax: 051-390144
Email: info@osheas-hotel.com
Web: www.osheas-hotel.com
GPS: N +52° 9' 35.54" W -7° 9' 1.03"

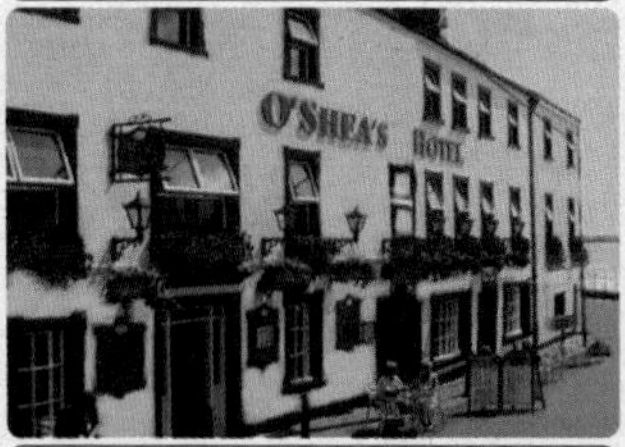

Noreen & Joe O'Shea are the proud owners of this intimate family-run hotel that opened its doors to guests in 1968 & has maintained an outstanding reputation for customer care, good food & genuine hospitality. Located by the sea in downtown Tramore, minutes from "Splashworld" (discount for our guests). Bedrooms are located in either the main hotel or the annexe. We specialise in the best of Irish foods, served in the Copper Room Restaurant (breakfast served all day) or in O'Shea's Bar where good food, customer satisfaction, comfort & value for money prevails. Secure car-park. Golfing, surfing & racing packages.

An IHF Quality Employer

Bookable on www.irelandhotels.com
Special Offer: www.irelandhotels.com/offers

Room Rate from €69.00 to €129.00

Joe & Noreen O'Shea
Proprietors

29

Food for Kids *Activities:*

Closed 23 - 26 December

Sands Hotel (The)

HOTEL ★★★ MAP 4 L 5

Strand Road,
Tramore,
Co. Waterford

Tel: 051-381355 Fax: 051-393869
Email: enquiries@sands-hotel-tramore.com
Web: www.sands-hotel-tramore.com
GPS: N +52° 9' 39.98" W -7° 8' 57.63"

Nestled in the heart of Tramore, overlooking a three mile golden beach, The Sands Hotel offers the very best in accommodation and entertainment with unbelievable offers. It is the perfect venue whether you are visiting for business or pleasure. Many rooms offer outstanding views of the beautiful coastline. The Sands hotel boasts an ideal location just minutes away from all the attractions, entertainment and the beautiful beach our town is famous for.

Bookable on www.irelandhotels.com

B&B from €35.00 to €80.00
Suites from €120.00 to €200.00

Paul Mitchell
General Manager

20

Activities:

Closed 24 - 25 December

B&B Rates are per Person Sharing per Night incl. Breakfast.
or Room Rates are per Room per Night - **See also Page 8**

Arlington Lodge Town House & Restaurant

HOTEL ★★★★ MAP 4 L 5

John's Hill,
Waterford City

Tel: 051-878584 Fax: 051-878127
Email: info@arlingtonlodge.com
Web: www.arlingtonlodge.com
GPS: N +52° 14' 58.89" W -7° 6' 17.24"

Arlington Lodge is the perfect base for touring the south east. Based in a quiet residential area of Waterford City with private off road parking. As a member of Good Food Ireland, we are all about local seasonal food. Our breakfast is an experience - choose from a menu where every dish is cooked to order. Waterford Blaa, Pancakes, Flavahans Porridge and of course the traditional "Full Irish". Experience real Irish country house hospitality in modernised Georgian surroundings with complementary broadband in every room. Maurice and his team make the perfect hosts for a memorable stay.

Member of Good Food Ireland

Bookable on www.irelandhotels.com

B&B from €55.00 to €95.00
Suites from €170.00 to €220.00

Maurice Keller
Manager / Proprietor

20

Food for Kids

Closed 24 December - 02 January

Athenaeum House Hotel

HOTEL ★★★★ MAP 4 L 5

Christendom,
Ferrybank,
Waterford

Tel: 051-833999 Fax: 051-833977
Email: info@athenaeumhousehotel.com
Web: www.athenaeumhousehotel.com
GPS: N +52° 15' 38.56" W -7° 5' 52.56"

Athenaeum House Hotel is a 4**** boutique hotel set amidst 6 acres of parkland on the banks of the River Suir overlooking Waterford City. Offering a lifestyles elegance, with modern chic décor. Providing the ultimate in comfort and luxury for discerning travellers. Featuring Zaks Restaurant, state of the art meeting rooms, all bedrooms, including de luxe rooms & suites, are individually designed with TV, mini-hi-fi, mini-bar, voicemail and broadband.

An IHF Quality Employer

Member of Manor House Hotels

Bookable on www.irelandhotels.com
Special Offer: www.irelandhotels.com/offers

B&B from €50.00 to €75.00
Suites from €180.00 to €220.00

Mailo & Stan Power
Joint Proprietors

29

Food for Kids

Closed 24 - 28 December

Belfry Hotel

HOTEL ★★★ MAP 4 L 5

Conduit Lane,
Waterford

Tel: 051-844800 Fax: 051-844814
Email: info@belfryhotel.ie
Web: www.belfryhotel.ie
GPS: N +52° 15' 41.05" W -7° 6' 38.33"

The Belfry Hotel is a family-run hotel that has a special ambience, combining traditional charm with superb modern amenities. Bedrooms are spacious and luxurious. Riada's Restaurant offers a well chosen and varied à la carte menu for dinner, while an extensive bar menu is available daily in the popular and stylish Chapter House Bar. City centre location, close to bus and rail station. Superb range of golf courses nearby. Golf packages available. Please enquire about Facilities for Persons with Disabilities.

Bookable on www.irelandhotels.com
Special Offer: www.irelandhotels.com/offers

B&B from €35.00 to €99.00
Suites from €120.00 to €250.00

Sharon Mansfield
General Manager

61

Food for Kids

Closed 21 - 30 December

B&B Rates are per Person Sharing per Night incl. Breakfast.
or Room Rates are per Room per Night - See also Page 8

Waterford City

Coach House

GUESTHOUSE ★★★ MAP 4 L 5

Butlerstown Castle,
Butlerstown, Cork Road,
Waterford

Tel: 051-384656 Fax: 051-384751
Email: coachhse@iol.ie
Web: www.butlerstowncastle.com
GPS: N +52° 13' 41.36" W -7° 11' 1.10"

Built during the late 1700s, remodelled by Sir Samuel Ferguson in 1874 and restored in 1992 - retaining many original features - the Coach House offers the best of traditional country home en suite accommodation in a tranquil and unique historical setting (walled cottage garden, 13th century castle ruins on grounds). Situated in countryside, 5 mins from Waterford city which has excellent pubs and restaurants. Michelin recommended. Included in Alastair Sawday's Special Places to Stay.

Bookable on www.irelandhotels.com

B&B from €55.00 to €62.50

Des O'Keeffe
Proprietor

7

Closed 01 November - 01 April

Diamond Hill Country House

GUESTHOUSE ★★★ MAP 4 L 5

Slieverue,
Waterford

Tel: 051-832855 Fax: 051-832254
Email: info@stayatdiamondhill.com
Web: www.stayatdiamondhill.com
GPS: N +52° 16' 38.56" W -7° 4' 48.10"

Situated 2.5km from Waterford City off the Rosslare Waterford Road N25. Convenient to ferries. A long established guesthouse of considerable charm and friendliness, set in its own national award-winning gardens. The house has been extensively refurbished incorporating family heirlooms and antiques resulting in a countryside oasis, a haven of luxury and tranquillity, yet only minutes from the bustling city of Waterford. Recommended by Frommers, Foders, Michelin, AA 4 Yellow Stars. Member of Premier Guesthouses. Please enquire about Facilities for Persons with Disabilities.

Member of Premier Guesthouses

Bookable on www.irelandhotels.com

B&B from €35.00 to €45.00

Bernard Smith-Lehane
Proprietor

17

Closed 20 - 28 December

Dooley's Hotel

HOTEL ★★★ MAP 4 L 5

The Quay,
Waterford

Tel: 051-873531 Fax: 051-870262
Email: hotel@dooleys-hotel.ie
Web: www.dooleys-hotel.ie
GPS: N +52° 15' 46.46" W -7° 6' 56.99"

The waters of the River Suir swirl past the door of this renowned hotel, which is situated on The Quay in Waterford. Dooley's is an ideal choice for a centrally located hotel, close to all amenities, cultural and business centres. This family owned & managed hotel caters for the corporate/leisure traveller. The hotel has a purpose-built conference centre with full facilities. Enjoy the style & comfort of The New Ship Restaurant & Dry Dock Bar. Dooley's Hotel serving the customer for three generations. 24 hour online booking www.dooleys-hotel.ie. Please enquire about Facilities for Persons with Disabilities.

An IHF Quality Employer

Member of Holiday Ireland Hotels

Bookable on www.irelandhotels.com
Special Offer: www.irelandhotels.com/offers

B&B from €39.00 to €99.00

Margaret & Tina Darrer
Directors

113

Food for Kids Activities:

Closed 25 - 28 December

B&B Rates are per Person Sharing per Night incl. Breakfast.
or Room Rates are per Room per Night - See also Page 8

Fitzwilton Hotel

HOTEL ★★★★ MAP 4 L 5

Bridge Street,
Waterford

Tel: 051-846900 Fax: 051-878650
Email: info@fitzwiltonhotel.ie
Web: www.fitzwiltonhotel.ie
GPS: N +52° 15' 47.78" W -7° 7' 12.63"

Break away from the norm to Boutique Luxury in the heart of Waterford City. The Fitzwilton Hotel offers beautifully appointed rooms & suites, many of which have floor to ceiling glass windows offering fantastic views across the city. Sample the in-house restaurant Chez K's, which has established itself as one of Waterford's "Must Do" restaurants with a well deserved reputation for fine food & outstanding service. Or why not unwind at the Met Bar-Café, serving an array of classic drinks & quirky cocktails with an exquisite bar menu also available. In-house Beauty Salon and Gymnasium. Free on-site parking. Free Wi-Fi

Bookable on www.irelandhotels.com
Special Offer: www.irelandhotels.com/offers

B&B from €39.50 to €85.00
Suites from €179.00 to €349.00

Aiden Fleming
General Manager

88

Closed 23 - 28 December

B&B Rates are per Person Sharing per Night incl. Breakfast.
or Room Rates are per Room per Night - **See also Page 8**

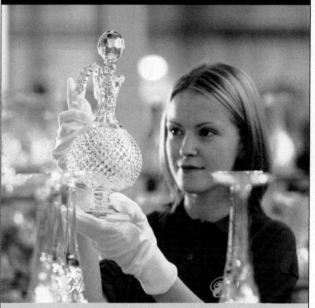

Waterford City

Granville Hotel

HOTEL ★★★ MAP 4 L 5

Meagher Quay,
Waterford

Tel: 051-305555 Fax: 051-305566
Email: stay@granville-hotel.ie
Web: www.granville-hotel.ie
GPS: N +52° 15' 43.58" W -7° 6' 43.87"

One of Waterford's most prestigious city centre hotels, overlooking the River Suir. This family-run hotel is one of Ireland's oldest with significant historical connections. Justly proud of the Granville's heritage, owners Liam and Ann Cusack today vigourously pursue the Granville's long tradition of hospitality, friendliness and comfort. It has been elegantly refurbished, retaining its old world Georgian character. Award-winning Bianconi Restaurant, Thomas Francis Meagher Bar. Bookable now on www.granville-hotel.ie Please enquire about Facilities for Persons with Disabilities.

An IHF Quality Employer

Bookable on www.irelandhotels.com

B&B from €40.00 to €90.00

Ann & Liam Cusack
Managers / Proprietors
98

Closed 24 - 27 December

Ramada Viking Hotel

HOTEL ★★★ MAP 4 L 5

Cork Road,
Waterford

Tel: 051-336933 Fax: 051-336969
Email: info@vikinghotel.ie
Web: www.ramadavikinghotel.ie
GPS: N +52° 14' 32.23" W -7° 9' 53.07"

Comfort, great service & value for money along with ample free parking, broadband and Sky Movies can be enjoyed during your stay. Unwind in the evening with a meal in Asgard Bar or Valhalla Restaurant or enjoy a workout or swim with the compliments of the hotel at an off-site leisure centre. Easily found on the N25 our hotel is an ideal base to explore all that Ireland's oldest city has to offer as well as the surrounding renowned beaches & golf courses. Please enquire about Facilities for Persons with Disabilities.

Bookable on www.irelandhotels.com
Special Offer: www.irelandhotels.com/offers

Room Rate from €49.00 to €99.00

Gavin Lonergan
General Manager
100

Closed 24 - 26 December

Rhu Glenn Country Club Hotel

HOTEL ★★★ MAP 4 L 5

Luffany,
Slieverue,
Waterford
Tel: 051-832242 Fax: 051-832242
Email: info@rhuglennhotel.com
Web: www.rhuglennhotel.com
GPS: N +52° 17' 50.27" W -7° 3' 15.07"

Built within its own grounds with parking for cars, coaches, etc., the hotel is family-run. Situated on the N25 Rosslare to Waterford Road, convenient to ferries, it offers a superb location whether your pleasure be golfing, fishing, or simply exploring the South East. All rooms are en suite with direct dial phone and multi-channel TV. Our Luffany Restaurant is renowned for its service of fine food. Relax and enjoy our Sliabh Mór lounge bars and the Country Club for ballroom dancing with live entertainment provided by Ireland's top artistes. Please enquire about Facilities for Persons with Disabilities.

Bookable on www.irelandhotels.com

B&B from €40.00 to €70.00

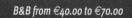

Liam Mooney
Proprietor
30

Activities:

Closed 24 - 25 December

B&B Rates are per Person Sharing per Night incl. Breakfast.
or Room Rates are per Room per Night - See also Page 8

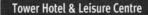

St. Albans Guesthouse

GUESTHOUSE ★★ MAP 4 L 5

Cork Road,
Waterford

Tel: 051-358171 / 379393 Fax: 051-358171
Email: stalbansbandb@yahoo.com
Web: www.irelandhotels.com
GPS: N +52° 15' 5.43" W -7° 7' 0.87"

St. Albans is a well established family-run guesthouse. Ideally located minutes walk from Waterford City centre and Waterford Crystal. Our very spacious superbly appointed rooms are all en suite with multi-channel TV, tea/coffee facilities and hairdryer. Secure parking at rear of premises. 4 championship golf courses in vicinity. Horse riding 3km. Tennis courts, swimming pool 2 minutes. Several local beaches and breathtaking scenery. Bus and train station a short distance. UK Freephone: 0800 912 3910. Tel: 051 379 393. Mobile: 086 8072153. Please enquire about Facilities for Persons with Disabilities.

B&B from €40.00 to €40.00

Helen & Tom Mullally
Proprietors

8

Open All Year

Tower Hotel & Leisure Centre

HOTEL ★★★ MAP 4 L 5

The Mall,
Waterford

Tel: 051-862300 Fax: 051-870129
Email: reservations@thw.ie
Web: www.towerhotelwaterford.com
GPS: N +52° 15' 36.27" W -7° 6' 17.97"

An FBD Hotel, with its riverside location in the heart of Waterford City and 135 guest rooms offering every modern amenity, the Tower Hotel is the flagship hotel of FBD Hotels. The Tower Hotel is the ideal base to discover this wonderful city & county, with two restaurants - traditional carvery & award-winning bistro, Adelphi Riverside Bar, leisure centre with 20m pool, Reznu treatment rooms, extensive conference facilities & private guest car park. Free internet access in each guest bedroom. Special online offers available on www.fbdhotels.com. Please enquire about Facilities for Persons with Disabilities.

An IHF Quality Employer

Member of FBD Hotels

Bookable on www.irelandhotels.com
Special Offer: www.irelandhotels.com/offers

B&B from €35.00 to €85.00

Alicia Maguire
General Manager

135

Food for Kids Activities:

Closed 24 - 28 December

Waterford Marina Hotel

HOTEL ★★★ MAP 4 L 5

Canada Street,
Waterford

Tel: 051-856600 Fax: 051-856605
Email: info@waterfordmarinahotel.com
Web: www.waterfordmarinahotel.com
GPS: N +52° 15' 30.03" W -7° 6' 6.23"

The Waterford Marina Hotel is ideally located in the heart of Waterford City, nestled on the banks of the River Suir, 5 minutes walk from the city centre. 81 superbly appointed en suite guest rooms, all offering the essentials for an enjoyable stay. Relax by the River Suir in our Waterfront Bar and Restaurant. Other facilities include a range of conference suites, our riverside terrace and complimentary on-site parking. Free WiFi installed in all bedrooms, bar, lobby and conference suites. Please enquire about Facilities for Persons with Disabilities.

An IHF Quality Employer

Bookable on www.irelandhotels.com
Special Offer: www.irelandhotels.com/offers

B&B from €39.00 to €120.00

Karen Dollery
General Manager

81

Food for Kids Activities:

Closed 20 - 27 December

B&B Rates are per Person Sharing per Night incl. Breakfast.
or Room Rates are per Room per Night - **See also Page 8**

Waterford City / Barntown / Bunclody

Woodlands Hotel (The)

HOTEL ★★★ MAP 4 L 5

Dunmore Road,
Waterford

Tel: 051-392700 Fax: 051-304575
Email: info@woodlandshotel.ie
Web: www.woodlandshotel.ie
GPS: N +52° 14' 21.11" W -7° 3' 51.92"

The Woodlands Hotel prides itself on delivering unrivalled care and attention to our guests. Located on the Dunmore Road in Waterford city we have 47 modern spacious bedrooms, lively "Brasscock" bar and the Stylish Arbutus Restaurant. In addition we are a superb wedding and conference venue with generous private car park and free WiFi throughout the hotel. Please enquire about Facilities for Persons with Disabilities.

Bookable on www.irelandhotels.com
Special Offer: www.irelandhotels.com/offers

Room Rate from €49.00 to €169.00

Barry Howard
General Manager

47

Food for Kids

Closed 24 - 25 December

Stanville Lodge Hotel

HOTEL ★★★ MAP 4 N 6

Barntown,
Co. Wexford

Tel: 053-913 4300 Fax: 053-913 4989
Email: info@stanville.ie
Web: www.stanville.ie
GPS: N +52° 20' 24.92" W -6° 34' 49.52"

This modern and family run hotel, guarantees top quality food in a relaxed atmosphere. Centrally located off the N25 just 5 mins from Wexford town, The Stanville Lodge provides easy access to Wexford's many attractions; the Irish National Heritage Park, Johnstown Castle, Dunbrody Tall Ship and many beautiful Wexford beaches. Please enquire about Facilities for Persons with Disabilities.

Bookable on www.irelandhotels.com
Special Offer: www.irelandhotels.com/offers

B&B from €25.00 to €90.00

Anne Marie Neville
General Manager

30

Closed 25 - 27 December

Carlton Millrace Hotel & C-Spa

HOTEL ★★★★ MAP 8 N 7

Riversedge,
Bunclody,
Co. Wexford

Tel: 053-937 5100 Fax: 053-937 5124
Email: reservations.millrace@carlton.ie
Web: www.carlton.ie/millrace
GPS: N +52° 39' 18.99" W -6° 39' 21.21"

Located on the edge of the Bunclody Golf & Fishing Club & the River Slaney. This 4**** hotel has 60 well appointed bedrooms including family suites. Lady Lucy's fine dining rooftop restaurant overlooks the picturesque town of Bunclody. The C Spa is a real treasure with 10 treatment suites and dedicated relaxation room with heated loungers. Bunclody is situated on the N80 between Carlow and Enniscorthy, 80 mins drive from Dublin, 45 mins from Rosslare. Conference facilities for up to 350 delegates. Room Reservations LoCall 1890 288 288. Newly opened Bunclody Golf & Fishing Club on site.

An IHF Quality Employer

Member of Carlton Hotel Group

Bookable on www.irelandhotels.com
Special Offer: www.irelandhotels.com/offers

B&B from €49.00 to €129.00
Suites from €180.00 to €310.00

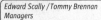

Edward Scally / Tommy Brennan
Managers

60

Closed 24 - 27 December

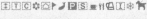

B&B Rates are per Person Sharing per Night incl. Breakfast.
or Room Rates are per Room per Night - **See also Page 8**

Courtown Harbour / Curracloe / Enniscorthy

Courtown Hotel

HOTEL ★★ MAP 8 O 7

Courtown Harbour,
Gorey,
Co. Wexford

Tel: 053-942 5210 Fax: 053-942 5304
Email: info@courtownhotel.ie
Web: www.courtownhotel.ie
GPS: N +52° 38' 43.75" W -6° 13' 43.08"

The family-run Courtown Hotel & Leisure Centre is renowned for its friendly atmosphere and excellent cuisine. This hotel features our new Bistro V for excellent food in stylish surroundings and a selection of lounge bars. Our Pear Tree beer garden offers food from 1pm to 8pm daily. All rooms are en suite with TV and direct dial telephone. Residents enjoy complimentary use of our leisure facilities which include an indoor heated swimming pool, sauna, jacuzzi & steam room. Regular live Entertainment throughout the year.

B&B from €50.00 to €70.00

Paul & Sandra Kinch
Manager/Proprietor

22

Closed 31 October - 16 March

Hotel Curracloe

HOTEL ★★ MAP 4 O 6

Curracloe,
Co. Wexford

Tel: 053-913 7308 Fax: 053-913 7587
Email: hotelcurracloe@eircom.net
Web: www.hotelcurracloe.com
GPS: N +52° 23' 36.53" W -6° 23' 38.17"

Hotel Curracloe is ideally situated, only five miles from Wexford Town, minutes from Blue/Green Flag beaches and central to golfing, angling, bird-watching, hill walking and horse riding amenities. Our 29 rooms are en suite with modern facilities and our award-winning Blake Restaurant and Tavern Pub serve the best of home produce. The Brent Banqueting Room will cater for every special occasion. Our friendly staff will ensure that Hotel Curracloe is the perfect base for your leisure time in the sunny South East. Please enquire about Facilities for Persons with Disabilities.

B&B from €35.00 to €60.00

John & Margaret Hanrahan
Owners

29

Open All Year

Lemongrove House

GUESTHOUSE ★★★ MAP 4 N 6

Blackstoops,
Enniscorthy,
Co. Wexford

Tel: 053-923 6115 Fax: 053-923 6115
Email: info@lemongrovehouse.ie
Web: www.lemongrovehouse.ie
GPS: N +52° 30' 51.78" W -6° 33' 43.47"

Elegant country house 1km north of Enniscorthy just off roundabout on Dublin/Rosslare Road (N11). Lemongrove House is set in mature gardens with private parking. All rooms are en suite with direct dial phone, TV, hairdryer and tea/coffee making facilities. Recommended by Guide du Routard and other leading guides. Within walking distance of a choice of restaurants, pubs and new pool and leisure centre. Locally we have beaches, golf, horse riding, walking and quad track. Please enquire about Facilities for Persons with Disabilities.

B&B from €35.00 to €45.00

Colm & Ann McGibney
Owners

9

Closed 20 - 29 December

B&B Rates are per Person Sharing per Night incl. Breakfast.
or Room Rates are per Room per Night - **See also Page 8**

Enniscorthy / Foulksmills / Gorey

Riverside Park Hotel and Leisure Club

HOTEL ★★★★ MAP 4 N 6

The Promenade,
Enniscorthy,
Co. Wexford

Tel: 053-923 7800 Fax: 053-923 7900
Email: info@riversideparkhotel.com
Web: www.riversideparkhotel.com
GPS: N +52° 29' 51.10" W -6° 34' 0.98"

Nestling along the scenic banks of the River Slaney, the Riverside Park Hotel and Leisure Club is an ideal base for touring the treasures of the sunny South East. With a choice of two superb restaurants, The Moorings and The Alamo, Tex-Mex at its best. A luxurious bar with spectacular views. Relax and unwind in our indoor swimming pool, sauna, steam room, jacuzzi and gym. Please enquire about Facilities for Persons with Disabilities.

Bookable on www.irelandhotels.com

Special Offer: www.irelandhotels.com/offers

B&B from €43.00 to €105.00
Suites from €150.00 to €200.00

Jim Maher
General Manager

62

Activities:

Closed 24 - 26 December

Horse and Hound Hotel

HOTEL ★★★ MAP 4 N 5

Ballinaboola,
Foulksmills,
Co. Wexford

Tel: 051-428323 Fax: 051-428471
Email: info@horseandhoundinn.ie
Web: www.horseandhoundinn.ie
GPS: N +52° 22' 9.85" W -6° 50' 13.62"

The Horse and Hound Hotel is a family-run hotel in picturesque Ballinaboola, a small village on the N25 from Rosslare. Accommodation is provided in 27 tastefully decorated guest rooms. Catering for all needs - from private parties and weddings to conferences. A haven for weary tourists or busy delegate. Food served all day in our renowned restaurant. You are sure of a friendly welcome from the Murphy family and their professional staff.

B&B from €40.00 to €85.00

Christy & Brendan Murphy

27

Closed 25 - 26 December

Amber Springs Hotel & Health Spa

HOTEL ★★★★ MAP 8 O 7

Wexford Road,
Gorey,
Co. Wexford

Tel: 053-948 4000 Fax: 053-948 4494
Email: info@ambersspringshotel.ie
Web: www.ambersspringshotel.ie
GPS: N +52° 40' 5.28" W -6° 17' 25.16"

A Redmond Hotel Group member & sister hotel to Ashdown Park Hotel, the newest 4**** luxury hotel in Gorey, Amber Springs Hotel & Health Spa is centrally located only walking distance from both the train station & town centre, Situated only 50 minutes from Dublin, exit 23 off the main N11 route from Dublin to Rosslare. Offering 69 luxurious spacious guest rooms with 11 executive suites, Kelbys Bistro, Brookes Bar, state of the art conference & banqueting facilities, fully equipped leisure centre & Cocoon Health & Beauty Spa. Complimentary car parking. Please enquire about Facilities for Persons with Disabilities.

Bookable on www.irelandhotels.com

B&B from €85.00 to €115.00

Sandra Wogan
General Manager

80

Activities:

Closed 23 - 25 December

B&B Rates are per Person Sharing per Night incl. Breakfast.
or Room Rates are per Room per Night - **See also Page 8**

Ashdown Park Hotel Conference & Leisure Centre

HOTEL ★★★★ MAP 807

Coach Road,
Gorey,
Co. Wexford

Tel: 053-948 0500 Fax: 053-948 0777
Email: info@ashdownparkhotel.com
Web: www.ashdownparkhotel.com
GPS: N +52° 40' 44.01" W -6° 17' 5.40"

The Ashdown Park has 79 beautifully appointed guest rooms and suites, each tastefully designed. Enjoy the food on offer all day or just relax with regular live entertainment. Facilities include conference & banqueting, the award-winning Rowan Tree Restaurant, Ivy & Coach Bars, Leisure Club and complimentary car park. All public areas are wheelchair friendly. The Ashdown Park Hotel has been awarded RAC **** AA **** Fáilte Ireland ****. Please enquire about Facilities for Persons with Disabilities.

An IHF Quality Employer

Bookable on www.irelandhotels.com

Special Offer: www.irelandhotels.com/offers

B&B from €55.00 to €99.00
Suites from €160.00 to €295.00

Liam Moran
General Manager

79

Food for Kids *Activities:*

Closed 24 - 26 December

Marlfield House Hotel

HOTEL ★★★★ MAP 807

Gorey,
Co. Wexford

Tel: 053-942 1124 Fax: 053-942 1572
Email: info@marlfieldhouse.ie
Web: www.marlfieldhouse.com
GPS: N +52° 40' 06" W -6° 16' 46"

This fine Regency period house is set in 36 acres of grounds and filled with antiques. The Bowe family opened its doors to guests in 1978 and has maintained an outstanding reputation for food, comfort and service ever since. The 19 bedrooms are filled with antiques, paintings and flowers and all have marble bathrooms. There are six sumptuous state rooms overlooking the lake. Member of Relais & Châteaux, AA Red Star & Ireland's Blue Book. Highly acclaimed conservatory restaurant. Please enquire about Facilities for Persons with Disabilities.

An IHF Quality Employer

Member of Relais et Châteaux

Bookable on www.irelandhotels.com

B&B from €90.00 to €138.00
Suites from €203.00 to €383.00

Mary, Margaret & Laura Bowe
Proprietors

19

Activities:

Closed 03 January - 28 February

Irish National Heritage Park

Ferrycarrig, Co. Wexford

Tel: +353 53 9120733
Fax: +353 53 9120911
Email: info@inhp.com
Web: www.inhp.com

"Over 9000 years of History"

Stroll through the park with its homesteads, places of ritual, burial modes and long forgotten remains.

Opening Times
May-Aug 9.30am-6.30pm
Sept-Apr 9.30am-5.30pm

Facilities:
- Guided Tours
- Restaurant
- Gift & Craft Shop
- Free car / coach parking

B&B Rates are per Person Sharing per Night incl. Breakfast.
or Room Rates are per Room per Night - **See also Page 8**

Gorey / New Ross / Newbawn

Seafield Golf & Spa Hotel

HOTEL ★★★★ MAP 8 O 7

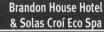

Ballymoney,
Gorey,
Co. Wexford
Tel: 053-942 4000 Fax: 053-942 4050
Email: sales@seafieldhotel.com
Web: www.seafieldhotel.com
GPS: N +52° 40' 31.19" W -6° 12' 55.09"

The stunning Seafield Golf & Spa Hotel is set on 160 acres of lush parkland grounds just an hour south of County Dublin on the sands of the Ballymoney shore. Designed by Italian architect Francesco Beia in a clean contemporary style, natural daylight floods through & awe-inspiring sea views have been maximized. This four star venue has something for everyone with its fabulous hotel, exquisite Spa and championship 18 hole golf course as designed by Peter McEvoy. Please enquire about Facilities for Persons with Disabilities.

Bookable on www.irelandhotels.com
Special Offer: www.irelandhotels.com/offers

B&B from €75.00 to €130.00

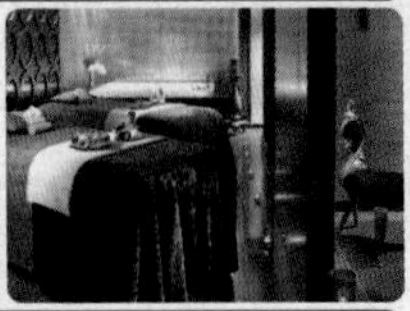

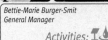

Micheal Cunningham
General Manager

102

Activities:

Closed 21 - 27 December

Brandon House Hotel & Solas Croí Eco Spa

HOTEL ★★★★ MAP 4 M 6

New Ross,
Co. Wexford
Tel: 051-421703 Fax: 051-421567
Email: info@brandonhousehotel.ie
Web: www.brandonhousehotel.ie
GPS: N +52° 23' 13.39" W -6° 56' 40.11"

Combining an eclectic mix of de luxe Old Country Manor House with State-of-the-art Spa and comfortable accommodation, the Brandon House Hotel & Solas Croí Eco Spa is set in landscaped gardens, with panoramic views of the River Barrow. Catering to family breaks, designer weddings, restorative treatments and much more. The Solas Croí Eco Spa facilitates all therapies, with specialised true Ayurvedic treatments. Please enquire about Facilities for Persons with Disabilities.

An IHF Quality Employer

Bookable on www.irelandhotels.com
Special Offer: www.irelandhotels.com/offers

Room Rate from €59.00 to €149.00
Suites from €120.00 to €249.00

Bettie-Marie Burger-Smit
General Manager

79

Activities:

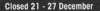

Closed 24 - 26 December

Cedar Lodge Hotel & Restaurant

HOTEL ★★★★ MAP 4 N 6

Carrigbyrne,
Newbawn, (Near New Ross),
Co. Wexford
Tel: 051-428386 Fax: 051-428222
Email: info@cedarlodgehotel.ie
Web: www.cedarlodgehotel.ie
GPS: N +52° 21' 51.34" W -6° 46' 25.80"

Charming boutique country hotel located in a picturesque setting, 30 minutes drive from Rosslare Port on the N25 New Ross Road. All bedrooms en suite with direct dial phone and TV. The restaurant, which concentrates on freshly prepared produce, is noted for its good food. Recommended by Michelin, Good Hotel Guide, AA. Forest walks nearby. Golf, horse riding, JF Kennedy Park, county museum, heritage park and sandy beaches within easy driving distance. Free Parking.

Member of CMV Hotels

Bookable on www.irelandhotels.com
Special Offer: www.irelandhotels.com/offers

B&B from €80.00 to €100.00

Thomas Martin
Proprietor

28

Closed 25 December - 01 February

B&B Rates are per Person Sharing per Night incl. Breakfast.
or Room Rates are per Room per Night - See also Page 8

Danby Lodge Hotel

HOTEL ★★★ MAP 405

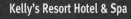

Rosslare Road,
Killinick, Rosslare,
Co. Wexford

Tel: 053-915 8191 Fax: 053-915 8758
Email: info@danbylodge.ie
Web: www.danbylodge.ie
GPS: N +52° 15' 28.29" W -6° 26' 48.03"

Newly refurbished 3* hotel, built in the 1730s boasts seven hectares of beautiful landscaped gardens and is located 5 mins from Rosslare Euro Port & 10 mins from Wexford Town. From the moment you walk through the door, you receive a warm welcome, gracious hospitality & personal service that is second to none. The Danby's reputation for good food & friendly service will ensure you have a more than memorable stay. With beautifully appointed bedrooms, confrence facilities & function room, the Danby Lodge Hotel is the ideal venue for any event. Please enquire about Facilities for Persons with Disabilities.

B&B from €45.00 to €60.00

Gavin McGuire
General Manager

29

Open All Year

Kelly's Resort Hotel & Spa

HOTEL ★★★★ MAP 405

Rosslare,
Co. Wexford

Tel: 053-913 2114 Fax: 053-913 2222
Email: info@kellys.ie
Web: www.kellys.ie
GPS: N +52° 16' 31.77" W -6° 23' 16.09"

Since 1895 the Kelly Family has personally overseen this truly fine beach side resort hotel. Locally produced food, specially selected wines and nightly entertainment are very much part of the tradition as well as tennis, snooker, bowls, croquet and a choice of local championship golf courses. Pamper yourself & relax in our luxurious 14,000sq ft 'SeaSpa', incorporating thermal spa, 12 treatment rooms, seaweed bath & serail Mud Chamber. Focus on health & well-being in our Aqua Club and gym or come for our special activity midweek breaks in Spring & Autumn. Please enquire about Facilities for Persons with Disabilities.

An IHF Quality Employer

Member of Good Food Ireland

Bookable on www.irelandhotels.com

Special Offer: www.irelandhotels.com/offers

B&B from €88.00 to €104.00
Suites from €390.00 to €460.00

Mr. Bill Kelly
Manager / Director

118

Food for Kids *Activities:*

Closed 05 December - 11 February

Best Western Hotel Rosslare

HOTEL ★★★ MAP 405

Rosslare Harbour,
Co. Wexford

Tel: 053-913 3110 Fax: 053-913 3386
Email: reservations@hotelrosslare.ie
Web: www.hotelrosslare.ie
GPS: N +52° 14' 59.95" W -6° 20' 11.97"

Occupying a panoramic cliff top position in Rosslare Harbour, we are the ideal base for touring Wexford and the Sunny South East. We are located 2 minutes drive from Rosslare Europort, Ideal for Ferry travel. 25 en suite rooms, many with sea views and private balcony. Relax in our trendy Portholes Bar with weekend music, or dine in style in the Fort Restaurant. Pamper yourself in our new health and beauty salon where a wide variety of relaxing treatments are available. Please enquire about Facilities for Persons with Disabilities.

Bookable on www.irelandhotels.com

B&B from €60.00 to €75.00

Deirdre Kelly
Manager

25

Closed 24 - 26 December

B&B Rates are per Person Sharing per Night incl. Breakfast.
or Room Rates are per Room per Night - See also Page 8

Rosslare Harbour

Ferryport House

GUESTHOUSE ★★★ MAP 405

Rosslare Harbour,
Co. Wexford

Tel: 053-913 3933 Fax: 053-916 1707
Email: info@ferryporthouse.com
Web: www.ferryporthouse.com
GPS: N +52° 14' 56.74" W -6° 20' 36.49"

Ferryport House is a 3*** guesthouse approved by the Irish Tourist Board, which includes Fusion Restaurant serving fresh seafood, steaks and Chinese cuisine. Ferryport House is situated on the N25 beside church in Rosslare Harbour. 2 minutes by car to ferry terminal. We provide breakfast from 7am to accommodate guests on early morning services. Our accommodation is of the highest standard, with all rooms en suite with telephone, TV and Tea/Coffee. Local amenities include golf, horse riding and fishing.

B&B from €35.00 to €50.00

Billy & Patricia Roche
Proprietors

16

Closed 24 - 27 December

Harbour View Hotel

HOTEL ★★★ MAP 405

Rosslare Harbour,
Co. Wexford

Tel: 053-916 1450 Fax: 053-916 1455
Email: info@harbourviewhotel.ie
Web: www.harbourviewhotel.ie
GPS: N +52° 15' 3.77" W -6° 20' 31.53"

A charming hotel overlooking Rosslare Europort, situated ideally on the N25 with access to ferries, trains and coaches - an ideal base for touring the sunny south east. All our beautifully appointed guest rooms are en suite with modern facilities including private safe. Renowned for our excellent food and friendly service, both our Mailboat Bar and Seasons Chinese Restaurant offer a wide range of Chinese and European cuisines. Local amenities include Golf, Angling, Horse Riding and sandy beaches. Special golf packages available. Please enquire about Facilities for Persons with Disabilities.

Bookable on www.irelandhotels.com

B&B from €45.00 to €75.00

James & Grace Chan

24

Food for Kids

Open All Year

St. Helens Hotel

HOTEL ★★★ MAP 405

Rosslare Harbour,
Co. Wexford

Tel: 053-913 3233 Fax: 053-913 3543
Email: res@sthelenshotel.ie
Web: www.sthelenshotel.ie
GPS: N +52° 15' 2.21" W -6° 20' 25.38"

In Rosslare Harbour, a favourite resort, St. Helens Hotel provides a warm welcome with traditional hospitality. The hotel is beautifully situated on a cliff-top overlooking Rosslare Harbour. All rooms are en suite with TV, radio, hairdryer and tea/coffee facilities. Enjoy the leisure centre with indoor swimming pool, jacuzzi, steam room, the comfortable lounges and excellent food of the Mariner's Restaurant.

An IHF Quality Employer

Bookable on www.irelandhotels.com
Special Offer: www.irelandhotels.com/offers

B&B from €35.00 to €61.50

Eoin O'Sullivan
General Manager

100

Food for Kids

Closed 08 November - 18 March

B&B Rates are per Person Sharing per Night incl. Breakfast or Room Rates are per Room per Night - See also Page 8

Drinagh Court Hotel

HOTEL ★★★ MAP 4 N 6

Drinagh,
Near Wexford Town,
Co. Wexford

Tel: 053-914 3295 Fax: 083-914 5827
Email: info@drinaghcourthotel.com
Web: www.drinaghcourthotel.com
GPS: N +52° 18' 27.60" W -6° 27' 25.27"

Located just off the N25 and within easy reach of Wexford Town and just 8 miles from Rosslare Ferry Port, a warm welcome awaits you in this family-run hotel. Daniel & Susan Finnerty with their dedicated team of staff are committed to the highest standards of service & customer care. The hotel, renovated in 2006, integrates the traditional with the contemporary. The interior features clean lines of natural stonework and wood, while the luxurious leather and textured fabrics ensure that comfort is not sacrificed for style. Please enquire about Facilities for Persons with Disabilities.

B&B from €49.00 to €60.00

Daniel & Susan Finnerty

21

Closed 24 - 27 December

Faythe Guest House

GUESTHOUSE ★★★ MAP 4 O 6

The Faythe,
Swan View,
Wexford

Tel: 053-912 2249 Fax: 053-912 1680
Email: damian@faytheguesthouse.com
Web: www.faytheguesthouse.com
GPS: N +52° 19' 59.00" W -6° 27' 25.00"

Family-run guesthouse in a quiet part of the town centre, is built on the grounds of a former castle of which one wall remains today. All rooms refurbished recently to the highest standard. Some of our rooms overlook Wexford Harbour. All rooms have bathroom en suite, colour TV, DVD player, direct dial phone, clock radios and tea/coffee facilities. Rosslare Ferry Port is only 15 minutes drive (early breakfast on request). We also have a large private car park. We are a non smoking house. Please enquire about Facilities for Persons with Disabilities.

Member of Premier Guesthouses

Bookable on www.irelandhotels.com

Special Offer: www.irelandhotels.com/offers

B&B from €35.00 to €55.00

Damian & Siobhan Lynch
Proprietors

10

Closed 25 - 27 December

Ferrycarrig Hotel

HOTEL ★★★★ MAP 4 N 6

Ferrycarrig,
Wexford

Tel: 053-912 0999 Fax: 053-912 0982
Email: reservations@ferrycarrighotel.com
Web: www.ferrycarrighotel.ie
GPS: N +52° 20' 59.24" W -6° 30' 16.28"

Renowned Ferrycarrig Hotel has one of the most spectacular locations of any hotel in Ireland, with every room providing memorable views of the River Slaney Estuary. Offers contemporary luxurious, spacious bedrooms, award-winning service, excellent waterfront dining, award-winning waterfront bar, 5***** health and fitness club with 20m pool, on-site Beauty and Wellness Lodge and hair salon. An abundance of historic, cultural and sporting amenities, including golf, are nearby. Excellent conference facilities for 4 - 400 delegates. Please enquire about Facilities for Persons with Disabilities.

An IHF Quality Employer

Bookable on www.irelandhotels.com

Special Offer: www.irelandhotels.com/offers

B&B from €65.00 to €150.00
Suites from €250.00 to €350.00

Jeanette O'Keeffe
General Manager

102

Food for Kids Activities:

Open All Year

B&B Rates are per Person Sharing per Night incl. Breakfast.
or Room Rates are per Room per Night - See also Page 8

Wexford Town

Maldron Hotel Wexford

HOTEL ★★★ MAP 406

Ballindinas,
Barntown,
Wexford

Tel: 053-917 2000 Fax: 053-917 2001
Email: info.wexford@maldronhotels.com
Web: www.maldronhotels.com
GPS: N +52° 20' 14.94" W -6° 30' 51.20"

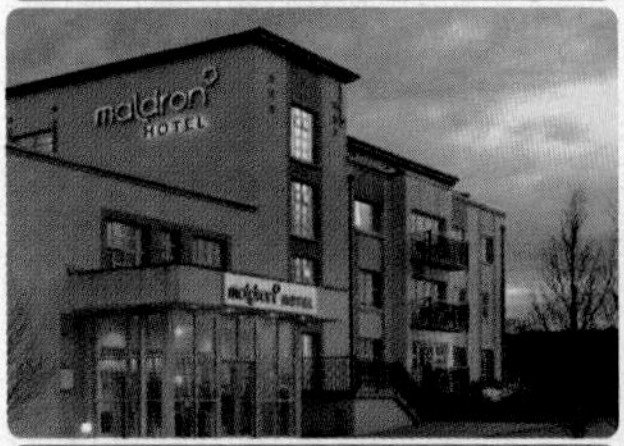

This modern 3 star hotel comprises 108 spacious rooms including family, interconnecting and balcony rooms as well as Stir Restaurant and lively Glenville Bar with entertainment at the weekends and during the summer. Free WiFi and broadband internet access and Club Vitae Health and Fitness Club and treatment rooms available. Supervised crèche and outdoor playground and new 18 hole crazy golf course on-site. Extensive complimentary parking. Please enquire about Facilities for Persons with Disabilities.

An IHF Quality Employer

Member of Maldron Hotels

Bookable on www.irelandhotels.com

Special Offer: www.irelandhotels.com/offers

B&B from €49.00 to €109.00

Rory Fitzpatrick
General Manager

108

Food for Kids

Closed 21 - 27 December

Newbay Country House

GUESTHOUSE ★★★ MAP 406

Newbay,
Wexford

Tel: 053-914 2779 Fax: 053-914 6318
Email: newbay@newbayhouse.com
Web: www.newbaycountryhouse.com
GPS: N +52° 19' 41.53" W -6° 30' 50.10"

Newbay Country House is a beautiful Georgian guesthouse in an idyllic countryside setting, yet only 5 minutes from the historic town of Wexford. Most bedrooms boast traditional 4 poster beds as well as views of the well manicured gardens. We are fully licensed and serve a la carte and bar food 7 days a week. AA Rosette restaurant. Newbay Casino Club and tennis courts open daily. Please enquire about Facilities for Persons with Disabilities.

B&B from €39.00 to €65.00
Suites from €90.00 to €120.00

Alex Scallan
General Manager

11

Food for Kids

Closed 25 December

Riverbank House Hotel

HOTEL ★★★ MAP 406

The Bridge,
Wexford

Tel: 053-912 3611 Fax: 053-912 3342
Email: info@riverbankhousehotel.com
Web: www.riverbankhousehotel.com
GPS: N +52° 20' 40.52" W -6° 27' 18.61"

The Riverbank House Hotel commands magnificent views of the old Viking town, the River Slaney and the miles of golden beach surrounding Wexford. The hotel boasts an excellent à la carte menu, delicious bar food together with an exciting wine list. Benefiting from its own private car park, the hotel offers easy access to five of the best golf courses in the South East, sea angling sites and shooting - ensuring that whatever your stay, business or leisure, it will be most enjoyable. Conference facilities available. Please enquire about Facilities for Persons with Disabilities.

Bookable on www.irelandhotels.com

B&B from €39.00 to €85.00

Colm Campbell
General Manager

23

Food for Kids Activities:

Closed 25 December

B&B Rates are per Person Sharing per Night incl. Breakfast
or Room Rates are per Room per Night - See also Page 8

St. George Guest House

GUESTHOUSE ★★ MAP 406

Upper Georges Street,
Wexford

Tel: 053-914 3474 Fax: 053-912 4814
Email: info@stgeorgeguesthouse.com
Web: www.stgeorgeguesthouse.com
GPS: N +52° 20' 22.14" W -6° 28' 0.40"

We are 3 minutes' walk from the town centre and bus station. All our bedrooms are en suite with TV and Tea/Coffee making facilities. Free Wi-Fi and private parking is also free. Our varied breakfast menu proves popular with customers and can be served early if required. Most credit cards accepted. Michael & Staff will be available to help make your stay most enjoyable. Ground floor bedrooms available for mobility impaired persons. Canine friendly section available also. Please enquire about Facilities for Persons with Disabilities.

Bookable on www.irelandhotels.com

B&B from €35.00 to €45.00

Michael & Catherine Power — 10

Closed 20 December - 04 January

Wexford Town

Talbot Hotel Conference and Leisure Centre

HOTEL ★★★★ MAP 4 O 6

On The Quay,
Wexford Town

Tel: 053-912 2566 Fax: 053-912 3377
Email: sales@talbothotel.ie
Web: www.talbothotel.ie
GPS: N +52° 20' 8.53" W -6° 27' 26.38"

Overlooking the quay in the heart of Wexford Town, the Talbot dates back to 1905 and offers all that is best in traditional style and hospitality. Luxuriously appointed guest rooms, Ballast Bank Bar & Grill with live music weekly. Award-winning Oyster Lane Restaurant, Conference & Banqueting Centre, Quay Leisure Centre, Younique Health & Beauty. Complimentary car parking. Enjoy hospitality at its best, upgrade to the Talbot Hotel, a locally owned and managed hotel. Please enquire about Facilities for Persons with Disabilities.

An IHF Quality Employer

Member of Talbot Hotel Group

Bookable on www.irelandhotels.com

Special Offer: www.irelandhotels.com/offers

B&B from €55.00 to €99.00

Declan Moriarty
General Manager

107

Food for Kids Activities:

Closed 23 - 26 December

Whites of Wexford

HOTEL ★★★★ MAP 4 O 6

Abbey Street,
Wexford

Tel: 053-912 2311 Fax: 053-914 5000
Email: info@whitesofwexford.ie
Web: www.whitesofwexford.ie
GPS: N +52° 20' 25.28" W -6° 27' 50.68"

Centrally located in Wexford Town, Whites of Wexford is the ideal base for touring the sunny South East. Facilities include 157 guestrooms and luxury suites, Tranquillity Spa, leisure facilities, Cryotherapy Clinic, extensive conference facilities and underground car parking. We cater for all palates with our Terrace Restaurant, Library Bar, La Speranza Café Bar and outdoor courtyard to dine alfresco. Close to sandy beaches, golf courses and tourist attractions. Beside Wexford train and bus station. Please enquire about Facilities for Persons with Disabilities.

An IHF Quality Employer

Member of Maldron Hotels - Partner Hotel

Bookable on www.irelandhotels.com

Special Offer: www.irelandhotels.com/offers

B&B from €49.00 to €105.00
Suites from €250.00 to €298.00

Peter Wilson
General Manager

157

Food for Kids Activities:

Closed 24 - 26 December

Whitford House Hotel Health & Leisure Club

HOTEL ★★★★ MAP 4 N 5

New Line Road,
Wexford

Tel: 053-914 3444 Fax: 053-914 6399
Email: info@whitford.ie
Web: www.whitford.ie
GPS: N +52° 19' 26.73" W -6° 30' 0.33"

The 4**** Whitford, one of Ireland's leading family-run hotels, is situated 2km from Wexford Town and central to all local amenities and activities. Renowned for its luxury accommodation, spectacular leisure facilities & excellence in food and customer care. Enjoy fine dining in our awarded Seasons Restaurant & Courtyard or for more informal dining try our awarded Forthside Bistro. With hair & beauty salon, kiddies playground and live entertainment, you can relax and unwind in this truly remarkable hotel.

Bookable on www.irelandhotels.com

Special Offer: www.irelandhotels.com/offers

B&B from €45.00 to €99.00

The Whitty Family

36

Food for Kids

Closed 24 - 26 December

B&B Rates are per Person Sharing per Night incl. Breakfast or Room Rates are per Room per Night - See also Page 8

Ireland West

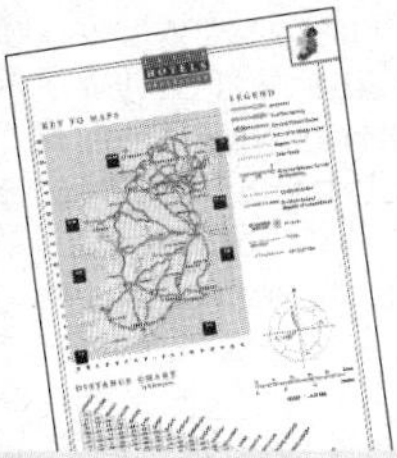

See page 365 for map with access points and driving distances

For Detailed Maps of this Region See Pages 365-380. Each Hotel or Guesthouse has a Map Reference to these detailed maps under their photograph.

Ireland West

Clare, Donegal, Galway, Leitrim, Limerick, Mayo, Roscommon, Sligo
(see pages 2 & 3 for full County listing)

The Green Carpet is out and ready for you … in Ireland's Western Regions.

Ireland's Western Regions are a beautiful part of a magical island. Come to Ireland's North West, West and Shannon Regions and discover a special place, rich in history and wild in spirit.

This is the Ireland made famous in poetry, song and film. It's the essence of Ireland and the part you can't miss if you want to see the real country. Come to the Western Regions where the best of the past mingles effortlessly with a pulsating, contemporary present. The magic is all in the blend.

The scenery might be just the beginning, but what a way to start! A dramatic Atlantic coastline running from Donegal to Clare. Towering cliffs contrast with golden sandy beaches; the Cliffs of Moher, Keem Bay and Black Head. Inland, nature offers lakes and mountains, the splendour of Connemara, the fragile beauty of the Burren and a series of beautiful National Parks.

No matter when you visit you'll find a festival in full swing somewhere. It could be traditional music at the Willie Clancy Festival, match making in Lisdoonvarna, Arts or Oysters in Galway, perhaps a Salmon Festival in Ballina or the time honoured Mary from Dungloe. Learn to play the Bodhran on the Aran Islands, play music in Sligo or try out one of the many summer schools scattered throughout the region.

We have so many places to visit and attractions to see. Ancient castles, forts and abbeys; sea life centres, waterworlds, folk parks, museums, show-caves, steam-trains, pet-farms, island and dolphin-watching boat trips, island safaris, river boat tours and much more. Some are world famous - Bunratty,

Fanad Lighthouse, Co. Donegal

Calendar of Events | GUINNESS

July

Ballina Arts Festival, Ballina, Co. Mayo

'illie Clancy Summer School, Milltown Malbay, Co. Clare

July/August

Ballyshannon Traditional and Folk Music Festival, Ballyshannon, Co. Donegal

Guinness Galway Racing Festival, Galway City

September/October

Guinness Galway International Oyster Festival, Galway City

Horse Racing, Co. Galway

n Aenghus, Cong and the Quiet Man Cottage. A host of ers are just waiting to be discovered, by you.

a playground for sports - on dry land or in the water. er 80 golf links and parkland courses compete for ention, so golfers will be in their element. Challenge urself on some of the top courses in the country, and be asantly surprised at the green fees. Fishermen find their pia. Casting a line in Ballina, The Salmon Capital, is nost a rite of passage for the game fisherman. The eat Western Lakes teem with trout and coarse ermen will find healthy fishing waters all around the ion. The best sea angling waters in the country tempt eryone from the novice to the expert. Watch out for npetitions throughout the year to test yourself against best.

e geography of the region lends itself perfectly to king trails and paths. Beaches, woodland, mountains, mlin and lakeland compete for attention. Marked long tance walks criss-cross the country and many towns d communities have their own shorter walks for visitors enjoy. Take only pictures, leave only footprints.

ors plot courses through picturesque islands, and a wing supply of visitor moorings and marinas. The at River Shannon offers idyllic cruising waters with ghtful stop off villages and pubs along the banks. Wind fers, snorkellers, surfers, body boarders, canoeists and mmers can take their choice of a hundred beaches, many with EU Blue Flag status. Deep sea divers revel in pristine waters of perfect clarity. It's no wonder the West is known as the Adventure Capital of Ireland.

Don't feel obliged to take part, try some spectator sports. Come horse racing and join in the fun at the big Galway race festival or at one of the smaller traditional racecourses. It's the heart of real Ireland. Go to the dogs at a greyhound track or catch a rugby match. The West is home to the mighty red army of Munster and Connaught Rugby Teams.

The West is the home of traditional music and melodies spill from pubs and sessions every night of the week. Music is an intrinsic part of the culture and spontaneous singing or playing are part of every event all year around. Festivals abound and visitors are enthusiastically welcomed into the celebrations.

Don't forget our cities and towns. **Sligo**, **Galway** and **Limerick** are great centres for shopping, dining and nightlife. They're full of character, colour and life and they're just waiting here for you.

Wherever you visit, you'll always remember the West.

Ireland West

Equestrian

Whether you are looking for an exhilarating beach ride, a leisurely trek or a week long trail across some of Ireland's most famous landscapes, the West has it all. Trail riding is very popular on the west coast and the more experienced rider will enjoy getting out and about and off the beaten track across varied terrain.
Check out www.discoverireland.ie/equestrian

Family Fun

You and your family will have a great holiday in Bundoran. Perched on wonderful Donegal Bay, this town offers great family friendly accommodation as well as an impressive natural playground.
Why not plan your trip to coincide with something from Bundoran's impressive and eclectic calendar of free events? Choose from sand sculpting competitions, street carnivals, or music sessions.
For more information visit www.discoverireland.ie/family

Traditionally Irish

Take in some traditional music in one of the many venues in the West, be it an intimate music session in a cosy pub or a spectacular music and dance show in a theatre setting. Engage in the traditions of old, Irish music, song and dance at Cnoc Suain, Spiddal, Co. Galway a pre-famine hill village set in 200 acres of pristine wilderness. Or reconnect with the Gaelic language at Oideas Gael, Glencolumcille, Co. Donegal. For more information check out
www.discoverireland.ie

Top Attractions

1 Dun Aenghus, Aran Islands, Co. Galway
2 Kylemore Abbey & Gardens, Co. Galway
3 Druid Theatre Company, Galway
4 Connemara National Park, Co. Galway
5 Glenveagh National Park, Co. Donegal
6 National Museum of Country Life, Castlebar, Co. Mayo
7 Cliffs of Moher, Co. Clare
8 Bunratty Castle & Folk Park, Co. Limerick
9 Strokestown House & Famine Museum, Co. Roscommon
10 Ceide Fields, Co. Mayo
11 Burren National Park, Co. Clare
12 Yeats Grave, Drumcliff, Co. Sligo

Angling

Ireland's western landscape is heavily punctuated by the large limestone lakes of Loughs Corrib, Mask and Carra. These superb wild brown trout lakes provide a quality of game fishing hard to equal anywhere in Europe. Co. Mayo boasts the most prolific salmon river in Ireland with the town of Ballina known as the 'Salmon Capital of Ireland'. The River Drowes which flows through the counties of Leitrim and Donegal regularly produces the first salmon of the year, usually right on January 1st!
For more information and the lists of towns that are part of our anglers welcome initiative visit
www.discoverireland.ie/angling

Adventure

Wherever you go you'll find spectacular opportunities to discover the great outdoors with scenic cycling on quiet, twisty roads, magnificent walking on dramatic hills, bracing horse riding on pristine beaches, and a range of adrenaline-fuelled adventure activities that make the most of dramatic surroundings. Surfers gravitate towards the West Coast and especially the seaside villages of Strandhill, Enniscrone Bundoran and Achill. For more information visit
www.discoverireland.ie/adventure

10 Key Walks

1 Diamond hill loops, Co. Galway
2 Inishbofin island, Co. Galway
3 Carrateigue loops, Co. Mayo
4 Croagh Patrick, Co. Mayo
5 Lough Key Forest, Co. Roscommon
6 Mullaghmore & Rosses Point, Co. Sligo
7 Glencolmcille loops, Co. Donegal
8 Glenveigh National Park, Co. Donegal
9 The Burren, Co. Clare
10 Ballyhoura, Co. Limerick

Maps for these walks and the other 200 looped walks across Ireland can be downloaded on
www.discoverireland.ie/walking

Ireland's Islands

Get away from it all to the rugged islands off the coast of Galway, Mayo and Donegal. Be it a yoga weekend on Clare Island (Mayo), diving off Tory Island (Donegal), or walking on Inishbofin (Galway), there's something there for everyone. For more information on Ireland's islands, including how to get there check out www.discoverireland.ie

Ballyvaughan Lodge

GUESTHOUSE ★★★ MAP 6 F 10

Ballyvaughan,
Co. Clare

Tel: 065-707 7292 Fax: 065-707 7287
Email: ballyvau@iol.ie
Web: www.ballyvaughanlodge.com
GPS: N +53° 6' 57.96" W -9° 8' 47.15"

Located in the heart of Ballyvaughan, a small fishing village overlooking Galway Bay. A custom built modern guesthouse, dedicated to the comfort and relaxation of our guests. Each room is en suite having TV, direct dial phone, tea/coffee making facilities, etc. Allow us to plan your carefree days in the most unspoilt natural environment imaginable, The Burren, including Neolithic caves, sea fishing, hill walking, cycling, Cliffs of Moher and the Aran Islands. WiFi available. Garden for visitors use.

B&B from €37.50 to €45.00

Pauline Burke
Owner

11

Closed 24 - 26 December

Gregans Castle Hotel

HOTEL ★★★★ MAP 6 F 10

The Burren,
Ballyvaughan,
Co. Clare

Tel: 065-707 7005 Fax: 065-707 7111
Email: stay@gregans.ie
Web: www.gregans.ie
GPS: N +53° 4' 36.62" W -9° 11' 3.60"

Family-run 4 star, luxurious retreat. Set among the rugged unspoilt beauty of the Burren hills. Overlooking Galway Bay. Extensive gardens, country house comforts and turf fires. Fresh, organic and local food. Individually decorated bedrooms. Andrew Harper's Grand Award 2009. Swimming, hill walking, horse riding, day trips to Aran Islands. Cliffs of Moher. Golf at Lahinch, Gort and Doonbeg. Situated halfway between Kerry and Connemara. 50 minutes from both Shannon and Galway Airports. Book online at www.gregans.ie. Please enquire about Facilities for Persons with Disabilities.

An IHF Quality Employer

Member of Ireland's Blue Book

Bookable on www.irelandhotels.com

B&B from €97.50 to €117.50
Suites from €295.00 to €450.00

Simon Haden
Managing Director

20

Closed 29 November - 11 February

Hyland's Burren Hotel

HOTEL ★★★ MAP 6 F 10

Ballyvaughan,
Co. Clare

Tel: 065-707 7037 Fax: 065-707 7131
Email: info@hylandsburren.com
Web: www.hylandsburren.com
GPS: N +53° 6' 54.99" W -9° 8' 57.39"

Hyland's Burren Hotel is a charming hotel, dating back to the 18th century and now tastefully maintained. It is located in the picturesque village of Ballyvaughan, nestling in the unique Burren landscape of County Clare. Experience bygone charm with the best of modern facilities, open turf fires, informal bars and restaurants specialising in the finest local seafood. An ideal base for golfing and walking enthusiasts and truly an artist's haven.

An IHF Quality Employer

Member of Irish Country Hotels

Bookable on www.irelandhotels.com

B&B from €50.00 to €80.00

Tony McDermott

30

Closed Christmas Day & 05 Jan - 05 Feb

B&B Rates are per Person Sharing per Night incl. Breakfast.
or Room Rates are per Room per Night - See also Page 8

Bunratty / Doolin

Bunratty Castle Hotel & Angsana Spa

HOTEL ★★★ MAP 6 G 7

Bunratty,
Co. Clare

Tel: 061-478700 Fax: 061-364891
Email: info@bunrattycastlehotel.com
Web: www.bunrattycastlehotel.com
GPS: N +52° 41' 46.58" W -8° 48' 54.18"

Bunratty Castle Hotel Leisure Club and Luxury Spa is a luxury hotel situated 8km from Shannon Airport, in the centre of Bunratty Village, overlooking the historic Bunratty Castle. You will discover excellent furnishings and superb facilities that create a haven of relaxation, enabling you to begin your day rested and rejuvenated. Experience sheer indulgence in our Angsana Spa where our Thai therapists offer a wide range of holistic treatments that will rejuvenate your body and soul. Please enquire about Facilities for Persons with Disabilities.

Member of Blarney Group Hotels

Bookable on www.irelandhotels.com
Special Offer: www.irelandhotels.com/offers

B&B from €75.00 to €90.00
Suites from €160.00 to €200.00

Lee Gregson
General Manager

144

Activities:

Closed 24 - 26 December

Bunratty Grove

GUESTHOUSE ★★★ MAP 6 G 7

Low Road,
Bunratty,
Co. Clare

Tel: 061-369579 Fax: 061-369561
Email: bunrattygrove@eircom.net
Web: www.bunrattygrove.com
GPS: N +52° 42' 36.56" W -8° 48' 30.77"

Bunratty Grove is a purpose built luxurious guesthouse. This guesthouse is located within 3 minutes drive of Bunratty Castle and Folk Park and is 10 minutes from Shannon Airport. Fishing, golfing and historical interests are within a short distance. Ideally located for tourists arriving or departing Shannon Airport. Bookings for Bunratty and Knappogue Banquets taken on request. All rooms are en suite with multi-channel TV, hairdryer, tea/coffee facilities and direct dial phone. Free Internet access.

B&B from €30.00 to €35.00

Joe & Maura Brodie
Proprietors

6

Open All Year

Aran View House Hotel & Restaurant

HOTEL ★★★ MAP 5 E 9

Coast Road,
Doolin,
Co. Clare

Tel: 065-707 4061 Fax: 065-707 4540
Email: info@aranview.com
Web: www.aranview.com
GPS: N +53° 1' 40.55" W -9° 21' 57.90"

Aran View Country House is a wonderful Georgian hotel set in the magnificent wilderness of the Burren. Built in 1736, it has a unique position commanding panoramic views of the islands & the wild Irish coastline, all of which can be experienced from our unique bedrooms. It has been in the Linnane family name for generations. While it retains much of the atmosphere of that era, the house has been totally refurbished in the Irish country house style. Menus are based on the best of local produce, fish being a speciality. All rooms with private bathroom, TV & DD phone. Visitors are assured of a warm and embracing welcome.

Bookable on www.irelandhotels.com

B&B from €50.00 to €80.00
Suites from €120.00 to €160.00

Theresa & John Linnane
Proprietors

19

Activities:

Closed 27 October - 10 April

B&B Rates are per Person Sharing per Night incl. Breakfast.
or Room Rates are per Room per Night - **See also Page 8**

Ballinalacken Castle Country House & Restaurant

HOTEL ★★★★ MAP 5 E 9

Coast Road,
Doolin,
Co. Clare
Tel: 065-707 4025 Fax: 065-707 4025
Email: ballinalackencastle@eircom.net
Web: www.ballinalackencastle.com
GPS: N +53° 2' 47.02" W -9° 20' 16.29"

A romantic peaceful oasis steeped in history and ambience offering the most spectacular views of the Cliffs of Moher, Aran Islands, Atlantic Ocean and Connemara Hills. Built in 1840 as the home of Lord O'Brien. Family members radiate a warm friendly welcome. Peat and log fires add to the cosy atmosphere. Ideal base for exploring Clare. Recommended by Egon Ronay, Michelin, Fodor, Frommer, Charming Hotels of Ireland, New York Times, Washington Post and London Times. The restaurant with its great views has many culinary delights and specialises in local seafood.

Bookable on www.irelandhotels.com

B&B from €65.00 to €100.00
Suites from €180.00 to €300.00

Mary & Denis O'Callaghan
Proprietors

12

Closed 01 November - 15 April

B&B Rates are per Person Sharing per Night incl. Breakfast.
or Room Rates are per Room per Night - **See also Page 8**

Doolin

Cullinan's Seafood Restaurant & Guesthouse

GUESTHOUSE ★★★ MAP 5 E 9

Doolin,
Co. Clare

Tel: 065-707 4183 Fax: 065-707 4239
Email: cullinans@eircom.net
Web: www.cullinansdoolin.com
GPS: N +53° 0' 59.03" W -9° 22' 38.37"

Unique setting overlooking the Aille River, centrally located in the heart of Doolin. Elegant bedrooms have spacious bathrooms with power showers, tea/coffee making facilities, DD phones & hairdryers. Complimentary WiFi throughout. Private car parking. Imaginative menus for breakfast & dinner are carefully chosen by the chef/owner, specializing in locally caught seafood. Reservations advisable. Highly recommended by Michelin, Fodors, Bridgestone, Georgina Campbell. AA & Le Guide du Routard. Accredited Best Restaurant Award 2007.

B&B from €35.00 to €50.00

James & Carol Cullinan
Owners

8

Closed 13 December - 26 February

Hotel Doolin

HOTEL ★★★★ MAP 5 E 9

Doolin,
Co. Clare

Tel: 065-707 4111 Fax: 065-707 5772
Email: info@hoteldoolin.ie
Web: www.hoteldoolin.ie
GPS: N +53° 0' 58.01" W -9° 22' 37.32"

A warm Irish welcome awaits you at Hotel Doolin, located in the heart of Doolin, traditional Irish Music & Culture capital of Ireland. Against the backdrop of the Cliffs of Moher & on the fringes of the Burren National Park, Hotel Doolin village streetscape consists of 17 de luxe bedrooms, South Sound Restaurant, Fitzpatrick's Bar, Café Sonas, Pizza Café, banqueting suite, Atrium Bar, Doolin Massage Therapy and Healing, Morrisson Art Gallery, selection of retail outlets, outdoor terraces & tourist information point. Nearby attractions include Cliffs of Moher, Aran Islands, Doolin Cave, Lahinch & Doonbeg Golf Courses

Bookable on www.irelandhotels.com

B&B from €50.00 to €85.00

John J. Burke
Director

17

Closed 25 December

O'Connors Guesthouse

GUESTHOUSE ★★★ MAP 5 E 9

Doolin,
Co. Clare

Tel: 065-707 4498 Fax: 065-707 4314
Email: joan@oconnorsdoolin.com
Web: www.oconnorsdoolin.com
GPS: N +53° 0' 58.91" W -9° 22' 48.51"

Spacious modern guesthouse situated in the heart of Doolin, within 5 minutes stroll from pubs, shops and restaurants. Home-baking, breakfast menu and laundry facilities. We offer a high standard of accommodation in comfortable spacious bedrooms. All rooms are en suite with direct dial telephones, television, tea/coffee facilities and hairdryers. Recommended by travel writers. Tourism award winners. A warm Irish welcome awaits you. Group rates available on request. 2 purpose-built bathrooms to cater for people with disabilities. Complimentary WiFi throughout. Please enquire about Facilities for Persons with Disabilities.

Bookable on www.irelandhotels.com

B&B from €35.00 to €45.00

Joan O'Connor
Owner

10

Closed 30 November - 01 February

B&B Rates are per Person Sharing per Night incl. Breakfast.
or Room Rates are per Room per Night - See also Page 8

Discover The Wonders Of Ireland's Shannon Region

Shannon Development
Delivering a Better Future

Ireland's Shannon Region

A journey through the Shannon Region is more than just a holiday, it is the starting point for priceless memories. Whether on your own, with a partner or with family, whether you are driving, cycling or walking, in the Shannon Region fun and adventure is just around the corner. Your journey throughout the Region will take you on a magical ride through South Offaly's rugged landscape, North Tipperary's fertile pastures, Limerick's medieval past and Clare's sandy beaches and award winning golf courses.

Limerick City is a cocktail of modern and medieval, a combination of old and new. You can marvel at the medieval city and soak up the atmosphere from Viking time and the Siege of Limerick and experience what it would be like to live in King John's 13th century castle.

If city life isn't for you why not revel in the delectable delights that are on offer in the countryside, from Limerick's Ballyhoura Mountain walkways to the Slieve Bloom Mountains' trials in the unspoilt backdrop that is County Offaly. Adare, winner of the much-coveted title of 'the Prettiest Village in Ireland' is an extraordinary village. A drive along the Shannon Estuary will surprise you with delights of all kind - the forest park with the most astounding walking trials; a visitor farm; adventure centre and the Flying Boat Museum in the portside village of Foynes, home of the Irish Coffee.

Why not take a cruise along the River Shannon and help us celebrate the renaissance of Limerick's Riverside city, and if you are lucky you may even see a dolphin or two. Or go north along the Shannon and journey through the spectacular Lough Derg.

While cruising along the lake why not try your hand at a spot of fishing. Fish in the lake are plentiful; brown trout, pike and coarse fish. Or why not stop off in Tipperary's Ballina and let the rolling pastures be the setting for a luscious meal or continue on to Terryglass for a bit of craic and ceol, you could even learn to Irish dance!!! Whilst in Tipperary, a stop in Thurles to 'Clash the Ash' and a visit to Lar na Pairce, an intriguing museum where the history of the Gaelic Games comes alive, are a must.

A trip to the Shannon Region would not be complete without a visit to County Clare, from the lunar like terrain of the world famous Burren National Park to the stunning Cliffs of Moher where losing yourself in the overwhelming views of the Aran Islands is a regular occurrence for many. While in the area a visit to Doolin Cave is a must. The cave boasts one of the world's largest Stalactites.

Clare is also said to be home of traditional Irish music and Ennis is most certainly the musical hub of Clare. Ennis has an array of pubs that has Traditional Irish Music every night where a good 'seisun' is always guaranteed. Clare has so much to offer from the many fishing lakes of East Clare to the scenic drives and water based activities of the West Coast from Kilkee to Ballyvaughan. Why not stop off in any of the towns and villages with rustic charm and character like Lahinch, Miltown Malbay, and Doonbeg. A visit to Clare however would not be complete without a stop at Bunratty Castle and Folk Park. The park boasts a majestic 15th century castle alongside its folk park that recreates 19th century Irish life over 26 acres.

For fantastic value and great holiday choice visit

www.SHORTBREAKSIRELAND.ie

Festival & Events

March
5th - 7th Ennis Book Club Festival, Co. Clare

May
Bankholiday weekend - Riverfest, Limerick City

August
Birr Vintage Week, Birr, Co. Offaly
Terryglass Arts Festival, Terryglass, Co. Tipperary

For further information contact:
Tourist Information Office
Arthur's Quay, Limerick
Tel 061 317522
Fax 061 317939
www.shortbreaksireland.ie

Ennis

Ardilaun Guesthouse

GUESTHOUSE ★★★ MAP 6 F 8

Galway Road,
Ennis,
Co. Clare
Tel: 065-682 2311 Fax: 065-684 3989
Email: purcells.ennis@eircom.net
Web: www.ardilaun.com
GPS: N +52° 52' 8.23" W -8° 58' 34.90"

Ardilaun is a triple award-winning 3* architect designed guesthouse overlooking the River Fergus & Ballyalia Lake amenity area. Most rooms enjoy panoramic views of the river & all are superbly decorated with en suite, phone, TV, hairdryer, tea/coffee facilities. Our gym, sauna & fishing facilities also overlook the River Fergus & are available to guests only. Ardilaun is just a 3 min drive to Ennis Town centre. 20 mins drive from Shannon Airport on N18. Ideal touring base for the West of Ireland.

Bookable on www.irelandhotels.com

B&B from €35.00 to €40.00

Anne Purcell
Proprietress
10

Closed 23 - 28 December

Ashford Court Boutique Hotel

HOTEL ★★★ MAP 6 F 8

Old Mill Road,
Ennis,
Co. Clare
Tel: 065-689 4444 Fax: 065-689 4455
Email: info@ashfordcourt.ie
Web: www.ashfordcourt.ie
GPS: N +52° 50' 42.23" W -8° 59' 23.19"

The Ashford Court Hotel is a new boutique style hotel, conveniently located within walking distance of Ennis town centre. Each of the individually decorated rooms is en suite with power shower, satellite TV, DD phone, computer/internet access, ironing facilities and hairdryer. Kingsize beds & crisp white linens offer the ultimate in luxury, comfort & style. Juliano's Restaurant specialises in local seafood, Italian cuisine & certified Irish Angus Beef. Ideally situated within minutes of Shannon Airport, the Burren, Cliffs of Moher, Bunratty Castle, Ailwee Caves, Dunbeg & Lahinch Golf Courses. Meeting rooms. Parking.

Bookable on www.irelandhotels.com

B&B from €30.00 to €60.00

Corinne Mannion
Proprietor
28

Open All Year

Auburn Lodge Hotel & Leisure Centre

HOTEL ★★★ MAP 6 F 8

Galway Road,
Ennis,
Co. Clare
Tel: 065-682 1247 Fax: 065-682 1232
Email: stay@irishcourthotels.com
Web: www.auburnlodge.com
GPS: N +52° 51' 54.83" W -8° 58' 51.27"

The Auburn Lodge Hotel & River Lodge Health & Fitness Club provides 108 en suite bedrooms, swimming pool, gymnasium, jacuzzi, steam room & sauna. The River Lodge has four beauty treatment rooms including Massage, Facial, Pedicures plus a whole range of other treatments. Enjoy excellent homemade cuisine, Irish Traditional Music in our Tailor Quiley's Pub. Complimentary WiFi throughout. Banquet & conference facilities available. Barney's Kids Club next door. Car park on site. Ideal for touring the West of Ireland, Bunratty, Burren & Cliffs of Moher. Convenient to golf courses. Shannon Airport 15km.

Member of Irish Court Hotels

Bookable on www.irelandhotels.com
Special Offer: www.irelandhotels.com/offers

B&B from €50.00 to €99.00
Suites from €120.00 to €280.00

Angela Lyne
Proprietor
108

Closed 24 - 26 December

B&B Rates are per Person Sharing per Night incl. Breakfast. or Room Rates are per Room per Night - See also Page 8

Magowna House Hotel

HOTEL ★★★ MAP 6 F 8

Inch,
Ennis,
Co. Clare
Tel: 065-683 9009 Fax: 065-683 9258

GPS: N +52° 49' 41.28" W -9° 4' 7.17"

We are a beautifully located, country house hotel with extensive gardens and lovely views. Ideal for an active or purely relaxing break. Close to excellent golf courses, angling and walks. (Mid-Clare Way 1.5km). Shannon Airport, Cliffs of Moher, The Burren, Doolin, Bunratty Castle, Killimer Car Ferry to Kerry within easy reach. Close to new Ennis bypass. Function/Conference room (capacity 200). Enjoy hospitality, comfort, good food and a genuine welcome in the heart of County Clare. Also contactable on 086 602 1390. Please enquire about Facilities for Persons with Disabilities.

B&B from €35.00 to €35.00

Martin Walsh

10

Closed 24 - 27 December

Old Ground Hotel

HOTEL ★★★★ MAP 6 F 8

O'Connell Street,
Ennis,
Co. Clare
Tel: 065-682 8127 Fax: 065-682 8112
Email: reservations@oldgroundhotel.ie
Web: www.flynnhotels.com
GPS: N +52° 50' 32.50" W -8° 58' 59.41"

Ivy-clad manor house dates to the 18th century. The hotel offers 83 de luxe rooms and luxurious new rooms with king beds and spacious suites. Our elegant formal dining room is renowned for excellent cuisine. Visit our recently opened Town Hall Café. The hotel is located in the heart of Ennis, 20 minutes drive from Shannon Airport, close to the Cliffs of Moher, The Burren, Bunratty Castle and many superb challenging golf courses, such as Doonbeg and Lahinch. GDS Access LE. Online reservations at www.flynnhotels.com.

Member of Flynn Hotels

Bookable on www.irelandhotels.com
Special Offer: www.irelandhotels.com/offers

B&B from €62.50 to €85.00
Suites from €180.00 to €230.00

Allen Flynn, Managing Director
Mary Gleeson, Gen Manager

83

Food for Kids

Closed 24 - 25 December

Temple Gate Hotel

HOTEL ★★★ MAP 6 F 8

The Square,
Ennis,
Co. Clare
Tel: 065-682 3300 Fax: 065-682 3322
Email: info@templegatehotel.com
Web: www.templegatehotel.com
GPS: N +52° 50' 36.72" W -8° 58' 54.16"

This charming town house hotel, family owned & managed, is truly a haven in the heart of Ennis. Built on the site of a 19th century convent, it offers a unique combination of historical beauty & exceptional service. Preachers Pub features live music & an acclaimed bar menu. Legends Restaurant – awarded the prestigious AA Rosette for 11 consecutive years. The Great Hall & The Great Hall Foyer – Conference, Wedding & Banqueting suite, a unique venue. Near Shannon International Airport, Bunratty, Cliffs of Moher and Lahinch & Doonbeg Golf courses. Awarded Ireland's Best Service Excellence Award 2004.

An IHF Quality Employer

Bookable on www.irelandhotels.com
Special Offer: www.irelandhotels.com/offers

B&B from €39.50 to €99.50
Suites from €129.00 to €249.00

Paul Madden
Managing Director

70

Activities:

Closed 24 - 27 December

Ennis / Ennistymon

Westbrook House

GUESTHOUSE ★★★ MAP 6 F 8

Galway Road,
Ennis,
Co. Clare

Tel: 065-684 0173 Fax: 065-686 7777
Email: westbrook.ennis@eircom.net
Web: www.westbrookhouse.net
GPS: N +52° 51' 30.74" W -8° 59' 1.42"

Westbrook House is a recently built luxury guesthouse in Ennis. All rooms are fitted to exceptionally high standards. Within walking distance of the centre of historic Ennis, with its friendly traditional pubs and fantastic shopping. Ideal base for golfing holidays, special discounts with local golf courses. A short drive to the majestic Cliffs of Moher, The Burren or Bunratty Castle and Folk Park. Only 15 minutes from Shannon Airport. Mobile: 087 798 5859. Member of Irish Hotels Federation. Please enquire about Facilities for Persons with Disabilities.

B&B from €40.00 to €45.00

Sheelagh & Domhnall Lynch
Proprietors

10

Closed 22 - 28 December

Falls Hotel & Spa

HOTEL ★★★ MAP 5 E 9

Ennistymon,
Co. Clare

Tel: 065-707 1004 Fax: 065-707 1367
Email: reservations@fallshotel.ie
Web: www.fallshotel.ie
GPS: N +52° 56' 26.20" W -9° 17' 55.53"

Falls Hotel & Spa is conveniently located for touring The Burren, Cliffs of Moher and for the Golfer, the Ch'ship Lahinch Golf Course is a mere 3km, with Doonbeg only a 30 mins drive. The hotel itself is surrounded by 50 acres of woodland and riverside walks. The hotel has 140 spacious bedrooms, 9 duplex apartments, the Dylan Thomas Bar, 2 restaurants, large leisure club, the River Spa and Conference/ Banqueting facilities for up to 350 people. Carvery is served in the bar from 12.30 - 2.30pm daily and a full bar menu is available until 9pm. Please enquire about Facilities for Persons with Disabilities.

An IHF Quality Employer

Member of Select Hotels of Ireland

Bookable on www.irelandhotels.com

Special Offer: www.irelandhotels.com/offers

B&B from €55.00 to €85.00
Suites from €190.00 to €240.00

John & Michael McCarthy
Directors

140

Food for Kids Activities:

Open All Year

Grovemount House

GUESTHOUSE ★★★ MAP 5 E 9

Lahinch Road,
Ennistymon,
Co. Clare

Tel: 065-707 1431 Fax: 065-707 1823
Email: grovmnt@eircom.net
Web: www.grovemount-ennistymon.com
GPS: N +52° 56' 22.91" W -9° 18' 13.00"

Grovemount House is a family-run guesthouse situated on the outskirts of Ennistymon Town. From here you can access with ease the renowned Cliffs of Moher and the spectacular and unique Burren. Just 5 minutes drive away is Lahinch Championship Golf Links and Blue Flag Beach. Whatever is your pleasure: fishing, golfing, sightseeing, horse riding or the best traditional music, enjoy and then return to luxurious tranquillity in Grovemount House. Please enquire about Facilities for Persons with Disabilities.

Member of Premier Guesthouses of Ireland

Bookable on www.irelandhotels.com

Special Offer: www.irelandhotels.com/offers

B&B from €35.00 to €40.00

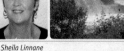

Sheila Linnane
Owner

7

Activities:

Closed 01 November - 30 April

B&B Rates are per Person Sharing per Night incl. Breakfast
or Room Rates are per Room per Night - See also Page

Halpin's Townhouse Hotel

HOTEL ★★★ MAP 5 D 7

Erin Street,
Kilkee,
Co. Clare
Tel: 065-905 6032 Fax: 065-905 6317
Email: halpinshotel@iol.ie
Web: www.halpinshotel.com
GPS: N +52° 40' 49.76" W -9° 38' 46.86"

Highly acclaimed 3* townhouse hotel. Combination of old world charm, fine food, vintage wines & modern comforts - overlooking old Victorian Kilkee, near Shannon Airport & Killimer car ferry. Ideal base for touring Cliffs of Moher, Bunratty, The Burren & Loop drive. Nearby major golf courses - Lahinch, Doonbeg & Ballybunion. Complimentary WiFi access. Accolades - Times, Best Loved Hotels. News: Sister property in Dublin 4, Blakes Hotel & Spa, opening luxurious Austrian themed Spa & Wellness facility for 2010.
USA toll free 1800 617 3178.
Global free phone +800 128 38155.
Direct Dial +353 65 905 6032.

Member of Epoque Hotels

Bookable on www.irelandhotels.com
Special Offer: www.irelandhotels.com/offers

B&B from €49.00 to €99.00

Pat Halpin & Ann Keane
Proprietors

12

Activities:

T C U P S I

Closed 15 November - 15 March

Kilkee Thalassotherapy Centre & Guesthouse

GUESTHOUSE ★★★ MAP 5 D 7

Grattan Street,
Kilkee,
Co. Clare
Tel: 065-905 6742 Fax: 065-905 6762
Email: info@kilkeethalasso.com
Web: www.kilkeethalasso.com
GPS: N +52° 40' 51.45" W -9° 38' 41.55"

Kilkee Thalassotherapy Centre & Guesthouse is a magnificent premises with 5 en suite rooms, offering natural seaweed baths, algae body wraps, beauty salon and other thalassotherapy treatments. Non-smoking. Children over 16 welcome. Ideal for those looking for a totally unique and relaxing break. Situated in beautiful Kilkee with golfing, scuba diving, deep sea angling, dolphin watching, swimming, pony trekking and spectacular cliff walks, nearby. Private car parking. Winner Best Day Spa 2004 - Irish Beauty Industry.

B&B from €38.00 to €60.00

Eileen Mulcahy
Proprietor

5

Activities:

T P S I

Closed 15 - 27 December

Strand Guest House

GUESTHOUSE ★★★ MAP 5 D 7

The Strand Line,
Kilkee,
Co. Clare
Tel: 065-905 6177 Fax: 065-905 6177
Email: thestrandkilkee@eircom.net
Web: www.clareguesthouse.com
GPS: N +52° 40' 49.95" W -9° 38' 49.21"

Situated on the seafront in Kilkee, one of the most westerly seaside resorts in Europe. Kilkee is built around a 1.5km beach, considered one of the best and safest bathing places in the west with breathtaking coastal walks. The Strand makes an ideal touring base - visit The Burren, Cliffs of Moher, Ailwee Caves. For golf enthusiasts there is a local 18 hole course, Kilrush 13km, Doonbeg 13km, Lahinch 42km or Ballybunion 40km (via car ferry). Our restaurant is fully licensed and specialises in local seafood.

Member of Clare Marketing Group

Bookable on www.irelandhotels.com
Special Offer: www.irelandhotels.com/offers

B&B from €38.00 to €48.00

Johnny & Caroline Redmond

6

T U I

Open All Year

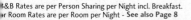

Lahinch

Dough Mor Lodge

GUESTHOUSE ★★★ MAP 5 E 9

Station Road,
Lahinch,
Co. Clare
Tel: 065-708 2063 Fax: 065-707 1384
Email: dough@gofree.indigo.ie
Web: www.doughmorlodge.com
GPS: N +52° 56' 0.16" W -9° 20' 2.77"

Purpose-built family-run guesthouse with residents' lounge and dining room. Private car parking and large garden. You can see Lahinch's famous golf links from the house. Tee times can be booked and arranged for guests. This is an ideal location for golfing, touring The Burren or visiting the Cliffs of Moher. The beach is within 5 minutes walk. Lahinch Sea World has a fine heated indoor swimming pool. The ideal place to unwind and enjoy your holiday.

Bookable on www.irelandhotels.com

B&B from €40.00 to €55.00

Jim Foley

6

Activities:

Closed 01 November - 28 February

Greenbrier Inn Guesthouse

GUESTHOUSE ★★★ MAP 5 E 9

Lahinch,
Co. Clare
Tel: 065-708 1242 Fax: 065-708 1247
Email: gbrier@indigo.ie
Web: www.greenbrierinn.com
GPS: N +52° 56' 3.04" W -9° 20' 29.46"

Luxurious 3* guesthouse, overlooking Lahinch Golf Links and the Atlantic Ocean. Situated 300 yards from Lahinch Village with its excellent restaurants, pubs & shops. All rooms are en suite with antique style pine furnishings, pressurised showers, orthopaedic beds, DD phones, multi-channel TV, tea/coffee making facilities. An excellent base from which to visit the Cliffs of Moher, play the famous Lahinch Golf Links or the spectacular Greg Norman designed Doonbeg Golf Links 18 miles away. "Come and enjoy our home while away from your own". Broadband internet via your own laptop is available.

Member of Premier Guesthouses of Ireland

B&B from €40.00 to €85.00

Margaret & Victor Mulcahy
Proprietors

14

Activities:

Closed 20 November - 07 March

Lahinch Golf & Leisure Hotel

HOTEL ★★★★ MAP 5 E 9

Lahinch,
Co. Clare
Tel: 065-708 1100 Fax: 065-708 1228
Email: info@lahinchgolfhotel.com
Web: www.lahinchgolfhotel.com
GPS: N +52° 55' 54.25" W -9° 20' 43.44"

Situated on the former site of the Aberdeen Arms, this property has undergone an extensive renovation, which has transformed the hotel into a luxurious property in the heart of Lahinch. Relax in the cosy atmosphere of the Aberdeen Bar or de-stress in our leisure centre. Only 5 mins from Lahinch Golf Course, the hotel is an ideal base for the discerning golfer. The Blue Flag beach at Lahinch is only a stroll away. The perfect base for touring the Burren and West Clare. Please enquire about Facilities for Persons with Disabilities.

Bookable on www.irelandhotels.com

B&B from €50.00 to €95.00
Suites from €180.00 to €280.00

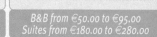

John O' Meara
General Manager

144

Closed 01 December - 01 February

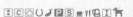

B&B Rates are per Person Sharing per Night incl. Breakfas
or Room Rates are per Room per Night - See also Page

Moy House

GUESTHOUSE ★★★★ MAP 5 E 9

Lahinch,
Co. Clare

Tel: 065-708 2800 Fax: 065-708 2500
Email: moyhouse@eircom.net
Web: www.moyhouse.com
GPS: N +52° 55' 5.15" W -9° 20' 56.53"

Moy House prevails over the breathtaking seascape of Lahinch Bay, set on 15 acres of ground, adorned by mature woodland and a picturesque river. Major restoration has transformed this 18th century country house in keeping with present day expectations of superior standards, yet preserving its unique character style and period ambience. Dining at Moy House is a truly memorable experience in the new classical conservatory restaurant overlooking the Atlantic, with local ingredients that are prepared in a modern Irish style. Personal attention and outstanding service makes for an unforgettable experience.

Member of Ireland's Blue Book

B&B from €95.00 to €140.00
Suites from €270.00 to €360.00

Brid O'Meara
General Manager

9

Closed 01 January - 14 February

Sancta Maria Hotel

HOTEL ★★ MAP 5 E 9

Lahinch,
Co. Clare

Tel: 065-708 1041 Fax: 065-708 1529
Email: info@sancta-maria.ie
Web: www.sancta-maria.ie
GPS: N +52° 56' 1.41" W -9° 20' 36.86"

The McInerney Family have welcomed holiday makers to the Sancta Maria for over 50 years. Many of the attractive bedrooms overlook the famous Lahinch Golf Links and golden beach, which are within 100 metres of the hotel. Our restaurant specialises in fresh produce and special emphasis is placed on local seafoods and home-baking. The Sancta Maria is the ideal base for touring The Burren or visiting the Cliffs of Moher and Aran Islands. Please enquire about Facilities for Persons with Disabilities.

Bookable on www.irelandhotels.com
Special Offer: www.irelandhotels.com/offers

B&B from €48.00 to €58.00

Thomas McInerney
Proprietor

24

Activities: ✓

Closed 02 November - 01 March

Vaughan Lodge and Seafood Restaurant

HOTEL ★★★★ MAP 5 E 9

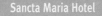

Ennistymon Road,
Lahinch,
Co Clare

Tel: 065-708 1111 Fax: 065-708 1011
Email: info@vaughanlodge.ie
Web: www.vaughanlodge.ie
GPS: N +52° 56' 0.73" W -9° 20' 28.11"

In a country gone daft on designer this and global brand that, how refreshing then that there are still 4th generation hotel families like the Vaughans running smart 4 star lodges where traditional values still abound. Built in 2005 with power showers, spacious rooms, free broadband and WiFi. There's a drying room for the wetter Irish days. A superb seafood restaurant and Clubby Lounge round off this award-winning luxury retreat. The informal style and professional service and care will have you returning again. Bookable on www.vaughanlodge.ie. Please enquire about Facilities for Persons with Disabilities.

Bookable on www.irelandhotels.com
Special Offer: www.irelandhotels.com/offers

B&B from €75.00 to €110.00

Maria & Michael Vaughan
Owners / Managers

22

Food for Kids Activities: ✓

Closed 01 November - 30 March

B&B Rates are per Person Sharing per Night incl. Breakfast.
or Room Rates are per Room per Night - **See also Page 8**

Lisdoonvarna

Rathbaun Hotel

HOTEL ★★ MAP 5 E 9

Main Street,
Lisdoonvarna,
Co. Clare
Tel: 065-707 4009 Fax: 065-707 4009
Email: rathbaunhotel@eircom.net
Web: www.rathbaunhotel.com
GPS: N +53° 1' 43.43" W -9° 17' 22.77"

Rathbaun Hotel is the most renowned hotel in Co. Clare for Irish Music - played nightly from June to September. Our hotel offers the best quality and value in accommodation and home-cooked food, with genuinely personal service. We offer maps and helpful information on The Burren, Aran Islands and Cliffs of Moher, etc. A welcoming and happy atmosphere is the hallmark of the Rathbaun Hotel. Shannon and Galway airports 60km. Céad Míle Fáilte. Please enquire about Facilities for Persons with Disabilities.

Member of Countrywide Hotels - MinOtel

Bookable on www.irelandhotels.com

B&B from €30.00 to €80.00

Lynn and John Connolly

10

Closed 10 October - 31 March

Sheedy's Country House Hotel

HOTEL ★★★★ MAP 5 E 9

Lisdoonvarna,
Co. Clare
Tel: 065-707 4026 Fax: 065-707 4555
Email: info@sheedys.com
Web: www.sheedys.com
GPS: N +53° 1' 48.09" W -9° 17' 22.21"

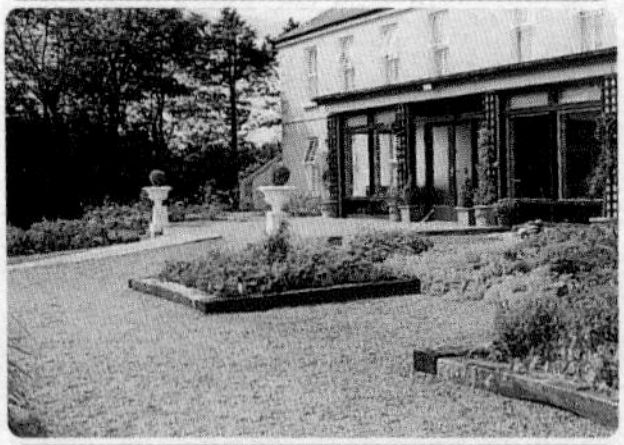

Situated 8km from majestic Cliffs of Moher and only 6km from Doolin, Sheedys is the perfect base for your holiday. A lovely four star, family-run hotel, we offer a high level of hospitality and comfort. Restaurant holds two rosettes from AA and Best Breakfast Awards. Host of the Year 2008. Local Irish music in village. Free on site car parking and internet access. Shannon Airport 45 minutes.

An IHF Quality Employer

Member of Manor House Hotels

Bookable on www.irelandhotels.com

B&B from €65.00 to €90.00
Suites from €200.00 to €230.00

John & Martina Sheedy

11

Closed 01 October - Easter

Wild Honey Inn

GUESTHOUSE ★★★ MAP 5 E 9

Lisdoonvarna,
Co. Clare
Tel: 065-707 4300 Fax: 065-707 4490
Email: info@wildhoneyinn.com
Web: www.wildhoneyinn.com
GPS: N +53° 1' 43.15" W -9° 17' 45.36"

Wild Honey Inn has a wealth of old world charm and character. Open log fires, a walled garden and 14 en suite bedrooms with views of the surrounding countryside. Guests can enjoy chef proprietor Aidan McGrath's cooking. The emphasis is on fresh, seasonal, organic & local produce, combined with the intimate service of a family-run hotel. An ideal base when visiting the Burren, Cliffs of Moher and Aran Islands. Please enquire about Facilities for Persons with Disabilities.

Member of Signpost Premier Hotels

Bookable on www.irelandhotels.com

B&B from €35.00 to €65.00

Aidan McGrath & Kate Sweeney
Proprietors

14

Closed 01 November - 31 March

B&B Rates are per Person Sharing per Night incl. Breakfast or Room Rates are per Room per Night - See also Page 8

Newmarket-on-Fergus / Shannon Airport

Dromoland Castle

HOTEL ★★★★★ MAP 6 G 8

Newmarket-on-Fergus,
Co. Clare

Tel: 061-368144 Fax: 061-363355
Email: sales@dromoland.ie
Web: www.dromoland.ie
GPS: N +52° 46' 57.44" W -8° 54' 23.63"

Located 13km from Shannon Airport. Stately halls, elegant public areas and beautifully furnished guest rooms are steeped in a timeless atmosphere that is unique to Dromoland. The international reputation for excellence is reflected in the award-winning cuisine in the castle's Earl of Thomond Restaurant & The Fig Tree Restaurant in the Dromoland Golf & Country Club. Estate activity abound; 18 hole c'ship golf, which is complemented by the Golf Academy with 10 fully automated driving bays, fishing, clay shooting, archery, falconry. The Spa at Dromoland with 6 treatment rooms, hair salon & exterior hydro therapy pool.

An IHF Quality Employer

Member of Preferred Hotels & Resorts WW

Bookable on www.irelandhotels.com

Special Offer: www.irelandhotels.com/offers

Room Rate from €238.00 to €607.00
Suites from €499.00 to €1,365.00

Mark Nolan
General Manager

99

Food for Kids

Closed 24 - 27 December

Hunters Lodge

GUESTHOUSE ★★★ MAP 6 G 8

The Square,
Newmarket-on-Fergus,
Co. Clare

Tel: 061-368577 Fax: 061-368057
Email: reservations@hunterslodge.ie
Web: www.hunterslodge.ie
GPS: N +52° 45' 38.42" W -8° 53' 48.07"

We at Hunters Lodge extend a very warm welcome to all our guests. Our rooms are stylish and modern, yet cosy, relaxed and homely. Each room offers very comfortable beds, Flat screen TV, direct dial telephone, free internet access, hairdryer and tea/coffee making facilities. The bar and restaurant serve good quality fresh food daily. Many tourist attractions and golf courses are within easy driving distance and Shannon Airport is only 12km away.

B&B from €40.00 to €50.00

Kathleen & Robert Healy
Proprietors

6

Open All Year

Oakwood Arms Hotel

HOTEL ★★★ MAP 6 G 7

Shannon,
Co. Clare

Tel: 061-361500 Fax: 061-361414
Email: reservations@oakwoodarms.com
Web: www.oakwoodarms.com
GPS: N +52° 42' 46.33" W -8° 52' 27.47"

The Oakwood Arms enjoys an enviable location in the centre of Shannon just 3 kms from Shannon Airport and a 20 minute drive from Ennis and Limerick. The hotel sets the standard on quality with its elegantly furnished guest rooms, state of the art gymnasium, sauna and steam room. Enjoy a relaxing drink or a light lunch in "Sophie's Lounge" or book a table in our "Palm Court" Restaurant. Please enquire about Facilities for Persons with Disabilities.

Bookable on www.irelandhotels.com

Special Offer: www.irelandhotels.com/offers

B&B from €45.00 to €65.00
Suites from €150.00 to €250.00

Victor O'Sullivan
Managing Director

100

Activities:

Closed 24 - 26 December

B&B Rates are per Person Sharing per Night incl. Breakfast.
or Room Rates are per Room per Night - See also Page 8

Shannon Airport / Ardara / Ballybofey

Park Inn Shannon

HOTEL ★★★ MAP 6 G 7

Shannon Airport,
Shannon,
Co. Clare

Tel: 061-471122 Fax: 061-471982
Email: reservations.shannon-airport@rezidorparkinn.com
Web: www.shannon.parkinn.ie
GPS: N +52° 41' 26.40" W -8° 55' 9.99"

Park Inn Shannon Airport is a hotel with exceptional style and comfort within walking distance of the terminal building at Shannon Airport. All 114 rooms are en suite with direct dial phone, TV, tea/coffee making facilities, hairdryer, trouser press and iron & ironing board. Leisure facilities include a gym and steam room. Within a short driving distance of Bunratty Castle, The Burren, Cliffs of Moher and the world famous Lahinch and Doonbeg Golf Links. Wireless internet available. Partly refurbished in 2008. Shannon Golf Club is only 1 mile away. Please enquire about Facilities for Persons with Disabilities.

An IHF Quality Employer

Member of Radisson Blu Hotels & Resorts

Bookable on www.irelandhotels.com
Special Offer: www.irelandhotels.com/offers

Room Rate from €79.00 to €150.00

Roderick Smith
General Manager

114

Activities:

Closed 24 - 27 December

Woodhill House

GUESTHOUSE ★★★ MAP 13 H 18

Wood Road,
Ardara,
Co. Donegal

Tel: 074-954 1112 Fax: 074-954 1516
Email: yates@iol.ie
Web: www.woodhillhouse.com
GPS: N +54° 45' 30.10" W -8° 24' 10.80"

An historic country house, the site dates back to the 17th century. In its own grounds, with an old Walled Garden overlooking the Donegal Highlands. There is a quality traditional French style restaurant, seafood a speciality, with full bar & occasional music. The area is famous for its Donegal tweeds & woollens, salmon & trout fishing, pony trekking, golf, boating, cycling, beaches, archaeological sites, Sheskinmore Wildlife Reserve, Glenveagh National Park, Slieve League & some of the most unspoilt scenery in Europe. Special Packages available. Please enquire about Facilities for Persons with Disabilities.

An IHF Quality Employer

Bookable on www.irelandhotels.com
Special Offer: www.irelandhotels.com/offers

B&B from €55.00 to €75.00

Nancy & John Yates
Owners

13

Closed 21 - 27 December

Jackson's Hotel, Conference & Leisure Centre

HOTEL ★★★ MAP 13 J 19

Ballybofey,
Co. Donegal

Tel: 074-913 1021 Fax: 074-913 1096
Email: enquiry@jacksons-hotel.ie
Web: www.jacksons-hotel.ie
GPS: N +54° 47' 59.90" W -7° 47' 4.83"

Situated on the banks of the River Finn and Drumboe Woods. Jackson's Hotel is the ideal base for touring Donegal and the North West of Ireland. Jackson's Hotel is an award-winning family run property providing an array of amenities including 137 beautifully appointed guest rooms. Relax in our award-winning "Glue Pot" bar, or beside the log fire and enjoy breathtaking views of the River Finn & Drumboe Woods. Sample delicious dishes in the Ballybuffet Bistro or Garden Restaurant or unwind in the state of the art Leisure Centre with 22m Swimming Pool, Jacuzzi, Sauna and fully equipped gym.

An IHF Quality Employer

Bookable on www.irelandhotels.com

B&B from €45.00 to €80.00

Margaret & Barry Jackson
Proprietors

137

Activities:

Open All Year

B&B Rates are per Person Sharing per Night incl. Breakfast. or Room Rates are per Room per Night - See also Page 8

Ballybofey / Ballyliffin / Ballyshannon

Kee's Hotel & Leisure Club

HOTEL ★★★ MAP 13 J 19

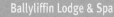

Stranorlar,
Ballybofey,
Co. Donegal
Tel: 074-913 1018 Fax: 074-913 1917
Email: info@keeshotel.ie
Web: www.keeshotel.ie
GPS: N +54° 48' 16.68" W -7° 46' 8.54"

Established in 1845 as a coaching inn, this historical hotel has been in the Kee family since 1892. In the twin towns of Stranorlar and Ballybofey, the hotel is perfectly situated for exploring the mountains and beaches. The old world elegance and atmosphere of the hotel has been gracefully retained, even with developments through the years, each bedroom being individually decorated and furnished with charm and warmth. The restaurant offers the finest local specialities and is recommended by food writer Georgina Campbell, Michelin listed. Leisure centre with swimming pool, jacuzzi, sauna, steam room, gym and in house beautician.

Bookable on www.irelandhotels.com

Special Offer: www.irelandhotels.com/offers

B&B from €79.00 to €89.00

Richard, Jayne & Vicky Kee
Proprietors / Managers — 53

Open All Year

Ballyliffin Lodge & Spa

HOTEL ★★★★ MAP 14 K 21

Shore Road,
Ballyliffin,
Co. Donegal
Tel: 074-937 8200 Fax: 074-937 8985
Email: info@ballyliffinlodge.com
Web: www.ballyliffinlodge.com
GPS: N +55° 16' 49.28" W -7° 23' 43.24"

The first thing to strike you about Ballyliffin Lodge is the panoramic views of the famous Ballyliffin Golf Club and Malin Head. Private and intimate and set in the heart of the village, the drama of its views is continued as you enter its beautifully designed interior, where traditional charm and luxury is woven into the very fabric of the exquisite décor. A stay in Ballyliffin Lodge & Spa whether for golf, wedding, walking or chilling out will calm your spirit, relax your body and rejuvenate your soul. Please enquire about Facilities for Persons with Disabilities.

B&B from €70.00 to €115.00

Cecil Doherty
General Manager — 40

Activities:

Closed 25 December

Creevy Pier Hotel (The)

HOTEL ★ MAP 13 I 17

Kildoney Glebe,
Ballyshannon,
Co. Donegal
Tel: 071-985 8355 Fax: 071-985 8356
Email: info@creevy.ie
Web: www.creevy.ie
GPS: N +54° 31' 33.66" W -8° 15' 9.68"

Hidden on the shores of Donegal Bay lies Creevy Pier Hotel, which offers the very best in international standards, fine dining and traditional Irish hospitality. The Creevy Pier Hotel has developed into one of the North West's best loved hotels. It will be our pleasure to welcome you to the Creevy Pier Hotel.

B&B from €30.00 to €55.00

Keith McBride & Jason Horkan
Proprietor / General Manager — 10

Food for Kids

Open All Year

B&B Rates are per Person Sharing per Night incl. Breakfast.
or Room Rates are per Room per Night - See also Page 8

Ballyshannon / Bunbeg

Dorrians Imperial Hotel

HOTEL ★★★ MAP 13 1 17

Main Street,
Ballyshannon,
Co. Donegal

Tel: 071-985 1147 Fax: 071-985 1001
Email: info@dorriansimperialhotel.com
Web: www.dorriansimperialhotel.com
GPS: N +54° 30' 7.88" W -8° 11' 29.61"

Town centre family-run hotel (built 1781). All rooms are en suite with TV, telephone and tea/coffee facilities. Private car park. Open fire. The hotel was recently renovated, embracing old and new décor and has an elevator. Ideally suited for touring North West and North East Ireland and ideally located for golfing, fishing & beaches. Sligo 45km, Belfast 202km, Dublin 216km.

Bookable on www.irelandhotels.com
Special Offer: www.irelandhotels.com/offers

B&B from €60.00 to €80.00

Ben & Mary Dorrian
Proprietors

47

Closed 22 December - 24 January

Heron's Cove

GUESTHOUSE ★★★ MAP 13 I 17

Creevy, Rossnowlagh Road,
Ballyshannon,
Co. Donegal

Tel: 071-982 2070 Fax: 071-982 2075
Email: info@heronscove.ie
Web: www.heronscove.ie
GPS: N +54° 31' 14.75" W -8° 13' 45.40"

Located close to the magnificent beach at Rossnowlagh and the little harbour at Creevy Pier in South Donegal, Heron's Cove is the ideal, intimate destination to explore the wonderful coastline & countryside of the North West. The excellent family-run restaurant, with charming quiet accommodation, offers the best of Irish cuisine and hospitality. Many of Ireland's finest golf links courses are within driving distance. Excellent sea angling, surfing, hill walking & pony trekking are all available locally. Please enquire about Facilities for Persons with Disabilities.

Member of Irish Country Hotels

B&B from €35.00 to €60.00

Tony McDermott

10

Food for Kids

Closed 05 January - 05 February

Sea View Hotel

HOTEL ★★★ MAP 13 I 20

Bunbeg,
Letterkenny,
Co. Donegal

Tel: 074-953 1159 Fax: 074-953 2238
Email: info@seaviewhotel.ie
Web: www.visitgweedore.com
GPS: N +55° 3' 1.68" W -8° 17' 27.32"

In an area where nature remains untouched, the air is rich and pure, ensuring a heavy appetite. In the Seaview Hotel, guests are treated to wonderful food. The à la carte menu always includes a seasonal selection of fresh, local seafood dishes, with salmon, trout, lobster and oysters a speciality.

An IHF Quality Employer

B&B from €40.00 to €70.00

James Boyle
General Manager

36

Closed 24 - 27 December

B&B Rates are per Person Sharing per Night incl. Breakfast.
or Room Rates are per Room per Night - **See also Page 8**

Inishowen Gateway Hotel

HOTEL ★★★ MAP 14 K 20

Railway Road,
Buncrana, Inishowen,
Co. Donegal
Tel: 074-936 1144 Fax: 074-936 2278
Email: info@inishowengateway.com
Web: www.inishowengateway.com
GPS: N +55° 7' 33.01" W -7° 27' 25.75"

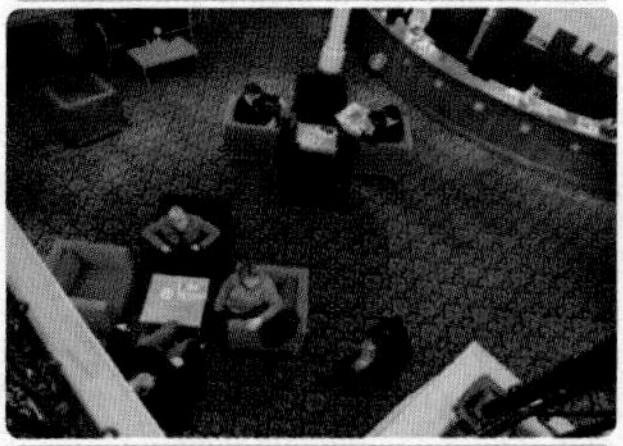

Located on the shores of Lough Swilly on the Inishowen Peninsula, this hotel offers a picturesque & convenient location to explore the North West. 80 bedrooms with all the features of a modern 3*** hotel. Health club includes steam room, jacuzzi, sauna, & 20m pool. Seagrass Wellbeing Centre caters for all your beauty & pampering needs. The Peninsula Restaurant is renowned for its à la carte & dinner menus serving the finest local produce. Offering free golf on the adjacent 9 hole Buncrana and within 20 mins of three 18 hole link courses including Ballyliffin. Planet Active soft adventure play centre.

Bookable on www.irelandhotels.com

Special Offer: www.irelandhotels.com/offers

B&B from €65.00 to €85.00
Suites from €170.00 to €240.00

Patrick Doherty
Proprietor

80

Food for Kids *Activities:*

Open All Year

Grand Central Hotel

HOTEL ★★★ MAP 13 I 17

Main Street,
Bundoran,
Co. Donegal
Tel: 071-984 2722 Fax: 071-984 2656
Email: info@grandcentralbundoran.com
Web: www.grandcentralbundoran.com
GPS: N +54° 28' 47.48" W -8° 16' 35.63"

The Grand Central Hotel, located in the heart of Bundoran, has always been recognised as the best value 3*** hotel in Bundoran. Along with our 62 bedrooms, we have sea views, a Féile Bia approved restaurant, Coffee Dock, WiFi broadband and music every weekend and nightly during the summer season. The Grand Central Hotel also offers the perfect location to enjoy golfing, surfing, horse riding, angling and hill walking, all of which can be arranged by the hotel. Please enquire about Facilities for Persons with Disabilities.

Room Rate from €39.00 to €59.00

Tony Herra
Manager

62

Open All Year

Great Northern Hotel

HOTEL ★★★★ MAP 13 I 17

Bundoran,
Co. Donegal
Tel: 071-984 1204 Fax: 071-984 1114
Email: reservations@greatnorthernhotel.com
Web: www.greatnorthernhotel.com
GPS: N +54° 29' 7.40" W -8° 16' 36.15"

Great Northern Hotel, Conference & Leisure Centre Bundoran. The hotel is situated in the middle of an 18 hole championship golf course overlooking Donegal Bay. 4**** hotel with 96 bedrooms with top leisure facilities for all the family. This hotel has all en suite bedrooms, a restaurant, grill room, lounge, ballroom and syndicate rooms. State of the art Leisure Facilities with swimming pool, gymnasium, sauna, steam room, childrens' area. Conference & banquet centre. Please enquire about Facilities for Persons with Disabilities.

An IHF Quality Employer

Member of Brian McEniff Hotels

Bookable on www.irelandhotels.com

Special Offer: www.irelandhotels.com/offers

B&B from €70.00 to €125.00
Suites from €250.00 to €350.00

Philip McGlynn
General Manager

96

Food for Kids *Activities:*

Open All Year

B&B Rates are per Person Sharing per Night incl. Breakfast.
or Room Rates are per Room per Night - See also Page 8

Carrigart / Donegal Town

Carrigart Hotel

HOTEL ★★★ MAP 13 J 21

Carrigart,
Co. Donegal

Tel: 074-915 5114 Fax: 074-915 5250
Email: info@carrigarthotel.com
Web: www.carrigarthotel.com
GPS: N +55° 10' 39.56'' W -7° 47' 35.15''

The Carrigart Hotel is a heritage hotel. It is a listed building and has a wealth of ambience. Holiday makers have been coming here since the 1880s. The Carrigart Hotel is situated in the picturesque Victorian estate village of Carrigart. As a family-run hotel, we offer a warm combination of traditional hospitality and modern facilities. Please enquire about Facilities for Persons with Disabilities.

B&B from €55.00 to €65.00

Cormac Walsh
General Manager

39

Food for Kids

Closed 01 October - 01 April

Ard Na Breátha

GUESTHOUSE ★★★ MAP 13 I 18

Drumrooske Middle,
Donegal Town

Tel: 074-972 2288 Fax: 074-974 0720
Email: info@ardnabreatha.com
Web: www.ardnabreatha.com
GPS: N +54° 39' 46.24" W -8° 6' 4.31"

Ard na Breatha Restaurant & Guesthouse, described by many as a hidden treasure, is located 1.5km from Donegal Town just off the road to lovely Lough Eske. You will be assured of a warm welcome in our cosy lounge, complete with open hearth, with views of the Bluestack Mountains. Our en suite bedrooms (all with bath) have tea/coffee facilities, TV, phone, WiFi and hairdryer. Our fully licensed restaurant specialises in modern Irish cuisine with an emphasis on local & organic food where possible and an extensive wine list. AA 4*. Georgina Campbell Guesthouse of the Year 2009. EU Flower Award for Eco Tourism.

Member of Donegal Direct

Bookable on www.irelandhotels.com
Special Offer: www.irelandhotels.com/offers

B&B from €40.00 to €55.00

Theresa & Albert Morrow
Proprietor

6

Closed 01 November - 14 February

Atlantic Guesthouse

GUESTHOUSE ★★ MAP 13 I 18

Main Street,
Donegal Town,
Donegal

Tel: 074-972 1187
Email: atlanticguesthouse@yahoo.ie
Web: www.atlanticguesthouse.ie
GPS: N +54° 39' 13.46'' W -8° 6' 28.65''

Atlantic Guesthouse is one of the longest established guesthouses in the heart of Donegal Town, family run for over 40 years, with worldwide visitors returning year after year. Located in the centre of Donegal Town. Convenient to shops, nightlife and many of the North West's attractions. This guesthouse offers you en suite rooms and standard rooms with tea & coffee facilities, hairdryer, television, free WiFi internet & complimentary breakfast. Free parking.

Bookable on www.irelandhotels.com

B&B from €30.00 to €40.00

Lorraine Browne
Manager

11 5

Open All Year

B&B Rates are per Person Sharing per Night incl. Breakfast.
or Room Rates are per Room per Night - See also Page 8

Donegal Town

Donegal Manor

GUESTHOUSE ★★★★ MAP 13 | 18

Letterkenny Road,
Donegal Town,
Co. Donegal
Tel: 074-972 5222 Fax: 074-972 5688
Email: info@donegalmanor.com
Web: www.donegalmanor.com
GPS: N +54° 39' 34.72" W -8° 4' 11.27"

A warm Celtic welcome awaits all our 2009 guests. Donegal Town's only 4* guesthouse offers style, comfort, location & value. Near to Lough Eske and 1 mile from Donegal Town. Awarded Guesthouse of the Year and Hosts of the Year 2008 from Emerald Awards. Delicious Breakfasts and lots of local knowledge. De luxe, standard & spacious family rooms available. New cookery school open early 2009. Highly rated on www.tripadvisor.com.

Bookable on www.irelandhotels.com
Special Offer: www.irelandhotels.com/offers

B&B from €45.00 to €70.00
Suites from €150.00 to €200.00

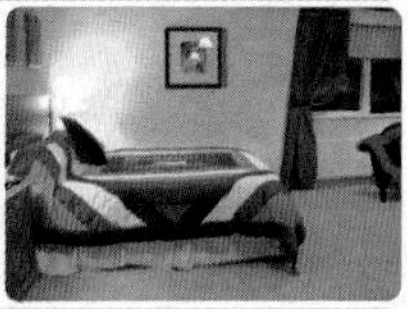

Sian, Michelle & Staff
Hosts

9

Closed 02 January - 01 March

Harvey's Point Hotel

HOTEL ★★★★ MAP 13 | 18

Lough Eske,
Donegal Town,
Co. Donegal
Tel: 074-972 2208 Fax: 074-972 2352
Email: sales@harveyspoint.com
Web: www.harveyspoint.com
GPS: N +54° 41' 45.29" W -8° 3' 13.31"

Set in a magical location amidst the natural beauty of the Bluestack Mountains & on the edge of the shimmering Lough Eske, Harvey's Point is an island of serenity and a truly unforgettable experience. Lavish accommodation with fine gourmet dining steeped in elegance & sophistication, 6km from Donegal Town. Michelin & Good Hotel Guide listed, AA and Fáilte Ireland 4****, 2 AA Rosettes, Optimus Award of Best Practice 2005/6/7. Owned & managed by the Swiss Family Gysling since 1989. AA Hotel of the Year 2007. Closed Sun, Mon & Tue nights from November to Easter.

An IHF Quality Employer

Bookable on www.irelandhotels.com
Special Offer: www.irelandhotels.com/offers

B&B from €79.00 to €125.00
Suites from €290.00 to €580.00

Deirdre McGlone &
Marc Gysling
Proprietors

70

Activities:

Open All Year

Mill Park Hotel, Conference Centre & Leisure Club

HOTEL ★★★★ MAP 13 | 18

The Mullins,
Donegal Town,
Co. Donegal
Tel: 074-972 2880 Fax: 074-972 2640
Email: info@millparkhotel.com
Web: www.millparkhotel.com
GPS: N +54° 39' 32.83" W -8° 7' 5.52"

The luxurious Mill Park Hotel is located only a few minutes stroll from Donegal Town. The interior design of the hotel is a fusion of traditional & contemporary styles with the main feature being the Granary Foyer at the heart of the hotel. Each of the 95 rooms and 5 suites reflect the luxury and comfort offered throughout the hotel. Enjoy a choice of restaurants, superb leisure facilities, including: swimming pool, jacuzzi, wellness centre.

Member of Irish Country Hotels

Bookable on www.irelandhotels.com

B&B from €45.00 to €115.00
Suites from €170.00 to €320.00

Tony McDermott

100

Activities:

Closed 24 - 27 December

B&B Rates are per Person Sharing per Night incl. Breakfast.
or Room Rates are per Room per Night - **See also Page 8**

Donegal Town / Downings / Dunfanaghy

Solis Lough Eske Castle

HOTEL ★★★★★ MAP 12 I 18

Lough Eske,
Donegal Town,
Co. Donegal

Tel: 074-972 5100 Fax: 074-972 3762
Email: reservations.lougheske@solishotels.com
Web: www.solislougheskecastle.com
GPS: N +54° 41' 18.02" W -8° 3' 57.77"

A beautifully restored 17th century castle set amidst 43 acres of forest woodland hugging the shores of Lough Eske near the famous Bluestack Mountains, just 5 km from Donegal Town. From the Spa to the Dining table Solis provide a truly accommodating environment taking care of every detail while guests relax in gracious surroundings. A perfect blend of Irish country charm and modern comforts for a corporate event or private weekend retreat.

B&B from €87.50 to €212.50
Suites from €225.00 to €1,650.00

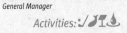

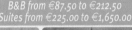

Andrew Turner
General Manager
95

Activities:

Open All Year

Downings Bay Hotel

HOTEL ★★★ MAP 13 J 19

Downings,
Letterkenny,
Co. Donegal

Tel: 074-915 5586 Fax: 074-915 4716
Email: info@downingsbayhotel.com
Web: www.downingsbayhotel.com
GPS: N +55° 11' 40.42" W -7° 50' 8.36"

Situated on Sheephaven Bay & the picturesque Atlantic Drive. Spacious bedrooms, many of them interconnecting, are luxuriously finished. The Sheephaven Suite is available for 20 - 350 people. JC's Bar & The Haven Dining Rooms serve locally sourced fresh food daily. Magherabeg Leisure Centre & Kidz Kingdom are complimentary to hotel guests. Local activities include golf, fishing, horse riding & water sports. Within driving distance of Glenveagh National Park & Horn Head.

Bookable on www.irelandhotels.com
Special Offer: www.irelandhotels.com/offers

B&B from €40.00 to €70.00

Eileen Rock
Manager
40

Activities:

Closed 24 - 27 December

Arnolds Hotel

HOTEL ★★★ MAP 13 J 21

Dunfanaghy,
Co. Donegal

Tel: 074-913 6208 Fax: 074-913 6352
Email: enquiries@arnoldshotel.com
Web: www.arnoldshotel.com
GPS: N +55° 10' 59.77" W -7° 58' 11.86"

Established in 1922 the hotel has been in the Arnold Family for three generations. Situated at the entrance to the village and overlooking Horn Head and Sheephaven Bay, we are an ideal base for touring North Donegal, Glenveagh National Park and Gardens close by. Enjoy one of the many activities organised by the hotel, horse riding from the hotel stables, golf on the local golf courses, fishing, walking, painting tuition, photography weekends and creative writing. Also bookable on www.irishcountryhotels.com. Please enquire about Facilities for Persons with Disabilities.

An IHF Quality Employer
Member of Irish Country Hotels

Bookable on www.irelandhotels.com

B&B from €55.00 to €91.00

Arnold Family
Proprietors
30

Activities:

Closed 01 November - 26 March

B&B Rates are per Person Sharing per Night incl. Breakfast.
or Room Rates are per Room per Night - See also Page 8

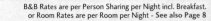

Dunfanaghy / Glenties / Killybegs

Shandon Hotel Spa and Wellness

HOTEL ★★★★ MAP 13 J 21

Marble Hill Strand,
Port-na-Blagh, Dunfanaghy,
Co. Donegal
Tel: 074-913 6137 Fax: 074-913 6430
Email: info@shandonhotel.com
Web: www.shandonhotel.com
GPS: N +55° 10' 47.56" W -7° 54' 24.32"

Discover the perfect getaway and the ultimate spa experience in Donegal. A family-run resort hotel situated beside the sea and the mile long sandy shore of Marble Hill Strand. Leisure centre, play house, tennis courts, pitch & putt and Resort Spa. Located near many amenities and national parks family holidays and spa destination. Three and half hours from Dublin Airport on the M1, exit 14 to Ardee, N2 North, from Letterkenny, take the N56.
Please enquire about Facilities for Persons with Disabilities.

An IHF Quality Employer

Bookable on www.irelandhotels.com

B&B from €80.00 to €130.00
Suites from €260.00 to €520.00

Dermot & Catherine McGlade

50

Closed 01 November - 12 February

Highlands Hotel

HOTEL ★★ MAP 13 I 19

Glenties,
Co. Donegal
Tel: 074-955 1111 Fax: 074-955 1564
Email: highlandhotel@eircom.net
Web: www.thehighlandshotel.com
GPS: N +54° 47' 45.09" W -8° 16' 54.07"

The Highlands Hotel is situated in the pretty town of Glenties. The town has won awards both in the Tidy Towns and the European Entente Florale competition. The surrounding glens are a haven for the hill walkers and a series of marked walks meander through the countryside. Enjoy a meal in our restaurant and try our famous Donegal seafood chowder.

B&B from €45.00 to €60.00

Boyle Family

24

Activities:

Closed 24 - 27 December

Bay View Hotel & Leisure Centre

HOTEL MAP 13 H 18

Main Street,
Killybegs,
Co. Donegal
Tel: 074-973 1950 Fax: 074-973 1856
Email: info@bayviewhotel.ie
Web: www.bayviewhotel.ie
GPS: N +54° 38' 12.49" W -8° 26' 31.92"

Built to a 3*** specification. One of Donegal's finest hotels, overlooking the splendour of Donegal Bay. The hotel has 40 en suite bedrooms with satellite TV, hairdryer, trouser press, DD telephone and Tea/Coffee making facilities, wheelchair accessible rooms and a lift. There is a traditional Irish bar, carvery, bistro and a leisure centre with gym, swimming pool, steam room, sauna and Jacuzzi. Harmony in Health Treatments can be booked directly with the hotel. Locally, there is deep sea and fresh water fishing, golf, hill walking, equestrian centres, boating and boat trips. Private function rooms for parties, weddings, meetings and conferences.

An IHF Quality Employer

Member of Countrywide Hotels

B&B from €45.00 to €75.00

Bernard O'Callaghan & Mary Kearns
Directors

40

Closed 24 - 27 December

B&B Rates are per Person Sharing per Night incl. Breakfast.
or Room Rates are per Room per Night - **See also Page 8**

Laghey / Letterkenny

Moorland Guesthouse

GUESTHOUSE ★★★ MAP 13 I 18

Laghey, R.232,
Donegal Town,
Co. Donegal
Tel: 074-973 4319 Fax: 074-973 4319
Email: moorland@eircom.net
Web: www.moorland-guesthouse.com
GPS: N +54° 35' 58.24" W -8° 0' 20.46"

Have a break from the hustle and bustle. A guesthouse with family character, situated in a wild, high moor/hill landscape. We offer good cuisine. Available on the premises: treatment with reflexology, body massage, cosmetics salon and sauna. Lounge with open fire and TV. Special relaxing breaks. Arrangements made for golf and fishing. Excellent 18-hole golf links not far away. Ideal place for relaxation. Very quiet and remote. German spoken.

Bookable on www.irelandhotels.com
Special Offer: www.irelandhotels.com/offers

B&B from €38.00 to €45.00

Rosemarie & Walter Schaffner
Proprietors
8

Closed 01 November - 31 January

Castle Grove Country House Hotel

HOTEL ★★★★ MAP 13 J 19

Ramelton Road,
off the R245,
Letterkenny
Tel: 074-915 1118 Fax: 074-915 1384
Email: reservations@castlegrove.com
Web: www.castlegrove.com
GPS: N +54° 59' 13.15" W -7° 38' 53.62"

Castle Grove is a 17th century country house set on its own rolling estate overlooking Lough Swilly. Its bedrooms are spacious and with all modern facilities. Downstairs in both drawing room and library you find a perfect blend of old and new. The dining room offers excellent cuisine, much of its produce from the Walled Garden. To the discerning guest Castle Grove has to be visited to be appreciated. While here you can fish, golf, or simply enjoy the locality. This house may be exclusively booked for family or business functions. Please enquire about Facilities for Persons with Disabilities.

Bookable on www.irelandhotels.com
Special Offer: www.irelandhotels.com/offers

B&B from €60.00 to €95.00
Suites from €200.00 to €350.00

Raymond & Mary T. Sweeney
Owners
1 15

Activities:

Closed 22 - 29 December

Gleneany House

GUESTHOUSE ★★★ MAP 13 J 19

Port Road,
Letterkenny,
Co. Donegal
Tel: 074-912 6088 Fax: 074-912 6090
Email: gleneanyhouse@eircom.net
Web: www.gleneany.com
GPS: N +54° 57' 10.24" W -7° 43' 45.46"

Gleneany House, located in the town centre, opposite the bus station in the heart of Letterkenny, offers both corporate & leisure clientèle an excellent level of personal & friendly service. Renowned for its consistency in excellent cuisine, food is served all day. Our 19 en suite rooms have satellite TV & DD phone. Our lounge bar is the ideal place for a quiet relaxing drink. An ideal base for touring beautiful Donegal, private car parking available. A warm welcome awaits all at the Gleneany House. So when next in town, call & experience for yourself our hospitality. For special offers go to www.gleneany.com.

B&B from €49.00 to €75.00

Paul Kelly
19

Closed 22 - 28 December

B&B Rates are per Person Sharing per Night incl. Breakfast. or Room Rates are per Room per Night - See also Page 8

Radisson Blu Hotel

HOTEL ★★★★ MAP 13 J 19

Paddy Harte Road,
Letterkenny,
Co. Donegal
Tel: 074-919 4444 Fax: 074-919 4455
Email: info.letterkenny@radissonblu.com
Web: www.radissonblu.ie/hotels-letterkenny
GPS: N +54° 56' 49.16" W -7° 44' 0.83"

Radisson Blu Hotel Letterkenny is designed with a contemporary Irish style, with comfort of both business & leisure guests in mind. The superior 4 star hotel features modern, bright bedrooms, award winning TriBeCa Restaurant, Oak Grill Bar, the Palm Lounge & the Nintendo Wii lounge & our fully equipped health & fitness centre. There is ample free parking & complimentary high speed internet access. The hotel is conveniently located in the centre of Letterkenny town. The main shopping district, theatre, cinemas, pubs & restaurants are all within walking distance.

Member of Radisson Blu Hotels & Resorts

Bookable on www.irelandhotels.com
Special Offer: www.irelandhotels.com/offers

B&B from €55.00 to €75.00
Suites from €220.00 to €250.00

Brian Gleeson
General Manager
114

Open All Year

Silver Tassie Hotel

HOTEL ★★★ MAP 13 J 19

Ramelton Road,
Letterkenny,
Co. Donegal
Tel: 074-912 5619 Fax: 074-912 4473
Email: info@silvertassiehotel.ie
Web: www.silvertassiehotel.com
GPS: N +54° 59' 9.82" W -7° 40' 13.89"

This luxurious hotel offers the best of both worlds - a rural setting gazing across Lough Swilly whilst only a 5 min drive from the bustling town of Letterkenny. The Blaney family have been welcoming guests to their hotel for 10 years & are always adding little touches to make your stay memorable. Relax by quiet fireside corners or unwind in the tranquillity of the impressive oak beamed foyer. Renowned for friendly service & excellent food. Free WiFi & all the latest technology. Complimentary use of Aura Leisure Centre. Spa and Hair Salon recently opened to guests.

Member of Select Hotels of Ireland

Bookable on www.irelandhotels.com
Special Offer: www.irelandhotels.com/offers

B&B from €40.00 to €85.00
Suites from €120.00 to €220.00

Rose & Ciaran Blaney
36

Food for Kids Activities:

Closed 24 - 26 December

Malin Hotel

HOTEL ★★ MAP 14 L 21

Malin Town,
Inishowen,
Co. Donegal
Tel: 074-937 0606 Fax: 074-937 0770
Email: info@malinhotel.ie
Web: www.malinhotel.ie
GPS: N +55° 17' 43.05" W -7° 15' 40.66"

Situated at the tip of the Inishowen Peninsula, the Malin Hotel offers the very best in luxury boutique hotel accommodation. The beauty of the surrounding area is breathtaking, and the Malin Hotel is the perfect base to explore local attractions. The quality of the food preparation is evident in the award-winning Jack Yeats Restaurant, which is highly recommended in the Bridgestone and Georgina Campbell Guide. Please enquire about Facilities for Persons with Disabilities.

Bookable on www.irelandhotels.com
Special Offer: www.irelandhotels.com/offers

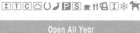

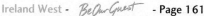

B&B from €65.00 to €85.00
Suites from €150.00 to €170.00

Volker Eichinger
Head Chef
18

Activities:

Closed 25 December

Milford / Moville / Portnoo

Best Western Milford Inn Hotel

HOTEL ★★★ MAP 13 J 20

Milford,
Co. Donegal

Tel: 074-915 3313 Fax: 074-915 3388
Email: info@milfordinnhotel.com
Web: www.milfordinndonegal.com
GPS: N +55° 4' 36.07" W -7° 40' 51.17"

Recently refurbished Best Western Milford Inn Hotel is located 5km from the heritage town of Ramelton. Set in some of Donegal's most stunning countryside. Ideal hotel for those seeking splendid relaxation, peace and tranquillity. It is the perfect base to explore some of Donegal's best kept secrets or simply head out for a day of golfing or fishing. The Best Western Milford Inn Hotel will spoil you, pamper you and remind you of the real meaning of hospitality.

Member of Blaney Group

Bookable on www.irelandhotels.com

Special Offer: www.irelandhotels.com/offers

B&B from €35.00 to €80.00

Mandy & Neil Blaney

33

Activities:

Closed 24 - 26 December

Carlton Redcastle Hotel & C-Spa

HOTEL ★★★★ MAP 14 L 21

Inishowen Peninsula,
Moville,
Co. Donegal

Tel: 074-938 5555 Fax: 074-938 5444
Email: info.redcastle@carlton.ie
Web: www.carlton.ie
GPS: N +55° 9' 31.43" W -7° 7' 21.90"

Nestled along the banks of Lough Foyle, the Carlton Redcastle Hotel is perfect for a relaxing leisure break. Discover one of the most beautiful regions in the country, world-class golf courses, ancient monuments & Blue Flag beaches. 93 luxury rooms & suites all with spectacular views; fine dining Waters Edge Restaurant, Captains Bar, & spacious banqueting & conference Ocean Suite with panoramic views. The C-Spa offers Thalasso spa & beauty treatments, complimentary use of the heated, multi-jet seawater Thalasso pool & gym. Room Reservations LoCall 1890 288 288.

An IHF Quality Employer

Member of Carlton Hotel Group

Bookable on www.irelandhotels.com

Special Offer: www.irelandhotels.com/offers

B&B from €49.00 to €129.00
Suites from €170.00 to €510.00

Matt Doherty
Sales Executive

93

Closed 24 - 27 December

Lake House Hotel

HOTEL ★★★ MAP 13 H 19

Narin,
Portnoo,
Co. Donegal

Tel: 074-954 5123 Fax: 074-954 5444
Email: lakehouse@iol.ie
Web: www.lakehousehotel.ie
GPS: N +54° 50' 15.42" W -8° 25' 43.67"

A country house hotel overlooking Narin golf course, minutes away from the Blue Flag Beach at Narin. 14 en suite luxury bedrooms decorated with a feeling of elegance and spaciousness, with television, DD telephone, hairdryer and complimentary tea/coffee making facilities. Family rooms available. The hotel boasts dining experiences from fine dining in the award-winning restaurant to a grill/bar menu in the lounge. Conference and banqueting facilities also available. Please note the hotel is also closed 19 - 27 December. Please enquire about Facilities for Persons with Disabilities.

Member of irish Countrywide Hotels

B&B from €40.00 to €60.00

Frank Barber
Managing Director

14

Closed 05 January -17 March

B&B Rates are per Person Sharing per Night incl. Breakfast.
or Room Rates are per Room per Night - **See also Page 8**

Fort Royal Country House

HOTEL ★★★ MAP 14 K 20

Rathmullan,
Co. Donegal

Tel: 074-915 8100 Fax: 074-915 8103
Email: fortroyal@eircom.net
Web: www.fortroyal.ie
GPS: N +55° 6' 14.14" W -7° 31' 40.90"

One of the most beautifully situated houses in Ireland with 7 hectares of lovely grounds and gardens, beside Lough Swilly including a sandy beach, hard tennis court, par 3 golf course. Especially friendly welcome accounts for the large number of regular visitors from all parts of the world to this peaceful unspoilt part of Donegal. Irish Tourist Board and AA***.

Bookable on www.irelandhotels.com

B&B from €70.00 to €80.00

Tim & Tina Fletcher
Proprietor / Manager

11

Closed 01 November - 31 March

Waters Edge (The)

HOTEL ★★★ MAP 14 K 20

Rathmullan,
Co. Donegal

Tel: 074-915 8182 Fax: 074-915 8314
Email: info@thewatersedge.ie
Web: www.watersedgedonegal.com
GPS: N +55° 5' 32.08" W -7° 33' 1.12"

Set in an exclusive location, this boutique hotel boasts some of the most spectacular views that Donegal has to offer. All rooms offer breathtaking sea views equipped with all mod cons, TV, DVD, tea/coffee making facilities, hairdryer, robes, slippers. Food & wine is what we are famous for, come join us in our waterfront restaurant. Dine on the finest of fare as you enjoy panoramic views of Lough Swilly. The ideal location for golf, horse riding, surfing or hiking. Private weddings catered for. Member of Private Ireland. Please enquire about Facilities for Persons with Disabilities.

Member of Blaney Group

B&B from €40.00 to €80.00

Mandy & Neil Blaney

10

Activities:

Closed 25 - 26 December

Ard Einne Guesthouse

GUESTHOUSE ★★★ MAP 5 D 10

Inismor,
Aran Islands,
Co. Galway

Tel: 099-61126 Fax: 099-61388
Email: ardeinne@eircom.net
Web: www.ardeinne.com
GPS: N +53° 6' 0.55" W -9° 39' 20.04"

Árd Einne is a 3 star family run guesthouse. Provides high standard of comfortable accommodation and service. Its cosy atmosphere has spectacular views from bedroom windows and over-looks own beach. Located in an unspoilt area on the island, the ideal base to 'Get Away' for one to experience and explore the magnificence of Inis Mór, while enjoying a unique, peaceful and relaxing break. Near cliffs and monastic ruins. Beside air-strip and 2km from Cillronan Pier. Please enquire about Facilities for Persons with Disabilities.

Member of Premier Collection of Ireland

Bookable on www.irelandhotels.com

B&B from €45.00 to €60.00

Clodagh Ni Ghoill
Manager

8

Closed 30 November - 01 February

B&B Rates are per Person Sharing per Night incl. Breakfast.
or Room Rates are per Room per Night - **See also Page 8**

Aran Islands

Kilmurvey House

GUESTHOUSE ★★★ MAP 5 D 10

Kilronan,
Inismor, Aran Islands,
Co. Galway
Tel: 099-61218 Fax: 099-61397
Email: kilmurveyhouse@eircom.net
Web: www.kilmurveyhouse.com
GPS: N +53° 7' 50.41" W -9° 45' 29.82"

Kilmurvey House is a 150 year old country house once the home of "The Ferocious O'Flahertys". We are situated at the foot of Dun Aonghus, just beside Dun Aonghus Visitor Centre. Just 3 minutes walk from a Blue Flag beach, we are an ideal location for cyclists, walkers and those who just wish to relax. Group rates available. Free access to Dun Aonghus National Monument available to our guests. Recommended by several travel guides including Bridge Stone and Georgina Campbell.

B&B from €45.00 to €65.00

Treasa Joyce
Proprietor

12

Activities:

Closed 1 November - 27 March

Pier House

GUESTHOUSE ★★★ MAP 5 D 10

Kilronan,
Aran Islands,
Co. Galway
Tel: 099-61417 Fax: 099-61122
Email: pierh@iol.ie
Web: www.pierhousearan.com
GPS: N +53° 7' 11.99" W -9° 39' 56.51"

Pier House is perfectly located less than 100m from Kilronan Village, within walking distance of sandy beaches, pubs and historical remains. This modern house is finished to a very high standard and has many extra facilities, TV, tea/coffee facilities in bedrooms and a restaurant on the premises. The bedrooms are well appointed and have perfect sea and landscape views. If it is comfort and old fashioned warmth and hospitality you expect, then Pier House is the perfect location to enjoy it.

B&B from €45.00 to €60.00

Maura Joyce
Proprietor

12

Closed 30 November - 17 March

Tigh Fitz

GUESTHOUSE ★★★ MAP 5 D 10

Killeany, Kilronan,
Inishmore, Aran Islands,
Co. Galway
Tel: 099-61213 Fax: 099-61386
Email: penny@tighfitz.com
Web: www.tighfitz.com
GPS: N +53° 6' 20.07" W -9° 39' 51.01"

Tigh Fitz, a family-run guesthouse is in Killeany, Inishmore. Offering luxurious accommodation in this unspoilt area of the Aran Isles. Tigh Fitz is unique in its situation, in its spaciousness and proximity to beaches and areas of archaeological and historical remains. In this area are the tall Cliffs of Aran and the magnificent pre-historic forts. Tigh Fitz is 1.6km from the island capital Kilronan and close to the Aer Arann airstrip.

B&B from €45.00 to €60.00

Penny Fitzpatrick
Proprietor

10

Closed 08 - 29 December

B&B Rates are per Person Sharing per Night incl. Breakfast.
or Room Rates are per Room per Night - **See also Page 8**

Raheen Woods Hotel Tranquillity Spa & Kardio Kids

HOTEL ★★★ MAP 6 G 10

Athenry,
Galway

Tel: 091-875888 Fax: 091-875444
Email: info@raheenwoodshotel.ie
Web: www.raheenwoodshotel.ie
GPS: N +53° 18' 2.31" W -8° 45' 42.29"

Raheen Woods Hotel & Tranquillity Leisure/Pool & Spa is "that special place", contemporary in style. Located in Athenry, a designated walled Heritage Town. 50 bright well appointed spacious bedrooms & suites, all areas wheelchair accessible by lift from basement car park. Good food in McHales Bar or dine in The Clarin Bistro. The N6 is mins away & Galway Airport just 15 mins. We welcome guests with reduced mobility. Our friendly staff will be happy to assist you with your plans. Kardio Kids: our in-house kids activity centre caters for kids needs from 6mths - 12yrs. Please visit our website for upcoming events.

Bookable on www.irelandhotels.com
Special Offer: www.irelandhotels.com/offers

B&B from €45.00 to €125.00
Suites from €145.00 to €245.00

Frank Corby
General Manager

50

Food for Kids Activities:

Closed 24 - 26 December

Carlton Shearwater Hotel & C-Spa

HOTEL ★★★★ MAP 6 I 11

Marina Point,
Ballinasloe,
Co. Galway

Tel: 0909-630400 Fax: 0909-630401
Email: info.shearwater@carlton.ie
Web: www.carlton.ie/shearwater
GPS: N +53° 19' 35.35" W -8° 13' 12.23"

Carlton Shearwater Hotel, a property adjoining the Marina in Ballinasloe, Co. Galway. It has 104 deluxe rooms including suites, Marengo's Restaurant offers the very best in fine dining using top quality local produce, a contemporary style bar, a C-Spa and leisure centre. A state of the art conference and banqueting centre with 9 meeting rooms and the Plaza Suite. This central location - the Gateway to the West is the perfect destination to tour Ireland. Room Reservations LoCall 1890 288 288. Please enquire about Facilities for Persons with Disabilities.

An IHF Quality Employer

Bookable on www.irelandhotels.com
Special Offer: www.irelandhotels.com/offers

B&B from €49.00 to €99.00
Suites from €180.00 to €298.00

Dermot Birchall
General Manager

104

Closed 24 - 26 December

Ballynahinch Castle Hotel

HOTEL ★★★★ MAP 5 D 11

Ballinafad,
Recess, Connemara,
Co. Galway

Tel: 095-31006 Fax: 095-31085
Email: bhinch@iol.ie
Web: www.ballynahinch-castle.com
GPS: N +53° 27' 36.68" W -9° 51' 44.51"

Once home to the O'Flaherty Chieftains, pirate queen Grace O'Malley, Humanity Dick Martin & Maharajah Ranjitsinji, Ballynahinch is now a 4**** hotel. With casual country elegance, overlooking both river & mountains, offering an unpretentious service & an ideal centre from which to tour the West. Log fires & a friendly fisherman's pub complement a restaurant offering the best in fresh game, fish & local produce. Voted in the Top 20 Hotels in the World by Fodor's, Ballynahinch is the jewel in Connemara's crown. RAC 2 Rosettes Dining Award and Food & Wine Magazine Hotel Restaurant of the Year.

An IHF Quality Employer

Member of Manor House Hotels

Bookable on www.irelandhotels.com

B&B from €80.00 to €185.00
Suites from €340.00 to €420.00

Patrick O'Flaherty
General Manager

40

Activities:

Closed Christmas Week & February

B&B Rates are per Person Sharing per Night incl. Breakfast.
or Room Rates are per Room per Night - **See also Page 8**

Caherlistrane / Carna / Cashel

Lisdonagh House

GUESTHOUSE ★★★★ MAP 10 F 12

Caherlistrane,
Co. Galway

Tel: 093-31163 Fax: 093-31528
Email: cooke@lisdonagh.com
Web: www.lisdonagh.com
GPS: N +53° 29' 30.65" W -9° 3' 20.84"

Lisdonagh House is located 20 mins from Galway City in a glorious tranquil setting. The house is early Georgian with commanding views over Lough Hackett. Over 100 acres of woodland on the estate where guests can meander on country walks. Fishing & horse riding can be arranged. Your hosts, John & Finola Cooke, have elegantly restored the house retaining the classical proportions. The oval entrance hall has murals depicting four virtues dating from 1790. The cooking is superb, innovatively using the best of local ingredients. A warm welcome is extended to guests at Lisdonagh House.

Member of Ireland's Blue Book

B&B from €70.00 to €140.00

John & Finola Cooke

9

Closed 01 Novemeber - 01 May

Carna Bay Hotel

HOTEL ★★★ MAP 9 D 11

Carna,
Connemara,
Co. Galway

Tel: 095-32255 Fax: 095-32530
Email: carnabay@iol.ie
Web: www.carnabay.com
GPS: N +53° 19' 35.10" W -9° 50' 19.75"

Carna Bay Hotel is located in the most magical scenery in Ireland. Connemara: unique landscape, flora and fauna, unspoilt beaches, mountain ranges. Beautiful Western Way walking routes. Our kitchen offers the finest fresh Irish produce. Locally: St. McDara's Island, Connemara National Park, Kylemore Abbey, Aran and Inisbofin Ferry 40 minutes drive. Bar, A la carte & dinner menu available. Wireless Broadband. Please enquire about Facilities for Persons with Disabilities.

Member of Irish Country Hotels

Bookable on www.irelandhotels.com

Special Offer: www.irelandhotels.com/offers

B&B from €45.00 to €130.00

Michael & Sheamus Cloherty
Proprietors

24

Closed 23 - 27 December

Cashel House Hotel

HOTEL ★★★★ MAP 5 D 11

Cashel,
Connemara,
Co. Galway

Tel: 095-31001 Fax: 095-31077
Email: res@cashel-house-hotel.com
Web: www.cashel-house-hotel.com
GPS: N +53° 25' 10.37" W -9° 48' 28.62"

Elegance in a wilderness on the shores of the Atlantic. It is set amidst the most beautiful gardens in Ireland. Enjoy long walks, cycling and fishing. Later, relax in front of a peat fire in this elegant residence appointed with antique furniture and period paintings. Most guest rooms look onto the gardens and some onto the sea. Dine on bounty from the sea and garden - enjoy vintage wine. New for 2009, Garden School with courses in planting, pruning, and plant shrub identification. Please enquire about Facilities for Persons with Disabilities.

Member of Ireland's Blue Book

Bookable on www.irelandhotels.com

Special Offer: www.irelandhotels.com/offers

B&B from €85.00 to €150.00
Suites from €250.00 to €360.00

Ray Doorley & Frank McEvilly
Manager & Proprietor

30

Open All Year

B&B Rates are per Person Sharing per Night incl. Breakfast.
or Room Rates are per Room per Night - See also Page 8

Abbeyglen Castle Hotel

HOTEL ★★★★ MAP 9 C 12

Sky Road,
Clifden,
Co. Galway
Tel: 095-21201 Fax: 095-21797
Email: info@abbeyglen.ie
Web: www.abbeyglen.ie
GPS: N +53° 29' 17.88" W -10° 1' 53.85"

Abbeyglen Castle Hotel was built in 1832 in the heart of Connemara by John D'Arcy of Clifden Castle. Romantically set in beautiful gardens with babbling brooks & streams, panoramic views of Clifden and the bay with a backdrop of the Twelve Bens. Abbeyglen has a new beauty & relaxation centre (Yon-Ka) and a long list of most indoor/outdoor facilities, international cuisine, unique qualities of peace, serenity & ambience. Complimentary afternoon tea a speciality. Superior rooms available at a supplement. Please enquire about Facilities for Persons with Disabilities.

Member of Manor House Hotels

Bookable on www.irelandhotels.com

B&B from €99.00 to €125.00

Brian / Paul Hughes
Manager / Proprietor

45

Activities:

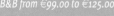

Closed 10 January - 04 February

All The Twos Guesthouse

GUESTHOUSE MAP 9 C 12

Galway Road,
Clifden, Connemara,
Co. Galway
Tel: 095-22222
Email: allthetwos@gmail.com
Web: www.clifden-allthetwos-connemara.com
GPS: N +53° 29' 17.99" W -10° 0' 44.20"

Built to a 4**** specification. Clifden's newest guesthouse, family run, non smoking. Built to exceptionally high standards (fire certificate) on the edge of Clifden only 1km from the centre of town. Ground Floor rooms. A lift available. Large luxurious bedrooms, king size beds, LCD satellite TV, radio, DD phone, tea/coffee, hairdryer, free WiFi. En suite bathrooms with power showers and many with separate baths. Enjoy the best of both worlds, the peace and quiet of the country but a few minutes walk from "the craic" in Clifden's great pubs and restaurants. Please enquire about Facilities for Persons with Disabilities.

Bookable on www.irelandhotels.com

B&B from €45.00 to €65.00

Brendan & Maureen Lavin

12

Open All Year

Ardagh Hotel & Restaurant

HOTEL ★★★ MAP 9 C 12

Ballyconneely Road,
Clifden,
Co. Galway
Tel: 095-21384 Fax: 095-21314
Email: ardaghhotel@eircom.net
Web: www.ardaghhotel.com
GPS: N +53° 28' 7.53" W -10° 1' 3.05"

A quiet family-run 3*** hotel, 2km from Clifden on Ardbear Bay, AA recommended. Bedrooms individually decorated with television, telephone and tea/coffee facilities. Award-winning restaurant, 2 AA Rosettes. Specialises in lobsters, oysters and Connemara lamb with homegrown vegetables and a wide selection of wines. Local amenities: golf, fishing and beaches. Reservations by post, phone, fax, email and website. Superior suites with bay view available. WiFi available.

Member of Irish Country Hotels

Bookable on www.irelandhotels.com

B&B from €60.00 to €110.00
Suites from €130.00 to €220.00

Stephane & Monique Bauvet
Proprietors / Manager / Chef

17

Closed 26 October - 02 April

Clifden

Ben View House

GUESTHOUSE ★★ MAP 9 C 12

Bridge Street,
Clifden, Connemara,
Co. Galway
Tel: 095-21256 Fax: 095-21226
Email: benviewhouse@ireland.com
Web: www.benviewhouse.com
GPS: N +53° 29' 19.51" W -10° 1' 14.87"

Dating from 1848, Ben View has been owned and managed by our family since 1926. See our history on website. Recommended by Frommer, Le Guide du Routard and Le Petit Fute Guides. AA 3 Star approved. Enjoy all the modern comforts of this elegant guesthouse, surrounded by antiques and old world atmosphere. Ben view is within walking distance of all amenities, harbour and seaside. Free overnight on-street parking. Lock-up garage available for motorcycles and bicycles. Your hostess Eileen wishes everyone a safe and pleasant journey.

Member of Connemara Toursim

B&B from €35.00 to €45.00

Eileen Morris
Proprietor

9

Activities:

Closed 24 - 26 December

Buttermilk Lodge

GUESTHOUSE ★★★ MAP 9 C 12

Westport Road,
Clifden,
Co. Galway
Tel: 095-21951 Fax: 095-21953
Email: info@buttermilklodge.com
Web: www.buttermilklodge.com
GPS: N +53° 29' 31.53" W -10° 1' 24.83"

A warm, friendly home from home, 400 metres (5 mins walk) from Clifden centre. All rooms en suite with WiFi & every modern convenience. Your warm welcome includes afternoon tea by the turf fire where there is always a cuppa available. Our extensive breakfast menu, free-range eggs, home baking, tasteful décor, stunning mountain views, friendly Connemara ponies, free WiFi, computer and printer for guests use and many extra touches ensure return visits. Laundry service, packed lunches, early breakfasts, no problem! ITB 3***, AA****. Children over 5 welcome.

Bookable on www.irelandhotels.com
Special Offer: www.irelandhotels.com/offers

B&B from €40.00 to €50.00

Cathriona & Patrick O'Toole
Proprietors / Hosts

11

Closed 20 - 27 December

Clifden Station House Hotel

HOTEL ★★★ MAP 9 C 12

Clifden,
Connemara,
Co. Galway
Tel: 095-21699 Fax: 095-21667
Email: info@clifdenstationhouse.com
Web: www.clifdenstationhouse.com
GPS: N +53° 29' 19.63" W -10° 1' 3.70"

Anyone who loves shopping, wining and dining will feel instantly at home at the Clifden Station House. Here on your break, to get away from it all, you can do all those things you love to do but in a relaxed contemporary environment. In the courtyard surrounding the hotel is a wonderful selection of speciality shops, hair salon, body and skincare clinic, full leisure facilities, self catering apartments, multi purpose venue, comprising of a theatre, music venue, cinema and museum. Please enquire about Facilities for Persons with Disabilities.

An IHF Quality Employer

Bookable on www.irelandhotels.com
Special Offer: www.irelandhotels.com/offers

B&B from €50.00 to €120.00
Suites from €120.00 to €200.00

Wilson Bird
General Manager

78

Activities:

Open All Year

B&B Rates are per Person Sharing per Night incl. Breakfast.
or Room Rates are per Room per Night - See also Page 8

Connemara Country Lodge

GUESTHOUSE ★★★ MAP 9 C 12

Westport Road,
Clifden,
Co. Galway
Tel: 095-22122 Fax: 095-21122
Email: connemara@unison.ie
Web: www.connemaracountrylodge.com
GPS: N +53° 29' 28.90" W -10° 1' 16.29"

Delightful Georgian home with spacious bedrooms, 2 minutes walk from Clifden, on extensive grounds with large private car park. All bedrooms are en suite with TV, tea/coffee making facilities, telephones, safes and hairdryers. Why not join Mary for an evening of traditional Irish music and song in her large lounge - a truly unique experience - as Mary is a well known performer. Her home and ballad singing have been recorded for broadcasting on American TV. French and German spoken by Mary. Home-baking a speciality. Please enquire about Facilities for Persons with Disabilities.

Member of Guide Bleu

B&B from €35.00 to €45.00

Mary Corbett
Proprietress

10

Open All Year

Dun Ri Guesthouse

GUESTHOUSE ★★★ MAP 9 C 12

Hulk Street,
Clifden,
Co. Galway
Tel: 095-21625 Fax: 095-21635
Email: michael@dunri.ie
Web: www.dunri.ie
GPS: N +53° 29' 16.35" W -10° 1' 6.37"

Centrally located on a quiet street in the heart of picturesque Clifden. Dun Ri offers private parking with secure motorcycle parking. Our spacious rooms have private bathrooms (many with bath tubs), DD phone and TVs. The guest lounge is an ideal place to relax over a coffee/tea after a day of exploring Connemara. We are just 1 minute's walk from the town centre, its excellent restaurants, traditional pubs and a short pleasant drive to beaches, golf horse riding and many more attractions.

B&B from €35.00 to €50.00

Michael & Aileen King
Proprietors

13

Closed 19 - 26 December

Foyles Hotel

HOTEL ★★★ MAP 9 C 12

Clifden,
Connemara,
Co. Galway
Tel: 095-21801 Fax: 095-21458
Email: info@foyleshotel.com
Web: www.foyleshotel.com
GPS: N +53° 29' 19.06" W -10° 1' 22.06"

One of Connemara's longest established hotels, trading since 1836 and owned by the Foyles for nearly a century. The hotel is situated in the centre of Clifden and is an ideal central point for exploring Connemara. The hotel's old world elegance and atmosphere have been gracefully retained through recent renovations, each room being individually decorated and furnished with charm and warmth. The Foyles and their staff offer you a warm welcome and will be happy to assist you in enjoying the area.

An IHF Quality Employer

Bookable on www.irelandhotels.com

B&B from €40.00 to €75.00

Eddie Foyle
Proprietor

25

Closed 08 January - 18 February

Clifden / Clonbur (An Fháirche) / Furbo

Quay House (The)

GUESTHOUSE ★★★★ MAP 9 C 12

Beach Road,
Clifden,
Co. Galway
Tel: 095-21369 Fax: 095-21608
Email: thequay@iol.ie
Web: www.thequayhouse.com
GPS: N +53° 29' 8.59" W -10° 1' 48.14"

The Quay House is Clifden's oldest building, c.1820. It now comprises 14 individually furnished rooms, some with balconies and working fireplaces, and has a wonderful collection of Georgian furniture and family portraits. It's just 7 minutes walk into town. Fishing, golf, pony-trekking, etc. are all nearby. Owned by Julia and Paddy Foyle whose family have been innkeepers in Connemara since 1917. Staying at the Quay House is a completely different experience. Outright winner of "Cesar" Award for Ireland 2003. Awarded Georgina Campbell's Guesthouse of the Year 2006. Please enquire about Facilities for Persons with Disabilities.

Member of Hidden Ireland

B&B from €65.00 to €80.00

Paddy & Julia Foyle
Owners

14

Closed 1 November - 12 March

Fairhill House Hotel

HOTEL ★★★ MAP 9 E 12

Clonbur (An Fháirche),
Connemara,
Co. Galway
Tel: 094-954 6176 Fax: 094-954 6176
Email: fairhillhouse@eircom.net
Web: www.fairhillhouse.com
GPS: N +53° 32' 39.89" W -9° 21' 52.19"

Established 1830, located in one of the most scenic parts of Connemara. Clonbur is nestled between the magical lakes of Lough Mask & Lough Corrib. One of the best regions in Europe for free fishing. Tuition & guides arranged. Abundance of golf courses, outdoor pursuits - abseiling, canoeing, windsurfing, hill walking. Close to Galway, Castlebar & Westport, known for excellent shopping. Famous for its seafood menu, old world bar, open fires, traditional music entertainment & friendly atmosphere. You could meet anybody in Clonbur! Group rates. A walker's paradise. Please enquire about Facilities for Persons with Disabilities.

Bookable on www.irelandhotels.com

B&B from €45.00 to €75.00

Edward Lynch
Proprietor

20

Activities:

Closed 23 - 26 December

Connemara Coast Hotel

HOTEL ★★★★ MAP 6 F 10

Furbo,
Galway
Tel: 091-592108 Fax: 091-592065
Email: info@connemaracoast.ie
Web: www.sinnotthotels.com
GPS: N +53° 14' 55.03" W -9° 12' 1.64"

An award winning hotel with dedicated staff extend a warm welcome in this spectacular setting, just ten minutes from Galway city. Superb facilities, fine food, an indoor leisure centre and grounds that sweep down to the shores of the bay are all here and more. Live entertainment available on selected evenings.
Bookable on www.sinnotthotels.com.
Please enquire about Facilities for Persons with Disabilities.

An IHF Quality Employer

Member of Sinnott Hotels Ireland

Bookable on www.irelandhotels.com
Special Offer: www.irelandhotels.com/offers

B&B from €70.00 to €175.00
Suites from €300.00 to €600.00

Ann Downey
General Manager

130

Activities:

Open All Year

B&B Rates are per Person Sharing per Night incl. Breakfast.
or Room Rates are per Room per Night - **See also Page 8**

Amber House Hotel (The)

HOTEL ★★★ MAP 6 F 10

Deoch Uisce,
Merlin Park,
Galway

Tel: 091-746666 Fax: 091-746667
Email: info@theamberhousehotel.com
Web: www.theamberhousehotel.com
GPS: N +53° 17' 1.87" W -8° 58' 53.04"

Welcome to The Amber House Hotel. Situated off the old Galway - Dublin Road and less than 8 minutes from Galway City. With free secure parking you'll be just steps away from Galway Race Course, Galway Clinic and Galway Airport. The Amber House Hotel boasts 20 tastily designed guest bedrooms, D'Arcy's Bar, our Galway Races themed bar, with live entertainment and fabulous food served all day and the Killanin Room which is ideal for conference, functions and parties alike. We look forward to welcoming you to The Amber House Hotel. Please enquire about Facilities for Persons with Disabilities.

B&B from €49.50 to €69.50

Amber Accommodation Group

20

Closed 24 - 26 December

Anno Santo Hotel

HOTEL ★★ MAP 6 F 10

Threadneedle Road,
Salthill,
Galway

Tel: 091-523011 Fax: 091-522110
Email: gerry@annosantohotel.com
Web: www.annosantohotel.com
GPS: N +53° 15' 47.64" W -9° 5' 19.29"

Small family-run hotel located in quiet residential area. Galway's major tennis/badminton and squash club lies opposite the hotel. The golf club is also close by (1km), while Galway City and beaches are within easy reach. We are also on a main bus route. All rooms are en suite, with TV, complimentary tea/coffee and direct dial telephone. Your hosts, the Vaughan family, provide high class service in comfortable bedrooms at budget prices.

Bookable on www.irelandhotels.com

Room Rate from €45.00 to €155.00

Gerard & Joanna Vaughan
Proprietors

14

Activities:

Closed 20 December - 20 January

Ardilaun Hotel, Conference Centre & Leisure Club

HOTEL ★★★★ MAP 6 F 10

Taylor's Hill,
Galway City

Tel: 091-521433 Fax: 091-521546
Email: info@theardilaunhotel.ie
Web: www.theardilaunhotel.ie
GPS: N +53° 16' 3.30" W -9° 4' 51.15"

The Ardilaun Hotel is a family owned and established 4 Star Hotel, on it's own landscaped grounds only 1 mile from Galway City centre and Galway bay. Facilities include 125 luxurious bedrooms, beautiful gardens with terrace patio, spacious lounges, award winning Camilaun restaurant, Blazers Bar & Bistro, superb leisure club, Avalon beauty salon, conferencing & banqueting facilities, free broadband, business centre & free car parking. Please enquire about Facilities for Persons with Disabilities.

An IHF Quality Employer

Member of Select Hotels of Ireland

Bookable on www.irelandhotels.com
Special Offer: www.irelandhotels.com/offers

B&B from €55.00 to €135.00
Suites from €175.00 to €370.00

John Ryan
Managing Director

125

Closed 22 - 27 December

Galway City

Atlantic View Guesthouse

GUESTHOUSE ★★★ MAP 6 F 10

4 Ocean Wave,
Dr. Colohan Road,
Galway
Tel: 091-582109 Fax: 091-582109
Email: atlanticbandb@hotmail.com
Web: www.atlanticbandb.com
GPS: N +53° 15' 50.64" W -9° 4' 9.18"

Atlantic View guesthouse is a luxurious haven overlooking Galway Bay with a large sun balcony. Some of our rooms have stunning views of the sea, with balconies. We are an ideal base to tour Connemara, Cliffs of Moher and The Burren. We are only a short walk to the city centre and are ideally located for shopping, theatres, art galleries, museums, pubs, restaurants and clubs. Free secure car parking. Free wireless internet. We are situated on the famous salthill promenade across the road from the beach. Mobile: 086 - 852 4579. Please enquire about Facilities for Persons with Disabilities.

B&B from €35.00 to €95.00

Tara Treacy
Proprietor

5

Closed 23 - 27 December

Best Western Flannery's Hotel

HOTEL ★★★ MAP 6 F 10

Dublin Road,
Galway
Tel: 091-755111 Fax: 091-753078
Email: reservations@flanneryshotel.net
Web: www.flanneryshotel.net
GPS: N +53° 16' 41.71" W -9° 0' 53.73"

Flannerys Hotel is long established in Galway as a hotel offering comfort and style within relaxed surroundings. A welcome choice for the business traveller or leisure guest. We take pride in ensuring that a special emphasis is placed on guest comfort enhanced by a genuinely caring and efficient service. Recently refurbished, the hotel features 134 modern, comfortable bedrooms, restaurant and bar. Member of Best Western Hotels. Free extensive on-site car parking. Free WiFi throughout entire Hotel. Please enquire about Facilities for Persons with Disabilities.

An IHF Quality Employer

Member of Best Western Hotels

Bookable on www.irelandhotels.com

Special Offer: www.irelandhotels.com/offers

B&B from €35.00 to €170.00

Mary Flannery
Proprietor

134

Food for Kids *Activities:*

Closed 20 - 29 December

Claregalway Hotel

HOTEL ★★★ MAP 6 11 G

Claregalway Village,
Galway
Tel: 091-738300 Fax: 091-738311
Email: stay@claregalwayhotel.ie
Web: www.claregalwayhotel.ie
GPS: N +53° 20' 37.13" W -8° 56' 38.31"

The Claregalway Hotel is an award winning family-run hotel in Claregalway, conveniently located only 3km from Galway Airport on the location of the N17 and N18 routes, making it an ideal base for your Galway visit. We have comfortable bedrooms, fun bars, a contemporary restaurant, a modern luxurious leisure centre, swimming pool and spa suites incorporating seaweed baths. The Claregalway Hotel looks forward to welcoming you in the future. Please enquire about Facilities for Persons with Disabilities.

Bookable on www.irelandhotels.com

Special Offer: www.irelandhotels.com/offers

B&B from €50.00 to €100.00
Suites from €130.00 to €300.00

Paul & Nora Gill
Directors

3 45

Activities:

Closed 24 - 26 December

B&B Rates are per Person Sharing per Night incl. Breakfast.
or Room Rates are per Room per Night - **See also Page 8**

Clayton Hotel Galway

HOTEL ★★★★ MAP 6 F 10

Ballybrit,
Galway

Tel: 091-721900 Fax: 091-721901
Email: info@clayton.ie
Web: www.claytonhotelgalway.ie
GPS: N +53° 17' 29.51'' W -8° 59' 18.88''

The 4* Clayton Hotel Galway is located only minutes from Galway city centre, Galway airport and ballybrit racecourse, home to the Galway races. Hotel facilities comprise 195 well-appointed guest rooms, excellent conference facilities and a spacious ballroom which can accommodate up to 800 delegates. Other facilities include Tribes Restaurant & Enclosure bar. Leisure facilities include a 20m swimming pool, steam room & sauna. Please enquire about Facilities for Persons with Disabilities.

Member of Maldron Hotels - Partner Hotel

Bookable on www.irelandhotels.com

Special Offer: www.irelandhotels.com/offers

B&B from €50.00 to €175.00
Suites from €200.00 to €350.00

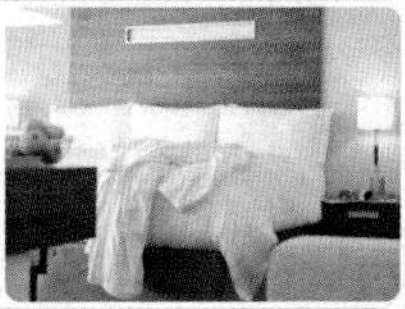

Edward Sweeney
General Manager

195

Closed 23 - 26 December

Corrib Haven Guest House

GUESTHOUSE ★★★ MAP 6 F 10

107 Upper Newcastle,
Galway

Tel: 091-524171 Fax: 091-582414
Email: corribhaven@eircom.net
Web: www.corribhaven.net
GPS: N +53° 17' 12.94" W -9° 4' 11.40"

Corrib Haven's motto is quality hospitality for discerning people. Located in Galway City on the N59 leading to Connemara. All rooms en suite, power showers, posture sprung beds, cable TV, DD phones. Tea/coffee facility, breakfast menu, private parking. Convenient to city centre, swimming pool 2 mins. Ideal for touring Connemara, Aran Islands. Smooth professionalism with personal warmth to our visitors. Non-smoking. 20 mins drive from Galway Airport. Close to NUI Galway & hospital. Bus No.4 to city centre. Close to Westwood House Hotel & Glenlo Abbey Hotel. Wireless broadband throughout.

Member of Premier Guesthouses

Bookable on www.irelandhotels.com

B&B from €30.00 to €60.00

Tom & Angela Hillary
Proprietors

9

Closed 16 - 31 December

Courtyard Marriott Galway

HOTEL ★★★★ MAP 6 F 10

Headford Point,
Headford Road,
Galway City

Tel: 091-513200 Fax: 091-513201
Email: galway.reservations@courtyardgalway.com
Web: www.galwaycourtyard.com
GPS: N +53° 17' 8.56" W -9° 2' 42.49"

Located at Headford Point within walking distance of Eyre Square & Shop St, the Courtyard Marriott is the ideal base to explore Galway City & its surrounds. Our 104 rooms are spacious & comfortable featuring high speed internet access, air-con, pay per view movies, built in mini fridge & safe. The Olive Tree Bistro features popular Irish cuisine with a contemporary & Mediterranean influence. Additional facilities: the Point Bar, the Spa, a fitness suite, business centre & conference suites with secure underground car parking.

An IHF Quality Employer

Member of Marriott Hotel Group

Bookable on www.irelandhotels.com

Room Rate from €99.00 to €350.00
Suites from €150.00 to €500.00

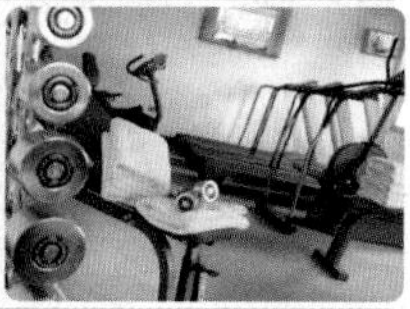

Cian Landers
General Manager

104

Food for Kids *Activities:*

Open All Year

B&B Rates are per Person Sharing per Night incl. Breakfast.
or Room Rates are per Room per Night - See also Page 8

Galway City

Eyre Square Hotel

HOTEL ★★★ MAP 6 F 10

Forster Street,
Galway

Tel: 091-569633 Fax: 091-569641
Email: eyresquarehotel@eircom.net
Web: www.eyresquarehotel.com
GPS: N +53° 16' 27.34" W -9° 2' 50.60"

The Eyre Square Hotel is situated right in the heart of Galway adjacent to both bus and rail stations. The Eyre Square Hotel caters for both the tourist and business person offering a very high standard of accommodation. Rooms en suite with direct dial phone, satellite TV and tea/coffee making facilities. Enjoy excellent cuisine in our Red's Bistro or visit the lively Red Square Pub. A warm and friendly welcome awaits you at the Eyre Square Hotel.

Member of Byrne Hotel Group

Bookable on www.irelandhotels.com

B&B from €35.00 to €150.00

Roger Carey
General Manager

52

Closed 20 - 28 December

Forster Court Hotel

HOTEL ★★★ MAP 6 F 10

Forster Street,
Galway City

Tel: 091-564111 Fax: 091-539839
Email: sales@forstercourthotel.com
Web: www.forstercourthotel.com
GPS: N +53° 16' 38.64" W -9° 2' 40.56"

Galway's most central hotel, located adjacent to Eyre Square, has it all. All rooms have recently been refurbished to the highest possible standard, with contemporary, luxurious furnishings. Morgan's Bar provides sumptuous food, fine wines and premium spirits. The perfect location for a romantic getaway or the business client. Free WiFi throughout. Close to bus & train station, servicing all of Ireland. Airport transfers available.

Member of Select Hotels of Ireland

Bookable on www.irelandhotels.com
Special Offer: www.irelandhotels.com/offers

B&B from €35.00 to €150.00

Ronan Lawless
Proprietor

48

Open All Year

g Hotel (The)

HOTEL ★★★★★ MAP 6 F 10

Wellpark,
Galway

Tel: 091-865200 Fax: 091-865203
Email: info@theg.ie
Web: www.theg.ie
GPS: N +53° 16' 55.25" W -9° 1' 55.75"

Awarded one of the top three hotels in the world for ambience and design in the 2009 Condé Nast Traveler Magazine's Gold List. The g hotel is situated overlooking Lough Atalia & Galway Bay. The exquisite creation of world renowned milliner, Philip Treacy, the hotel has been created for both the business & leisure traveller, where thoughtful service meets sophisticated style. Matz at the g offers a contemporary Irish menu with a European influence; inspired by the use of local, seasonal produce. Award-winning ESPA at the g, located on the upper two floors, is set amidst a Zen rooftop garden.

Bookable on www.irelandhotels.com
Special Offer: www.irelandhotels.com/offers

Room Rate from €150.00 to €420.00
Suites from €240.00 to €2,500.00

Damien O'Riordan

98

Activities:

Closed 23 - 27 December

B&B Rates are per Person Sharing per Night incl. Breakfast.
or Room Rates are per Room per Night - See also Page 8

Galway Bay Hotel, Conference & Leisure Centre

HOTEL ★★★★ MAP 6 F 10

The Promenade,
Salthill,
Galway

Tel: 091-520520 Fax: 091-520530
Email: info@galwaybayhotel.com
Web: www.galwaybayhotel.com
GPS: N +53° 15' 31.37" W -9° 5' 5.94"

Award-winning Galway Bay Hotel, has all the advantages of a city centre location while being situated overlooking the famous Galway Bay and Salthill's Blue Flag beach. Facilities include Gymnasium, Pool, Steam Room, Sauna, "Calmer Waters" Beauty Salon and seasonal Kids Club. The Lobster Pot Restaurant offers international cuisine with seafood specialities prepared by Ciaran Gantly and this team. Complimentary broadband access in all guest bedrooms and meeting rooms. Please enquire about Facilities for Persons with Disabilities.

An IHF Quality Employer

Bookable on www.irelandhotels.com

Special Offer: www.irelandhotels.com/offers

B&B from €65.00 to €210.00
Suites from €170.00 to €460.00

Dan Murphy
General Manager

153

Food for Kids

Open All Year

Glenlo Abbey Hotel

HOTEL ★★★★★ MAP 6 F 10

Bushypark,
Galway

Tel: 091-526666 Fax: 091-527800
Email: info@glenloabbey.ie
Web: www.glenlo.com
GPS: N +53° 18' 0.70" W -9° 5' 53.13"

Glenlo Abbey Hotel - an 18th century country estate, is located on a 138 acre lakeside golf course just 4km from Galway City. A Fáilte Ireland rated 5***** hotel, Glenlo Abbey is one of the most entertaining properties in the West of Ireland. All 46 rooms are de luxe standard. There is a choice for dining including the Pullman Restaurant aboard the Orient Express. Golf, fishing, lake boating all on site with a spa being developed in the near future. Galway City 5 mins drive. Choice of suites available - enquire with reservations. Please enquire about Facilities for Persons with Disabilities.

An IHF Quality Employer

Member of Ireland's Blue Book

Bookable on www.irelandhotels.com

Room Rate from €250.00 to €400.00
Suites from €550.00 to €980.00

John & Peggy Bourke
Proprietors

46

Food for Kids

Closed 23 - 27 December

Hotel Meyrick

HOTEL ★★★★ MAP 6 F 10

Eyre Square,
Galway

Tel: 091-564041 Fax: 091-566704
Email: reshm@monogramhotels.ie
Web: www.hotelmeyrick.ie
GPS: N +53° 16' 25.80" W -9° 2' 52.73"

Hotel Meyrick is a 4 star luxury hotel located right in the heart of Galway City overlooking Eyre Square. It is an exquisite combination of old world charm and modern luxuries. Its 99 guest bedrooms offer a range of Standard and Executive rooms, Junior and Executive suites. The hotel's Oyster Bar and Grill Restaurant has an extensive menu to suit all tastes. Relax, unwind and indulge in The Square Spa and Health Club on level 5 with an array of treatments to choose from. Please enquire about Facilities for Persons with Disabilities.

An IHF Quality Employer

Bookable on www.irelandhotels.com

Special Offer: www.irelandhotels.com/offers

Room Rate from €115.00 to €356.00
Suites from €215.00 to €650.00

Cian O'Broin
General Manager

99

Closed 24 - 27 December

B&B Rates are per Person Sharing per Night incl. Breakfast.
or Room Rates are per Room per Night.- See also Page 8

Galway City

House Hotel (The)

HOTEL ★★★★ MAP 6 F 10

Spanish Parade,
Galway

Tel: 091-538900 Fax: 091-568262
Email: info@thehousehotel.ie
Web: www.thehousehotel.ie
GPS: N +53° 16' 12.02" W -9° 3' 11.65"

Welcome to the House, a luxurious boutique hotel located in the heart of Galway City. The House Hotel represents the ideal "Home away from home" with its cosy atmosphere, chic style, excellent facilities and personalised service. Features of the guestrooms include flat screen TVs, with internet access, laptop safe and crisp white linen. The Parlour Bar and Grill specialises in modern international cuisine. Please enquire about Facilities for Persons with Disabilities.

An IHF Quality Employer

Bookable on www.irelandhotels.com

B&B from €49.50 to €120.00
Suites from €160.00 to €450.00

Niall Dalton
General Manager

40

Closed 24 - 27 December

Huntsman Inn

HOTEL ★★★ MAP 6 F 10

164 College Road,
Galway

Tel: 091-562849 Fax: 091-561985
Email: info@huntsmaninn.com
Web: www.huntsmaninn.com
GPS: N +53° 16' 52.77" W -9° 2' 2.06"

Situated one kilometre from Eyre Square, this stylish, comfortable boutique hotel offers excellent standards of accommodation and décor. All bedrooms are en suite with direct dial phone, internet access, flat screen TV, DVD player, safe and tea/coffee making facilities. Enjoy excellent food in our modern dining room or relax in our spacious lounge bars. Free car parking on site. Recommended in numerous guides including, Georgina Campbell, Bridgestone Guides and Lucinda O'Sullivan. Please enquire about Facilities for Persons with Disabilities.

Bookable on www.irelandhotels.com

B&B from €40.00 to €80.00
Suites from €129.00 to €159.00

Cathrina McManamon
Manager

12

Closed 24 - 28 December

Inishmore House

GUESTHOUSE ★★★ MAP 6 F 10

109 Fr. Griffin Road,
Lower Salthill,
Galway

Tel: 091-582639 Fax: 091-589311
Email: inishmorehouse@eircom.net
Web: www.irishgolf.de
GPS: N +53° 16' 1.61" W -9° 4' 1.03"

A charming family residence with secure carpark within 5 minutes walk of city and beach. All rooms contain direct dial phone, multi-channel TV and hairdryers. Tea/coffee and ironing facilities available. German spoken. An ideal base for touring the Aran Islands, Burren and Connemara. All day tours can be organised. Recommended by many leading travel guides. Specialise in Golf Holidays. WiFi available.

Bookable on www.irelandhotels.com

B&B from €35.00 to €70.00

Marie & Peter
Proprietors

8

Activities: ✓

Open All Year

B&B Rates are per Person Sharing per Night incl. Breakfast.
or Room Rates are per Room per Night - **See also Page 8**

Maldron Hotel Galway

HOTEL ★★★ MAP 6 F 10

Oranmore,
Galway

Tel: 091-792244 Fax: 091-792246
Email: info.galway@maldronhotels.com
Web: www.maldronhotels.com
GPS: N +53° 16' 40.27" W -8° 55' 38.63"

The Maldron Hotel Galway is superbly located just a 10 minute drive from Galway City centre. Comprising 113 guest rooms, Stir Restaurant and Q Bar with entertainment programme. Free Wi-Fi and broadband internet access. Club Vitae Health and Fitness Club with 20m pool, gym, spa pool, steam room, sauna and beauty salon. Free car parking, playroom and outdoor playground. Adjacent to the hotel is an Omniplex Cinema and City Limits Entertainment Centre. Please enquire about Facilities for Persons with Disabilities.

An IHF Quality Employer

Member of Maldron Hotels

Bookable on www.irelandhotels.com

Special Offer: www.irelandhotels.com/offers

B&B from €39.00 to €119.00

Dermot Comerford
General Manager

113

Food for Kids

Closed 24 - 26 December

Marian Lodge Guesthouse

GUESTHOUSE ★★★ MAP 6 F 10

Knocknacarra Road,
Salthill Upper,
Galway

Tel: 091-521678 Fax: 091-528103
Email: celine@iol.ie
Web: www.marian-lodge.com
GPS: N +53° 15' 33.34" W -9° 6' 9.21"

AA 4 Stars "A home from home". Family-run. Adjacent to promenade/beach in Salthill. Private parking. Daily tours arranged Connemara/Burren/Aran Islands. City bus route. Home baking. Bedrooms en suite, cable TV, DD phone, orthopaedic beds, hairdryers, tea/coffee facilities. Iron, trouser press available. Large family rooms. Children welcome. Close to nightly entertainment, Leisureland, Aquarium, tennis, windsurfing, fishing, horse-riding, Galway Bay, Ardilaun, Clybaun & Salthill hotels. Beside golf course, driving range, restaurant, pubs & shops. Internet. Also contactable on 087 6184128.

Member of Premier Guesthouses of Ireland

B&B from €38.00 to €55.00

Celine Molloy

6

Closed 23 - 28 December

Menlo Park Hotel

HOTEL ★★★★ MAP 6 F 10

Terryland,
Headford Road,
Galway

Tel: 091-761122 Fax: 091-761222
Email: reservations@menloparkhotel.com
Web: www.menloparkhotel.com
GPS: N +53° 17' 16.40" W -9° 2' 48.73"

The four star Menlo Park Hotel is located only half a mile from the city centre, offering 70 bedrooms including 14 superior rooms with extra luxury decor and kingsize beds. Food is served daily in MPS Bar & Oliver McGlynn Restaurant. We offer complimentary WiFi throughout, free parking, weekend entertainment and extensive conference and banqueting facilities. Awarded the Optimus Service Excellence Award 2009-2010. Please enquire about Facilities for Persons with Disabilities.

An IHF Quality Employer

Bookable on www.irelandhotels.com

Special Offer: www.irelandhotels.com/offers

B&B from €60.00 to €180.00

Elaine Brennan
General Manager

70

Closed 24 - 25 December

B&B Rates are per Person Sharing per Night incl. Breakfast.
or Room Rates are per Room per Night - **See also Page 8**

Galway City

Oranmore Lodge Hotel, Conference & Leisure Centre

HOTEL ★★★★ MAP 6 G 10

Oranmore,
Galway

Tel: 091-794400 Fax: 091-790227
Email: info@oranmorelodge.ie
Web: www.oranmorelodgehotel.ie
GPS: N +53° 16' 33.63" W -8° 55' 51.28"

This family owned manor house hotel is located in Galway City East, 10 minutes from the city centre, adjacent to picturesque Oranmore which overlooks Galway Bay, 4km to Galway Airport/Racecourse. Our rooms and suites are furnished to the highest standard. Ultra modern conference facilities and relaxing leisure centre. Your host and friendly staff look forward to welcoming you to sample our superb food and excellent service in the best traditions of Irish hospitality. Please enquire about Facilities for Persons with Disabilities.

An IHF Quality Employer

Bookable on www.irelandhotels.com
Special Offer: www.irelandhotels.com/offers

B&B from €45.00 to €150.00
Suites from €180.00 to €400.00

Brian J. O'Higgins
Managing Director

68

Closed 22 - 27 December

Radisson Blu Hotel & Spa Galway

HOTEL ★★★★ MAP 6 F 10

Lough Atalia Road,
Galway

Tel: 091-538300 Fax: 091-538380
Email: sales.galway@radissonblu.com
Web: www.radissonhotelgalway.com
GPS: N +53° 16' 26.10" W -9° 2' 36.81"

Located overlooking Lough Atalia, the Radisson Blu Hotel & Spa Galway is a few steps away from Eyre Square and the main bus and railway stations. Restaurant Marinas is famous for its seafood & guests can choose from a range of fresh local fare & international cuisine. The Atrium Bar & Veranda Lounge are perfect for relaxing. Live Lounge is Galway's Entertainment venue. Multi - award winning Spirit One Spa offers unique thermal suite & luxury pampering treatments. LEVEL 5, the luxurious executive floor offers secure members-only access, terraces, club lounge, and business centre.

An IHF Quality Employer

Member of Radisson Blu Hotels & Resorts

Bookable on www.irelandhotels.com

B&B from €75.00 to €200.00
Suites from €299.00 to €2,000.00

Stephen Hanley
General Manager

261

Food for Kids

Open All Year

Salthill Hotel

HOTEL ★★★ MAP 6 F 10

The Promenade,
Salthill,
Galway

Tel: 091-522711 Fax: 091-521855
Email: salthillhotel@eircom.net
Web: www.salthillhotel.com
GPS: N +53° 15' 31.38" W -9° 5' 14.56"

A Byrne Hotel, 50m from Salthill's sandy beach. All rooms en suite, direct dial phone, tea making facilities, hairdryer. Excellent cuisine and service. Live entertainment nightly with a choice of live bands or Trad on the Prom, which is a contemporary Irish show featuring an electrifying mix of music, song and dance. Overlooking Galway Bay with a large car park. Less than 2 miles from the mediaeval City of Galway. Our new Ocean Fitness & Leisure Centre will open autumn 2009.

Member of Byrne Hotel Group

Bookable on www.irelandhotels.com

B&B from €75.00 to €105.00
Suites from €200.00 to €350.00

Pauline Griffin
General Manager

160

Closed 23 - 27 December

B&B Rates are per Person Sharing per Night incl. Breakfast.
or Room Rates are per Room per Night - See also Page 8

Skeffington Arms Hotel

HOTEL ★★★ MAP 6 F 10

Eyre Square,
Galway

Tel: 091-563173 Fax: 091-561679
Email: reception@skeffington.ie
Web: www.skeffington.ie
GPS: N +53° 16' 26.64" W -9° 3' 0.52"

The Skeffington Arms Hotel is ideally located in an enviable position, overlooking Eyre Square, within distance of rail & bus terminals & just a short stroll from an array of shops, restaurants, bars & theatres. Now boasting 24 newly refurbished stylish, spacious & modern bedrooms, oozing comfort, style & personality. Elements such as crisp white sheets, colourful throws & minimalistic décor help to soothe and relax. The Hotel also boasts the famous Skeff Bar & Restaurant. Please enquire about Facilities for Persons with Disabilities.

Bookable on www.irelandhotels.com

B&B from €50.00 to €190.00

Lisa Moore
Front Office Manager

24

Closed 25 - 26 December

Twelve (The)

HOTEL ★★★★ MAP 6 F 10

Barna Coast Road,
Galway

Tel: 091-597000 Fax: 091-597003
Email: enquire@thetwelvehotel.ie
Web: www.thetwelvehotel.ie
GPS: N +53° 15' 5.04" W -9° 9' 9.76"

A stone's throw from Galway City, on the fringe of Connemara, traditional and the new Ireland come together as one. The award-winning Twelve combines a modern and fun design with a uniquely refreshing and personal experience. Dine in West, a world class restaurant, pamper yourself with selected in-room treatments and enjoy a 'trad' session in the bar. As the sun sets on Galway Bay, step into your stylish suite and think…"I have arrived".

Bookable on www.irelandhotels.com
Special Offer: www.irelandhotels.com/offers

B&B from €50.00 to €112.00
Suites from €130.00 to €650.00

Fergus O'Halloran
General Manager / Sommelier

48

Food for Kids *Activities:*

Open All Year

Victoria Hotel

HOTEL ★★★ MAP 6 F 10

Victoria Place,
Eyre Square,
Galway

Tel: 091-567433 Fax: 091-565880
Email: victoriahotel@eircom.net
Web: www.victoriahotelgalway.com
GPS: N +53° 16' 23.06" W -9° 2' 52.12"

The Victoria Hotel is centrally located just 100 yards off Eyre Square, within walking distance of all shops, theatres, pubs and cinemas. Each of the 57 spacious en suite rooms is beautifully appointed with direct dial phone, TV, tea/coffee making facilities and hairdryer. The hotel restaurant serving à la carte dinner, along with a lively bar serving lunches, will all add up to make your stay at the Victoria as enjoyable as possible. The Victoria is your enclave in the city, dedicated to pleasing you. Please enquire about Facilities for Persons with Disabilities.

An IHF Quality Employer

Member of Byrne Hotel Group

Bookable on www.irelandhotels.com
Special Offer: www.irelandhotels.com/offers

B&B from €35.00 to €150.00

Mary T.Cullinane
General Manager

57

Activities:

Closed 23 - 27 December

B&B Rates are per Person Sharing per Night incl. Breakfast.
or Room Rates are per Room per Night - **See also Page 8**

Galway City / Gort

Westwood Hotel (The)

HOTEL ★★★★ MAP 6 F 10

Dangan,
Upper Newcastle,
Galway City
Tel: 091-521442 Fax: 091-521400
Email: resmanager@westwoodhousehotel.com
Web: www.westwoodhousehotel.com
GPS: N +53° 17' 21.22" W -9° 4' 30.44"

The Westwood stands amidst a rural landscape of greenery and combines a mellow taste of the countryside with the city's cutting edge. The hotel has recently completed a major refurbishment of all 58 guest bedrooms, hotel foyer, Meridian Restaurant, and banqueting suites. The hotel is air-conditioned throughout and offers complimentary internet access in all areas, and free private parking. Winner of CIE National Award of Excellence 2003/4. Locall 1850 366 000. Please enquire about Facilities for Persons with Disabilities.

An IHF Quality Employer

Bookable on www.irelandhotels.com

B&B from €49.50 to €169.50
Suites from €139.00 to €339.00

David Kelly
General Manager

58

Food for Kids Activities:

Closed 24 - 26 December

Lady Gregory Hotel, Conference & Leisure Club

HOTEL ★★★ MAP 6 G 9

Ennis Road,
Gort,
Co. Galway
Tel: 091-632333 Fax: 091-632332
Email: info@ladygregoryhotel.ie
Web: www.ladygregoryhotel.ie
GPS: N +53° 3' 40.38" W -8° 48' 53.74"

Situated in the West of Ireland, near Coole Park, in the town of Gort, with its many local and historical attractions. A warm friendly welcome awaits you as you enter the architectural splendor of the Lady Gregory Hotel. 87 beautifully appointed rooms, Copper Beech Restaurant, lively Jack B. Yeats Bistro Bar and magnificent Gregory Suite for banqueting and conferencing, with broadband WiFi. Leisure Club incorporates an 18m swimming pool, children's pool, Technogym gymnasium, herb sauna, crystal steam, Jacuzzi, and a unique salt grotto with health showers - thus offering a hydro and thermal relaxing experience.

Bookable on www.irelandhotels.com
Special Offer: www.irelandhotels.com/offers

B&B from €55.00 to €85.00

Brian Morrissey
Operations Manager

87

Activities:

Closed 24 - 27 December

Sullivan's Royal Hotel

HOTEL ★★ MAP 6 G 9

The Square,
Gort,
Co. Galway
Tel: 091-631257
Email: sullivansroyalhotel@eircom.net
GPS: N +53° 4' 2.84" W -8° 49' 10.65"

Sullivan's Hotel is family-run hotel with 12 newly refurbished bedrooms, between Galway City (25 mins) and Shannon Airport (30 mins). Dining Pub of the Year winner 2000 - 2008 for service, quality and value. Additional phone number: 091-631401. Additional email sullivanshotel@eircom.net

B&B from €38.00 to €55.00

Johnny & Annie Sullivan
Proprietors

12

Open All Year

B&B Rates are per Person Sharing per Night incl. Breakfast.
or Room Rates are per Room per Night - See also Page 8

Headford / Inishbofin Island

Anglers Rest Hotel

HOTEL ★★ MAP 10 F 12

Headford,
Co. Galway

Tel: 093-35528 Fax: 093-35749
Email: anglersresthotel@eircom.net

GPS: N +53° 28' 10.13" W -9° 6' 24.08"

The Anglers Rest Hotel has been owned and managed by the Heneghan family since 1905. Just 3 miles from the eastern shore of Lough Corrib and 16 miles from Galway City. It is an ideal centre for the tourist or angler. With 16 bedrooms, dining room, 2 bars, open lounge, residents lounge and a function room with dining facilities. Meeting and conference facilities for over 100 people are also available on request. Please enquire about Facilities for Persons with Disabilities.

B&B from €45.00 to €65.00

Frank Heneghan
Manager

16

Closed 23 - 27 December

Doonmore Hotel

HOTEL ★★ MAP 9 C 12

Inishbofin Island,
Co. Galway

Tel: 095-45814 Fax: 095-45804
Email: info@doonmorehotel.com
Web: www.doonmorehotel.com

GPS: N +53° 36' 50.48" W -10° 13' 41.56"

Uniquely situated on a beautiful and historic island, commanding magnificent views of the surrounding sea and islands. Inishbofin, a haven for artists, fishermen, bird watchers, nature lovers or those who just wish to escape from the hectic pace of life. Fine sandy beaches. Sea trips and boat angling can be arranged. Facilities for divers. Excellent shore fishing. Doonmore Hotel is owned and managed by the Murray family, unpretentious but friendly and comfortable. Please enquire about Facilities for Persons with Disabilities.

B&B from €48.00 to €65.00

Aileen Murray
Manager

19

Activities:

Closed 30 September - 30 March

Inishbofin House Hotel

HOTEL ★★★ MAP 9 C 12

Inishbofin Island,
Connemara,
Co. Galway

Tel: 095-45809 Fax: 095-45803
Email: info@inishbofinhouse.com
Web: www.dayshotel.ie

GPS: N +53° 36' 49.38" W -10° 12' 21.96"

Inishbofin lies 6 miles off the Galway coast and is one of Ireland's most thriving and beautiful islands. A 30 minute ferry journey from the north Connemara village of Cleggan. Inishbofin is a physical gem and a favourite haven among botanists, geologists and environmentalists due to its huge diversity of natural life. Inishbofin House is a de luxe hotel with a marine spa which commands exquisite views of the beautiful harbour. Built on the site of the old Day's Hotel, this family owned hotel offers a warm welcome, friendly and efficient service and excellent food, particularly seafood!

B&B from €50.00 to €90.00

Reception

34

Activities:

Closed 30 November - 01 March

B&B Rates are per Person Sharing per Night incl. Breakfast.
or Room Rates are per Room per Night - **See also Page 8**

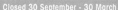

Kylemore / Leenane

Kylemore Pass Hotel

HOTEL ★★ MAP 9 D 12

Kylemore,
Connemara,
Co. Galway

Tel: 095-41141 Fax: 095-41377
Email: passinn@indigo.ie
Web: www.kylemore-pass-hotel-connemara.com
GPS: N +53° 33' 50.65" W -9° 50' 1.76"

Beautifully situated, in the foot hills of the "Twelve Bens", overlooking some of Connemara's most spectacular scenery. There is something that will appeal to everyone in this "wild & wonderful" part of Ireland. Ideal for touring, walking, fishing etc, or "just a quiet relaxing break". Splendidly remote, with clean mountain air, and our own mountain spring water. The benign waters of Kylemore Lake lap peacefully below your bedroom window. Our restaurant has one of the most stunning views, also Sailors-Bar beer garden, both offer appetising home cooked meals.

Member of Countrywide Hotels

Bookable on www.irelandhotels.com

Special Offer: www.irelandhotels.com/offers

B&B from €39.00 to €59.00

Stuart & Rose Rima
Hosts

11

Open All Year

Delphi Mountain Resort

HOTEL ★★★★ MAP 9 D 12

Leenane,
Co. Galway

Tel: 095-42208 Fax: 095-42223
Email: info@delphiescape.com
Web: www.delphimountainresort.com
GPS: N +53° 37' 21.62" W -9° 45' 16.59"

Delphi Mountain Resort is a four star resort with spa and adventure centre. Surrounded by some of the most breaktaking scenery in Ireland, it truly is a unique destination. With no TVs or phone reception, it is a complete escape to a more natural, peaceful haven. Whether you want to rest and relax in the spa or challenge yourself with outdoor activities, there is something for everyone here.

B&B from €69.00 to €99.00
Suites from €299.00 to €299.00

Jackie Lydon
Reservations Manager

36

Activities:

Open All Year

Leenane Hotel

HOTEL ★★★ MAP 9 D 12

Leenane,
Connemara,
Co. Galway

Tel: 095-42249 Fax: 095-42376
Email: info@leenanehotel.com
Web: www.leenanehotel.com
GPS: N +53° 35' 40.35" W -9° 42' 17.79"

On the shores of Killary Harbour, Ireland's only Fjord, lies Ireland's oldest Coaching Inn. The Leenane Hotel, recently refurbished to the highest of standards, boasts the most spectacular views in Ireland. Being a family-run hotel, we understand the appreciation for traditional home-cooking. Fresh seafood from the harbour and vegetables and herbs from the hotel garden are brought in every day. The hotel's position makes it without doubt the best base for exploring Connemara, the most romantic and unspoiled region of Ireland. Please enquire about Facilities for Persons with Disabilities.

Bookable on www.irelandhotels.com

Special Offer: www.irelandhotels.com/offers

B&B from €39.00 to €65.00

Conor Foyle
Manager

29

Closed 22 November - 14 March

B&B Rates are per Person Sharing per Night incl. Breakfast.
or Room Rates are per Room per Night - See also Page 8

Portfinn Lodge & Fjord Restaurant

GUESTHOUSE ★★ MAP 9 D 12

Clifden Road,
Leenane,
Co. Galway
Tel: 095-42265 Fax: 095-42315
Email: info@portfinn.com
Web: www.portfinn.com
GPS: N +53° 35' 43.56" W -9° 41' 50.29"

Portfinn, run by the Daly family since 1977, is located overlooking the picturesque village of Leenane and Killary Harbor in Co. Galway. We offer 8 comfortable rooms all en suite with either a sea or mountain views. Portfinn has a renowned seafood restaurant serving only locally caught and sourced fish, meat and poultry. Activities such as scuba diving, fishing, hiking, golf and much more is available at our door step. We look forward to hosting you in the future. Fáilte Ireland approved.

B&B from €35.00 to €45.00

Óran Daly

8

Closed 20 December - 01 March

Rosleague Manor Hotel

HOTEL ★★★★ MAP 9 C 12

Letterfrack,
Connemara,
Co. Galway
Tel: 095-41101 Fax: 095-41168
Email: info@rosleague.com
Web: www.rosleague.com
GPS: N +53° 32' 55.56" W -9° 58' 27.59"

Rosleague is a Regency manor now run as a first class country house hotel by Mark Foyle & Eddie Foyle. It lies 7 miles north west of Clifden on the coast overlooking a sheltered bay & surrounded by the Connemara Mountains, beside the National Park. It is renowned for its superb cuisine personally supervised by the owners & amenities expected by today's discerning guest. Cesar Award for Hotel of the Year Ireland 2010 - Good Hotel Guide. Recommended in Bridgestone 100 Best Places to Stay, Georgina Campbell's Best of the Best, Karen Brown, Alastair Sawday's Special Places & Guide Michelin.

Member of I.C.H.R.A. (Ireland's Blue Book)

B&B from €75.00 to €115.00
Suites from €190.00 to €250.00

Eddie Foyle / Mark Foyle
Owner / Manager

20

Closed 15 November - 15 March

Lough Rea Hotel & Spa

HOTEL MAP 6 H 10

Galway Road,
Loughrea,
Co. Galway
Tel: 091-880088 Fax: 091-880080
Email: sales@loughreahotelandspa.com
Web: www.loughreahotelandspa.com
GPS: N +53° 12' 17.17'' W -8° 35' 52.80''

Built to a 4**** specification. Lough Rea Hotel & Spa situated on the main Galway road in the heart of Loughrea. The beautiful Lough Rea Hotel & Spa boasts 91 luxury rooms, conference centre, dedicated meeting rooms, free broadband throughout. Shore Island Spa with 10 treatment rooms dedicated to relaxation. Playtown for families and fun. Complimentary secure car parking. For reservations log on to www.loughreahotelandspa.com.

B&B from €79.00 to €150.00

Barry Kilroy
Operations Manager

91

Activities:

Closed 24 - 27 December

B&B Rates are per Person Sharing per Night incl. Breakfast.
or Room Rates are per Room per Night - **See also Page 8**

Loughrea / Oughterard

Meadow Court Hotel

HOTEL ★★★ MAP 6 H 10

Clostoken,
Loughrea,
Co. Galway
Tel: 091-841051 Fax: 091-842406
Email: meadowcourthotel@eircom.net
Web: www.meadowcourthotel.com
GPS: N +53° 12' 37.00" W -8° 38' 10.37"

Charming boutique hotel tucked in to the tranquil West of Ireland countryside. This family-run hotel prides itself in offering first class service. At its award-winning restaurant, experience culinary delights in the midst of cosy open fires, elegant oak panelled surroundings, beautiful paintings, antique furniture & imagine this setting enhanced by the sound of classical music & gentle illuminating candle light. We offer freshly prepared home cooked food & free car parking. All luxurious bedrooms are individually designed & decorated with your comfort & relaxation in mind. Please enquire about Facilities for Persons with Disabilities.

B&B from €45.00 to €80.00
Suites from €160.00 to €160.00

Tommy & Margaret Corbett
Proprietors

21

Activities:

Closed 24 - 26 December

Corrib Wave Guest House

GUESTHOUSE ★★★ MAP 5 E 11

Portacarron,
Oughterard, Connemara,
Co. Galway
Tel: 091-552147 Fax: 091-552736
Email: cwh@gofree.indigo.ie
Web: www.corribwave.com
GPS: N +53° 25' 55.95" W -9° 17' 19.56"

Panoramic lakeside guesthouse - the home of Michael & Maria Healy. As our guests, you are assured of a warm welcome to a family home with every comfort and Irish hospitality, superb home-cooking, excellent wines, beautiful en suite bedrooms (all with double and single beds), TVs, hairdryers, spectacular views, turf fire, peace and tranquility. Angling specialists, boats, engines, for hire. Lakeside walks. 18 hole golf 1km. Recommended by Le Guide Routard & Georgina Campbell Best Places to Stay. For more info contact us direct. Please enquire about Facilities for Persons with Disabilities.

B&B from €33.00 to €40.00

Maria & Michael Healy
Proprietors

10

Activities:

Closed 01 December - 15 January

Mountain View Guest House

GUESTHOUSE ★★★ MAP 5 E 11

Aughnanure,
Oughterard,
Co. Galway
Tel: 091-550306 Fax: 091-550133
Email: tricia.oconnor@eircom.net
Web: www.mountainviewgalway.com
GPS: N +53° 24' 43.49" W -9° 16' 39.77"

Situated just off the N59, 24kms from Galway City and within 2.4 km of Oughterard, with the Connemara mountains in the distance and Lough Corrib nearby. Leisure activities include golf at the renowned Oughterard Golf Club, established walks along scenic routes, a stroll around Brigit's Gardens, a visit to the picturesque Aughnanure Castle, a tour of Glengowla Silver and Lead Mines, boating or fishing on Lough Corrib. All bedrooms en suite, with TV, direct dial phones, tea/coffee making facilities and hairdryers. Free WiFi available. Please enquire about Facilities for Persons with Disabilities.

Bookable on www.irelandhotels.com
Special Offer: www.irelandhotels.com/offers

B&B from €32.00 to €40.00

Richard & Patricia O'Connor
Proprietors

10

Closed 22 - 28 December

B&B Rates are per Person Sharing per Night incl. Breakfast.
or Room Rates are per Room per Night - **See also Page 8**

Ross Lake House Hotel

HOTEL ★★★★ MAP 5 E 11

Rosscahill,
Oughterard,
Co. Galway
Tel: 091-550109 Fax: 091-550184
Email: rosslake@iol.ie
Web: www.rosslakehotel.com
GPS: N +53° 23' 31.73" W -9° 16' 50.75"

Ross Lake House is a wonderful Georgian house set in the magnificent wilderness of Connemara. Six acres of mature gardens surround the house creating an air of peace and tranquillity. Hosts Henry and Elaine Reid have beautifully restored this manor house to its former glory. A high quality Irish menu is prepared daily featuring a tempting variety of fresh produce from nearby Connemara hills, streams and lakes as well as fish straight from the Atlantic.

Member of Private Ireland

Bookable on www.irelandhotels.com

Special Offer: www.irelandhotels.com/offers

B&B from €75.00 to €100.00
Suites from €225.00 to €300.00

Elaine & Henry Reid
Proprietors

13

Closed 01 November - 16 March

Shannon Oaks Hotel & Country Club

HOTEL ★★★ MAP 6 I 9

Portumna,
Co. Galway
Tel: 090-974 1777 Fax: 090-974 1357
Email: sales@shannonoaks.ie
Web: www.shannonoaks.ie
GPS: N +53° 5' 24.77" W -8° 13' 25.78"

An idyllic setting close by the serene shores of the river Shannon's Lough Derg and adjoining the magnificent Portumna Forest Park. Enjoy a choice of three luxurious accommodation types: comfortable bedrooms, lodges and de luxe two bedroom suites. Award-winning Leisure Centre featuring gym, pool, jacuzzi and treatment rooms. Dining facilities comprise The Castle Gates Restaurant, Upper Deck Bistro and the Idle Hour Bar. Please enquire about Facilities for Persons with Disabilities.

An IHF Quality Employer

Bookable on www.irelandhotels.com

Special Offer: www.irelandhotels.com/offers

B&B from €35.00 to €90.00

Karl Reinhardt
General Manager

63

Activities:

Open All Year

Renvyle House Hotel

HOTEL ★★★ MAP 9 C 12

Renvyle,
Connemara,
Co. Galway
Tel: 095-43511 Fax: 095-43515
Email: info@renvyle.com
Web: www.renvyle.com
GPS: N +53° 36' 32.41" W -10° 0' 6.04"

Historic coastal hotel set amid the magical beauty of sea, lake and mountains, the keynotes are warmth and comfort with award-winning fine fare. Turf fires and cosy lounges make you relax and feel at home. Golf, tennis, swimming pool (seasonal - outdoor, heated), snooker, boating, fishing are the facilities to name but a few. Wonderful walking and cycling routes throughout an area that hosts a vast National Park. Additional facilities include claypigeon shooting, canoeing, beauty treatment centre. Now with 6 seater Canadian hot tub & infra-red sauna. Please enquire about Facilities for Persons with Disabilities.

Bookable on www.irelandhotels.com

Special Offer: www.irelandhotels.com/offers

B&B from €30.00 to €125.00
Suites from €80.00 to €300.00

Zoe Fitzgerald
Sales & Marketing Manager

70

Closed 29 Nov- 23 Dec & 08 Jan-11 Feb

B&B Rates are per Person Sharing per Night incl. Breakfast.
or Room Rates are per Room per Night - **See also Page 8**

Roundstone / Spiddal

Roundstone House Hotel

HOTEL ★★ MAP 9 C 11

Roundstone,
Connemara,
Co. Galway

Tel: 095-35864 Fax: 095-35944
Email: vaughanshotel@eircom.net
Web: www.irishcountryhotels.com
GPS: N +53° 23' 42.46" W -9° 55' 8.82"

Roundstone House Hotel is a family hotel situated in the picturesque village of Roundstone. Roundstone is a fascinating place for a holiday offering a wide range of interests for the holidaymakers. Many outdoor activities are available locally including sea angling, watersports, hill walking, pony trekking and a championship 18 hole golf course nearby. Come to beautiful Roundstone for a holiday to remember. Please enquire about Facilities for Persons with Disabilities.

Member of Irish Country Hotels

Bookable on www.irelandhotels.com

B&B from €55.00 to €65.00

Maureen Vaughan
Proprietor

12

Closed 31 October - 01 April

An Crúiscín Lán Hotel

HOTEL ★★ MAP 5 E 10

Spiddal,
Co. Galway

Tel: 091-553148 Fax: 091-553712
Email: ancruiscinlanhotel@gmail.com
GPS: N +53° 14' 38.34" W -9° 18' 23.52"

An Crúiscín Lán Hotel is located in the heart of the Irish speaking Spiddal Village perfectly suited for touring the Gaeltacht, Connemara and the Islands. The hotel comprises a snug bar showing your favourite sports events, a lounge bar for meeting friends and making new ones and a dining conservatory with views of the Burren, Galway Bay and the Islands. We serve food all day long and are well known for quality.

B&B from €50.00 to €80.00

David Concannon

14

Closed 25 December

Park Lodge Hotel

HOTEL ★★★ MAP 5 E 10

Park,
Spiddal,
Co. Galway

Tel: 091-553159 Fax: 091-553494
Email: parklodgehotel@eircom.net
Web: www.parklodgehotel.com
GPS: N +53° 14' 49.35" W -9° 15' 52.31"

The Park Lodge Hotel is owned and run by the Foyle Family. It is situated on the coast road from Galway to Connemara, 16km west of Galway City and just east of Spiddal Village. Most of the 23 bedrooms have a view of Galway Bay. There are also seven detached cottages on the grounds, each self-catering and fully equipped for 5 persons. Cottages open all year. Please enquire about Facilities for Persons with Disabilities.

B&B from €50.00 to €60.00

Jane Marie Foyle
Manager

23

Activities:

Closed 01 October - 31 May

B&B Rates are per Person Sharing per Night incl. Breakfast.
or Room Rates are per Room per Night - **See also Page 8**

Corralea Court

HOTEL ★★★ MAP 10 G 12

The Square,
Tuam,
Galway

Tel: 093-24188 Fax: 093-52794
Email: info@corraleacourthotel.com
Web: www.corraleacourthotel.com
GPS: N +53° 30' 52.38" W -8° 51' 3.62"

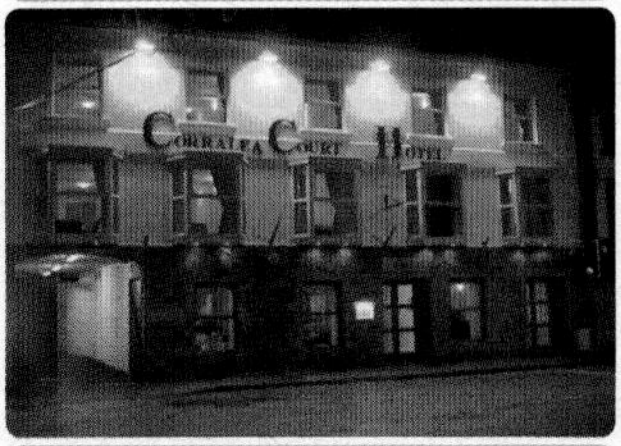

Located in the heart of Tuam, this modern 3 star hotel is only a short drive from Galway & Knock making it the perfect meeting place for both business and pleasure. Krugers Bar - weekend entertainment, Food served daily 7.30am - 9.30pm, Sunday Carvery 12 - 4.00pm. Corrals Restaurant serving the finest and freshest local products. Mitre and O'Connor Suite - Catering for all your banqueting needs. Please enquire about Facilities for Persons with Disabilities.

Bookable on www.irelandhotels.com

B&B from €45.00 to €90.00

Gerry Synott
General Manager

24

Closed 24 - 25 December

Commercial & Tourist Hotel

HOTEL ★★ MAP 11 J 15

Ballinamore,
Co. Leitrim

Tel: 071-964 4675 Fax: 071-964 4679
Email: commercialhotel@gmail.com
Web: www.hotelcommercial.com
GPS: N +54° 3' 10.45" W -7° 48' 1.67"

Ideally situated in the centre of the greenest & most uncluttered part of Ireland in the heart of lovely Leitrim. Completely re-built to 3* de luxe standard. Large comfortable rooms with queen size beds all en suite. Private car parking & elevator along with excellent cuisine & personal service. Local amenities include river cruising on the Shannon - Erne Waterway, scenic drives, hill walking & golfing. Fishing in the area is an absolute must. Special rates for golfers & commercial travellers. The Commericial Hotel is your ideal base for breathtaking tours or business. Dublin/Belfast 2 hrs, Shannon 3 hrs. Complimentary WiFi.

Bookable on www.irelandhotels.com

B&B from €55.00 to €65.00

Karen Walsh
Director

28

Closed 25 December

Aisleigh Guest House

GUESTHOUSE ★★★ MAP 10 I 14

Dublin Road,
Carrick-on-Shannon,
Co. Leitrim

Tel: 071-962 0313 Fax: 071-962 0675
Email: aisleigh@eircom.net
Web: www.aisleighguesthouse.com
GPS: N +53° 56' 33.14" W -8° 4' 11.55"

A warm welcome awaits you at our family-run guesthouse situated 1km from the picturesque town of Carrick-on-Shannon, Ireland's best kept secret. Facilities include en suite bedrooms with TV, direct dial telephones. Internet access, games room and sauna. Local genealogy a speciality. Private car parking. Ideal attractions-Aura Leisure Centre, Docks Theatre & Gallery. Arigna Mining Museum, Strokestown House and Lough Key Forest Park, golfing, cruising, fishing (tackle & bait supplies) horse riding, walking, cycling, etc.

Bookable on www.irelandhotels.com
Special Offer: www.irelandhotels.com/offers

B&B from €35.00 to €50.00

Sean & Charlotte Fearon
Owners

10

Open All Year

B&B Rates are per Person Sharing per Night incl. Breakfast.
or Room Rates are per Room per Night - **See also Page 8**

Carrick-on-Shannon

Bush Hotel

HOTEL ★★★ MAP 10 | 14

Carrick-on-Shannon,
Co. Leitrim

Tel: 071-967 1000 Fax: 071-962 1180
Email: info@bushhotel.com
Web: www.bushhotel.com
GPS: N +53° 56' 45.94" W -8° 5' 38.40"

Welcome to the Bush Hotel - one of Ireland's oldest, steeped in history, tradition, charm and character and many memorabilia from the past; sympathetically restored as a boutique hotel with open fires, theme lounges, carvery/coffee shop, bistro bar, 50 luxurious rooms. Town centre location with mature gardens, secure parking, banqueting and conference facilities. Free WiFi throughout. The Bush is Ireland's first Ecolabel Hotel recognising exceptional environmental care and awareness. Please enquire about Facilities for Persons with Disabilities.

An IHF Quality Employer

Member of Irish Country Hotels

Bookable on www.irelandhotels.com

Special Offer: www.irelandhotels.com/offers

B&B from €69.50 to €89.50
Suites from €175.00 to €199.00

Joseph Dolan
Managing Director

50

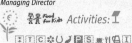

Food for Kids Activities:

Closed 24 - 31 December

Ciúin House

GUESTHOUSE ★★★★ MAP 10 | 4

Hartley,
Carrick-on-Shannon,
Co. Leitrim

Tel: 071-967 1488 Fax: 071-967 1487
Email: info@ciuinhouse.com
Web: www.ciuinhouse.com
GPS: N +53° 57' 15.02" W -8° 5' 22.67"

The essence of style, luxury, comfort, relaxation, tranquility & calm. Close to the town centre & an abundance of amenities & visitor attractions. Bedrooms are all en suite with orthopaedic mattresses, bath/power shower, tea/coffee, hairdryer & TV. Superior rooms have queen-size beds, jacuzzi bath, dressing gown, slippers, herbal bath products, safe & trouser press. Licensed premises serving homecooking. Guest lounge, plasma TV, free WiFi. CCTV monitored premises/carpark. Non-Smoking. Local attractions, Leisure Centre, Theatre, Leitrim Design House, Arigna Mining Museum, Lough Key Forest Park.

An IHF Quality Employer

Bookable on www.irelandhotels.com

Special Offer: www.irelandhotels.com/offers

B&B from €47.50 to €55.00
Suites from €119.00 to €130.00

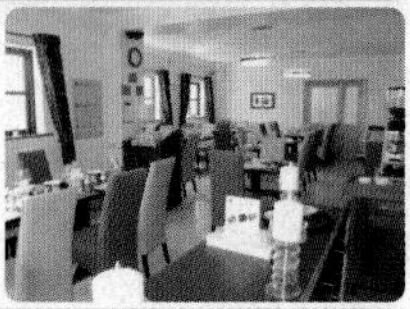

Fiona & Barry Reynolds

15

Open All Year

Landmark Hotel

HOTEL ★★★★ MAP 10 | 14

Carrick-on-Shannon,
Co. Leitrim

Tel: 071-962 2222 Fax: 071-962 2233
Email: reservations@thelandmarkhotel.com
Web: www.thelandmarkhotel.com
GPS: N +53° 56' 36.73" W -8° 5' 34.33"

Located in the heart of the beautiful riverside town of Carrick-on-Shannon, the landmark hotel is ideally located just 1 hour 40 minutes away from Dublin, 2 hours from Galway, 30 minutes from Sligo. Offering breathtaking views of the River Shannon, warm hospitality and a choice of fabulous restaurants and bars, the Landmark is an ideal retreat whether you are on business, attending a wedding or taking a short leisure break. Please enquire about Facilities for Persons with Disabilities.

B&B from €49.00 to €85.00
Suites from €138.00 to €210.00

Ciaran Kelly
Manager

60

Closed 25 December

B&B Rates are per Person Sharing per Night incl. Breakfast.
or Room Rates are per Room per Night - **See also Page 8**

Ramada Hotel & Suites at Lough Allen

HOTEL ★★★★ MAP 10 I 15

Drumshanbo,
Co. Leitrim

Tel: 071-964 0100 Fax: 071-964 0101
Email: info@loughallenhotel.com
Web: www.loughallenhotel.com
GPS: N +54° 3' 14.34" W -8° 2' 46.79"

Close to the picturesque town of Drumshanbo, located on the shores of Lough Allen. Many rooms with balconies, decking area with stunning view of the lake. The best base for touring the surrounding countryside. Yeat's Country, verdant County Fermanagh, rocky coastline of Co. Mayo, the many lakes of County Leitrim. In a word IDYLLIC! Please enquire about Facilities for Persons with Disabilities.

Bookable on www.irelandhotels.com

Special Offer: www.irelandhotels.com/offers

B&B from €39.50 to €90.00
Suites from €190.00 to €225.00

Erik Speekenbrink
Resort General Manager

64

Food for Kids Activities:

Closed 25 - 27 December

Adare Manor Hotel & Golf Resort

HOTEL ★★★★★ MAP 6 G 7

Adare,
Co. Limerick

Tel: 061-396566 Fax: 061-396124
Email: reservations@adaremanor.com
Web: www.adaremanor.com
GPS: N +52° 33' 50.05" W -8° 46' 40.16"

Located 20 miles from Shannon Airport. Adare Manor Hotel & Golf Resort provides a historical backdrop for a romantic getaway, a golfing break or a group event. Unique and individual accommodation, the best of contemporary Irish food in an incomparable setting are hallmarks of the manor experience. Play golf on the Robert Trent Jones Sr. designed golf course. Other pursuits include fishing on the River Maigue which flows through the estate, archery, laser clay target shooting & falconry. Facilities include an indoor heated swimming pool, fitness room and Elemis treatment rooms.

An IHF Quality Employer

Bookable on www.irelandhotels.com

Special Offer: www.irelandhotels.com/offers

B&B from €145.00 to €247.00
Suites from €350.00 to €420.00

Anita Higgins
General Manager

62

Closed 24 - 27 December

Adare / Castleconnell

Dunraven Arms Hotel

HOTEL ★★★★ MAP 6 G 7

Adare,
Co. Limerick

Tel: 061-605900 Fax: 061-396541
Email: reservations@dunravenhotel.com
Web: www.dunravenhotel.com
GPS: N +52° 33' 54.68" W -8° 47' 13.74"

Established in 1792, a 4**** old world hotel surrounded by ornate thatched cottages, in Ireland's prettiest village. Each bedroom, including 24 junior suites and interconnecting rooms, is beautifully appointed with antique furniture, dressing room and bathroom en suite. Award-winning restaurant, AA Two Red Rosettes. Leisure centre comprised of a 17m pool, steam room, gymnasium and massage and beauty therapy rooms. Equestrian and golf holidays a speciality. 30 minutes from Shannon Airport. Hotel of the Year 2004 - Georgina Campbell Jameson Guide. Complimentary WiFi access throughout the hotel.

An IHF Quality Employer

Member of Small Luxury Hotels of the World

Bookable on www.irelandhotels.com
Special Offer: www.irelandhotels.com/offers

Room Rate from €135.00 to €200.00
Suites from €225.00 to €325.00

Hugh Murphy
Manager

86

Activities:

Open All Year

Fitzgeralds Woodlands House Hotel & Spa

HOTEL ★★★ MAP 6 G 7

Knockanes,
Adare,
Co. Limerick

Tel: 061-605100 Fax: 061-396073
Email: reservations@woodlands-hotel.ie
Web: www.woodlands-hotel.ie
GPS: N +52° 33' 46.90" W -8° 45' 57.32"

Sink into a duck down pillow topped mattress and experience a sleep like never before. Choose from fine dining in our Brennan Room Restaurant or traditional Irish fayre in Timmy Mac's Bistro, then spend the evening in our lively Piano Bar. With Leisure Club including 20M pool, our extensive revas spa, and Woodies Kids Club, the Fitzgerald family look forward to welcoming you to the Woodlands House Hotel & Spa in beautiful Adare. Please enquire about Facilities for Persons with Disabilities.

An IHF Quality Employer

Member of Irish Country Hotels

Bookable on www.irelandhotels.com
Special Offer: www.irelandhotels.com/offers

B&B from €25.00 to €87.50

Mary & David Fitzgerald
Hosts

94

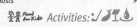

Food for Kids *Activities:*

Closed 24 - 25 December

Castle Oaks House Hotel & Country Club

HOTEL ★★★ MAP 6 H 7

Castleconnell,
Co. Limerick

Tel: 061-377666 Fax: 061-377717
Email: info@castleoaks.ie
Web: www.castleoaks.ie
GPS: N +52° 42' 34.28" W -8° 30' 30.60"

Castle Oaks House Hotel and Holiday Village set on 26 acres of landscaped gardens in a tranquil setting only 10 minutes from city centre. Guest accommodation comprises of 62 bedrooms and 19 4star holiday homes. Award winning restaurant. Guests can avail of leisure centre, day spa, tennis courts, playground, fishing, riverside walks and lakeside activities. Equestrian and golf holidays a speciality. Conferencing facilities for up to 250 delegates. 30 minutes from Shannon airport.

Member of Select Hotels

Bookable on www.irelandhotels.com
Special Offer: www.irelandhotels.com/offers

Room Rate from €79.00 to €160.00
Suites from €120.00 to €300.00

Gobnait O'Connell
Managing Director

62

Closed 23 - 26 December

B&B Rates are per Person Sharing per Night incl. Breakfast.
or Room Rates are per Room per Night - See also Page 8

Deebert House Hotel

HOTEL ★★★ MAP 6 H 6

Deebert,
Kilmallock,
Co. Limerick
Tel: 063-31200 Fax: 063-31212
Email: info@deeberthousehotel.com
Web: www.deeberthousehotel.com
GPS: N +52° 24' 2.96" W -8° 34' 14.33"

Nestled at the foothills of the Ballyhoura mountains in the historic town of Kilmallock, the charm of Deebert House Hotel awaits you. Originally a flour mill dating back to 1807, the new building has many unique and individual features which have been maintained in the current design. The hotel offers 20 elegant bedrooms Restaurant and bar, meeting room and banqueting facilities for 100 delegates. Experience the true taste of Ballyhoura country where walking and mountain biking holidays are our specialty.

Bookable on www.irelandhotels.com
Special Offer: www.irelandhotels.com/offers

B&B from €50.00 to €75.00

Margaret Atalla
Manager

20

Activities:

Closed 24 - 28 December

Absolute Hotel & Spa

HOTEL ★★★★ MAP 6 H 7

Sir Harry's Mall,
Limerick
Tel: 061-463600 Fax: 061-463601
Email: info@absolutehotel.com
Web: www.absolutehotel.com
GPS: N +52° 40' 2.27" W -8° 37' 11.07"

The Absolute Hotel & Spa is located in the heart of Limerick city. Features of our guestrooms include complimentary broadband internet access, rain-dance showers, plasma screen TVs, air-conditioning, hairdryer, tea and coffee making facilities. Relax and enjoy great food in either our Riverbank restaurant or bar. Our breathtaking Escape Spa has the perfect treatment to help you relax. Please enquire about Facilities for Persons with Disabilities.

Bookable on www.irelandhotels.com
Special Offer: www.irelandhotels.com/offers

B&B from €44.50 to €119.50
Suites from €189.00 to €299.00

Donnacha Hurley
General Manager

99

Activities:

Open All Year

Best Western Pery's Hotel

HOTEL ★★★ MAP 6 H 7

Glentworth Street,
Limerick
Tel: 061-413822 Fax: 061-413073
Email: info@perys.ie
Web: www.perys.ie
GPS: N +52° 39' 37.95" W -8° 37' 40.52"

Located in the heart of Georgian Limerick, Pery's has achieved the Ireland's Best Award for Service Excellence 3 years running and prides itself in creating exceptional service surrounded by a friendly and welcoming atmosphere. Bus and rail station, shopping, theatres, museums, restaurants, nightlife all within minutes. Gym, sauna, car park and comlimentary WiFi. Shannon Airport 20 minutes drive. "Limerick's friendliest hotel...where people matter". Please enquire about Facilities for Persons with Disabilities.

Member of Best Western

Bookable on www.irelandhotels.com
Special Offer: www.irelandhotels.com/offers

B&B from €35.00 to €90.00

Marie Tynan
Hotel Manager

62

Food for Kids

Closed 24 - 26 December

Limerick City

Carlton Castletroy Park Hotel

HOTEL ★★★★ MAP 6 H 7

Dublin Road,
Limerick

Tel: 061-335566 Fax: 061-331117
Email: reservations.castletroy@carlton.ie
Web: www.carlton.ie/castletroy
GPS: N +52° 40' 0.69" W -8° 34' 36.94"

The Carlton Castletroy Park Hotel, one of the leading hotels in Limerick reopened in 2009 as part of Carlton Hotel Group. Located just 3 miles from the city and opposite the internationally acclaimed UL Sports Arena and Concert Hall. For leisure breaks or business trips, you will find what you are looking for at Limerick's finest hotel. Room Reservations LoCall 1890 288 288. Please enquire about Facilities for Persons with Disabilities.

An IHF Quality Employer

Bookable on www.irelandhotels.com

Special Offer: www.irelandhotels.com/offers

B&B from €59.00 to €109.00
Suites from €200.00 to €320.00

Philip Lee
General Manager

107

Closed 24 - 27 December

Clifton House

GUESTHOUSE ★★★ MAP 6 H 7

Ennis Road,
Limerick

Tel: 061-451166 Fax: 061-451224
Email: cliftonhouse@eircom.net
Web: www.cliftonhouse.ie
GPS: N +52° 40' 6.60" W -8° 39' 1.23"

Set in 1 acre of landscaped gardens. All sixteen rooms are en suite, with multi-channel TV, trouser press, hairdryers and direct dial telephone. Complimentary tea/coffee is available in our spacious TV lounge. We are situated on the main Limerick / Shannon Road. Within 15 minutes walk of city centre. 22 space car park. AA listed. Friendly welcome awaits you. 15 minutes walk from Thomand Park Rugby Grounds and the Gaelic grounds are 5 minutes walk away.

Bookable on www.irelandhotels.com

B&B from €40.00 to €45.00

Michael & Mary Powell
Proprietors

16

Closed 20 December - 02 January

Kilmurry Lodge Hotel

HOTEL ★★★ MAP 6 H 7

Dublin Road,
Castletroy,
Limerick

Tel: 061-331133 Fax: 061-330011
Email: info@kilmurrylodge.com
Web: www.kilmurrylodge.com
GPS: N +52° 40' 7.20" W -8° 33' 11.67"

The Kilmurry Lodge Hotel set among four acres of landscaped gardens is perfectly located adjacent to the University of Limerick on the Dublin road (N7), whilst still only minutes from the thriving city centre. The business and conference services (for up to 300 people) exceed the highest of expectations and the hotel's "Olde World" character and charm is complemented by the latest in technology including free broadband access in all guest bedrooms. Please enquire about Facilities for Persons with Disabilities.

An IHF Quality Employer

Bookable on www.irelandhotels.com

Special Offer: www.irelandhotels.com/offers

Room Rate from €59.00 to €99.00

Siobhan Hoare
Proprietor

100

Closed 24 - 27 December

B&B Rates are per Person Sharing per Night incl. Breakfast.
or Room Rates are per Room per Night - See also Page 8

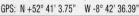

Maldron Hotel Limerick

HOTEL ★★★ MAP 6 H 7

Southern Ring Road,
Roxboro,
Limerick

Tel: 061-436100 Fax: 061-436110
Email: info.limerick@maldronhotels.com
Web: www.maldronhotels.com
GPS: N +52° 38' 50.44" W -8° 37' 6.97"

Conveniently located off the Southern Ring Road and just 5 minutes drive from Limerick City, the Maldron Hotel Limerick is the perfect choice for your visit to Limerick. Our 143 superior guest rooms, 26 two bedroom suites and 4 one bedroom suites with superb Club Vitae Health and Fitness Club offer an excellent accommodation choice. Additional facilities include Stir restaurant and bar; free WiFi and broadband internet access as well as complimentary car parking. Please enquire about Facilities for Persons with Disabilities.

An IHF Quality Employer

Member of Maldron Hotels

Bookable on www.irelandhotels.com

Special Offer: www.irelandhotels.com/offers

Room Rate from €59.00 to €199.00

Emma Dalton
General Manager

199

Food for Kids

Closed 20 - 27 December

No 1 Pery Square, Hotel & Spa

HOTEL MAP 6 H 7

Georgian Quarter,
Pery Square,
Limerick

Tel: 061-402 402 Fax: 061-313 060
Email: info@oneperysquare.com
Web: www.oneperysquare.com
GPS: N +52° 39' 29.67" W -8° 37' 47.72"

Built to a 4**** specification. A listed Georgian townhouse, Hotel & Spa situated in Limerick's historic Georgian quarter. 20 individual bedrooms with great views of red brick Limerick, the Peoples' Park & our own beautiful terrace garden. Enjoy pre & after dinner drinks in park room lounge followed by lunch or dinner, wine classes, private dining, lots to choose from whatever the occasion. All our food is prepared from local produce & has a strong French influence. The real urban retreat is our spa located in the vaults where you can enjoy a full spa experience away from the city crowds. The hotel has its very own dedicated wine room.

Member of Private Ireland

B&B from €82.50 to €97.50
Suites from €250.00 to €350.00

Patricia Roberts

20

Activities:

Closed 24 - 28 December

Radisson Blu Hotel & Spa

HOTEL ★★★★ MAP 6 H 7

Ennis Road,
Limerick

Tel: 061-456200 Fax: 061-327418
Email: sales.limerick@radissonblu.com
Web: www.radissonblu.ie/hotel-limerick
GPS: N +52° 41' 3.75" W -8° 42' 36.39"

Located on the N18, 5 minutes drive from Limerick City, 15 minutes from Shannon Airport. Set in landscaped gardens, the hotel boasts 154 spacious bedrooms. Dine in our award-winning restaurant or relax in one of our two bars. Complimentary WiFi in all areas. Ladies level and business class room available. Rain Spa & Wellness Clinic, offering Elemis products, includes 9 treatment rooms, thermal suite, hot tub, relaxation suite and wet treatment rooms.

An IHF Quality Employer

Member of Radisson Blu Hotels & Resorts

Bookable on www.irelandhotels.com

Special Offer: www.irelandhotels.com/offers

B&B from €57.50 to €92.50
Suites from €250.00 to €380.00

Louise O'Hara
General Manager

154

Food for Kids Activities:

Open All Year

B&B Rates are per Person Sharing per Night incl. Breakfast.
or Room Rates are per Room per Night - **See also Page 8**

Limerick City

Railway Hotel

HOTEL ★★ MAP 6 H 7

Parnell Street,
Limerick

Tel: 061-413653 Fax: 061-419762
Email: sales@railwayhotel.ie
Web: www.railwayhotel.ie
GPS: N +52° 39' 32.59" W -8° 37' 32.88"

Family-run hotel, owned and managed by the McEnery/Collins Family, this hotel offers Irish hospitality at its best. Personal attention is a way of life, along with an attractive lounge/bar, comfortable en suite accommodation and good home cooked food, one can't ask for more. Ideally situated, opposite rail/bus station, convenient to city centre, it is the perfect stop for the tourist and business person alike. All major credit cards accepted.

Room Rate from €30.00 to €80.00

Pat & Michele McEnery
Owners / Managers

5 25

Food for Kids

T C P

Closed 24 - 26 December

Savoy Hotel Limerick

HOTEL ★★★★★ MAP 6 H 7

City Central,
Henry Street,
Limerick

Tel: 061-448700 Fax: 061-448701
Email: reservations@savoylimerick.ie
Web: www.savoylimerick.ie
GPS: N +52° 39' 47.70" W -8° 37' 44.33"

Limerick City's only 5 star hotel situated in the heart of Limerick City close to the main shopping, business & tourist attractions. This elegant & sophisticated hotel includes suites, executive lounge, Aqua & Fitness Club (exclusive to guests), the Liszt Lounge featuring Afternoon Tea, the Savoy Bar & Limerick's most talked about restaurant, the now legendary Hamptons Bar & Grill. A range of banqueting & meeting facilities, including board rooms, can accommodate 220, whilst WiFi/Broadband & valet parking are complimentary. We invite you to be enchanted by our warm & unparalleled hospitality.

Bookable on www.irelandhotels.com
Special Offer: www.irelandhotels.com/offers

Room Rate from €99.00 to €195.00

Ronan Brannigan
General Manager

94

T C S I

Closed 25 - 26 December

Woodfield House Hotel

HOTEL ★★★ MAP 6 H 7

Ennis Road,
Limerick

Tel: 061-453022 Fax: 061-326755
Email: woodfieldhotel@eircom.net
Web: www.woodfieldhousehotel.com
GPS: N +52° 40' 3.94" W -8° 39' 2.41"

Enjoy a warm & friendly welcome at our family-run hotel. Situated a short stroll from Limerick City Centre on the upmarket Ennis Rd, close to Thomand Park & adjacent to the Gaelic Grounds. All rooms en suite, free parking. Excellent dining facilities. Range of conference suites available. Public areas and ground floor rooms WiFi enabled. Ideal for visiting all major attractions. Please enquire about Facilities for Persons with Disabilities.

An IHF Quality Employer
Member of MinOtel Ireland Hotel Group

Bookable on www.irelandhotels.com

Room Rate from €45.00 to €110.00

Dermot & Suzanne Fehily
Proprietors

26

C P S I

Closed 24 - 26 December

B&B Rates are per Person Sharing per Night incl. Breakfast.
or Room Rates are per Room per Night - **See also Page 8**

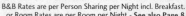

Courtenay Lodge Hotel

HOTEL ★★★ MAP 2 F 6

Newcastle West,
Co. Limerick

Tel: 069-62244 Fax: 069-77184
Email: res@courtenaylodge.iol.ie
Web: www.courtenaylodgehotel.com
GPS: N +52° 26' 55.41" W -9° 3' 7.39"

A warm welcome awaits you at the Courtenay Lodge Hotel situated on the main Limerick to Killarney Road and only 15 minutes from the picturesque village of Adare. The newly-built, tastefully decorated, en suite rooms complete with TV, direct dial phone, power showers, trouser press, tea/coffee facilities, etc. ensure a level of comfort second to none. The ideal base for touring the Shannon and South West regions and the perfect location for golfers to enjoy some of the most renowned courses.

An IHF Quality Employer

Bookable on www.irelandhotels.com

B&B from €55.00 to €75.00

Declan O'Grady
General Manager

39

Activities:

Closed 24 - 25 December

Rathkeale House Hotel

HOTEL ★★★ MAP 6 G 6

Lower Main Street,
Rathkeale,
Co. Limerick

Tel: 069-63333 Fax: 069-63300
Email: info@rathkealehousehotel.ie
Web: www.rathkealehousehotel.ie
GPS: N +52° 31' 22.75" W -8° 56' 29.84"

Rathkeale House Hotel, located just off the N21 Limerick to Killarney route and 4 miles west of Ireland's prettiest village, Adare. 26 superior en suite rooms, O'Deas Bistro open each evening 6-9.30pm. Chestnut Tree Bar where carvery lunch is available each day. Conference & banqueting facilities for 300 guests. Golf packages a speciality. Local courses, Adare, Adare Manor, Newcastle West (Ardagh), Charleville. Spacious gardens for your relaxation. A warm welcome awaits you. Please enquire about Facilities for Persons with Disabilities.

An IHF Quality Employer

Bookable on www.irelandhotels.com

B&B from €50.00 to €70.00
Suites from €250.00 to €350.00

Gerry O'Connor
General Manager

26

Activities:

Closed 24 - 25 December

Achill Cliff House Hotel

HOTEL ★★★ MAP 9 C 14

Keel,
Achill Island,
Co. Mayo

Tel: 098-43400 Fax: 098-43007
Email: info@achillcliff.com
Web: www.achillcliff.com
GPS: N +53° 58' 33.90" W -10° 4' 52.44"

This Superbly located hotel is renowned for its excellent cuisine & fine wines. Our dining room boasts beautiful views of Minaun Cliffs, Atlantic Ocean and Tramore Beach. Local mountain lamb & freshly caught fish is a speciality. RAC Dining Awards 2005. The large spacious bedrooms offer comfortable, luxurious accommodation. Nearby is the Deserted Village, Tramore Beach, Keem Bay, Minaun Heights. No night club. Featured on TV's "No Frontiers" in February and May 2009. Check our website for special offers. Please enquire about Facilities for Persons with Disabilities.

An IHF Quality Employer

Bookable on www.irelandhotels.com
Special Offer: www.irelandhotels.com/offers

B&B from €40.00 to €80.00

Teresa McNamara
Proprietor

10

Open All Year

B&B Rates are per Person Sharing per Night incl. Breakfast.
or Room Rates are per Room per Night - See also Page 8

Achill Island / Ballina

Ostán Oileán Acla

HOTEL ★★★ MAP 9 C 14

Achill Sound,
Achill,
Co. Mayo
Tel: 098-45138 Fax: 098-45198
Email: reservations@achillislandhotel.com
Web: www.achillislandhotel.com
GPS: N +53° 55' 58.55" W -9° 55' 10.05"

Enjoy the panoramic views of Achill Island from our new luxury hotel situated at the gateway to Achill Island. In our elegant Seafood Restaurant choose from a wide range of local produce. Relax and enjoy a drink in our friendly traditional bar. Convenient to 5 Blue Flag beaches, the highest cliffs in Europe, golf courses, pitch and putt course, outdoor activities. A warm friendly welcome awaits you at Ostán Oileán Acla. Please enquire about Facilities for Persons with Disabilities.

Bookable on www.irelandhotels.com

B&B from €35.00 to €60.00

Una McLoughlin
Proprietor
26

Closed 25 December

Ballina Manor Hotel

HOTEL MAP 10 F 15

Barrett Street,
Ballina,
Co. Mayo
Tel: 1890 238400
Email: info@ballinamanorhotel.com
Web: www.ballinamanorhotel.com
GPS: N +54° 6' 41.76" W -9° 9' 17.32"

Being refurbished to a 4 star standard, re-opening April 2010. Located in the heart of Ballina Town overlooking the River Moy & the Ridgepool - world famous for salmon fishing. Part of the Castle Hotel Group - a name synonymous with quality accommodation & friendly service. The hotel has a fully equipped leisure centre with a pool, sauna & steam room. The modern restaurant uses only the freshest locally sourced ingredients & has spectacular views overlooking the River Moy. An ideal base for guests touring the West & North West of Ireland. Please enquire about Facilities for Persons with Disabilities.

Member of Castle Hotel Group

Room Rate from €69.00 to €189.00

69

Activities:

Closed 24 - 27 December

Belleek Castle

HOTEL ★★★ MAP 10 F 15

Belleek,
Ballina,
Co. Mayo
Tel: 096-22400 Fax: 096-71750
Email: belleekcastlehotel@eircom.net
Web: www.belleekcastle.com
GPS: N +54° 7' 59.79" W -9° 8' 42.08"

Historic, romantic, set in 1000 acres of woodland on banks of River Moy - wine/dine till midnight - Gourmet organic food enthusiasts welcomed - 'Perchance to Dream' in a four poster. For your added pleasure: tour of 16th century castle armoury, giant fossil exhibits, Spanish Armada Bar, dramatic artefacts and timbers salvaged from Galleons wrecked off the Irish West Coast 1588. Sporting: international surfing, golf, fishing, tennis, riding, ten stables in castle. Please enquire about Facilities for Persons with Disabilities.

B&B from €80.00 to €95.00

Jacqueline Doran
Host
15

Closed 09 January - 25 March

B&B Rates are per Person Sharing per Night incl. Breakfast.
or Room Rates are per Room per Night - **See also Page 8**

Downhill House Hotel & Eagles Leisure Club

HOTEL ★★★ MAP 10 F 15

Ballina,
Co. Mayo

Tel: 096-21033 Fax: 096-21338
Email: info@downhillhotel.ie
Web: www.downhillhotel.ie
GPS: N +54° 7' 2.79" W -9° 8' 8.41"

Celebrating 75 years as a family run business in 2010. Set within a haven of landscaped gardens on the banks of the Brosna, a tributary of the River Moy. Located on the periphery of Ballina, Co. Mayo - the "Salmon Capital of Ireland" - explore the beautiful and rugged west of Ireland. Foxford Woollen Mills, Ceide Fields, Knock Shrine. Homemade cuisine. Eagles Leisure Club incorporates 2 indoor heated swimming pools. Large conference centre. Enjoy close proximity to championship golf at Enniscrone, Carne and Ballina. Fantastic golf, fishing, walking and cookery package.

Bookable on www.irelandhotels.com
Special Offer: www.irelandhotels.com/offers

B&B from €86.00 to €103.00
Suites from €250.00 to €350.00

Karen Moylett
Managing Director
60

Food for Kids *Activities:* ✓

Closed 22 - 26 December

Downhill Inn

HOTEL ★★★ MAP 10 F 15

Sligo Road,
Ballina,
Co. Mayo

Tel: 096-73444 Fax: 096-73411
Email: info@downhillinn.ie
Web: www.downhillinn.com
GPS: N +54° 7' 9.90" W -9° 8' 6.19"

A family-run 3*** hotel, located 1 mile outside Ballina Town on the main Sligo Road (N59). Contemporary in its design with 45 well-appointed triple rooms. All rooms are en suite with multi-channel TV, hairdryer, tea/coffee facilities and DD phone. The region offers superb fishing on the River Moy, Lough Conn and Killala Bay. An excellent selection of golf courses: Enniscrone, Ballina, Carne, to mention but a few. Special green fees available with our golf packages - see our website. 2 B&B and 1 dinner with 3 golf from €180pps. Enjoy a drink at the bar or a meal in our Terrace Restaurant. Rest assured!

An IHF Quality Employer

Member of Holiday Ireland Hotels

Bookable on www.irelandhotels.com

B&B from €45.00 to €75.00

John Raftery / Nicola Moylett
Proprietors
45

Closed 20 - 27 December

Ramada Ballina

HOTEL ★★★★ MAP 10 F 15

Old Dublin Road,
Ballina,
Co. Mayo

Tel: 096-23600 Fax: 096-23623
Email: stay@ramadaballina.ie
Web: www.ramadaballina.ie
GPS: N +54° 6' 45.20" W -9° 9' 29.58"

Ramada Ballina is modern, spacious, stylish & comfortable. Enjoy the warmth of our charming town & experience a genuine Céad Míle Fáilte in the beautiful North West. Unwind in Tranquillity Spa or work out in the pool or gym. Relax in Mc Shane's Bar & Bistro. There's a lot to do in Ballina; fishing, golfing, water sports & family fun, we have it all. Choose Ballina, leave the rest to us. Please enquire about Facilities for Persons with Disabilities.

Member of Ramada Group

Bookable on www.irelandhotels.com
Special Offer: www.irelandhotels.com/offers

B&B from €60.00 to €230.00
Suites from €160.00 to €250.00

André Turnbull
General Manager
87

Closed 24 - 26 December

B&B Rates are per Person Sharing per Night incl. Breakfast.
or Room Rates are per Room per Night - **See also Page 8**

Ballyhaunis / Belmullet / Castlebar

Courthouse (The)

GUESTHOUSE MAP 10 G 13

Main Street,
Ballyhaunis,
Co. Mayo

Tel: 094-963 0068 Fax: 094-963 1854
Email: reservations@courthouse.ie
Web: www.courthouse.ie
GPS: N +53° 45' 49.32" W -8° 45' 59.47"

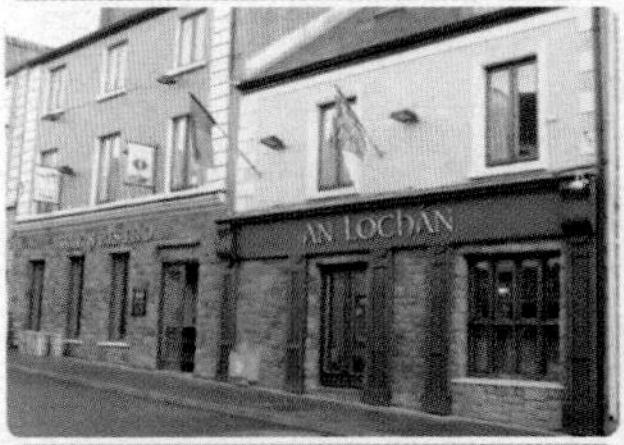

Built to a 3*** specification. The Courthouse is a family owned guesthouse in the heart of Connaught. The property, which was fully refurbished in 2009, is located just 10 minutes from Ireland West Airport which provides daily flights from Dublin & various UK destinations. Enjoy a pint in our newly decorated 'An Lochán' pub where we show all the main sporting events on Sky Sports and ESPN. Bar food is served throughout the day with a la carte available in our restaurant at weekends. Take in a round of golf in one of the many top class courses in the area or head for the water for coarse or game fishing.

B&B from €35.00 to €45.00

Tommy Leonard

10

Activities:

Open All Year

Sea Rod Inn

GUESTHOUSE ★★ MAP 9 C 16

Doohoma,
Ballina,
Co. Mayo

Tel: 097-86767 Fax: 097-86809
Email: info@thesearodinn.ie
Web: www.thesearodinn.ie
GPS: N +54° 4' 12.38" W -9° 57' 8.40"

Located on the southern shore of Doohoma Peninsula, The Sea Rod Inn is a fully licensed premises with a beautifully decorated bar and lounge, and nine magnificent bedrooms all of which are en suite with TV and central heating. Tea/coffee making facilities are all available in a separate sitting room, exclusive to guests, where you can enjoy panoramic views of Achill Island and the Atlantic Ocean. Our in-house entertainment during the summer months ensures that parents with young families can have a carefree holiday with no childcare worries.

Member of North & West Coast Links Ireland

B&B from €35.00 to €45.00

Michael & Bernadette Barrett

9

Activities:

Closed 23 - 26 December

Days Hotel Castlebar

HOTEL ★★★★ MAP 9 E 14

Lannagh Road,
Castlebar,
Co. Mayo

Tel: 094-928 6200 Fax: 094-928 6201
Email: res@dayshotelcastlebar.com
Web: www.dayshotelcastlebar.com
GPS: N +53° 51' 12.51" W -9° 18' 20.37"

Days Hotel Castlebar is Castlebar's only 4 star boutique hotel, located in the heart of the town, beside the shopping and theatre district and overlooking Lough Lannagh. The hotel is contemporary and chic in design. Complimentary broadband is offered in all guest bedrooms as well as the usual 4 star amenities, the Harlequin Restaurant is open daily, serving contemporary Irish and international cuisine. Days Hotel is the ideal choice for business and corporate guests with on site meeting room facilities. Please enquire about Facilities for Persons with Disabilities.

Member of Days Hotels Ireland

Bookable on www.irelandhotels.com
Special Offer: www.irelandhotels.com/offers

Room Rate from €69.00 to €189.00
Suites from €99.00 to €270.00

Lynda Foley
General Manager

90

Activities:

Closed 23 - 26 December

B&B Rates are per Person Sharing per Night incl. Breakfast.
or Room Rates are per Room per Night - See also Page 8

Castlebar / Charlestown

Kennys Guest House

GUESTHOUSE ★★★ MAP 9 E 14

Lucan Street,
Castlebar,
Co. Mayo
Tel: 094-902 3091
Email: info@kennysguesthouse.com
Web: www.kennysguesthouse.com
GPS: N +53° 51' 28.52" W -9° 17' 47.16"

Castlebar's only 3 star guesthouse offers luxury and comfort. Privacy when you want it WiFi when you need it. Decorated and furnished to a very high standard. All rooms are en suite with TV, DD telephone and hairdryer. Relax in the residents lounge with complimentary tea/coffee or avail of the numerous facilities nearby e.g. organised walks, fishing, bowling, swimming, golf, fine restaurants and entertainment. Location: town centre. Private car park. Mobile: 087 984 0759. Please enquire about Facilities for Persons with Disabilities.

Bookable on www.irelandhotels.com

Special Offer: www.irelandhotels.com/offers

B&B from €40.00 to €45.00

Susanna & Raymond Kenny

8

Open All Year

TF Royal Hotel & Theatre

HOTEL ★★★ MAP 9 E 14

Old Westport Road,
Castlebar,
Co. Mayo
Tel: 094-902 3111 Fax: 094-928 6161
Email: info@tfroyalhotel.com
Web: www.tfroyalhotel.com
GPS: N +53° 51' 11.50" W -9° 18' 14.48"

The TF Royal Hotel & Theatre is a luxury boutique 3*** family hotel adjacent to Castlebar Town centre. Renovation & refurbishment has provided luxurious bedrooms decorated to an excellent standard with air con, security safe, ISDN lines, TV, VCR, trouser press, hairdryer. Executive/master suites & connecting family rooms. Modern conference & theatre facility. Café Bar & Bistro. Tamarind Seed Restaurant. Dedicated business centre. Adjacent to Institute of Technology, Mayo General Hospital, Harlequin Shopping Centre and main shopping. New Royal Theatre. Please enquire about Facilities for Persons with Disabilities.

Member of Countrywide Hotels

Bookable on www.irelandhotels.com

B&B from €55.00 to €85.00

Pat & Mary Jennings
Proprietors

27

Closed 24 - 26 December

Riverside Guesthouse & Restaurant

GUESTHOUSE ★★ MAP 10 G 14

Church Street,
Charlestown,
Co. Mayo
Tel: 094-925 4200 Fax: 094-925 4207
Email: riversiderestaurant@eircom.net
Web: www.riversiderest.com
GPS: N +53° 57' 49.09" W -8° 47' 46.47"

Situated in town centre off the intersection of N17 & N5 routes. Leave the N5 by-pass taking the N17 exit to Sligo. 5 minutes to Knock international Airport, 20 minutes to Knock Shrine. Ideally located for Mayo & Ireland West. Family run guesthouse with en suite rooms & TV. Free car parking. Complimentary Wi-Fi access and tea/coffee facilities in residents lounge. Seasonal, locally sourced food served 7 days from 8am to 9.30pm in our Olde World restaurant by our friendly staff. Award-winning chef/owner. Licensed to serve alcohol to diners. An Irish welcome awaits you.

B&B from €43.00 to €44.00

Anthony & Anne Kelly
Proprietors

2 8

Closed 24 - 27 December

Cong / Kiltimagh / Knock

Ashford Castle

HOTEL ★★★★★ MAP 9 E 12

Cong,
Co. Mayo

Tel: 094-954 6003 Fax: 094-954 6260
Email: ashford@ashford.ie
Web: www.ashford.ie
GPS: N +53° 32' 4.23" W -9° 17' 7.12"

13th Century Castle located 40 minutes from Galway City. Once the estate of Lord Ardilaun and the Guinness Family. Ashford Castle opened as a luxury hotel in 1939. 83 guest rooms are of the highest standards with incredible lake or river views. We offer 9 hole golf and tennis complimentary to residents. Our activities include archery, clay pigeon, fishing, horseback riding, cruising on the lake and falconry. Our Health Centre comprises: sauna, jacuzzi, steam room, gym area and treatment rooms. Various suites and staterooms available. Email enquiries to reservations@ashford.ie.

An IHF Quality Employer

Member of The Leading Small Hotels of the World

Bookable on www.irelandhotels.com

Room Rate from €175.00 to €405.00
Suites from €475.00 to €950.00

Niall Rochford
General Manager

83

Food for Kids Activities:

Open All Year

Park Hotel Kiltimagh

HOTEL ★★★ MAP 10 F 14

Swinford Road,
Kiltimagh,
Mayo

Tel: 094-937 4922 Fax: 094-937 4924
Email: info@parkhotelmayo.com
Web: www.parkhotelmayo.com
GPS: N +53° 51' 26.15" W -8° 59' 35.91"

The Park Hotel Kiltimagh is located in east Mayo, 15 minutes from Ireland West Airport Knock, situated adjacent to the local wildlife park and a few minutes walk from the town centre. The hotel is an ideal base for touring the west. Enjoy our individually decorated de luxe or executive rooms, full fitness centre. Relax in our comfortable lobby or dine in our café bar or à la carte restaurant. A warm welcome awaits you at the Park Hotel Kiltimagh.

Member of Irish Country Hotels

B&B from €50.00 to €90.00
Suites from €170.00 to €270.00

Noel Lafferty
Manager

45

Activities:

Closed 24 - 27 December

Knock House Hotel

HOTEL ★★★ MAP 10 G 13

Ballyhaunis Road,
Knock,
Co. Mayo

Tel: 094-938 8088 Fax: 094-938 8044
Email: info@knockhousehotel.ie
Web: www.knockhousehotel.ie
GPS: N +53° 47' 27.68" W -8° 54' 51.63"

Located in over 100 acres of parkland and nestling close to the Basilica, this 10 year old hotel is a gem! With 68 comfortable bedrooms, of which 6 are designed for wheelchair users, every need is catered for. The superb Four Seasons Restaurant - open all day - and the glazed reception and lounge areas, surrounded by local limestone, overlook countryside. This well run, tranquil hotel will be hard to leave. Helipad available. Bookable on www.knockhousehotel.ie. Please enquire about Facilities for Persons with Disabilities.

An IHF Quality Employer

Bookable on www.irelandhotels.com

B&B from €60.00 to €84.00

Brian Crowley
General Manager

68

Activities:

Open All Year

B&B Rates are per Person Sharing per Night incl. Breakfast. or Room Rates are per Room per Night - See also Page 8

Mulranny / Newport / Pontoon

Mulranny Park Hotel

HOTEL ★★★★ MAP 9 D 14

Mulranny,
Westport,
Co. Mayo
Tel: 098-36000 Fax: 098-36899
Email: info@mulrannyparkhotel.ie
Web: www.mulrannyparkhotel.ie
GPS: N +53° 54' 21.63" W -9° 46' 57.55"

This stunning hotel is situated on a unique site, overlooking Clew Bay, Croagh Patrick and Clare Island. All rooms have spectacular sea or woodland views. Its original charm and character has been retained. Superb cuisine in the elegant Nephin Restaurant, lively Waterfront Bar and relaxing lounge. Listed as one of the best places to stay in Ireland this year, the hotel offers extensive leisure facilities. Overlooking the Blue Flag beach, walking, surfing, sailing, championship golf - is all at our doorstep. Please enquire about Facilities for Persons with Disabilities.

Bookable on www.irelandhotels.com

Special Offer: www.irelandhotels.com/offers

B&B from €75.00 to €120.00

Dermot Madigan
General Manager

41

Closed 03 - 29 January

Hotel Newport

HOTEL ★★★ MAP 9 E 14

Main Street,
Newport,
Co. Mayo
Tel: 098-41155 Fax: 098-42548
Email: info@hotelnewportmayo.com
Web: www.hotelnewportmayo.com
GPS: N +53° 53' 9.50" W -9° 32' 47.89"

A modern yet traditional hotel offering personal service and reflecting the heritage of Newport. Hotel Newport has 30 comfortable and spacious modern built guest rooms comprising of double rooms, family rooms and suites, offering panoramic views of the village and the Nephin Mountains. Special rates and packages are available. Hotel Newport offers Irish and European dining, specialising in seafood and steaks. A choice between the Cobblers Restaurant or the traditional Seven Arches Bistro.

B&B from €35.00 to €55.00
Suites from €110.00 to €150.00

Helen Deane
Manager

30

Closed 25 December

Healys Restaurant & Fishing Lodge

HOTEL ★★ MAP 9 F 14

Pontoon,
Foxford,
Co. Mayo
Tel: 094-925 6443 Fax: 094-925 6572
Email: info@healyspontoon.com
Web: www.healyspontoon.com
GPS: N +53° 58' 37.90" W -9° 12' 44.00"

"Probably the best Fishing and Golf location in the West of Ireland" - Healys Restaurant & Fishing Lodge located on the shores of Lough Conn & Cullen. A pre 1800 Country House, everything has changed but nothing has changed, still old world. The house has been home to great anglers/golfers for 160 years. Both peaceful and scenic, truly a place for all seasons. Our Coachmans Restaurant: Open daily from Breakfast at 8am to last orders for food at 8.30pm approx. Our Lough Cullen Dining Room: A superb lake view, boasts "probably the best food in the West". Open nightly 6pm to 9pm approx.

Member of Great Fishing Houses of Ireland

B&B from €35.00 to €45.00

John Dever & Josette Maurer
Proprietors

14

Activities:

Closed 25 December

B&B Rates are per Person Sharing per Night incl. Breakfast.
or Room Rates are per Room per Night - **See also Page 8**

Westport

Ardmore Country House Hotel and Restaurant

HOTEL ★★★★ MAP 9 E 13

The Quay,
Westport,
Co. Mayo
Tel: 098-25994 Fax: 098-27795
Email: ardmorehotel@eircom.net
Web: www.ardmorecountryhouse.com
GPS: N +53° 47' 45.89" W -9° 33' 7.33"

Ardmore House is a small exclusive 4**** boutique hotel offering individual style, superb cuisine and the highest level of personal service. Idyllically situated overlooking Clew Bay with breathtaking sunsets in the shadow of Croagh Patrick. A perfect home from home. All 13 bedrooms are non-smoking.

B&B from €60.00 to €95.00

Noreen & Pat Hoban

10

Closed 01 November - 01 April

Augusta Lodge

GUESTHOUSE ★★★ MAP 9 E 13

Golf Links Road,
Westport,
Co. Mayo
Tel: 098-28900 Fax: 098-28995
Email: info@augustalodge.ie
Web: www.augustalodge.ie
GPS: N +53° 48' 23.43" W -9° 31' 40.35"

Augusta Lodge is a purpose built 3*** guesthouse situated in the picturesque Heritage Town of Westport. Equipped with all modern conveniences, your stay will be a memorable one. An all-weather synthetic 9 hole putting green is on site for guests use. Listed in all leading guides.

Member of Premier Guesthouses

Bookable on www.irelandhotels.com
Special Offer: www.irelandhotels.com/offers

B&B from €30.00 to €45.00

Dave O'Regan

10

Closed 23 - 27 December

Boffin Lodge

GUESTHOUSE ★★★ MAP 9 E 13

The Quay,
Westport,
Co. Mayo
Tel: 098-26092 Fax: 098-28690
Email: info@boffinlodge.com
Web: www.boffinlodge.com
GPS: N +53° 47' 54.64" W -9° 32' 33.78"

Boffin Lodge was purpose built in 1999. It is located very close to the fashionable quay area of Westport where many of the town's best hotels, restaurants and pubs are located. Boffin Lodge has many special features such as a four poster room, a bedroom with a steam room and another with a jet stream bath. Our breakfast menu is extensive and can be seen on www.boffinlodge.com. We look forward to meeting you. Same rate applies all year round.

Member of Destination Westport

Bookable on www.irelandhotels.com

B&B from €35.00 to €45.00

Patrick Aylward
Proprietor

10

Closed 21 - 29 December

B&B Rates are per Person Sharing per Night incl. Breakfast.
or Room Rates are per Room per Night - **See also Page 8**

Carlton Atlantic Coast Hotel

HOTEL ★★★★ MAP 9 E 13

The Quay,
Westport,
Co. Mayo
Tel: 098-29000 Fax: 098-29111
Email: info@atlanticcoasthotel.com
Web: www.carlton.ie/atlantic
GPS: N +53° 47' 58.41" W -9° 32' 59.65"

Established as one of Westport's finest & most popular hotels, on the waterfront at Westport Quay overlooking Clew Bay. Superb contemporary cuisine in our unique top floor award-winning Blue Wave Restaurant. The Aqua Club features pool, gym, sauna, steam room and Float & Light Therapy treatment. The C Spa with 9 treatment rooms offers an extensive range of therapies & treatments. Championship golf, angling, scenic walks, island trips & Blue Flag beaches nearby. Room Reservations LoCall 1890 288 288. Please enquire about Facilities for Persons with Disabilities.

An IHF Quality Employer

Bookable on www.irelandhotels.com

Special Offer: www.irelandhotels.com/offers

B&B from €59.00 to €129.00
Suites from €180.00 to €310.00

Garrett McGuinness
General Manager

85

Food for Kids

Closed 21 - 27 December

Castlecourt Hotel Spa, Leisure, Conference

HOTEL ★★★ MAP 9 E 13

Castlebar Street,
Westport,
Co. Mayo
Tel: 098-55088 Fax: 098-28622
Email: info@castlecourthotel.ie
Web: www.castlecourthotel.ie
GPS: N +53° 48' 4.54" W -9° 31' 6.99"

When all you need is to get away and find space to breathe again, at the Castlecourt Hotel, you can do just that. Whether you're here on business, escaping with your partner or treating the family, you'll find everything you need for that well earned break. A family-run hotel, we have earned the reputation as a home away from home as well as being one of the largest leisure hotels in the West of Ireland. Leisure Centre and Resort Spa, Spa Sula now open. Please enquire about Facilities for Persons with Disabilities.

An IHF Quality Employer

Bookable on www.irelandhotels.com

Special Offer: www.irelandhotels.com/offers

B&B from €45.00 to €119.00
Suites from €130.00 to €340.00

Anne Corcoran / Joseph Corcoran
Managers

148

Activities:

Closed 24 - 26 December

B&B Rates are per Person Sharing per Night incl. Breakfast.
or Room Rates are per Room per Night - **See also Page 8**

Westport

Clew Bay Hotel

HOTEL ★★★ MAP 9 E 13

James Street,
Westport,
Co. Mayo
Tel: 098-28088 Fax: 098-25783
Email: info@clewbayhotel.com
Web: www.clewbayhotel.com
GPS: N +53° 48' 1.77" W -9° 31' 24.05"

Clew Bay Hotel is a family owned & managed hotel which combines a genuine welcome in an outstanding Westport location, in the town centre. Modern & contemporary in style it offers exceptional dining & wining options including Cocktails & Tapas in Madden's Bar, contemporary & value dining in Madden's Bistro & a fine dining experience in the Riverside Restaurant. Bedrooms offer comfort, luxury & relaxation when staying for either business or pleasure, including free WiFi in all rooms. Guests enjoy free access to Westport Leisure Park. The hotel is ideally located for exploring the stunning sites of the West.

An IHF Quality Employer

Member of Irish Country Hotels

Bookable on www.irelandhotels.com

Special Offer: www.irelandhotels.com/offers

B&B from €50.00 to €110.00

Maria Ruddy & Darren Madden
Proprietors

40

Food for Kids

Closed 19 - 28 December

Hotel Westport

HOTEL ★★★★ MAP 9 E 13

Newport Road,
Westport,
Co. Mayo
Tel: 098-25122 Fax: 098-26739
Email: reservations@hotelwestport.ie
Web: www.hotelwestport.ie
GPS: N +53° 48' 3.44" W -9° 31' 42.79"

Located in Ireland's Tidiest Town, Hotel Westport is set in private woodlands, just a short riverwalk into the town centre. This Award-Winning hotel is a place to truly relax and pamper yourself! Facilities include: refurbished premier bedrooms, Ocean Spirit Spa & Leisure, Ocean Wave Hair Salon, Islands Restaurant, Maple Bar, Riverside Gardens, outdoor children's play area. A variety of holidays available – Bridge, Bowling, Golf, Murder Mystery, Walking & Pottery Painting. Seasonal Family Holidays with Children's Panda Club. Lo-call Reservations (ROI) 1850 53 63 73 (NI/UK) 0870 876 54 32.

An IHF Quality Employer

Bookable on www.irelandhotels.com

B&B from €55.00 to €140.00
Suites from €150.00 to €345.00

Gerry Walshe
General Manager

129

Food for Kids Activities:

Open All Year

Knockranny House Hotel & Spa

HOTEL ★★★★ MAP 9 E 13

Westport,
Co. Mayo
Tel: 098-28600 Fax: 098-28611
Email: info@khh.ie
Web: www.khh.ie
GPS: N +53° 48' 7.68" W -9° 30' 28.52"

Beautifully appointed in secluded grounds over looking the picturesque town of Westport. Our suites have super king size beds, LCD TVs, Bose sound system, broadband and large bathrooms with spa baths. The restaurant, La Fougére, is renowned for excellent cuisine with emphasis on the finest local ingredients complimented by a selection of fine wines. The hotel spa Salveo is renowned as one of the best destination Spas in Ireland. Please enquire about Facilities for Persons with Disabilities.

An IHF Quality Employer

Member of Manor House Hotels

Bookable on www.irelandhotels.com

Special Offer: www.irelandhotels.com/offers

B&B from €70.00 to €145.00
Suites from €210.00 to €590.00

Geraldine & Adrian Noonan
Proprietors

97

Closed 22 - 26 December

B&B Rates are per Person Sharing per Night incl. Breakfast. or Room Rates are per Room per Night - See also Page 8

Mill Times Hotel

HOTEL ★★★ MAP 9 E 13

Town Centre,
Mill Street, Westport,
Co. Mayo
Tel: 098-29200 Fax: 098-29250
Email: info@milltimeshotel.ie
Web: www.milltimeshotel.ie
GPS: N +53° 47' 54.57" W -9° 31' 20.40"

Mill Times Hotel has undergone a major refurbishment, adding a state of the art banqueting & conference suite, fine dining Temptations Restaurant, Uncle Sams Bar is a vibrant retreat to relax and unwind, 34 spacious bedrooms & a friendly reception area. The hotel has limited, complimentary parking & a lift to all floors. The hotel is ideally located in the heart of Westport, a hive of activity. We pride ourselves in customer service at this warm & relaxing hotel. Directions - Take a left at the clock at the top of Bridge Street and we are situated on the left hand side on Mill Street. Please enquire about Facilities for Persons with Disabilities.

Bookable on www.irelandhotels.com

Special Offer: www.irelandhotels.com/offers

Room Rate from €60.00 to €219.00
Suites from €80.00 to €290.00

Joe O'Malley
Proprietor

34

Activities:

Closed 24 - 26 December

Quay West

GUESTHOUSE ★★ MAP 9 E 13

Quay Road,
Westport,
Co. Mayo
Tel: 098-27863 Fax: 098-28379
Email: quaywest@eircom.net
Web: www.quaywestport.com
GPS: N +53° 47' 55.00'' W -9° 32' 23.19''

Quay West is a purpose built house situated 10 minutes walk from town and 5 minutes from the harbour and directly opposite Westport Woods Hotel, where guests can enjoy the superb leisure facilities at discounted rates. Rooms are en suite with power showers, orthopaedic beds and TV. Lounge for guest comfort with tea/coffee facilities. Perfect base for touring beautiful Mayo, Connemara and relaxing in some of Westport's famous pubs and restaurants.

Bookable on www.irelandhotels.com

B&B from €32.00 to €40.00

David Kelly
Proprietor

6

Open All Year

Westport Plaza Hotel
Spa, Leisure, Conference

HOTEL ★★★★ MAP 9 E 13

Castlebar Street,
Westport,
Co. Mayo
Tel: 098-51166 Fax: 098-51133
Email: info@westportplazahotel.ie
Web: www.westportplazahotel.ie
GPS: N +53° 48' 3.73" W -9° 31' 9.96"

Step into the Westport Plaza Hotel and the world outside will seem far away. A fusion of contemporary chic and classic elegance awaits as you relax and unwind in ultimate luxury. Will it be an Indian head massage, sophisticated dining at the Restaurant Merlot or a peaceful night in one of luxurious suites? Just across the courtyard, in our resort leisure centre, you'll find a range of facilities to help you unwind, including a hair dressing salon. Our Resort Spa, Spa Sula, is now open. Please enquire about Facilities for Persons with Disabilities.

Bookable on www.irelandhotels.com

Special Offer: www.irelandhotels.com/offers

B&B from €65.00 to €129.00
Suites from €150.00 to €358.00

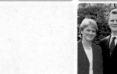

Anne Corcoran, Joseph Corcoran

88

Activities:

Open All Year

B&B Rates are per Person Sharing per Night incl. Breakfast.
or Room Rates are per Room per Night - **See also Page 8**

Westport / Ballaghaderreen

Westport Woods Hotel & Spa

HOTEL ★★★ MAP 9 E 13

Quay Road,
Westport,
Co. Mayo
Tel: 098-25811 Fax: 098-26212
Email: info@westportwoodshotel.com
Web: www.westportwoodshotel.com
GPS: N +53° 47' 57.42" W -9° 32' 26.07"

Ireland's greenest hotel is conveniently located in mature woodland between the charming town of Westport and the Quay. Superb facilities include award-winning leisure centre with pool, luxury Cedar Spa and popular horse riding centre. Enjoy fine dining in the Lakeview Restaurant or all day bar food in the atmospheric Bench Café Bar. Regular evening entertainment. Family holiday include Go!Kids! Club. Full programme of get!together! theme weeks and weekends. Please enquire about Facilities for Persons with Disabilities.

An IHF Quality Employer

Member of Brian McEniff Hotels

Bookable on www.irelandhotels.com

Special Offer: www.irelandhotels.com/offers

B&B from €65.00 to €120.00
Suites from €170.00 to €300.00

Michael Lennon & Joanne McEniff
Management Team

122

Activities:

Open All Year

Wyatt Hotel

HOTEL ★★★ MAP 9 E 13

The Octagon,
Westport,
Co. Mayo
Tel: 098-25027 Fax: 098-26316
Email: info@wyatthotel.com
Web: www.wyatthotel.com
GPS: N +53° 47' 57.06" W -9° 31' 31.03"

What a GEM of a hotel in the heart of Westport by the famous Octagon. Guests staying at this boutique hotel will enjoy a warm Irish Welcome! The atmosphere is intimate, mood tranquil, a haven in the shopping district. Award-winning JW's Brasserie, Bar & Courtyard serves an excellent menu popular with locals & visitors. Free access to Westport Leisure Park. Beauty/Wellness Suite. It's a must stay when in Westport! Please enquire about Facilities for Persons with Disabilities.

Member of Select Hotels of Ireland

Bookable on www.irelandhotels.com

Special Offer: www.irelandhotels.com/offers

B&B from €49.00 to €130.00
Suites from €150.00 to €300.00

Barney Clarke
General Manager

52

Activities:

Closed 20 - 28 December

Abbeyfield Hotel Conference and Leisure Centre

HOTEL MAP 10 H 14

Sligo Road,
Ballaghaderreen,
Co. Roscommon
Tel: 094-986 2100 Fax: 094-986 2738
Email: sales@abbeyfieldhotel.ie
Web: www.abbeyfieldhotel.ie
GPS: N +53° 53' 42.88" W -8° 34' 10.68"

Built to a 4**** specification. Luxurious 42 bedroom hotel located on mature grounds, once the setting of the bishops palace, the hotel is situated in the cathedral town of Ballaghaderreen, historically known as the gateway to the west. The hotel boasts a selection of superior executive & family suites, conference rooms, leisure & spa facilities including swimming pool, fitness club, spa bath & treatment rooms. Ideally located 15 minutes drive from Ireland West Airport Knock. Golf, angling & horse racing nearby. Please enquire about Facilities for Persons with Disabilities.

B&B from €55.00 to €90.00
Suites from €180.00 to €300.00

Martin Carty
Managing Director

42

Activities:

Closed 24 - 27 December

B&B Rates are per Person Sharing per Night incl. Breakfast. or Room Rates are per Room per Night - **See also Page 8**

Kilronan Castle Estate & Spa

HOTEL ★★★★ MAP 10 I 15

Ballyfarnon,
Co. Roscommon

Tel: 071-961 8000 Fax: 071-961 8001
Email: enquiries@kilronancastle.ie
Web: www.kilronancastle.ie
GPS: N +54° 3' 50.90" W -8° 10' 39.23"

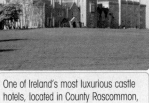

One of Ireland's most luxurious castle hotels, located in County Roscommon, Kilronan Castle is majestically set on the shores of Lough Meelagh and surrounded by over 40 acres of breathtaking scenery. The castle offers a wonderful mix of old world elegance and modern day comforts to make your stay most memorable. One step inside Kilronan Castle and you are at home. Please enquire about Facilities for Persons with Disabilities.

Bookable on www.irelandhotels.com
Special Offer: www.irelandhotels.com/offers

B&B from €44.50 to €99.50
Suites from €189.00 to €350.00

Michelle Coghlan
Resident Manager

84

Activities:

Open All Year

Gleesons Townhouse & Restaurant

GUESTHOUSE ★★★ MAP 10 I 12

Market Square,
Roscommon Town,
Co. Roscommon

Tel: 090-662 6954 Fax: 090-662 7425
Email: info@gleesonstownhouse.com
Web: www.gleesonstownhouse.com
GPS: N +53° 37' 51.31" W -8° 11' 29.31"

Overlooking the town's historic square, this lovingly restored 19th century townhouse's combination of locally sourced & organic sustainable food, excellent rooms, café, fully licensed restaurant, private car park, free internet access & Gleeson's charming hospitality creates an ideal setting when staying or dining in Roscommon. Gleeson's also offer you chance to bring home some amazing foods with you; visit their Artisan Food & Wine Shop located next door for a true taste of Roscommon. House in a building highly commended by SEI. Members of Good Food Ireland, Georgina Campbell's Guide to Ireland.

An IHF Quality Employer

Member of Good Food Ireland & Best Loved Hotels

Bookable on www.irelandhotels.com
Special Offer: www.irelandhotels.com/offers

B&B from €50.00 to €65.00
Suites from €150.00 to €190.00

Mary & Eamonn Gleeson
Proprietors

19

Closed 25 - 26 December

Castle Dargan Golf Hotel Wellness

HOTEL ★★★★ MAP 10 H 15

Ballygawley,
Co. Sligo

Tel: 071-911 8080 Fax: 071-911 8090
Email: info@castledargan.com
Web: www.castledargan.com
GPS: N +54° 11' 50.64" W -8° 26' 11.90"

Combining timeless opulence with a rich and romantic heritage to offer an unrivalled resort experience. The Edwardian House and crumbling Castle ruins stand testament to the wonderful sense of history that still lives in what is now a modern contemporary retreat for the discerning traveller. Presenting exquisite cuisine, accommodation and ambience. The Darren Clarke designed Golf Course is incredible with Icon the destination Medi Spa; luxury abounds at Castle Dargan. Please enquire about Facilities for Persons with Disabilities.

Bookable on www.irelandhotels.com
Special Offer: www.irelandhotels.com/offers

B&B from €80.00 to €150.00
Suites from €230.00 to €400.00

Noel Conlon
General Manager

22

Food for Kids Activities:

Closed 24 - 26 December

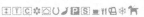

Collooney / Enniscrone / Mullaghmore

Markree Castle

HOTEL ★★★ MAP 10 H 15

Collooney,
Co. Sligo

Tel: 071-916 7800 Fax: 071-916 7840
Email: info@markreecastle.ie
Web: www.markreecastle.ie
GPS: N +54° 10' 26.63" W -8° 27' 42.14"

A spectacular castle set in lovely gardens and large estate, in the same ownership for over 350 years. Markree Castle offers a relaxing, friendly and quiet place to stay. Wonderful wood and plaster work complements the friendly service and the restaurant enjoys a reputation of excellence throughout Ireland. Please enquire about Facilities for Persons with Disabilities.

An IHF Quality Employer

Member of Manor House Hotels

Bookable on www.irelandhotels.com

B&B from €49.00 to €97.50

Charles & Mary Cooper
Proprietors

30

Closed 24 - 27 December

Diamond Coast Hotel

HOTEL ★★★★ MAP 10 F 15

Bartragh,
Enniscrone,
Co. Sligo

Tel: 096-26000 Fax: 096-26099
Email: info@diamondcoast.ie
Web: www.diamondcoast.ie
GPS: N +54° 12' 17.21" W -9° 6' 10.78"

The 4* Diamond Coast Hotel is situated in the spectacular Killala Bay region of County Sligo overlooking Enniscrone championship golf course and the stunning Dune lands. It is also a stones throw from the 5km golden beach - perfect for water sports, swimming and long walks and a mere 10 minute walk to Enniscrone town and Waterpoint Water Park. Facilities comprise 92 spacious guest rooms, a banqueting suite which can accommodate up to 450 guests, meeting rooms, Inishaven Bar and Coral Restaurant. Please enquire about Facilities for Persons with Disabilities.

Member of Maldron Hotels - Partner Hotel

Bookable on www.irelandhotels.com

Special Offer: www.irelandhotels.com/offers

B&B from €39.00 to €119.00

Brian Pierson

92

Closed 23 - 27 December

Pier Head Hotel, Spa and Leisure Centre

HOTEL ★★★ MAP 13 H 17

Mullaghmore,
Co. Sligo

Tel: 071-916 6171 Fax: 071-916 6473
Email: pierheadreception@eircom.net
Web: www.pierheadhotel.ie
GPS: N +54° 28' 0.75" W -8° 26' 51.41"

With its unique setting in the picturesque seaside village of Mullaghmore, the Pier Head Hotel has two bars and a very popular restaurant. All 40 rooms are en suite, many with balconies or access to the roof garden with stunning views of Mullaghmore Harbour and Donegal Bay. Nearby activities include surfing, sailing, horse riding, hiking and fishing to name a few. The hotel offers luxurious accommodation and excellent facilities such as swimming pool, hot tub and seaweed baths making it the ideal venue for your stay in the North West. Please enquire about Facilities for Persons with Disabilities.

Member of Sligo Marketing Forum

B&B from €50.00 to €70.00

John McHugh

40

Activities:

Closed 24 - 26 December

B&B Rates are per Person Sharing per Night incl. Breakfast.
or Room Rates are per Room per Night - See also Page 8

Rosses Point / Sligo Town

Yeats Country Hotel, Spa & Leisure Club

HOTEL ★★★ MAP 10 H 16

Rosses Point,
Co. Sligo

Tel: 071-917 7211 Fax: 071-917 7203
Email: info@yeatscountryhotel.com
Web: www.yeatscountryhotel.com
GPS: N +54° 18' 22.18" W -8° 33' 54.72"

A family-run, 3* hotel. All rooms en suite, cable TV, DD phone, tea/coffee facilities, hairdryer. Within walking distance of sandy beaches & Sligo's 18 hole championship golf courses. Our wonderful Eros Spa is located in the hotel offering seaweed baths, hydro baths, Yon-ka Paris body products & much more. Amenities: leisure club with 18m swimming pool, sauna, jacuzzi, steam room & hi-tech gym. Also available tennis, basketball. Supervised crèche & indoor play areas during the months of July & August & Bank Holiday Weekends. Local activities: golf, yachting, fishing, scenic drives. Also closed 20 - 27 Dec. WiFi.

Member of McEniff Hotels

Bookable on www.irelandhotels.com
Special Offer: www.irelandhotels.com/offers

B&B from €55.00 to €90.00

Fiona McEniff
Managing Director

98

Activities:

Closed 05 - 25 January

Radisson Blu Hotel & Spa Sligo

HOTEL ★★★★ MAP 10 H 16

Ballincar,
Rosses Point,
Sligo

Tel: 071-914 0008 Fax: 071-914 0005
Email: info.sligo@radissonblu.com
Web: www.radissonblu.ie/hotel-sligo
GPS: N +54° 17' 56.76" W -8° 30' 0.21"

Located in beautiful Rosses Point with stunning views of Sligo Bay. 132 luxurious bedrooms. Classiebawn Restaurant serving local and international cuisine and Benwiskin Bar with an extensive bar menu. Magnificent leisure facilities include 18m swimming pool, steam room, sauna, jacuzzi and outdoor Canadian hot tub. Solas Spa and Wellness centre boasts a relaxation suite, 7 modern treatment rooms, a luxurious thermal suite, a Balneotherapy bath and a dry floatation tank. Within easy reach of some of Ireland's best golf courses. Please enquire about Facilities for Persons with Disabilities.

An IHF Quality Employer

Member of Radisson Blu Hotels & Resorts

Bookable on www.irelandhotels.com

B&B from €40.00 to €90.00
Suites from €130.00 to €230.00

Fergus O'Donovan
General Manager

132

Food for Kids Activities:

Open All Year

Sligo City Hotel

HOTEL ★★★ MAP 10 H 16

Quay Street,
Sligo

Tel: 071-914 4000 Fax: 071-914 6888
Email: info@sligocityhotel.com
Web: www.sligocityhotel.com
GPS: N +54° 16' 23.48" W -8° 28' 34.47"

The Sligo City Hotel is located in the heart of Sligo Town, with immediate access to Sligo's new shopping centre and a host of lively bars on its doorstep. All 60 bedrooms are en suite with cable TV and direct dial phone, fast internet connections with broadband and tea/coffee making facilities. The Sligo City Hotel offers a warm welcome to all our guests and prides itself on delivering service excellence. Specialising in room only rates, commercial traveller rates and golfing holidays. Room only rate. Please enquire about Facilities for Persons with Disabilities.

Bookable on www.irelandhotels.com
Special Offer: www.irelandhotels.com/offers

Room Rate from €79.00 to €180.00
Suites from €99.00 to €250.00

Bernard Mullen & Michael Mulholland
Directors

60

Closed 24 December - 02 January

B&B Rates are per Person Sharing per Night incl. Breakfast.
or Room Rates are per Room per Night - **See also Page 8**

Sligo Town / Tubbercurry

Sligo Park Hotel & Leisure Club

HOTEL ★★★★ MAP 10 H 16

Pearse Road,
Sligo

Tel: 071-919 0400 Fax: 071-916 9556
Email: sligo@leehotels.com
Web: www.leehotels.com
GPS: N +54° 15' 14.97" W -8° 28' 14.19"

Situated one mile south of Sligo on the old Dublin Road, just a short walk or suburban bus ride into town. The Sligo Park Hotel is set in lush landscaped gardens. A 4 star hotel with 137 new bedrooms, and one of the finest health and leisure clubs in the country. In the heart of Yeats Country, surrounded by the most scenic countryside ranging from the majestic Benbulben to the gentle waters of Lough Gill. For that special break, the Sligo Park offers everything for your enjoyment. Please enquire about Facilities for Persons with Disabilities.

An IHF Quality Employer

Bookable on www.irelandhotels.com
Special Offer: www.irelandhotels.com/offers

B&B from €49.00 to €129.00

Gerard Moore
General Manager

137

Food for Kids Activities:

Open All Year

Cawley's Guesthouse

GUESTHOUSE ★★ MAP 10 G 15

Emmet Street,
Tubbercurry,
Co. Sligo

Tel: 071-918 5025 Fax: 071-918 5963
Email: cawleysguesthouse@eircom.net
Web: www.cawleysguesthouse.com
GPS: N +54° 3' 14.01" W -8° 43' 40.98"

Cawley's is a large 3 storey family-run guesthouse with full bar license. We offer high standards in accommodation with tastefully decorated rooms. Our home cooking and personal service make this premises your home for the duration of your stay. Private parking, landscaped gardens, easily accessed by air, rail and bus. Local amenities include fishing, 9 hole golf course and horse riding. Seaside resorts close by. Major credit cards accepted. For further information please contact a member of the Cawley family on 071-918 5025. Wirless internet in lobby. Please enquire about Facilities for Persons with Disabilities.

Bookable on www.irelandhotels.com

B&B from €32.50 to €39.50

Teresa Cawley / Pierre Krebs

3 14

Closed 24 - 30 December

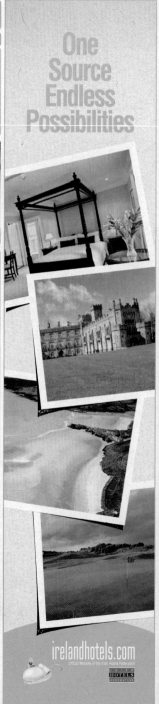

B&B Rates are per Person Sharing per Night incl. Breakfast.
or Room Rates are per Room per Night - See also Page 8

Northern Ireland

See page 365 for map with access points and driving distances

For Detailed Maps of this Region See Pages 365-380. Each Hotel or Guesthouse has a Map Reference to these detailed maps under their photograph.

Find your journey...
in Northern Ireland.
Northern Ireland Tourist Board
PEZ 2526

Northern Ireland
explore more
Get right inside the
Titanic story
Get up close to Belfast's famous lege
Visit the Pump House, once t
beating heart of Harland & Wol
construction of the White Star Line
Meet the 'Apprentic
Walk the full length of Thompson
Dock. And see the huge Caisson Ga
where she was unveiled to the wo
before her fateful maiden voya
It's a journey never to be forgott
discovernorthernireland.co
Titanic's Dock and Pump House Tour, Belfast
Northern Ireland Tourist Board

Dunsilly Hotel

HOTEL ★★★ MAP 15 O 18

20 Dunsilly Road,
Antrim BT41 2JH

Tel: 028-9446 2929 Fax: 028-9446 5801
Email: info@dunsillyhotel.com
Web: www.dunsillyhotel.com
GPS: N +54° 44' 33.32'' W -6° 14' 0.24''

The Dunsilly Hotel, an international award-winning hotel, is located at the junction 1 roundabout off the main M22 motorway. Just ten minutes from the International Airport and a 5 minute walk from the Junction 1 Shopping Centre, it makes the ideal location for business & leisure visitors alike. This hotel offers 40 luxury en suite bedrooms, designed with you, the guest, in mind. All rooms are flooded with natural daylight and are equipped with the latest in facilities and comforts. Please enquire about Facilities for Persons with Disabilities.

Bookable on www.irelandhotels.com

Special Offer: www.irelandhotels.com/offers

B&B from £34.50 to £64.50

Bridgene McKeever
Marketing Manager

40

Activities:

Closed 24 - 26 December

Marine Hotel

HOTEL MAP 15 O 21

1-3 North Street,
Ballycastle,
Co. Antrim BT54 6BN
Tel: 028-2076 2222 Fax: 028-2076 9507
Email: reception@marinehotel.net
Web: www.marinehotel.net
GPS: N +55° 12' 18.26" W -6° 14' 20.80"

Unclassified by Northern Ireland Tourist Board. Perfectly located on the Ballycastle seafront on the North Antrim coast between the Giant's Causeway and Glens of Antrim. Guests can relax and dine in the Front bar or Custom House Restaurant and have full use of the leisure club; in door pool, gym, sauna, steam room and jacuzzi. With the beach, marina, nearby tennis and golf courses on your doorstep, the Marine Hotel is the ideal venue for breaks, weddings and conferences. Please enquire about Facilities for Persons with Disabilities.

B&B from £22.50 to £70.00
Suites from £95.00 to £160.00

30

Closed 23 - 26 December

Galgorm Resort & Spa

HOTEL ★★★★ MAP 15 O 19

136 Fenaghy Road,
Ballymena,
Co. Antrim BT42 1EA
Tel: 028-2588 1001 Fax: 028-2588 0080
Email: sales@galgorm.com
Web: www.galgorm.com
GPS: N +54° 52' 37.61" W -6° 20' 46.01"

Set in 163 acres of lush parkland, Galgorm Resort & Spa is the perfect getaway for both business and pleasure. Following a £17 million refurbishment programme, Galgorm Resort & Spa has become one of Ireland's premier resort destinations. Whether you prefer to spend time luxuriating in our spa, eating delicious fare in one of our award winning restaurants, or lounging in our lobby soaking up the atmosphere, we can cater to your every whim.

B&B from £47.50 to £72.50
Suites from £205.00 to £295.00

Yvonne Moore
Manager

75

Activities:

Open All Year

B&B Rates are per Person Sharing per Night incl. Breakfast.
or Room Rates are per Room per Night - **See also Page 8**

Bushmills / Carnlough

Bushmills Inn Hotel

HOTEL ★★★ MAP 14 N 21

9 Dunluce Road,
Bushmills,
Co. Antrim BT57 8QG
Tel: 028-2073 3000 Fax: 028-2073 2048
Email: mail@bushmillsinn.com
Web: www.bushmillsinn.com
GPS: N +55° 12' 25.64" W -6° 31' 26.63"

In the village that is home to the world's oldest distillery between the Giant's Causeway and Royal Portrush Golf Club, this multi award-winning hotel, on the banks of the River Bush, with turf fires, oil lamps, nooks, crannies and even a secret room presents an extensive range of intriguing bedrooms, an atmospheric restaurant (new Irish cuisine), a turf-fired old kitchen and a Victorian bar still lit by gas light - you're welcome.

Bookable on www.irelandhotels.com

Special Offer: www.irelandhotels.com/offers

Room Rate from £138.00 to £298.00
Suites from £328.00 to £398.00

Alan Walls
Assistant Hotel Manager

41

Activities:

Open All Year

Causeway Hotel

HOTEL ★★ MAP 14 N 21

40 Causeway Road,
Bushmills,
Co. Antrim BT57 8SU
Tel: 028-2073 1226 Fax: 028-2073 2552
Email: reception@giants-causeway-hotel.co.uk
Web: www.giants-causeway-hotel.com
GPS: N +55° 14' 1.51" W -6° 31' 4.12"

Situated on the North Antrim Coast at the entrance to the world famous Giant's Causeway. This old family hotel established in 1836 has been tastefully renovated and restored to provide modern facilities while retaining its old grandeur and charm. The 28 centrally heated bedrooms have TV, tea/coffee making facilities and bathrooms en suite.

B&B from £35.00 to £45.00

Darrel Stevenson
Manager

28

Open All Year

Londonderry Arms Hotel

HOTEL ★★★ MAP 15 P 20

Glens of Antrim, 20 Harbour Rd,
Carnlough,
Co. Antrim BT44 0EU
Tel: 028-2888 5255 Fax: 028-2888 5263
Email: lda@glensofantrim.com
Web: www.glensofantrim.com
GPS: N +54° 59' 33.31" W -5° 59' 24.95"

This beautiful Georgian hotel was built in 1847. Once owned by Sir Winston Churchill, it is now owned and managed by Mr. Frank O'Neill. With its open log fires, private lounges and award-winning restaurant, this premier hotel in the Glens of Antrim is the perfect place to stay and discover the north eastern part of Ireland. Member of Irish Country Hotels. Ideal for incentive travel and close to the Giant's Causeway. The hotel suits tour parties, conferences and weddings. Please enquire about Facilities for Persons with Disabilities.

Member of Irish Country Hotels

Bookable on www.irelandhotels.com

B&B from £40.00 to £85.00

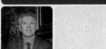

Frank O'Neill
Proprietor

35

Activities:

Closed 24 - 25 December

B&B Rates are per Person Sharing per Night incl. Breakfast.
or Room Rates are per Room per Night - See also Page 8

Ramada Portrush

HOTEL ★★★ MAP 14 N 21

73 Main Street,
Portrush,
Co. Antrim BT56 8BN
Tel: 028-7082 6100 Fax: 028-7082 6160
Email: info@ramadaportrush.com
Web: www.ramadaportrush.com
GPS: N +55° 12' 28.32" W -6° 39' 19.13"

Hotel of the Year 2004/5 (Northern Ireland Tourism Awards) - the award-winning Ramada Portrush is situated overlooking the Atlantic Ocean in the centre of Portrush. 69 en suite bedrooms with internet access, safe and lift. Ideal base for golfing, walking, cycling, angling, sightseeing, (Giant's Causeway), tour parties, conferences and functions. Golf at Royal Portrush, Portstewart, Castlerock, Ballycastle, Gracehill, Bushfoot and Galgorm Castle Golf Courses. Please enquire about Facilities for Persons with Disabilities.

Member of Ramada Worldwide

Bookable on www.irelandhotels.com

B&B from £34.50 to £90.00

Ann Donaghy
Group General Manager

69

Activities:

Open All Year

Royal Court Hotel

HOTEL ★★★ MAP 14 N 21

233 Ballybogy Road,
Portrush,
Co. Antrim BT56 8NF
Tel: 028-7082 2236 Fax: 028-7082 3176
Email: royalcourthotel@aol.com
Web: www.royalcourthotel.co.uk
GPS: N +55° 12' 16.11" W -6° 36' 25.10"

Situated overlooking the harbour town of Portrush and its world famous Royal Portrush Golf Club with panoramic views of County Donegal. It occupies one of the best positions on Northern Ireland's most famous coastline. Offering the perfect base not only for golfing, fishing and water sports. But also for those who wish to explore the Causeway Coast. Please enquire about Facilities for Persons with Disabilities.

Member of Causeway Coast and Glens

B&B from £40.00 to £49.50
Suites from £120.00 to £180.00

Barry Duffy
Manager

18

Closed 25 December

Ballymac

HOTEL ★★ MAP 15 O 18

7a Rock Road,
Stoneyford,
Co. Antrim BT28 3SU
Tel: 028-9264 8313 Fax: 028-9264 8312
Email: info@ballymachotel.co.uk
Web: www.ballymac.com
GPS: N +54° 34' 52.87" W -6° 6' 34.74"

The Ballymac Hotel set amid tranquil surroundings. Spectacularly reincarnated, the contemporarily designed 15 en suite bedrooms with excellent facilities including DD phones, modem facilities, hairdryers, TVs and hospitality trays. Our Grill Bar/Lounge and à la carte restaurant feature outstanding cuisine along with an extensive wine list. The Ballymac also boasts well-equipped function suites suitable for weddings, parties, trade shows and conferences. Extensive private parking is available in our grounds.

B&B from £45.00 to £65.00
Suites from £110.00 to £140.00

Ciaran Cunningham
General Manager

15

Closed 25 December

B&B Rates are per Person Sharing per Night incl. Breakfast.
or Room Rates are per Room per Night - **See also Page 8**

Templepatrick / Armagh City

Hilton Templepatrick

HOTEL ★★★★ MAP 15 O 18

Castle Upton Estate,
Templepatrick,
Co. Antrim BT39 0DD
Tel: 028-9443 5500 Fax: 028-9443 5511
Email: reservations.templepatrick@hilton.com
Web: www.hilton.co.uk/templepatrick
GPS: N +54° 42' 35.41" W -6° 5' 39.22"

A luxurious 4*, 129 bedroom hotel & country club, situated in the private grounds of the Castle Upton Estate. Centrally located & just 10mins from the sights & sounds of Belfast, this is the perfect base from which you can explore the award winning Antrim coastline. Accommodation ranges from standard to superior & family rooms, which offer an impressive combination of stylish furnishings & amenities. The hotel also boats a superb 18-hole championship golf course, tennis courts & a Livingwell Health Club with an 18m swimming pool, steam room & jacuzzi. Beauty rooms have both relaxation and therapeutic treatments on offer.

Bookable on www.irelandhotels.com
Special Offer: www.irelandhotels.com/offers

B&B from £32.00 to £77.00

Mark Walker
Area General Manager
129

Activities:

Open All Year

Templeton Hotel

HOTEL ★★★ MAP 15 O 18

882 Antrim Rd, Templepatrick,
Ballyclare,
Co. Antrim BT39 0AH
Tel: 028-9443 2984 Fax: 028-9443 3406
Email: reception@templetonhotel.com
Web: www.templetonhotel.com
GPS: N +54° 42' 13.82" W -6° 5' 32.24"

This privately owned hotel, 5 minutes from Belfast International Airport, 20 minutes from Belfast City centre and Belfast and Larne Ports, offers total quality for all tastes. With the choice of Raffles à la carte restaurant, the Upton Grill Room and the spacious lounge bar, you are guaranteed an enjoyable dining experience. Sam's Bar hosts a pub quiz every Monday evening and offers a late bar at weekends. Our 24 en suite bedrooms, including executive suites, are ideal for a relaxing and comfortable stay. Please enquire about Facilities for Persons with Disabilities.

B&B from £40.00 to £62.50
Suites from £100.00 to £125.00

Alison McCombe / Claire Kerr
General Manager /
Marketing Manager
24

Closed 25 - 26 December

Charlemont Arms Hotel

HOTEL ★★ MAP 14 N 16

57-65 English Street,
Armagh City,
Co. Armagh BT61 7LB
Tel: 028-3752 2028 Fax: 028-3752 6979
Email: info@charlemontarmshotel.com
Web: www.charlemontarmshotel.com
GPS: N +54° 21' 1.30" W -6° 39' 18.43"

A family-run hotel set in the city centre, offering the best of both worlds, traditional and modern. Convenient to shops, 18 hole golf course, leisure centre and all major tourist attractions including the 2 Cathedrals and other places of interest. 30 en suite bedrooms including one for the disabled, a 60 seat restaurant, 80 seat lounge bar, Turner's theme bar and Basement Bistro/Winebar that offers a unique dining experience for Armagh.

B&B from £45.00 to £55.00

The Forster Family
30

Closed 25 - 26 December

B&B Rates are per Person Sharing per Night incl. Breakfast. or Room Rates are per Room per Night - **See also Page 8**

Belfast City

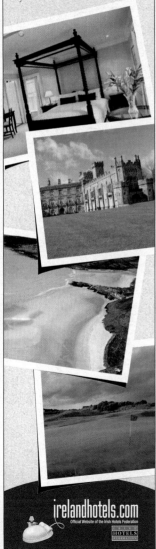

Hilton Belfast

HOTEL ★★★★★ MAP 15 P 18

4 Lanyon Place,
Belfast BT1 3LP

Tel: 028-9027 7000 Fax: 028-9027 7277
Email: reservations.belfast@hilton.com
Web: www.hilton.co.uk/belfast
GPS: N +54° 35' 46.89'' W -5° 55' 8.89''

Hilton Belfast is a 5* contemporary chic hotel, in the heart of Belfast city. With breathtaking views overlooking the city's architecture to the north & the Lagan River to the south, Hilton Belfast is Northern Ireland's only international 5* hotel. The hotel boasts 198 luxurious, air-conditioned bedrooms including a selection of stunning river-view corner suites & studios with views of the historic Harland & Wolfe shipyard which built the Titanic. Guestroom amenities include mini-bars, wide screen plasma TVs, in room-safes as well as a host of nibbles to make your welcome special. Livingwell Express Gym also on site.

Bookable on www.irelandhotels.com
Special Offer: www.irelandhotels.com/offers

B&B from £39.50 to £102.00

Mark Walker
Area General Manager
198

Activities:

Open All Year

La Mon Hotel & Country Club

HOTEL ★★★★ MAP 15 P 18

41 Gransha Road,
Castlereagh,
Belfast BT23 5RF

Tel: 028-9044 8631 Fax: 028-9044 8026
Email: info@lamon.co.uk
Web: www.lamon.co.uk
GPS: N +54° 32' 51.04" W -5° 49' 8.09"

This modern 4 star hotel offers 120 en suite bedrooms, excellent banqueting & conference facilities in a tranquil setting just 8 miles south east of Belfast City centre. Guests will enjoy the superb luxury leisure facilities including 15 metre swimming pool, childrens' pool, sauna, jacuzzi, steam room, gymnasium, hair studio & beauty salon. A wide range of dining options is also available with table d'hôte and à la carte menus in the Shakespeare Restaurant. Casual dining with a cosmopolitan flavour is also available in our lively bistro. An ideal venue for business or leisure.

Bookable on www.irelandhotels.com

B&B from £45.00 to £65.00
Suites from £110.00 to £200.00

Francis Brady
Managing Director
120

Activities:

Closed 24 - 26 December

B&B Rates are per Person Sharing per Night incl. Breakfast.
or Room Rates are per Room per Night - See also Page 8

Belfast City

Malone Lodge Hotel & Apartments

HOTEL ★★★★ MAP 15 P 18

60 Eglantine Avenue,
Malone Road,
Belfast BT9 6DY
Tel: 028-9038 8000 Fax: 028-9038 8088
Email: info@malonelodgehotel.com
Web: www.malonelodgehotelbelfast.com
GPS: N +54° 34' 54.36" W -5° 56' 33.66"

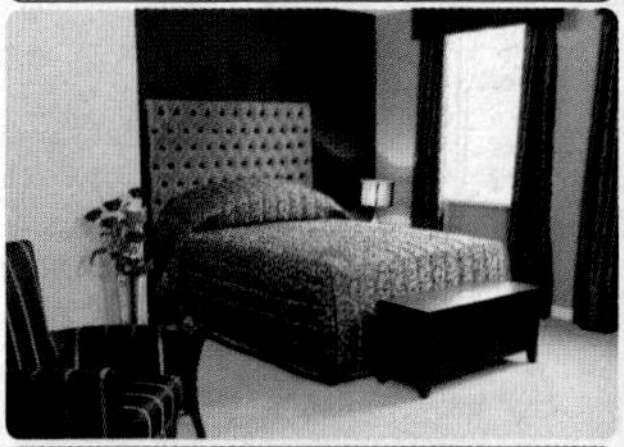

In the leafy suburbs of the university area of South Belfast, discover one of Northern Ireland's finest 4**** hotels. The centre piece of a beautiful Victorian terrace, the Malone Lodge Hotel offers you an oasis of calm and quiet elegance. The hotel offers luxury en suite accommodation, an award-winning restaurant, bar with big screen, conference & banqueting facilities and a fitness suite & sauna. Please enquire about Facilities for Persons with Disabilities.

Member of Select Hotels of Ireland

Bookable on www.irelandhotels.com

B&B from £37.50 to £55.00
Suites from £120.00 to £200.00

Mary & Brian Macklin

51

Activities:

Open All Year

Radisson Blu Hotel Belfast

HOTEL ★★★★ MAP 15 P 18

The Gasworks, 3 Cromac Place,
Ormeau Road,
Belfast BT7 2JB
Tel: 028-9043 4065 Fax: 028-9043 4066
Email: info.belfast@radissonblu.com
Web: www.radissonblu.co.uk/hotel-belfast
GPS: N +54° 35' 29.43" W -5° 55' 18.40"

Radisson Blu Hotel Belfast is an architecturally striking 120 bedroom hotel based in the city centre. Tourist attractions, entertainment, nightlife and shopping areas all within walking distance of the hotel. George Best Belfast City Airport only 4km away with bus and train stations a short walk away. Filini Bar and Restaurant on site. Please enquire about Facilities for Persons with Disabilities.

Member of Radisson Blu Hotels & Resorts

B&B from £54.50 to £60.00

Jan Hanak
General Manager

120

Open All Year

Ten Square Luxury Hotel

HOTEL ★★★★ MAP 15 P 18

10 Donegall Square South,
Belfast BT1 5JD
Tel: 028-9024 1001 Fax: 028-9024 3210
Email: reservations@tensquare.co.uk
Web: wwww.tensquare.co.uk
GPS: N +54° 35' 44.64" W -5° 55' 49.12"

With its distinctive charm & warmth in the heart of Belfast, overlooking City Hall, Ten Square is unrivalled in its service & setting. A highly acclaimed Boutique hotel, with 23 superbly appointed, unique & oversized guest rooms, featuring super king low slung beds & White Company amenities. The Grill Room & Bar is a vibrant & stylish 120 seater restaurant, focusing on the highest quality local ingredients. The menu is conceived with a view, to providing simple traditional dishes with a modern twist. The Porcelain Suite on the 1st floor is a refreshingly unique & contemporary setting for corporate events.

B&B from £85.00 to £85.00
Suites from £265.00 to £265.00

Kevin Smyth
General Manager

23

Closed 24 - 26 December

B&B Rates are per Person Sharing per Night incl. Breakfast.
or Room Rates are per Room per Night - **See also Page 8**

Brown Trout Golf & Country Inn

Hotel ★★★ Map 14 N 20

209 Agivey Road,
Aghadowey, Near Coleraine,
Co. Derry BT51 4AD
Tel: 028-7086 8209 Fax: 028-7086 8878
Email: jane@browntroutinn.com
Web: www.browntroutinn.com
GPS: N +55° 2' 13.71" W -6° 36' 9.25"

The Brown Trout Golf and Country Inn nestles near the River Bann only 12.8km from the picturesque Causeway Coast. This old inn with 15 rooms and four 5 star cottages, is Northern Ireland's first golf hotel. Gerry, Jane or Joanna will happily organise golf and fishing packages with professional tuition if required, or you can just enjoy a relaxing break and the craic with the locals. The warm hospitality and 'Taste of Ulster' Restaurant will make your stay enjoyable. Please enquire about Facilities for Persons with Disabilities.

Bookable on www.irelandhotels.com

Special Offer: www.irelandhotels.com/offers

B&B from £40.00 to £55.00

Jane O'Hara
Owner

15

Open All Year

Bushtown Hotel

Hotel ★★★ Map 14 N 20

283 Drumcroone Road,
Coleraine,
Co. Derry BT51 3QT
Tel: 028-7035 8367 Fax: 028-7032 0909
Email: bushtownhotel@btinternet.com
Web: www.bushhotel.co.uk
GPS: N +55° 6' 13.97" W -6° 41' 23.32"

The Bushtown Hotel is set amidst mature gardens on the outskirts of the university town of Coleraine & is only a stone's throw away from the beautiful Causeway Coast, Antrim Glens & world famous attractions. Originally a thatched cottage, it has evolved over the years to the Bushtown Hotel of today, a modern 3* hotel which has adapted comfort & elegance to the legacy and charm of that original cottage. Our Sunday carvery is renowned throughout the North West. Weddings of up to 220 guests are our speciality - please call for a brochure. Please enquire about Facilities for Persons with Disabilities.

B&B from £35.00 to £55.00
Suites from £130.00 to £170.00

Dermot Friel & Kieran McGilligan
Owners

38

Open All Year

Beech Hill Country House Hotel

Hotel ★★★★ Map 14 L 20

32 Ardmore Road,
Londonderry,
Co. Derry BT47 3QP
Tel: 028-7134 9279 Fax: 028-7134 5366
Email: info@beech-hill.com
Web: www.beech-hill.com
GPS: N +54° 58' 10.02" W -7° 16' 11.90"

Beech Hill is a privately owned country house hotel, 2 miles from Londonderry. It retains the elegance of country living & has been restored to create a hotel of charm, character & style. Its ambience is complemented by the surrounding grounds, planted with a myriad trees, including beech. Superb cuisine using local produce and homemade specialties. NITB Highly Commended Hotel of the Year 2008. John and Sally McKenna's Bridgestone Guide Top 100 Places to Stay in Ireland. Sauna, steam room, jacuzzi & gym available. Please enquire about Facilities for Persons with Disabilities.

Member of Manor House Hotels

Bookable on www.irelandhotels.com

B&B from £57.50 to £67.50
Suites from £190.00 to £230.00

Seamus Donnelly
Proprietor

27

Closed 24 - 26 December

B&B Rates are per Person Sharing per Night incl. Breakfast.
or Room Rates are per Room per Night - **See also Page 8**

Limavady / Newcastle / Newry

Radisson Blu Roe Park Resort

HOTEL ★★★★ MAP 14 M 20

Roe Park,
Limavady,
Co. Londonderry BT49 9LB
Tel: 028-7772 2222 Fax: 028-7772 2313
Email: limavady.reservations@radissonblu.com
Web: www.radissonroepark.com
GPS: N +55° 2' 19.58" W -6° 57' 17.97"

One of the north coast's only 4**** de luxe resorts, offers 118 spacious en suite bedrooms, Fairways Leisure Club with indoor pool and fitness suite, the Roe Spa with 12 treatment rooms offering Elemis treatments. Greens Restaurant offers international cuisine with local ingredients served in an elegant atmosphere and the Coach House Brasserie is perfect for the more informal occasion overlooking the 18 hole parkland golf course. Please enquire about Facilities for Persons with Disabilities.

Member of Radisson Blu Hotels & Resorts

Bookable on www.irelandhotels.com

B&B from £55.00 to £65.00
Suites from £170.00 to £190.00

George Graham

118

Activities:

Open All Year

Burrendale Hotel, Country Club & Spa

HOTEL ★★★ MAP 12 P 16

51 Castlewellan Road,
Newcastle,
Co. Down BT33 0JY
Tel: 028-4372 2599 Fax: 028-4372 2328
Email: reservations@burrendale.com
Web: www.burrendale.com
GPS: N +54° 13' 32.38" W -5° 53' 40.51"

Nestling between majestic Mourne Mountains & the glimmering Irish Sea, the Burrendale is a fine example of the very best in traditional hospitality. All of our 68 bedrooms are designed to suit everyone from family rooms to luxurious suites. Indulge in a world of relaxation & pampering in the comfort of the Burrendale Spa & Hair Salon, just opened in January 2009. The Spa also offers a choice of treatments including dry floatation bed, nail bar, tanning & relaxation suite & with a further 5 lavish treatment suites for your every need. In close proximity are 15 golf courses including RCD, beaches, nature walks, forest parks & pony trekking.

B&B from £60.00 to £75.00
Suites from £150.00 to £150.00

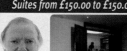

Denis Orr
General Manager

68

Activities:

Open All Year

Canal Court Hotel

HOTEL ★★★★ MAP 12 O 15

Merchants Quay,
Newry,
Co. Down BT35 8HF
Tel: 028-3025 1234 Fax: 028-3025 1177
Email: manager@canalcourthotel.com
Web: www.canalcourthotel.com
GPS: N +54° 10' 34.52" W -6° 20' 25.70"

This fabulous 4 star hotel is located in the heart of Newry City. The perfect location for a special break. With 112 beautiful bedrooms and suites and an extensive leisure complex, it is the ideal location to relax and unwind. Enjoy the shopping opportunities or visit the wealth of visitor and tourist attractions this city has to offer. Great weekend and midweek breaks available and guests can book online for all packages. This wonderful hotel has won many awards including Best Customer Service for 2 consecutive years, Eat Safe Award and NITB Hotel of the Year Award twice also. Please enquire about Facilities for Persons with Disabilities.

Bookable on www.irelandhotels.com
Special Offer: www.irelandhotels.com/offers

B&B from £65.00 to £150.00
Suites from £150.00 to £300.00

Patrick Murtagh
General Manager

112

Activities:

Closed 25 December

B&B Rates are per Person Sharing per Night incl. Breakfast.
or Room Rates are per Room per Night - See also Page 8

Cuan (The)

GUESTHOUSE ★★★ MAP 15 Q 17

6 - 10 The Square,
Strangford,
Co. Down BT30 7ND
Tel: 028-4488 1222
Email: info@thecuan.com
Web: www.thecuan.com
GPS: N +54° 22' 14.82" W -5° 33' 19.03"

The Cuan is located in the conservation village of Strangford on the shores of Strangford Lough, a world heritage site. Our reputation is built on providing wonderful accommodation and delicious food with exceptional customer service. Seafood is a speciality. The Cuan offers a wonderful base for the vast choice of activities on offer in Co. Down and beyond. Visit our website for more information. Please enquire about Facilities for Persons with Disabilities.

B&B from £37.50 to £42.50

Peter & Caroline McErlean

9

Closed 25 December

Killyhevlin Hotel

HOTEL ★★★★ MAP 11 K 16

Killyhevlin,
Enniskillen,
Co. Fermanagh BT74 6RW
Tel: 028-6632 3481 Fax: 028-6632 4726
Email: info@killyhevlin.com
Web: www.killyhevlin.com
GPS: N +54° 19' 47.16" W -7° 37' 11.55"

Killyhevlin Hotel and chalets are situated on the shores of scenic Lough Erne yet only 1km from the historic town of Enniskillen. All 70 spacious bedrooms, including suites, have been finished to an exceptional standard. Silks Restaurant and the Boathouse Grill offer a wide variety of menus daily. The Health Club and Elemis Spa are complete with pool, gym, outdoor hot tub and four treatment suites. Broadband Internet access available throughout the hotel. Please enquire about Facilities for Persons with Disabilities.

Member of Irish Country Hotels

Bookable on www.irelandhotels.com

B&B from £67.50 to £77.50
Suites from £210.00 to £230.00

Rodney J. Watson
Managing Director

70

Activities:

Closed 24 - 26 December

Manor House Resort Hotel

HOTEL ★★★★ MAP 14 K 16

Killadeas,
Enniskillen,
Co. Fermanagh BT94 1NY
Tel: 028-6862 2211 Fax: 028-6862 1545
Email: info@manorhouseresorthotel.com
Web: www.manorhouseresorthotel.com
GPS: N +54° 25' 46.31" W -7° 40' 43.54"

Set on the shores of Lough Erne, just north of Enniskillen, the Manor House is a journey back in time to a more elegant and tranquil age. But behind the stately surroundings of this 19th century manor is an hotel offering first class accommodation, leisure facilities and conference centre. The hotel boasts a wide range of bedrooms including beautifully appointed suites, executive and family rooms. Complimenting these facilities is the "Lady of the Lake" tour boat operating both public and private sailings.

B&B from £40.00 to £68.00
Suites from £275.00 to £275.00

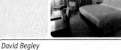

David Begley
General Manager

81

Activities:

Open All Year

B&B Rates are per Person Sharing per Night incl. Breakfast.
or Room Rates are per Room per Night - **See also Page 8**

Irvinestown / Clogher / Cookstown

Mahon's Hotel

HOTEL ★★★ MAP 13 K 17

Enniskillen Road,
Irvinestown,
Co. Fermanagh BT94 1GS
Tel: 028-6862 1656 Fax: 028-6862 8344
Email: info@mahonshotel.co.uk
Web: www.mahonshotel.co.uk
GPS: N +54° 28' 24.33" W -7° 37' 35.85"

Situated in the heart of the Fermanagh Lakeland. Ideal for visiting all major tourist attractions: Belleek Pottery 20 mins, Marble Arch Caves 30 mins, Necarne Equestrian Centre 5 mins, Lough Erne 5 mins, Donegal 20 mins. All rooms en suite, TV, tea making facilities. Bushmills Bar of the Year winner, entertainment at weekends, private car park. Family-run since 1883. Visit us in our third century. Cycling, horse riding, tennis & golf all available. Hotel has been upgraded to three star NITB and AA. Bedrooms have modem access, DVD and WiFi. Please enquire about Facilities for Persons with Disabilities.

B&B from £40.00 to £52.50

Joe Mahon
Manager

18

Activities: ✓

Closed 25 - 26 December

Corick House Hotel

HOTEL MAP 14 L 17

20 Corick Rd,
Clogher,
Co. Tyrone BT76 0BZ
Tel: 028-8554 8216 Fax: 028-8554 9531
Email: reservations@corickcountryhouse.com
Web: www.corickcountryhouse.com
GPS: N +54° 25' 30.99" W -7° 9' 45.86"

Unclassified By Northern Ireland Tourist Board. The only privately owned & managed 17th century country house with extensive gardens in Mid-Ulster. Meander through the walled garden & manicured lawns & savour the beauty of the Clogher Valley. Close to many tourist attractions for sightseeing and 8 mile fishing rights in River Blackwater. Carleton Licensed Restaurant: Major industry awards for imaginative menus, good service & hospitality, complemented by our Blackwater Bar & Conservatory. Garden Suite: Our new Orchid Site can seat 300+ for conferences & private events. Wedding Receptions at affordable prices.

B&B from £55.00 to £60.00

Jean Beacom
Proprietor

19

Open All Year

Tullylagan Country House Hotel

HOTEL ★★ MAP 14 M 18

40b Tullylagan Road,
Cookstown,
Co. Tyrone BT80 8UP
Tel: 028-8676 5100 Fax: 028-8676 1715
Email: info@tullylagan.com
Web: www.tullylagan.com
GPS: N +54° 35' 38.70" W -6° 46' 31.84"

This 19th century style manor is set in 30 acres of mature grounds & plantation, situated in the heart of Mid-Ulster. The rural setting lends itself to being the ideal place for a relaxing meal, short breaks, venue for a wedding or a business conference. This family-run hotel offers 15 en suite country style bedrooms. The hotel restaurant, with its warm & relaxed atmosphere, offers high quality food and friendly service in gracious surroundings. A welcome addition to the estate is our wine bar & restaurant. Certainly worth a visit! Suites available upon request. Taste of Ulster '09 Award. Member of the Good Food Circle.

B&B from £45.00 to £47.50
Suites from £120.00 to £130.00

Adrian Martin
Proprietor

15

Closed 24 - 27 December

B&B Rates are per Person Sharing per Night incl. Breakfast. or Room Rates are per Room per Night - **See also Page 8**

Bank House Hotel

HOTEL MAP 14 M 17

68 Irish Street,
Dungannon,
Co. Tyrone
Tel: 028-8772 8080 Fax: 028-8772 6847
Email: info@bhhd.co.uk
Web: www.@bhhd.co.uk
GPS: N +54° 30' 14.03" W -6° 46' 18.40"

Unclassified By Northern Ireland Tourist Board. Dungannon's premier hotel, centrally located in Dungannon Town, Co. Tyrone. This family owned and operated boutique style hotel has preserved history in modern elegant surroundings. Each of the superbly appointed en suite guest rooms has been designed with your comfort in mind. Coins Restaurant menu available every evening from 6pm-9pm. Gold Bar menu Mon-Fri 4pm-9pm, Sat 12-9pm, Sunday carvery 12-4pm. Live entertainment every Saturday night in Gold Bar. Perfect for intimate wedding of approximately 80 guests.

Room Rate from £95.00 to £135.00

17

Activities:

Open All Year

Valley Hotel (The)

HOTEL ★★ MAP 14 L 16

60 Main St,
Fivemiletown,
Co. Tyrone BT75 0PW
Tel: 028-8952 1505 Fax: 028-8952 1688
Email: info@thevalleyhotel.com
Web: www.thevalleyhotel.com
GPS: N +54° 22' 40.87" W -7° 18' 53.36"

This is truly a magnificent small AA 3 star contemporary family run-hotel offering excellent service, accommodation and award-winning cuisine. It is situated at the gateway to the famous Fermanagh Lakelands, a perfect base to explore many of the tourist attractions such as Marble Arch Caves, Belleek Pottery and the award-winning Ulster American Folk Park. Golf, fishing, walking, cycling and pony trekking are all available locally. Free WiFi & car parking available. Please enquire about Facilities for Persons with Disabilities.

Bookable on www.irelandhotels.com

B&B from £45.00 to £60.00
Suites from £100.00 to £120.00

Greg Williamson
General Manager

22

Closed 25 - 26 December

Silverbirch Hotel

HOTEL ★★★ MAP 14 L 18

5 Gortin Road,
Omagh,
Co. Tyrone BT79 7DH
Tel: 028-8224 2520 Fax: 028-8224 9061
Email: info@silverbirchhotel.com
Web: www.silverbirchhotel.com
GPS: N +54° 36' 37.04" W -7° 17' 58.94"

Silverbirch Hotel is located on the outskirts of Omagh on the B48 leading to the Gortin Glens, Sperrins and the Ulster American Folk Park. Set in its own spacious and mature grounds, the hotel has 64 bedrooms furnished to a 3*** standard. Other facilities include a newly refurbished Bar & Restaurant and also a new Business Centre complimenting our existing banqueting facilities. Now book online via our website providing a secure real-time booking with automated confirmation. Please enquire about Facilities for Persons with Disabilities.

B&B from £46.00 to £75.00

Allan Duncan
Manager

64

Closed 25 December

B&B Rates are per Person Sharing per Night incl. Breakfast.
or Room Rates are per Room per Night - **See also Page 8**

One Source
Endless Possibilities
irelandhotels.com
Official Website of the Irish Hotels Federation
IRISH
HOTELS
FEDERATION

Dublin & Ireland East

See page 365 for map with access points and driving distances

For Detailed Maps of this Region See Pages 365-380. Each Hotel or Guesthouse has a Map Reference to these detailed maps under their photograph.

Dublin & Ireland East

Cavan, Dublin, Kildare, Laois, Longford, Louth, Meath, Monaghan, Offaly, Westmeath, Wicklow
(see pages 2 & 3 for full County listing)

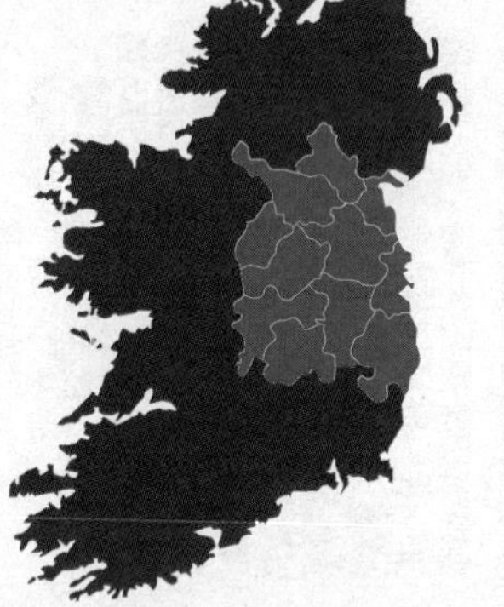

Feast your senses on bewitching scenery, fantastic city life, sensational sporting events and compelling historical sights.

The republic's capital city **Dublin** lies at the heart of a region that enchants the visitor with a selection of lakes, rivers and stretches of coastline. Dublin is usually the first port of call for visitors and this energetic, youthful city pulsates with a compelling mix of history, culture, hip bars and pubs, elegant architecture, great shopping and some of the country's most sophisticated restaurants. Cosmopolitan and diverse, Dublin is now one of Europe's top urban hotspots.

Ireland's capital is steeped in history and youthful energy. Dublin is a city where the charming and cosmopolitan converge in delightful diversity. Medieval, Georgian and modern architecture provide a backdrop to this friendly bustling port. Attractions are many, from castles, museums and art galleries to the lively spirit of Temple Bar. As one of the oldest cities in Europe, Dublin provides you with a multitude of cultural riches from the ancient to the ultra-modern and from history, architecture and literature to the performing arts. Dublin has lively pedestrian shopping streets at the heart of the city, alive with buskers and street performers, and there is a number of huge shopping centres in the outskirts offering excellent choice all under one roof, or go further a field to the surrounding towns and villages where you'll find boutiques and craft shops. Rich culture, gourmet cuisine, lively pubs, fabulous shopping, music for all and plenty of sport are just some of the experiences Dublin has to offer. There has never been a better time to visit Dublin! Visit the official online tourist office for Dublin **www.visitdublin.com**. The Dublin Pass offers the visitor the best in attraction, sightseeing, shopping, service and restaurant offers, all in one complete package. The purchase price of the pass covers entrance to over thirty of Dublin's top attraction and gives access to over twenty five special offers, added value and preferential rates at selected venues, theatres, retail outlets, restaurants, transport and tours. For more information see **www.dublinpass.ie**

Ireland East & Dublin will shower you with friendship and unforgettable memories and your adventures begin now…

Beyond Dublin, the east of Ireland tells a different story with the counties of Cavan, Kildare, Laois, Longford, Louth, Meath, Monaghan, Offaly, Westmeath and Wicklow offering a contrasting slice of life. This region is famed for its rich natural charms, ancient sites of Newgrange and Clonmacnoise, top golfing and world-renowned horseracing. The county of Kildare, in particular, is home to some of the world's finest thoroughbreds and of course the 2006 Ryder Cup.

But what really defines the east is the unspoilt countryside. With glistening lakes, tranquil rivers, authentic rural life, scenic pastureland, rolling hills and forest parks, this area is a haven for outdoors enthusiasts with cycling, watersports, walking, angling, golfing, horseriding and cruising in plentiful supply.

Cruising, fishing, golfing and equestrian enthusiasts should look no further than **Laois** and **Offaly.** The heritage town of Tullamore has put Offaly firmly on the map as a short break location and from here the ancient monastic site of Clonmacnoise, and of course the famous Tullamore Dew Heritage Centre, can be visited. For those who enjoy country walks and visiting gardens, Laois provides both. Tranquillity reigns along the banks of the Grand Canal at Vicarstown or the walking routes of the Slieve Blooms. Splendid gardens surround the Gandon House at Emo or the Lutyens Gardens at Heywood.

Kildare, host of the prestigious international Ryder Cup, is also home of the Irish horse. The county boasts three of the country's premier race courses as well as the Irish National Stud, Japanese and St. Fiachra's Gardens. Other attractions include Castletown House, Leixlip Castle, Ballindoolin Gardens and Mondello International Motor Race Course. Neighbouring **Wicklow**, known as the Garden of Ireland, contains outstanding scenery of mountains, valleys, lakes and coastlines. Renowned for its walking trails, The Wicklow Way is one of the most

Calendar of Events | GUINNESS

July
Guinness Seabreeze, Arklow, Co. Wicklow

August
Fleadh Cheoil na hÉireann, Tullamore, Co. Offaly
Tullamore Phoenix Festival, Tullamore, Co. Offaly

September
All Ireland Hurling Championship Final,
Croke Park, Dublin

High Cross, Co. Wicklow

mous. The ancient monastic site of Glendalough, owerscourt Gardens, Mount Usher Gardens, Wicklow aol and Parnell's Avondale House are some of the many tractions well worth a visit.

ne royal county of **Meath** has some of the most pectacular attractions in the country including the ssage Graves at Newgrange, the historic Trim Castle nd the famous Hills of Tara and Slane. The vibrant towns Navan, Trim and Kells provide the ideal base for touring. **uth** also has a rich medieval past. The town of Dundalk s connections with the mythical hero Cuchulainn. It is a brant shopping town and has a newly refurbished Town all & Basement Gallery, an award-winning County useum and the magnificent St. Patrick's Cathedral that ates back to 1837. Drogheda, on the River Boyne, has any fascinating buildings including St. Laurence's Gate, ilmount Motte and Martello Tower. The relics of St. iver Plunkett, martyred in 1681, are preserved in St. ter's Church. The heritage town of Carlingford displays past in King John's Castle and the interpretive centre.

avan is known as the Lake County. Discover the mystery d magic of the Lake County – a county with an ancient d colourful heritage. Come for a weekend, a week or nger and discover that Cavan is a fun place to visit. uzzing with friendly people, lively towns and villages, ectacular scenery, a vibrant arts and theatre scene, alks, cycle routes, museums, heritage centres, sparkling kes, fishing, cruising and activities, Cavan is a popular stination. Ireland's longest river – the mighty River annon rises in Dowra, Co. Cavan and forms part of the annon Erne Waterway. Why not hire a cruiser and meander your way through the longest navigable waterway in Europe. There is no better place to start than Cavan…

Monaghan has a landscape you can reach out and touch. It resounds with the poetry of Patrick Kavanagh. The renowned poet is celebrated in the Patrick Kavanagh Rural and Literary Resource Centre in Inniskeen – a must for anyone interested in the poet's life and work. Monaghan has long been known as an angler's paradise and with this attraction and so many more it is well worth a visit. There are several walking routes in the Sliabh Beagh area. These include the Sliabh Beagh Way, a 46km long distance walk, way marked from St. Patrick's Chair & Well in Co. Tyrone, entering Co. Monaghan at Lough More, going over Bragan Mountain, winding its way through Tully Forest and aptly ending at Donagh. There are also 36 loop walks, throughout the Sliabh Beagh region, all of which are way marked and vary in length from 4km – 15km. These routes take the walker through a variety of landscapes.

Counties **Longford** and **Westmeath** with their rivers, lakes and canal ensure many watersports are enjoyed here as well as top class angling with all species of coarse fish and brown trout. An area noted for its history and varied heritage, visitor attractions include the Heritage Centre in Ardagh, Corlea Trackway near Kenagh, the Bog Oak Sculptures in Newtowncashel, the magnificent Belvedere House and Gardens outside Mullingar, Athlone Castle and Locke's Distillery situated in the town of Kilbeggan which also hosts horse racing during the summer months. Literary associations include Maria Edgeworth, Padraic Colum, Oliver Goldsmith, James Joyce and Jonathan Swift.

Dublin & Ireland East

Equestrian

Ireland's East Coast offers some extraordinary equestrian experiences from horse racing, to horse riding, museums and studs to horse drawn caravan holidays.
The region is most famous for its horse racing so after a visit to the National Museum and Stud in Kildare why not take in one of our famous racing festivals like those at the Curragh or Punchestown. Ireland has over 300 race meetings every year across its many racecourses so finding a fixture that suits you is never a problem.
To find one near the hotel you are staying in, check out www.discoverireland.ie/equestrian

10 Key Walks

1 Howth looped walks, Co. Dublin
2 Bailieborough, Co. Cavan
3 Glendalough, Co. Wicklow
4 Crone Woods, Co. Wicklow
5 Tinahely, Co. Wicklow
6 Glenbarrow looped walks, Co. Laois
7 Kinnitty looped walks, Co. Offaly
8 Slieve Foye looped walks, Carlingford, Co. Louth
9 Donadea forest park, Co. Kildare
10 Drewstown woods, Co. Meath

Maps for these walks and the other 200 looped walks across Ireland can be downloaded on
www.discoverireland.ie/walking

Or why not get on your bike and follow one of 3 cycling trails surrounding Mullingar?

Top 10 Attractions

1 National Museum of Ireland
Kildare St, Dublin (Archaeology)
2 Guinness Storehouse, Dublin
3 National Museum of Ireland Collins
Barracks, Dublin (Decorative Art & History)
4 Kilmainham Jail, Dublin
5 Dublinia, Dublin
6 Glendalough, Co. Wicklow
7 Belvedere House & Gardens
Mullingar, Co. Westmeath
8 Clonmacnoise, Co. Offaly
9 Castletown House, Co. Kildare
10 Newgrange & Bru na Boinne, Co. Meath
11 Mellifont Abbey, Drogheda, Co. Louth
12 Japanese Gardens & National Stud, Co. Kildare
13 GAA Museum, Dublin

Angling

The mighty pike is most prevalent in the counties of Monaghan and Cavan. County Cavan boats 365 lakes alone! Major pike fisheries on the River Shannon include Loughs Allen, Ree, Derravaragh and Derg. Coarse anglers will find easily accessible stretches on the Grand and Royal canal systems running though the towns of Edenderry, Prosperous, Enfield and Leixlip. The River Fane in County Louth has a deservedly fine reputation for it's wild brown trout as has the River Boyne in the adjoining county of Meath.
For more information and the lists of towns that are part of our anglers welcome initiative visit
www.discoverireland.ie/angling

Cruising

What better way to enjoy Irelands' dramatic unspoilt inland lakes and rivers than to take a boat trip. This for the less experienced sailors, is the best way to sit back and relax and take in what Ireland has to offer.
Dotted with lakes, and criss-crossed by lovely rivers and historic canals, Ireland is a watery paradise for those looking to relax and go with the flow on a cruising holiday. But taking a cruising trip in Ireland – where no experience or license is required – goes far beyond the boat.
Take the mighty River Shannon. Once a major route through the country, it was used by Viking invaders to attack monastic settlements along its banks like Clonmacnoise. Surging from Yeats Country through the brimming bowl of Lough Derg – it is now a haven for anglers, water sports enthusiasts, golfers, historians and foodies. While the Shannon may be the jewel in the crown, you might prefer to choose your own personal gem from the many other scenic rivers, lakes and canals. And if our inland waterways aren't enough to float your boat, maybe you'll be tempted by an excursion to one of our many rugged islands.
For more information on where to hire a boat visit
www.discoverireland.ie

Historic Boyne Valley

Discover the ancient splendor of Ireland's heritage from the Battle of the Boyne to Cuchulainn – within a landscape which is abundant with history & tradition.
For more information check out *www.discoverireland.ie*

Breffni Arms Hotel

HOTEL ★★ MAP 11 K 14

Arvagh,
Co. Cavan

Tel: 049-433 5127 Fax: 049-433 5799
Email: breffniarms@hotmail.com
Web: www.breffniarms.com
GPS: N +53° 55' 27.89" W -7° 35' 0.39"

The Breffni Arms is a 12 bedroomed en suite family-run licensed hotel and leisure centre. Ideally situated for a choice of golf courses, fishing, horse riding and pitch & putt, etc. Facilities include 15m indoor swimming pool, sauna, steam room, jacuzzi and fitness room. All our rooms have TV, phone, computer point and tea/coffee making facilities. Please enquire about Facilities for Persons with Disabilities.

Bookable on www.irelandhotels.com

B&B from €50.00 to €75.00

Philomena & Eamonn Gray

12

Closed 24 - 26 December

Keepers Arms

GUESTHOUSE ★★ MAP 11 K 15

Bridge Street,
Bawnboy, Ballyconnell,
Co. Cavan

Tel: 049-952 3318 Fax: 049-952 3008
Email: info@keepersarms.com
Web: www.keepersarms.com
GPS: N +54° 7' 13.56" W -7° 40' 36.16"

Situated in West Cavan the village of Bawnboy boasts The Keepers Arms. It offers top of the range quality approved accommodation and fully licenced bar. Ideally based for fishing, golfing and walking holidays. All our nine en suite rooms have been decorated and equipped with your comfort in mind. (TVs, Tea/Coffee, DD Phone). So if you require a king, single, double, twin, or family room we are able to satisfy your needs. Our aim is to make your stay a comfortable one. Please enquire about Facilities for Persons with Disabilities.

Bookable on www.irelandhotels.com

B&B from €60.00 to €70.00

Sheila McKiernan

9

Closed 24 - 26 December

Slieve Russell Hotel Golf & Country Club

HOTEL ★★★★ MAP 11 K 15

Ballyconnell,
Co. Cavan

Tel: 049-952 6444 Fax: 049-952 6474
Email: enquiries@slieverussell.ie
Web: www.slieverussell.ie
GPS: N +54° 5' 46.44" W -7° 33' 30.13"

The Slieve Russell Hotel Golf & Country Club with Ciúin Spa & Wellness Centre, is a luxury 4 star resort with 222 stylish rooms set amidst 300 acres of landscaped gardens, including 50 acres of lakes. Our state of the art conference centre caters for conferences with up to 1200 delegates. For the golfer, our 18 hole Championship Golf Course ensures a challenging game. Our 9 hole par 3 course & driving range are also available. Located just 90 miles from Dublin & Belfast, the Slieve Russell Hotel offers a haven of comfort & relaxation. Please enquire about Facilities for Persons with Disabilities.

An IHF Quality Employer

Member of Quinn Hotels

Bookable on www.irelandhotels.com

B&B from €65.00 to €79.00
Suites from €230.00 to €259.00

Tony Walker
General Manager

222

Food for Kids   Activities:

Open All Year

B&B Rates are per Person Sharing per Night incl. Breakfast.
or Room Rates are per Room per Night - **See also Page 8**

Cavan Town / Kingscourt

Hotel Kilmore

HOTEL ★★★ MAP 11 L 14

Dublin Road,
Cavan Town,
Co. Cavan
Tel: 049-433 2288 Fax: 049-433 2458
Email: sales@hotelkilmore.ie
Web: www.hotelkilmore.ie
GPS: N +53° 59' 12.93" W -7° 19' 21.36"

On the doorsteps of Ireland's lakelands, the charming Hotel Kilmore offers guests a perfect blend of old world charm and contemporary design. Relax and enjoy the benefits of the afternoon sun in our Victorian sunroom bar, dine in sumptuous elegance in our Annalee Restaurant or enjoy a pint and a friendly chat in our Killykeen Lounge. A vibrant venue for any conference or private function. Please enquire about Facilities for Persons with Disabilities.

An IHF Quality Employer

Bookable on www.irelandhotels.com

B&B from €75.00 to €95.00
Suites from €175.00 to €220.00

Paul Henry
General Manager

38

Activities:

Closed 24 - 26 December

Radisson Blu Farnham Estate Hotel

HOTEL ★★★★ MAP 11 L 14

Farnham Estate,
Cavan,
Co. Cavan
Tel: 049-437 7700 Fax: 049-437 7701
Email: info@farnhamestate.com
Web: www.farnhamestate.com
GPS: N +54° 0' 6.97" W -7° 24' 1.35"

Among 1,300 acres of ancient forest, rolling meadows and pristine lakeland, this resort offers wonderful accommodation, healthy and delicious cuisine, full use of spa facilities and a holistic mix of fitness and outdoor activities. Enjoy walking through ancient woodland, biking, fishing and golf on our new Jeff Howes designed course. This is a wonderful place to find peace within while increasing vitality throughout. Enjoy! Please enquire about Facilities for Persons with Disabilities.

An IHF Quality Employer

Member of Radisson Blu Hotels & Resorts

Bookable on www.irelandhotels.com
Special Offer: www.irelandhotels.com/offers

B&B from €55.00 to €120.00
Suites from €160.00 to €390.00

John O'Carroll
General Manager

158

Food for Kids Activities:

Open All Year

Cabra Castle Hotel

HOTEL ★★★★ MAP 11 M 14

Kingscourt,
Co. Cavan
Tel: 042-966 7030 Fax: 042-966 7039
Email: sales@cabracastle.com
Web: www.cabracastle.com
GPS: N +53° 54' 49.72" W -6° 46' 29.79"

Follow in the footsteps of Oliver Cromwell and James II, and treat yourself to a stay in a castle. Cabra Castle stands on 88 acres of gardens and parkland, with its own nine hole golf course. The bar and restaurant offer views over countryside, famous for its lakes and fishing, as well as Dun a Ri Forest Park. An ideal venue for that holiday, specialising in golfing and equestrian holidays. Member of: Manor House Hotels Tel: 01-295 8900. www.manorhousehotels.com. Sister hotel of Ballyseede Castle Hotel, Tralee, Co. Kerry. Please enquire about Facilities for Persons with Disabilities.

Member of Manor House Hotels

Bookable on www.irelandhotels.com
Special Offer: www.irelandhotels.com/offers

B&B from €55.00 to €140.00
Suites from €190.00 to €500.00

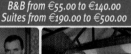

Howard Corscadden
Manager

86

Closed 23 - 26 December

B&B Rates are per Person Sharing per Night incl. Breakfast.
or Room Rates are per Room per Night - See also Page 8

Lakeside Manor Hotel

HOTEL ★★★ MAP 11 L 13

Dublin Road,
Virginia,
Co. Cavan

Tel: 049-854 8200 Fax: 049-854 8279
Email: info@lakesidemanor.ie
Web: www.lakesidemanor.ie
GPS: N +53° 49' 7.37" W -7° 3' 12.66"

This luxurious hotel located on the shores of scenic Lough Ramor offers something to suit everyone's taste. Relaxing in the Manor Bar with its breathtaking view of the lake and surrounding countryside. An excellent central location for golfing and all other leisure activities. For the fisherman, boat hire is available at your request and boat trips can also be arranged. This friendly hotel with its helpful and courteous staff is an ideal venue for a relaxing weekend or just to escape the hustle and bustle of the city. Please enquire about Facilities for Persons with Disabilities.

B&B from €50.00 to €75.00
Suites from €120.00 to €180.00

Meabh & Jim Brady
Proprietors

30

Activities:

Closed 24 - 26 December

Bracken Court Hotel

HOTEL ★★★ MAP 12 O 12

Bridge Street,
Balbriggan,
Co. Dublin

Tel: 01-841 3333 Fax: 01-841 5118
Email: info@brackencourt.ie
Web: www.brackencourt.ie
GPS: N +53° 36' 32.12" W -6° 10' 58.74"

An unexpected gem situated in the little fishing town of Balbriggan, North County Dublin. A boutique style hotel of timeless elegance & understated luxury, creating a haven of sophistication away from the hustle & bustle of Ireland's capital city. The building dates back to the 18th century, The Bracken Court Hotel successfully incorporates all the splendour of a by-gone age in its stunning design. Balbriggan's dramatic coastline & quaint harbour adds to the feeling of being away from it all. Home to Jack Doyles Bar & the 'Laveer' Restaurant. Please enquire about Facilities for Persons with Disabilities.

Member of The Moriarty Group

Bookable on www.irelandhotels.com

Special Offer: www.irelandhotels.com/offers

B&B from €55.00 to €75.00
Suites from €140.00 to €200.00

Luke Moriarty
Owner

66

Activities:

Closed 25 - 26 December

Airportview Hotel & Spa

HOTEL ★★★ MAP 8 O 11

Blakes Cross,
Lusk,
Co. Dublin

Tel: 01-843 8756 Fax: 01-807 1949
Email: gerry.butterly@gmail.com
Web: www.airportviewhotel.ie
GPS: N +53° 30' 23.18" W -6° 11' 48.12"

Airport View Hotel & Spa newly built 2007. Luxurious hotel 8 mins from Dublin Airport built on a 7 acre site, incorporates a state of the art spa, four poster bedroom with jacuzzi baths, DVD, TV, tea/coffee, fax, computer outlet facilities & large rooms, TV lounge, car park, conference rooms. Award-winning Winter's Restaurant with its excellent reputation for superb cuisine. Located on R129, 50yds off old main Dublin/Belfast Road, (R132). It has all the features of a 4* luxury Hotel. New health spa & spa pool, sauna, steam etc now open. See you there!! Also within 5 miles of 8 Golf courses (ideal for the perfect golf party).

Room Rate from €65.00 to €150.00
Suites from €130.00 to €150.00

Gerard Butterly / Annemarie Beggs
Proprietor

19

Activities:

Closed 24 - 26 December

B&B Rates are per Person Sharing per Night incl. Breakfast.
or Room Rates are per Room per Night - **See also Page 8**

Donabate / Dublin Airport

Waterside House Hotel & Signal Restaurant

HOTEL ★★★ MAP 12 O 12

Balcarrick Road,
Donabate,
Co. Dublin
Tel: 01-843 6153 Fax: 01-843 6111
Email: info@watersidehousehotel.ie
Web: www.watersidehousehotel.ie
GPS: N +53° 28' 44.08" W -6° 6' 55.74"

Overlooking Lambay Island, Ireland's Eye & Howth Head, this 3* property boasts 35 en suite recently refurbished bedrooms. It's ideal for golfers with 24 golf courses in the surrounding area & Corballis Golf Links on its doorstep. 20 mins from city centre & just 10 mins from Dublin Airport & Swords. The award-winning Signal Restaurant is open for breakfast, lunch & dinner daily. The Tower Bar & Bistro serves food from 7am-8.30pm. Telephone for special offers. Awarded two years in a row "Best Customer Service" Swords Fingal Chamber of Commerce. Tailor made packages available.

Bookable on www.irelandhotels.com
Special Offer: www.irelandhotels.com/offers

B&B from €30.00 to €130.00
Suites from €100.00 to €300.00

Chris & Thelma Slattery
Proprietors
35

Food for Kids Activities:

Open All Year

Bewley's Hotel Dublin Airport

HOTEL ★★★ MAP 12 O 12

Baskin Lane,
Swords,
Co. Dublin
Tel: 01-871 1000 Fax: 01-871 1001
Email: dublinairport@bewleyshotels.com
Web: www.bewleyshotels.com
GPS: N +53° 24' 41.32" W -6° 13' 0.25"

Bewleys Hotel, Dublin Airport, now part of the Moran Hotel Group, is one of the Airport's newest hotels. This contemporary styled hotel, located just off the M50/M1, offers the convenience of a complimentary 24hr shuttle service to & from the Airport Terminal every 20 mins. Oversized bedrooms, fluffy duvets, hypoallergenic pillows, tea & coffee facilities, in room safe, high speed internet access & multi channel TV are all standard features. The Brasserie Restaurant & Lounge Bar offer a range of tasty dishes for breakfast, lunch & dinner. Extensive short & long term car parking available for residents at highly competitive rates.

Member of Moran Hotel Group

Bookable on www.irelandhotels.com
Special Offer: www.irelandhotels.com/offers

Room Rate from €59.00 to €199.00

Tom Moran
Managing Director
466

Food for Kids Activities:

Closed 24 - 26 December

Carlton Dublin Airport Hotel

HOTEL ★★★★ MAP 12 O 11

Old Airport Road,
Dublin Airport,
Co. Dublin
Tel: 01-866 7500 Fax: 01-862 3114
Email: info.dublin@carlton.ie
Web: www.carlton.ie/dublinairport
GPS: N +53° 24' 55.23" W -6° 14' 25.22"

Conveniently located adjacent to Dublin Airport. Elegantly designed & built to the highest international 4* standards the Carlton offers every facility for both our business & leisure customers. 100 luxury suites & bedrooms. Incorporating a fully equipped conference centre boasting 19 meeting rooms. Rooftop Restaurant & Kitty Hawks Bistro, each with their own extensive menus using high quality produce in sumptuous surroundings. Park, Relax & Fly offers are available & include our complimentary 24hr shuttle service to & from the airport. Please enquire about Facilities for Persons with Disabilities.

An IHF Quality Employer

Member of Carlton Hotel Group

Bookable on www.irelandhotels.com
Special Offer: www.irelandhotels.com/offers

Room Rate from €89.00 to €250.00
Suites from €225.00 to €450.00

Declan Meagher
General Manager
100

Food for Kids

Closed 24 - 27 December

B&B Rates are per Person Sharing per Night incl. Breakfast. or Room Rates are per Room per Night - See also Page 8

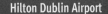

Crowne Plaza Dublin Northwood

HOTEL ★★★★ MAP 8 O 11

Northwood Park,
Santry,
Dublin 9
Tel: 01-862 8888 Fax: 01-862 8800
Email: info@crowneplazadublin.ie
Web: www.cpdublin.crowneplaza.com
GPS: N +53° 24' 16.20" W -6° 14' 43.89"

Crowne Plaza is a luxurious 4**** hotel with extensive conference facilities catering for 1000 delegates, 25 meeting rooms, 2 restaurants, bar and coffee lounge. Located in a mature parkland setting only 15 minutes from the City Centre and 5 minutes from Dublin Airport, close to M1/M50 motorways. Coach to/from Dublin Airport and large car park. AA Business Hotel of The Year 2006/2007. The Hotel is adjacent to the 3*** Express by Holiday Inn. Please enquire about Facilities for Persons with Disabilities.

An IHF Quality Employer

Member of Intercontintal Hotel Group

Bookable on www.irelandhotels.com

Room Rate from €89.00 to €300.00

Mary Buckley
General Manager

204

Activities:

Closed 24 - 26 December

Hilton Dublin Airport

HOTEL ★★★★ MAP 12 O 12

Northern Cross,
Malahide Road,
Dublin 17
Tel: 01-866 1800 Fax: 01-866 1866
Email: reservations.dublinairport@hilton.com
Web: www.dublinairport.hilton.com
GPS: N +53° 24' 13.16" W -6° 10' 48.21"

Your experience of Ireland's famously warm hospitality starts at the Hilton Dublin Airport. Purpose built with sleek design, the hotel is situated close to Dublin, the airport and Ireland's picturesque east coast. Its location, combined with second to none business facilities and an exceptionally welcoming environment, offers the very best in comfort and convenience for the business or leisure traveller. Please enquire about Facilities for Persons with Disabilities.

An IHF Quality Employer

Bookable on www.irelandhotels.com

B&B from €48.00 to €122.50
Suites from €136.00 to €285.00

Paul Flavin
General Manager

166

Food for Kids Activities:

Closed 24 - 26 December

Radisson Blu Hotel Dublin Airport

HOTEL ★★★★ MAP 12 O 11

Dublin Airport,
Co. Dublin
Tel: 01-844 6000 Fax: 01-8127265
Email: reservations.airport.dublin@radissonblu.com
Web: www.radissonblu.ie/hotel-dublinairport
GPS: N +53° 25' 35.45" W -6° 13' 56.81"

Situated within the airport complex, just two minutes from the main terminal and offering a 24h complimentary shuttle service to/from the terminal. This stylish contemporary hotel boasts 229 modern bedrooms and a wide range of conferences facilities catering up to 400 delegates. Radisson Blu Dublin Airport is ideal for both the leisure and business traveller. Please enquire about Facilities for Persons with Disabilities.

An IHF Quality Employer

Member of Radisson Blu Hotels & Resorts

Bookable on www.irelandhotels.com

Room Rate from €89.00 to €250.00
Suites from €250.00 to €250.00

Leah Morris

229

Open All Year

Dublin City

Abbott Lodge

GUESTHOUSE ★★ MAP 8 O 11

87/88 Lower Gardiner Street,
Dublin 1

Tel: 01-836 5548 Fax: 01-836 5549
Email: info@abbottlodge.com
Web: www.abbottlodge.com
GPS: N +53° 21' 7.86'' W -6° 15' 21.09''

Abbott Lodge is a warm and friendly, refurbished Georgian guesthouse situated in the heart of Dublin City. Located on the main bus route from Dublin Airport and close to all major tourist attractions, Temple Bar, shopping areas and nightlife. An excellent base for touring our wonderful city. All 29 guest rooms have en suite bathrooms, TV and tea/coffee making facilities. Our helpful staff at reception, which is open 24 hours, will be glad to help with tours, restaurant and theatre reservations. All rooms & public areas have free WiFi access. You can book online at www.abbottlodge.com.

B&B from €35.00 to €50.00

Patrick Healy
Assistant Manager

29

T C P I

Closed 22 - 27 December

Aberdeen Lodge

GUESTHOUSE ★★★★ MAP 8 O 11

53 Park Avenue,
Off Ailesbury Road, Ballsbridge,
Dublin 4

Tel: 01-283 8155 Fax: 01-283 7877
Email: aberdeen@iol.ie
Web: www.aberdeen-lodge.com
GPS: N +53° 19' 30.06" W -6° 12' 47.69"

The perfect balance of luxury, privacy & location, Aberdeen Lodge is one of Dublin's gems. The classic & de luxe bedrooms are spacious & elegant, several with four poster beds, spa baths, complimentary WiFi access, landscaped gardens & car park. Close to city centre, airport & car ferry terminals by DART or bus. Accolades: AA 5*, JDB Hotels, Times, Alaistair Sawdays, Bridgestone 100 Best Places to Stay Ireland 2009, The Good Hotel Guide, Best Loved Hotels. News: Sister property Blakes Hotel & Spa opening luxurious Austrian-themed Spa & wellness facility for 2010. USA toll free 1800 617 3178.

Member of Private Ireland

Bookable on www.irelandhotels.com

B&B from €69.00 to €99.00
Suites from €220.00 to €300.00

Pat Halpin & Ann Keane
Proprietors

20

Activities: ✓

T C U P S I

Open All Year

Adams Trinity Hotel

HOTEL ★★★ MAP 8 O 11

28 Dame Street,
Dublin 2

Tel: 01-670 7100 Fax: 01-670 7101
Email: adamstrinitygroup@eircom.net
Web: www.adamstrinityhoteldublin.ie
GPS: N +53° 20' 38.07" W -6° 15' 50.53"

What better location in Dublin than the Adams Trinity Hotel? Located mid-way between Dublin Castle, Grafton Street and Trinity College; it faces the vibrant Temple Bar area. Traditional style bedrooms are finished to an exceptionally luxurious standard. The hotel features the Mercantile Bar and Restaurant, O'Brien's Traditional Bar and café style Brokers Bar. The Adams Trinity Hotel offers all guests that same personal attention and warmth, it has that little something special. Special rates apply from Sunday - Thursday. Please enquire about Facilities for Persons with Disabilities.

Bookable on www.irelandhotels.com

B&B from €49.50 to €112.50

Fran Ryder / Peter Hanahoe
Proprietors

28

T C I

Closed 24 - 27 December

B&B Rates are per Person Sharing per Night incl. Breakfast.
or Room Rates are per Room per Night - See also Page 8

An Glen Guesthouse

GUESTHOUSE ★★ MAP 8 O 11

84 Lower Gardiner Street,
Dublin 1

Tel: 01-855 1374 Fax: 01-855 2506
Email: theglen@eircom.net
Web: www.glenguesthouse.com
GPS: N +53° 21' 5.89" W -6° 15' 17.33"

The Glen Guesthouse is an affordable and comfortable guesthouse located in the heart of Dublin city centre. Situated in North Dublin only half an hour from Dublin Airport, minutes from Temple bar, Grafton Street, the IFSC and all major attractions including Croke Park and the O2 - our guesthouse offers tourists the perfect base from which to explore and discover the city. Our ensuite guest rooms include TV, direct dial phones and tea and coffee facilities.

Bookable on www.irelandhotels.com

B&B from €20.00 to €125.00

Martin Tynan & Rossi Borisova
Joint Managers

15

T C P S I

Closed 23 - 27 December

Ardagh House

GUESTHOUSE ★★★ MAP 8 O 11

No.1 Highfield Road,
Rathgar,
Dublin 6

Tel: 01-497 7068 Fax: 01-497 3991
Email: enquiries@ardagh-house.ie
Web: www.ardagh-house.ie
GPS: N +53° 18' 46.66" W -6° 15' 50.84"

Having been recently totally refurbished, Ardagh House is conveniently situated in a premier residential area. This imposing turn of the century premises contains many of the gracious and spacious features of a fine detached residence of that era and yet incorporating modern creature comforts. Within easy distance of the city centre, RDS, etc. This fine property stands on approximately 1/2 acre with ample off street car parking and good gardens.

Bookable on www.irelandhotels.com

B&B from €40.00 to €75.00

Willie & Mary Doyle
Proprietors

19

T P I

Closed 21 December - 03 January

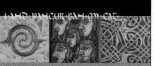

B&B Rates are per Person Sharing per Night incl. Breakfast.
or Room Rates are per Room per Night - See also Page 8

Dublin City

Ariel House

GUESTHOUSE ★★★★ MAP 8 O 11

50 - 54 Lansdowne Road,
Ballsbridge,
Dublin 4
Tel: 01-668 5512 Fax: 01-668 5845
Email: reservations@ariel-house.net
Web: www.ariel-house.net
GPS: N +53° 20' 2.95" W -6° 13' 51.97"

Ariel House is a charming Family run Guesthouse. The accommodation occupies three gracious Victorian mansions, on the doorstep of Aviva Stadium, Landsdowne Road. Beautifully restored yet incorporating the best of a modern boutique property Ariel house offers character and unrivalled dedication to hospitality. Located minutes from the DART station and RDS and close to the O2 arena & Dublin convention centre. Experience a warm welcome at a stylish address.

An IHF Quality Employer

Bookable on www.irelandhotels.com

Special Offer: www.irelandhotels.com/offers

B&B from €35.50 to €110.00

Deirdre McDonald
General Manager

37

Closed 22 - 27 December

Arlington Hotel O'Connell Bridge

HOTEL ★★★ MAP 8 O 11

Bachelors Walk,
O'Connell Bridge,
Dublin 1
Tel: 01-804 9100 Fax: 01-804 9152
Email: info@arlington.ie
Web: www.arlington.ie
GPS: N +53° 20' 50.07" W -6° 15' 39.45"

The most centrally located hotel in Dublin, overlooking the River Liffey at O'Connell Bridge. Dublin's top attractions and shopping districts on your doorstep. The Hotel boasts 131 en suite bedrooms, limited free underground parking, meeting room. Magnificent medieval Knightsbridge Bar with live Irish music and dancing 7 nights a week all year round (free admission). Carvery lunch and à la carte bar menu available, candle-lit Knights Bistro. Perfect base for business or pleasure. Please enquire about Facilities for Persons with Disabilities.

An IHF Quality Employer

Member of Fitzgerald Group

Bookable on www.irelandhotels.com

Special Offer: www.irelandhotels.com/offers

B&B from €45.00 to €130.00

Chris Carson
General Manager

131

Closed 24 - 26 December

Arlington Hotel Temple Bar

HOTEL ★★★ MAP 8 O 11

Lord Edward Street,
Temple Bar,
Dublin 2
Tel: 01-670 8777 Fax: 01-670 8787
Email: stay@arlingtonhoteltemplebar.com
Web: www.arlingtonhoteltemplebar.com
GPS: N +53° 20' 38.81" W -6° 16' 5.58"

The Arlington Hotel Temple Bar is located directly opposite Dublin Castle at the gateway to Dublin's Temple Bar. Visitors have a superb choice of bars, restaurants, theatres and shops on the doorstep. Minutes from Trinity College & Grafton Street. The hotel has 63 totally renovated rooms, and our new and busy Legends Bar offers the best in traditional Irish dishes with live Irish music & dancing 7 nights a week all year round (Free admission). Please call the hotel for superb theatre packages that include tickets to a show in the Olympia or Gaiety, pre-theatre meal & overnight accommodation with breakfast from just €99 per person.

Member of Fitzgerald Group

Bookable on www.irelandhotels.com

Special Offer: www.irelandhotels.com/offers

B&B from €44.50 to €149.50

Rory Keogh
General Manager

63

Closed 24 - 26 December

B&B Rates are per Person Sharing per Night incl. Breakfast.
or Room Rates are per Room per Night - **See also Page 8**

Ashling Hotel

HOTEL ★★★★ MAP 8 O 11

Parkgate Street,
Dublin 8

Tel: 01-677 2324 Fax: 01-679 3783
Email: info@ashlinghotel.ie
Web: www.ashlinghotel.ie
GPS: N +53° 20' 53.00" W -6° 17' 28.04"

Well established and highly recommended hotel in a central location. Recently extended and refurbished to a 4* finish. 225 excellent en suite bedrooms. Free car parking for overnight guests and complimentary internet access throughout. Short walk to city centre, or by bus, taxi or Luas. Adjacent to Heuston Rail Station, Guinness Brewery, Phoenix Park, Dublin Zoo and more. Easy access to M50 motorway and major routes. "Airlink" bus from Dublin Airport to Heuston Station. Wide range of meeting rooms available. Please enquire about Facilities for Persons with Disabilities.

An IHF Quality Employer

Member of Best Western Hotels

Bookable on www.irelandhotels.com

Special Offer: www.irelandhotels.com/offers

Room Rate from €79.00 to €310.00
Suites from €150.00 to €350.00

Alan Moody
General Manager
225

Food for Kids Activities:

Closed 24 - 26 December

Ballsbridge Inn & Towers

HOTEL ★★★ MAP 8 O 11

Pembroke Road,
Ballsbridge,
Dublin 4
Tel: 01-668 4468 Fax: 01-667 4381
Email: rooms@d4hotels.ie
Web: www.d4hotels.ie
GPS: N +53° 19' 56.62" W -6° 14' 3.80"

Offering you 3* quality accommodation, this hotel has a great location, friendly service & is excellent value for money, presenting a unique twist on a traditional hotel. The Ballsbridge Inn & Towers is located in Dublin's most exclusive address & is close to all major tourist attractions, theatre district, minutes walk from RDS & 5 minute bus or train from city centre. You will stay in rooms fitted with everything to make your stay in Dublin comfortable. We offer a special ground floor food hall with a number of well known & respected outlets serving you everything you need in the morning or revitalised during the day.

An IHF Quality Employer

Member of d4hotels.ie

Room Rate from €59.00 to €239.00
Suites from €99.00 to €300.00

Sarah Curran
General Manager
396

Activities:

Closed 24 - 26 December

Belvedere Hotel Parnell Square

HOTEL ★★★ MAP 8 O 11

Great Denmark Street,
Dublin 1

Tel: 01-873 7700 Fax: 01-873 7776
Email: info@belvederehotel.ie
Web: www.belvederehotel.ie
GPS: N +53° 21' 18.03" W -6° 15' 44.25"

Situated in the heart of Dublin City centre, the Belvedere Hotel Parnell Square is a historic, Georgian hotel offering great value close to O'Connell street, Croke Park, LUAS light rail services and all Dublin city centre attractions. It is the ideal base for your visit to Ireland's capital city. Facilities include 92 guest rooms, Belvedere Bar and Restaurant as well as two meeting rooms. Please enquire about Facilities for Persons with Disabilities.

An IHF Quality Employer

Member of Maldron Hotels - Partner Hotel

Bookable on www.irelandhotels.com

Special Offer: www.irelandhotels.com/offers

Room Rate from €79.00 to €299.00

Niamh Fitzpatrick
Hotel Manager
92

Closed 23 - 26 December

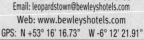

Dublin City

Best Western Premier Academy Plaza Hotel

HOTEL ★★★ MAP 8 O 11

Findlater Place,
Off O'Connell Street,
Dublin 1
Tel: 01-817 4141 Fax: 01-878 0600
Email: stay@academyplazahotel.ie
Web: www.academyplazahotel.ie
GPS: N +53° 21' 9.08" W -6° 15' 36.08"

Following the completion of our €30 million renovation, the Academy Plaza Hotel is now a Best Western Premier Member in the heart of Dublin, near Temple Bar, Trinity College & Croke Park. All the city transport is on our doorstep. We have 285 luxury bedrooms & suites, flatscreen TV, air-con & free WiFi. Dine or drink in Sir Harry's Bar & Bistro, Kendor Dine or Abacus Asian Restaurant. Conference & business facilities for 250 delegates. Gym, games room and Beauty Salon in hotel. Car parking nearby. Please enquire about Facilities for Persons with Disabilities.

Member of Best Western Premier

Bookable on www.irelandhotels.com

Room Rate from €79.00 to €299.00
Suites from €129.00 to €349.00

Peter Collins
Manager

285

Food for Kids *Activities:*

Closed 23 - 27 December

Bewley's Hotel Ballsbridge

HOTEL ★★★ MAP 8 O 11

Merrion Road,
Ballsbridge,
Dublin 4
Tel: 01-668 1111 Fax: 01-668 1999
Email: ballsbridge@bewleyshotels.com
Web: www.bewleyshotels.com
GPS: N +53° 19' 32.41" W -6° 13' 30.54"

Bewley's Hotel Ballsbridge, now part of the Moran Hotel Group, is located adjacent to the RDS grounds in the heart of Dublin's exclusive business district & embassy belt. This beautifully restored building was originally a 19th century Masonic school & is situated close to the city's many tourist attractions. Introducing Thomas Prior Hall, a magnificent new conference & banqueting venue. The oversized bedrooms boast fluffy duvets, tea & coffee facilities, in-room safe, high speed internet access & multi channel TV as standard. The Brasserie Restaurant & Tom's Bar offer a selection of dishes to suit all.

An IHF Quality Employer

Member of Moran Hotel Group

Bookable on www.irelandhotels.com

Room Rate from €59.00 to €199.00

Tom Moran
Managing Director

304

Food for Kids *Activities:*

Closed 24 - 26 December

Bewley's Hotel Leopardstown

HOTEL ★★★ MAP 8 O 11

Central Park,
Leopardstown Road,
Leopardstown, Dublin 18
Tel: 01-293 5000 Fax: 01-293 5099
Email: leopardstown@bewleyshotels.com
Web: www.bewleyshotels.com
GPS: N +53° 16' 16.73" W -6° 12' 21.91"

Bewleys Hotel Leopardstown, now part of the Moran Hotel Group, offers modern simplicity with the traditional touches that will guarantee a most enjoyable stay. Located only mins from Leopardstown Racecourse & Sandyford Ind Est. Convenient to the City Centre via the LUAS Lite Rail System. Oversized bedrooms, fluffy duvets, hypoallergenic pillows, tea & coffee facilities, in-room safe, high speed internet access & multi channel TV are all standard features. The Brasserie Restaurant has an excellent reputation locally & the bright, open plan lounge benefits from a south facing sun deck with views of the Dublin Mountains.

Member of Moran Hotel Group

Bookable on www.irelandhotels.com
Special Offer: www.irelandhotels.com/offers

Room Rate from €59.00 to €199.00

Tom Moran
Managing Director

352

Activities:

Closed 20 - 25 December

B&B Rates are per Person Sharing per Night incl. Breakfast.
or Room Rates are per Room per Night - **See also Page 8**

Dublin City

Bewley's Hotel Newlands Cross

HOTEL ★★★ MAP 8 O 11

Newlands Cross,
Naas Road (N7),
Dublin 22

Tel: 01-464 0140 Fax: 01-464 0900
Email: newlandscross@bewleyshotels.com
Web: www.bewleyshotels.com
GPS: N +53° 18' 48.94" W -6° 23' 33.41"

Bewley's Hotel Newlands Cross, now part of the Moran Hotel Group, offers quality & value in warm & friendly surroundings. Located at Dublin's gateway to the provinces (M50/N7 jct.) & convenient to the city centre via the LUAS Lite Rail system. Oversized bedrooms, fluffy duvets, hypoallergenic pillows, tea/coffee facilities, high speed internet access & multi channel TV are all standard features. The Brasserie Restaurant has an excellent reputation locally & offers a range of tasty dishes to suit the most discerning of palates. Please enquire about Facilities for Persons with Disabilities.

An IHF Quality Employer

Member of Moran Hotels

Bookable on www.irelandhotels.com

Special Offer: www.irelandhotels.com/offers

Room Rate from €59.00 to €199.00

Tom Moran
Managing Director

299

Activities:

Closed 24 - 26 December

Blakes Hotel & Spa

HOTEL MAP 8 O 11

50 Merrion Road,
Ballsbridge,
Dublin 4

Tel: 01-668 8324 Fax: 01-668 4280
Email: reservations@halpinprivatehotels.com
Web: www.halpinsprivatehotels.com
GPS: N +53° 19' 39.92" W -6° 13' 32.61"

UNDER CONSTRUCTION - OPENING FEBRUARY 2010

Built to a 5***** specification. New hotel & spa concept for Dublin. A sleek urban trendy hotel unique for its bold bathroom design and fitted out to a 5 star standard, Blakes is quickly making its mark with its unrivaled brand of contemporary luxury. This chic property with its avantgarde Austrian-themed spa and wellness centre is a first for Dublin. The spa suites and de luxe rooms offer the latest in-room technology – WIFI, air-con, plasma TV, CD and DVD. State of the art conference facility. Located in the south city centre embassy district. 20 mins by Aircoach to Dublin Airport. On Dublin DART & bus routes.

Member of Manor House Hotels of Ireland

Bookable on www.irelandhotels.com

B&B from €79.00 to €149.00
Suites from €229.00 to €399.00

Pat Halpin & Ann Keane
Proprietors

30

Activities:

Open All Year

Brooks Hotel

HOTEL ★★★★ MAP 8 O 11

Drury Street,
Dublin 2

Tel: 01-670 4000 Fax: 01-670 4455
Email: reservations@brookshotel.ie
Web: www.sinnotthotels.com
GPS: N +53° 20' 29.58" W -6° 15' 49.09"

Character, Style, Luxury, and Location are what distinguish Brooks from its peers. Add service excellence, superb food, with a warmth of welcome second to none and you have the obvious base for your stay in Dublin. All of Dublin's must 'Must See' sights are within minutes stroll and car parking facilities directly opposite. Bookable on www.sinnotthotels.com Please enquire about Facilities for Persons with Disabilities.

An IHF Quality Employer

Member of Small Luxury Hotels of the World

Bookable on www.irelandhotels.com

Room Rate from €160.00 to €395.00
Suites from €350.00 to €675.00

Mark O'Sullivan
General Manager

98

Activities:

Open All Year

B&B Rates are per Person Sharing per Night incl. Breakfast.
or Room Rates are per Room per Night - See also Page 8

Burlington (The)

HOTEL ★★★★ MAP 8 O 11

Upper Leeson Street,
Dublin 4

Tel: 01-618 5600 Fax: 01-668 8086
Email: info@burlingtonhotel.ie
Web: www.burlingtonhotel.ie
GPS: N +53° 19' 49.89" W -6° 14' 56.55"

A place that has inspired a thousand stories, The Burlington Hotel has held a special place in the heart of Dublin since 1972. Located just a 10 minute walk from St. Stephens Green. With our newly renovated Bellini's bar & lobby, renowned ballroom, modern conference facilities, opulent bedrooms, 2 spacious restaurants & expert chefs & friendly open staff, the hotel is the ideal choice for a stay in Dublin. Book online burlingtonhotel.ie. Please enquire about Facilities for Persons with Disabilities.

An IHF Quality Employer

Bookable on www.irelandhotels.com

Room Rate from €89.00 to €250.00
Suites from €199.00 to €350.00

John Clifton
General Manager

500

Activities:

Open All Year

Buswells Hotel

HOTEL ★★★ MAP 8 O 11

23/27 Molesworth Street,
Dublin 2

Tel: 01-614 6500 Fax: 01-676 2090
Email: buswells@quinn-hotels.com
Web: www.quinnhotels.com
GPS: N +53° 20' 26.71" W -6° 15' 20.93"

A hotel with special character and elegance - Buswells is a modern hotel within a unique Georgian setting. Ideally located in the heart of Dublin city centre, a short stroll from St. Stephen's Green, Trinity College, Grafton Street and many other visitor attractions. Our classic bedrooms allow you to relax and unwind after a long day in the busy city. Complimentary WiFi available in most bedrooms & all public areas. Secure overnight car parking available in Dawson St. Car Park to all our guests from 5.30pm to 9.30am. Please enquire about Facilities for Persons with Disabilities.

An IHF Quality Employer

Member of Quinn Hotels

Bookable on www.irelandhotels.com

Special Offer: www.irelandhotels.com/offers

B&B from €40.00 to €144.00
Suites from €90.00 to €194.00

Paul Gallagher
General Manager

67

Food for Kids Activities:

Closed 24 - 26 December

Butlers Town House

GUESTHOUSE ★★★★ MAP 8 O 11

44 Lansdowne Road,
Ballsbridge,
Dublin 4

Tel: 01-667 4022 Fax: 01-667 3960
Email: info@butlers-hotel.com
Web: www.butlers-hotel.com
GPS: N +53° 20' 2.56" W -6° 13' 56.32"

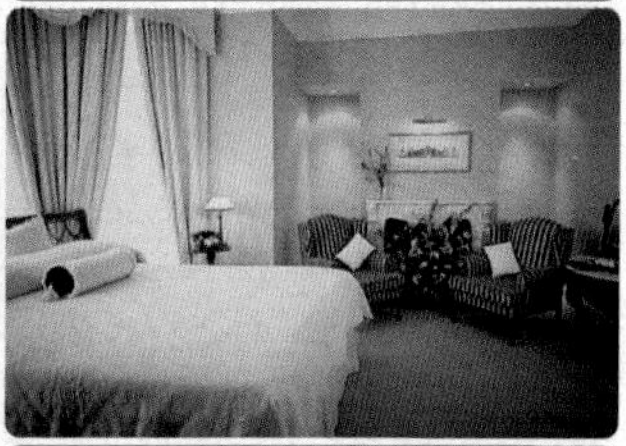

An oasis of country tranquillity in the heart of Dublin, Butlers Town House is an experience as opposed to a visit. Opened in March 1997, fully restored to reflect its former glory, but with all modern comforts from air-conditioning to WiFi. Butlers Town House is renowned for its elegance and premier guest service. Private secure car park available.

Member of Manor House Hotels

Bookable on www.irelandhotels.com

B&B from €70.00 to €80.00

Cecilia Farrell
Host

20

Closed 23 - 29 December

Dublin City

Camden Court Hotel

HOTEL ★★★ MAP 8 O 11

Camden Street,
Dublin 2

Tel: 01-475 9666 Fax: 01-475 9677
Email: sales@camdencourthotel.com
Web: www.camdencourthotel.com
GPS: N +53° 19' 59.15" W -6° 15' 52.32"

A highly recommended 3* hotel centrally located in the heart of Dublin. Situated within a 5 minute walk to St. Stephen's Green adjacent to Dublin's LUAS line. The hotel comprises 246 bedrooms and following a €10 million refurbishment programme, the hotel features an extensive range of conference facilities and the new Iveagh Restaurant. Enjoy our health club which includes a 16 meter pool, Jacuzzi and Sauna/ Steam room. Complimentary car parking on site subject to availability.

An IHF Quality Employer

Member of Cara Hotels

Bookable on www.irelandhotels.com

Special Offer: www.irelandhotels.com/offers

Room Rate from €99.00 to €200.00
Suites from €155.00 to €250.00

Stephen Hanna
General Manager

246

Food for Kids *Activities:*

Closed 23 - 28 December

Cassidys Hotel

HOTEL ★★★ MAP 8 O 11

Cavendish Row,
Upper O'Connell Street,
Dublin 1

Tel: 01-878 0555 Fax: 01-878 0687
Email: stay@cassidyshotel.com
Web: www.cassidyshotel.com
GPS: N +53° 21' 11.43" W -6° 15' 41.76"

"A little gem in the heart of Dublin" Cassidy's is a comfortable 113 bed-roomed boutique styled hotel located in 3 converted Georgian buildings opposite the famous Gate Theatre. Trinity College, shopping and the vibrant Temple Bar quarter are all a short walk away. Groomes Bar & Bistro adds a relaxing air and offers quality, character & comfort. On-site Fitness Suite free to guest. Guests can avail of complimentary WiFi.

An IHF Quality Employer

Bookable on www.irelandhotels.com

Special Offer: www.irelandhotels.com/offers

B&B from €45.00 to €145.00

Martin Cassidy
General Manager

113

Food for Kids *Activities:*

Closed 24 - 29 December

Castle Hotel

HOTEL ★★★ MAP 8 O 11

2-4 Gardiner Row,
Dublin 1

Tel: 01-874 6949 Fax: 01-872 7674
Email: info@castle-hotel.ie
Web: www.castle-hotel.ie
GPS: N +53° 21' 17.41" W -6° 15' 48.06"

Elegant Georgian hotel close to Dublin's main shopping, just 2 mins from O'Connell Street, close to Temple Bar, Croke Park & shopping- renowned for its friendly service. One of Dublin's oldest hotels. Authentically restored, the décor and furnishings offer modern comfort combined with old world features: crystal chandeliers, antique mirrors, marble fireplaces and period staircases. The individually decorated rooms are all en suite, with TV, DD phone, hairdryers and tea/coffee making facilities. The hotel has a restaurant, bar and private parking. Complimentary wireless internet access is available throughout the hotel.

Member of Castle Hotel Group

Bookable on www.irelandhotels.com

Room Rate from €69.00 to €189.00
Suites from €150.00 to €300.00

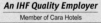

Yvonne O' Keeffe
General Manager

120

Closed 24 - 27 December

B&B Rates are per Person Sharing per Night incl. Breakfast.
or Room Rates are per Room per Night - **See also Page 8**

Castleknock Hotel and Country Club

HOTEL ★★★★ MAP 8 O 11

Porterstown Road,
Castleknock,
Dublin 15
Tel: 01-640 6300 Fax: 01-640 6303
Email: reservations@chcc.ie
Web: www.fbdhotels.com
GPS: N +53° 21' 57.50" W -6° 23' 23.34"

An exceptional 4 star hotel located just 15 minutes from the city centre, it offers all the comforts of a country retreat with a parkland golf course & and a relaxing day spa and leisure centre. It also includes 142 bedrooms, free parking and a choice of dining & bar facilities, which includes the AA Rosette award-winning Park Restaurant overlooking the golf course. Our extensive conference facilities & function rooms provide the perfect venue for our corporate guests & weddings. Special online offers available www.fbdhotels.com. Please enquire about Facilities for Persons with Disabilities.

An IHF Quality Employer

Member of FBD Hotels

Bookable on www.irelandhotels.com
Special Offer: www.irelandhotels.com/offers

B&B from €49.50 to €165.00
Suites from €160.00 to €330.00

Guy Thompson
General Manager

142

Activities:

Closed 24 - 28 December

Celtic Lodge Guesthouse

GUESTHOUSE ★★ MAP 8 O 11

81/82 Talbot Street,
Dublin 1
Tel: 01-878 8732 Fax: 01-878 8698
Email: info@celticlodge.ie
Web: www.celticlodge.ie
GPS: N +53° 21' 1.77" W -6° 15' 18.21"

Celtic Lodge is a newly renovated guesthouse, located in the city centre, just a few minutes walk from train, bus & tram. A stroll from our door is the vibrant Temple Bar district with its numerous pubs, restaurants, clubs, art galleries and markets. Trinity College, Dublin Castle, National Gallery, Christchurch & a number of theatres are within a stone's throw. All rooms are en-suite & equipped with TV and coffee/tea making facilities. Next door are our own traditional pub with live music and a new stylish restaurant. Airport transfer available.

Bookable on www.irelandhotels.com

B&B from €24.50 to €69.00

Brian Moloney
Director

29

Closed 23 - 27 December

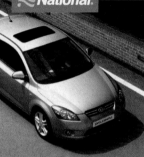

B&B Rates are per Person Sharing per Night incl. Breakfast.
or Room Rates are per Room per Night - **See also Page 8**

Dublin City

Charleville Lodge

GUESTHOUSE ★★★ MAP 8 O 11

268-272 North Circular Road,
Phibsborough,
Dublin 7
Tel: 01-838 6633 Fax: 01-838 5854
Email: info@charlevillelodge.ie
Web: www.charlevillelodge.ie
GPS: N +53° 21' 32.92" W -6° 16' 47.51"

Charleville Lodge, (former home of Lord Charleville), is a Victorian property located 15 minutes walk from the city centre, Trinity College, Temple Bar and en route to Dublin Airport and car ferry. Modernised to offer all the facilities normally associated with a larger hotel, while retaining the family-run atmosphere. There is a free car park, tea/coffee facility and broadband internet access. Group evening meals available upon request. 2 Nights B&B & 1 green fee in Island Golf Links from €150.00 to €200.00 per person sharing. Wireless internet access in all guestrooms, complimentary. Meeting room for up to 10 delegates.

An IHF Quality Employer

Member of Premier Collection

Bookable on www.irelandhotels.com

Special Offer: www.irelandhotels.com/offers

B&B from €27.50 to €125.00

Paul Stenson
Director

30

Activities:

T C P S I

Closed 20 - 26 December

Clarence (The)

HOTEL ★★★★ MAP 8 O 11

6-8 Wellington Quay,
Dublin 2
Tel: 01-407 0800 Fax: 01-407 0820
Email: reservations@theclarence.ie
Web: www.theclarence.ie
GPS: N +53° 20' 42.90" W -6° 16' 0.28"

Located on the River Liffey, in the heart of the city, The Clarence was built in 1852 and was transformed into a boutique hotel in 1996. Owned by Bono and The Edge of the rock group U2, The Clarence has 49 individually designed bedrooms and suites. A massage and treatment room, fitness room and valet parking are all available. The renowned Tea Room Restaurant and Octagon Bar, famous for its cocktails, are located here. Please enquire about Facilities for Persons with Disabilities.

Bookable on www.irelandhotels.com

Room Rate from €179.00 to €445.00
Suites from €349.00 to €2,800.00

Oliver Sevestre
General Manager

49

Activities:

T C P I

Closed 24 - 26 December

Clifden Guesthouse

GUESTHOUSE ★★★ MAP 8 O 11

32 Gardiner Place,
(off middle Gardiner Street),
Dublin 1
Tel: 01-874 6364 Fax: 01-874 6122
Email: info@clifdenhouse.com
Web: www.clifdenhouse.com
GPS: N +53° 21' 21.30" W -6° 15' 37.47"

200 year old 'listed' non-smoking Georgian home with 15 en suite rooms right in the heart of Dublin City centre with free secure car parking. Within a quick 5 min walk to O'Connell Street which offers convenient transport around the entire city. Experience the warm homely feel with its kind and friendly staff. We cater for single, double, twin, triple & family stays. All 15 rooms are en suite with shower in lower rooms and full bath/shower in rooms on 4th floor, no elevator, telephone, TV, tea/coffee making facilities, and WIFi. Luggage can be deposited at any time for early arrivals & left after checkout.

Member of Premier Collection

Bookable on www.irelandhotels.com

B&B from €25.00 to €100.00

Jack & Mary Lalor

15

T C P I

Closed 20 - 27 December

B&B Rates are per Person Sharing per Night incl. Breakfast.
or Room Rates are per Room per Night - See also Page 8

Clontarf Castle Hotel

HOTEL ★★★★ MAP 8 O 11

Castle Avenue,
Clontarf,
Dublin 3

Tel: 01-833 2321 Fax: 01-833 0418
Email: info@clontarfcastle.ie
Web: www.clontarfcastle.ie
GPS: N +53° 21' 53.32" W -6° 12' 25.25"

Clontarf Castle Hotel is part of a privately owned Irish hotel collection. Dating back to 1172 we offer the perfect blend of contemporary and traditional. From the strikingly historical exterior, to the warm Irish welcome waiting inside, the emphasis throughout is on luxury and glamour. 111 distinctively designed bedrooms and suites. 8 meeting rooms facilitating up to 600 delegates. Banqueting facilities for up to 450 guests. 2 bars; the chic Indigo Lounge & the time honoured Knights Bar. Our unique restaurant, Fahrenheit Grill, specialises in steak & fish. Please enquire about Facilities for Persons with Disabilities.

An IHF Quality Employer

Bookable on www.irelandhotels.com

Room Rate from €100.00 to €400.00
Suites from €140.00 to €420.00

Pius Furlong
General Manager

111

Activities:

Open All Year

Conrad Dublin

HOTEL ★★★★★ MAP 8 O 11

Earlsfort Terrace,
Dublin 2

Tel: 01-602 8900 Fax: 01-676 5424
Email: dublininfo@conradhotels.com
Web: www.conraddublin.com
GPS: N +53° 20' 5.79" W -6° 15' 26.17"

Conrad Dublin is a 5* luxury hotel located in the heart of Dublin opposite the National Concert Hall. The beautiful St. Stephens Green park and the fashionable Grafton Street popular with shopping enthusiasts are only a few mins walk. Guest rooms come with ergonomic work stations, broadband internet, multi-channel TV, CD player, air-con, bathrobes & slippers. Hotel offers two bars, restaurant, 24 hour room service, fitness centre, business centre & extensive conference & meeting facilities. Please enquire about Facilities for Persons with Disabilities.

An IHF Quality Employer

Member of Hilton Hotels Corporation

Bookable on www.irelandhotels.com

Special Offer: www.irelandhotels.com/offers

Room Rate from €189.00 to €400.00
Suites from €250.00 to €1,500.00

Martin Mangan
General Manager

191

Activities:

Open All Year

Croke Park Hotel (The)

HOTEL ★★★★ MAP 8 O 11

Jones's Road,
Dublin 3

Tel: 01-871 4444 Fax: 01-871 4400
Email: crokepark@doylecollection.com
Web: www.doylecollection.com
GPS: N +53° 21' 38.88" W -6° 15' 14.04"

Located a short distance from the city centre and within easy reach of Dublin's main retail and entertainment areas as well as business districts and the airport, The Croke Park Hotel is the perfect base for business or leisure trips. The hotel bridges the gap between home and work by providing spacious, luxurious bedrooms and bathrooms with entertainment systems, an excellent restaurant and bar serving fresh, healthy food. Meeting rooms feature state-of-the-art technology.

Member of The Doyle Collection

Bookable on www.irelandhotels.com

Special Offer: www.irelandhotels.com/offers

Room Rate from €79.00 to €399.00

Edward Stephenson
General Manager

232

Food for Kids

Closed 25- 28 December

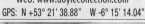

B&B Rates are per Person Sharing per Night incl. Breakfast.
or Room Rates are per Room per Night - **See also Page 8**

Dublin City

D4 Berkeley

HOTEL ★★★★ MAP 8 O 11

Lansdowne Road,
Ballsbridge,
Dublin 4

Tel: 01-668 4468 Fax: 01-667 4381
Email: rooms@d4hotels.ie
Web: www.d4hotels.ie
GPS: N +53° 19' 56.62" W -6° 14' 3.80"

Welcome to the 4* D4 Berkeley Hotel in Dublin 4. Located on the same site as the Ballsbridge Inn & Ballsbridge Towers, the D4 Berkeley (formerly the Ballsbridge Court Hotel) has been host to famous celebrities, incl... Madonna, Nelson Mandela, Elton John, Cher...to name but a few. This hotel offers discerning guests style, panache, quality service & amazing value for money for a 4* hotel. Guests can lounge in our Ballsbridge Bar & choose from a selection of cocktails & spirits. Dine at O'Connells Restaurant in South Dublin which is part of a famous Dublin institution. Exceptional food at great prices.

An IHF Quality Employer

Member of d4hotels.ie

Bookable on www.irelandhotels.com

Room Rate from €59.00 to €259.00
Suites from €109.00 to €300.00

Sarah Curran
General Manager

177

Activities:

Close 23 - 26 December

Dergvale Hotel

HOTEL ★★ MAP 8 O 11

4 Gardiner Place,
Dublin 1

Tel: 01-874 4753 Fax: 01-874 8276
Email: dergvale@indigo.ie
Web: www.dergvalehotel.com
GPS: N +53° 21' 21.99" W -6° 15' 38.69"

The Dergvale Hotel is located within walking distance of all principal shopping areas, cinemas, museums, Trinity College, Dublin Castle and airport bus. Most bedrooms with showers en suite, colour TV and direct dial telephone. Fully licensed. A courteous and efficient staff are on hand to make your stay an enjoyable one. The hotel is under the personal supervision of Gerard and Nancy Nolan.

Bookable on www.irelandhotels.com

B&B from €29.50 to €80.00

Gerard Nolan
Owner

3 17

Closed 23 December - 05 January

Drury Court Hotel

HOTEL ★★★ MAP 8 O 11

28-30 Lower Stephen Street,
Dublin 2

Tel: 01-475 1988 Fax: 01-478 5730
Email: reservations@drurycourthotel.com
Web: www.drurycourthotel.com
GPS: N +53° 20' 28.13" W -6° 15' 51.80"

Located in the heart of Dublin, beside Stephen's Green and Grafton Street. Convenient to the hotel are theatres, galleries, museums, Trinity College and Temple Bar. The hotel comprises 42 luxurious bedrooms all en suite with direct dial phone, free wireless internet service available, multi-channel TV/Radio and tea/coffee facilities. There is also the Bia Bar, a lively bar serving sumptuous food all day. The hotel is adjacent to secure public parking, just perfect for the leisure or business visitor. Please enquire about Facilities for Persons with Disabilities.

An IHF Quality Employer

Member of MinOtel Ireland Hotel Group

Bookable on www.irelandhotels.com
Special Offer: www.irelandhotels.com/offers

Room Rate from €55.00 to €190.00

Paul Hand
General Manager

42

Closed 23 - 28 December

B&B Rates are per Person Sharing per Night incl. Breakfast.
or Room Rates are per Room per Night - See also Page 8

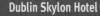

Dublin Citi Hotel

HOTEL ★★ MAP 8 O 11

46-49 Dame Street,
Dublin 2

Tel: 01-679 4455 Fax: 01-679 4496
Email: reservations@dublincitihotel.com
Web: www.dublincitihotel.com
GPS: N +53° 20' 39.57" W -6° 15' 49.11"

This hotel lies in the heart of Dublin City on the edge of Temple Bar. Boasting 26 guest rooms that have been designed with comfort and convenience in mind, the Dublin Citi Hotel offers great food and genuine Irish hospitality in a prime location. Attractions such as Trinity College, Grafton Street and Christchurch are right outside the door. Please Note: We have a very busy bar and nightclub within the hotel. As a result guests may experience noise late into the night and may not be suitable for families with children. Please enquire about Facilities for Persons with Disabilities.

Bookable on www.irelandhotels.com

Room Rate from €49.00 to €249.00

Philip Jaronski
Front Office Manager

26

Closed 24 - 26 December

Dublin Skylon Hotel

HOTEL ★★★ MAP 8 O 11

Upper Drumcondra Road,
Dublin 9

Tel: 01-884 3900 Fax: 01-837 2778
Email: reservations@dublinskylonhotel.com
Web: www.dublinskylonhotel.com
GPS: N +53° 22' 21.81" W -6° 15' 12.07"

A smart hotel on the northern approach, ten minutes from the airport and five from the city centre. Dublin Skylon Hotel has just the right blend of style and informality to make your stay special. Its restaurant and bar are welcoming and just as popular in the neighbourhood as with guests. Please enquire about Facilities for Persons with Disabilities.

An IHF Quality Employer

Member of Brian McEniff Hotels

Bookable on www.irelandhotels.com

Special Offer: www.irelandhotels.com/offers

Room Rate from €59.00 to €299.00
Suites from €129.00 to €499.00

Brian McEniff / Andrew Hyland
Proprietor / General Manager

126

Closed 24 - 26 December

Dylan Hotel

HOTEL ★★★★★ MAP 8 O 11

Eastmoreland Place,
Dublin 2

Tel: 01-660 3000 Fax: 01-660 3005
Email: info@dylan.ie
Web: www.dylan.ie
GPS: N +53° 20' 1.92" W -6° 14' 32.06"

By day the open plan lobby exudes warmth & elegance, by night Dylan is candles & champagne. Located on a leafy, affluent, residential street, Dylan is just minutes away from the heart of Dublin City centre; a short stroll over the canal along the historic Baggot Street leads to the city centre haven of St. Stephens Green & the world renowned Grafton Street, unrivalled for its top quality shopping and diverse street entertainment. Please enquire about Facilities for Persons with Disabilities.

An IHF Quality Employer

Member of Preferred Boutique

Bookable on www.irelandhotels.com

Room Rate from €225.00 to €395.00
Suites from €395.00 to €800.00

Siobhan Delaney
Hotel General Manager

44

Closed 25 - 26 December

Dublin City

Egan's Guesthouse

GUESTHOUSE ★★★ MAP 8 O 11

7/9 Iona Park,
Glasnevin,
Dublin 9
Tel: 01-830 3611 Fax: 01-830 3312
Email: info@eganshouse.com
Web: www.eganshouse.com
GPS: N +53° 22' 1.18" W -6° 15' 59.59"

Egan's House is an elegant terrace of Edwardian houses in a quiet area but only 1.7km from Dublin's city centre. All 23 guest rooms are en suite with television, telephone, hairdryer, electronic safe, ironing centre, power shower and tea/coffee facility. Free car parking. Dublin Airport is just 10 minutes by taxi and the car ferry is also close by, as is Croke Park, the O2 Arena, RDS and championship golf courses. Now wireless internet in all rooms.

Member of Premier Guesthouses

Bookable on www.irelandhotels.com

B&B from €35.00 to €85.00

Pat & Monica Finn
Proprietors
23

Open All Year

Ferryview House

GUESTHOUSE ★★★ MAP 8 O 11

96 Clontarf Road,
Clontarf,
Dublin 3
Tel: 01-833 5893 Fax: 01-853 2141
Email: ferryview@oceanfree.net
Web: www.ferryviewhouse.com
GPS: N +53° 21' 37.54" W -6° 12' 25.48"

Ferryview House is located in the exclusive coastal suburb of Clontarf, 2.5 miles from the city centre on a regular bus route. This is a totally refurbished family-run guesthouse. The house is close to Dublin Port, the O2 Arena, East Point Business Park (2km) and Dublin Airport is 15 minutes away. Local facilities include restaurants, coastal walks, Clontarf Rugby Club, tennis and 3 golf clubs.

B&B from €35.00 to €65.00

Margaret Allister
8

Open All Year

Fitzsimons Hotel

HOTEL ★★★ MAP 8 O 11

21-22 Wellington Quay,
Temple Bar,
Dublin 2
Tel: 01-677 9315 Fax: 01-677 9387
Email: info@fitzsimonshotel.com
Web: www.fitzsimonshotel.com
GPS: N +53° 20' 44.09" W -6° 15' 55.15"

Fitzsimons Hotel a boutique hotel situated on the banks of the River Liffey in the heart of Temple Bar. Its location offers the visitor doorstep access to this vibrant, exciting locale and all it has to offer, theatres, galleries, bars, restaurants, live music venues and alternative shops. Fitzsimons offers visitors a great place to socialise now with 4 floors of entertainment including our new open air Roof Terrace with bar, bars on all floors, restaurant and nightclub, seven nights a week. Please enquire about Facilities for Persons with Disabilities.

Bookable on www.irelandhotels.com

B&B from €45.00 to €100.00

Darina Howard
Host
22

Closed 24 - 25 December

B&B Rates are per Person Sharing per Night incl. Breakfast.
or Room Rates are per Room per Night - **See also Page 8**

Four Seasons Hotel Dublin

HOTEL ★★★★★ MAP 8 O 11

Simmonscourt Road,
Dublin 4

Tel: 01-665 4000 Fax: 01-665 4099
Email: reservations.dublin@fourseasons.com
Web: www.fourseasons.com/dublin
GPS: N +53° 19' 35.76" W -6° 13' 33.86"

The charm of Irish tradition & hospitality combine to provide the stage for Four Seasons Hotel Dublin. The hotel offers a location of cosmopolitan convenience in the prestigious embassy & residential district, bringing together exceptional guest rooms and suites with the finest facilities for business & leisure. Reflective of Dublin's architectural heritage, the hotel is just minutes from the cultural & entertainment options of the city centre. The hotel features 15,000 sq ft of meeting and banqueting space, fine dining in Seasons Restaurant, Ice Bar and an 11,000 sq ft full service spa.

An IHF Quality Employer

Member of Four Seasons Hotels & Resorts

Room Rate from €255.00 to €405.00
Suites from €530.00 to €610.00

Jose Soriano
General Manager

197

Open All Year

Glenogra House

GUESTHOUSE ★★★★ MAP 8 O 11

64 Merrion Road,
Ballsbridge,
Dublin 4

Tel: 01-668 3661 Fax: 01-668 3698
Email: info@glenogra.com
Web: www.glenogra.com
GPS: N +53° 19' 38.67" W -6° 13' 29.20"

A warm welcome awaits you at Glenogra, 4**** guesthouse. Set inside an elegant Edwardian period house, our relaxed ambience makes it the perfect place to stay for business or pleasure. Located in Ballsbridge, just 10 minutes from the city centre. All our bedrooms are en suite and have free WiFi. Glenogra is within easy reach of the RDS Exhibition Centre, Sandymount DART station and bus routes, the Air Coach, Lansdowne Road Stadium, the British and American Embassies, Dublin Port, Dun Laoghaire Port. Please enquire about Facilities for Persons with Disabilities.

Member of Premier Guesthouses

Bookable on www.irelandhotels.com

B&B from €39.50 to €99.50

Joseph Donohoe
Manager

13

Closed 23 - 27 December

Dublin City

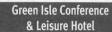

Grafton Capital Hotel

HOTEL ★★★ MAP 8 0 11

Stephens Street Lower,
Dublin 2

Tel: 01-648 1100 Fax: 01-648 1122
Email: info@graftoncapital-hotel.com
Web: www.graftoncapitalhotel.com
GPS: N +53° 20' 28.01" W -6° 15' 50.77"

The Grafton Capital Hotel is a traditional Georgian Townhouse which offers spacious accommodation and a warm ambiance. Located in the heart of Dublin City centre paces away from Grafton Street, entertainment and cultural attractions; this hotel is the perfect tourist choice. High standards of service and genuine Dublin hospitality are guaranteed during your stay. Break for the Border, the hotel's bar and restaurant, offers an extensive food and drinks menu. Please enquire about Facilities for Persons with Disabilities.

An IHF Quality Employer

Member of Capital Hotel Group

Bookable on www.irelandhotels.com

Special Offer: www.irelandhotels.com/offers

Room Rate from €69.00 to €200.00

Denyse Campbell
General Manager

75

Closed 24 - 27 December

Green Isle Conference & Leisure Hotel

HOTEL ★★★ MAP 8 0 11

Newlands Cross,
Dublin 22

Tel: 01-459 3406 Fax: 01-459 5828
Email: reservations@greenislehotel.com
Web: www.greenislehotel.com
GPS: N +53° 18' 34.37'' W -6° 24' 13.33''

The Green Isle hotel with newly refurbished bar & restaurant offers 270 superior bedrooms with a wide range of room types. Signature bedrooms with pillow-top mattresses, luxurious duvets and feather pillows ensure a great night's sleep. Leisure facilities include a 15m pool and extensive gym, Fusion Spa and hair salon. New conference centre can hold up to 650 delegates. Free parking. 10km from Dublin city, airport bus to door & LUAS only 5 mins away. Member of Brennan Hotels, Clonmel, Kilkenny, Arklow, Meath & Dublin. Please enquire about Facilities for Persons with Disabilities.

An IHF Quality Employer

Member of Brennan Hotel Group

Bookable on www.irelandhotels.com

Special Offer: www.irelandhotels.com/offers

Room Rate from €59.00 to €199.00

Padraig Blighe
General Manager

270

Closed 24 - 26 December

Gresham (The)

HOTEL ★★★★ MAP 8 0 11

23 Upper O'Connell Street,
Dublin 1

Tel: 01-874 6881 Fax: 01-878 7175
Email: info@thegresham.com
Web: www.gresham-hotels.com
GPS: N +53° 21' 5.96" W -6° 15' 37.17"

Elegant, sophisticated and offering unparalleled standards of hospitality and customer care. The Gresham has undergone an imaginative and tasteful transformation. Each room is equipped with air conditioning, complimentary WiFi and state of the art entertainment system. Other facilities include a renowned Clefs d'Or concierge service, two bars and afternoon tea in the luxurious lobby. Car parking (charges apply). AA approved.

An IHF Quality Employer

Member of Gresham Hotel Group

Bookable on www.irelandhotels.com

Special Offer: www.irelandhotels.com/offers

Room Rate from €140.00 to €600.00
Suites from €1,500.00 to €2,200.00

Paul McCracken
Operations Director

288

Activities:

Open All Year

B&B Rates are per Person Sharing per Night incl. Breakfast.
or Room Rates are per Room per Night - **See also Page 8**

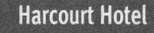

Hampton Hotel

HOTEL ★★★★ MAP 8 0 11

19-29 Morehampton Road,
Dublin 4

Tel: 01-668 0995 Fax: 01-667 6126
Email: info@hamptonhotel.ie
Web: www.hamptonhotel.ie
GPS: N +53° 19' 32.94" W -6° 14' 34.53"

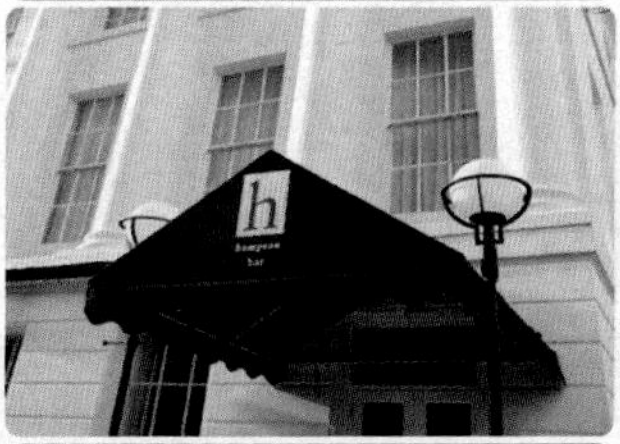

This 4-star boutique hotel offers luxury accommodation & is in close proximity to the RDS, National Concert Hall & a selection of Dublin's finest restaurants. With 24 beautifully styled guest bedrooms, this stunning period building has retained all its Georgian charm while providing a unique stylish touch & modern amenities. With its own private bar, the Morehampton Room is ideal for private gatherings, launches & meetings. From its informal bistro dining, designated function room & nightclub, the hotel offers every service that the modern visitor could need.

Bookable on www.irelandhotels.com

Room Rate from €99.00 to €379.00
Suites from €199.00 to €550.00

Bruno Gorisch
General Manager

24

Open All Year

Harcourt Hotel

HOTEL ★★★ MAP 8 0 11

60-65 Harcourt Street,
Dublin 2

Tel: 01-478 3677 Fax: 01-478 1557
Email: reservations@harcourthotel.ie
Web: www.harcourthotel.ie
GPS: N +53° 20' 3.91" W -6° 15' 45.97"

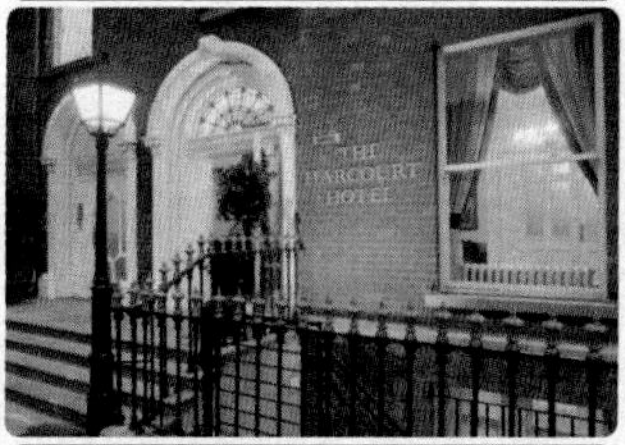

The Harcourt Hotel has a safe, fashionable, central location, close to Grafton Street and St. Stephen's Green. This boutique style hotel is famous for once being home to George Bernard Shaw. Its Georgian exterior conceals a contemporary interior. Facilities include a convivial bar, an all-weather beer garden and a nightclub (typically Wednesday to Saturday). Little Caesars Restaurant serves delicious Italian and international cuisine until midnight. Some rooms can suffer from noise. This is especially, but not exclusively, true at weekends.

Bookable on www.irelandhotels.com

Room Rate from €49.00 to €250.00

Danielle McGill
Operations Manager

51

Closed 24 - 26 December

Harding Hotel

HOTEL ★★★ MAP 8 0 11

Copper Alley,
Fishamble Street, Christchurch,
Dublin 2
Tel: 01-679 6500 Fax: 01-679 6504
Email: info@hardinghotel.ie
Web: www.hardinghotel.ie
GPS: N +53° 20' 38.12" W -6° 16' 11.72"

Newly renovated to an exceptional standard, The Harding Hotel is located within Dublin's Temple Bar district. All bedrooms have televisions, telephone, fridge, hairdryer, tea & coffee making facilities and free WiFi access. Relax and enjoy the drink and entertainment in Darkey Kelly's Bar or a wonderful meal in Copper Alley Bistro. Groups and individuals welcome. Please enquire about Facilities for Persons with Disabilities.

Bookable on www.irelandhotels.com

Room Rate from €45.00 to €200.00

Aine Hickey
Manager

52

Closed 24 - 25 December

Dublin City

Harrington Hall

GUESTHOUSE ★★★★ MAP 8 O 11

69-70 Harcourt Street,
Dublin 2

Tel: 01-475 3497 Fax: 01-478 1557
Email: harringtonhall@eircom.net
Web: www.harringtonhall.com
GPS: N +53° 20' 5.90" W -6° 15' 46.92"

Harrington Hall is centrally located on Harcourt St, just off the South West corner of St.Stephen's Green. It is convenient to the famous Shopping area of Grafton St. This boutique guesthouse features 29 magnificent bedrooms, including junior suites and family rooms. All bedrooms are en suite with direct dial phone, colour TV, tea/coffee making facilities and electric ceiling fan. All floors are serviced by an elevator. Free WiFi in public areas. Free car parking on site.

Member of Manor House Hotels

Bookable on www.irelandhotels.com

Room Rate from €69.00 to €199.00
Suites from €99.00 to €250.00

Paul Glynn

29

Open All Year

Harvey's Guest House

GUESTHOUSE ★★★ MAP 8 O 11

11 Upper Gardiner Street,
Dublin 1

Tel: 01-874 8384
Email: info@harveysguesthouse.com
Web: www.harveysguesthouse.com
GPS: N +53° 21' 26.45" W -6° 15' 35.96"

A family-run Georgian guesthouse with a household atmosphere, and we have time to chat with you. We are 1km from O'Connell Bridge. Close to the Abbey & Gate Theatres, the Writers Museum and James Joyce Centre and 500m from Croke Park. We look forward to meeting you and guiding you through your stay in Dublin and Ireland.

B&B from €35.00 to €70.00

Eilish Flood
Owner

16

Open All Year

Hilton Dublin

HOTEL ★★★★ MAP 8 O 11

Charlemont Place,
Dublin 2

Tel: 01-402 9988 Fax: 01-402 9852
Email: reservations.dublin@hilton.com
Web: www.hilton.com
GPS: N +53° 19' 52.25" W -6° 15' 33.69"

Hilton Dublin is located most conveniently next to the LUAS Charlemont stop which will bring you in 5 minutes to St. Stephen's Green. Completely refurbished in 2008 the hotel offers 193 Hilton de luxe rooms. Hilton Dublin can cater for meetings from 2 - 400 people. Try out UISCE, the *new* Irish restaurant serving Irish food made from Irish ingredients. Enjoy a night of flair bartending and *live* music in the eclectic STIL Bar and Lounge. Please enquire about Facilities for Persons with Disabilities.

An IHF Quality Employer

Member of Hilton International

Bookable on www.irelandhotels.com

B&B from €67.00 to €122.00

Erwin Verhoog
General Manager

193

Food for Kids *Activities:*

Closed 24 - 27 December

B&B Rates are per Person Sharing per Night incl. Breakfast.
or Room Rates are per Room per Night - See also Page 8

Hotel Isaacs

HOTEL ★★★ MAP 8 O 11

Store Street,
Dublin 1

Tel: 01-813 4700 Fax: 01-836 5390
Email: hotel@isaacs.ie
Web: www.hotelisaacs.com
GPS: N +53° 21' 0.32" W -6° 15' 10.05"

Situated in the heart of Dublin City, Hotel Isaacs, a converted wine warehouse, is the perfect location for any visitor to Dublin. Only a short walk to the IFSC, Temple Bar, O2 Arena, Croke Park, O'Connell Bridge and Busaras, this location cannot be beaten. All rooms are en suite with telephone, TV, tea/coffee, garment press, safe and hairdryer. Other facilities include Le Monde Café Bar, Il Vignardo Italian Restaurant, fitness room and Beresford conference and meeting facilities. Please enquire about Facilities for Persons with Disabilities.

Member of Isaacs Group

Bookable on www.irelandhotels.com

Room Rate from €50.00 to €260.00
Suites from €100.00 to €350.00

Justin Lowry
General Manager

103

Activities:

Closed 24 - 26 December

Hotel St. George

HOTEL ★★★ MAP 8 O 11

7 Parnell Square,
Dublin 1

Tel: 01-874 5611 Fax: 01-874 5582
Email: info@hotel-st-george.ie
Web: www.hotel-st-george.ie
GPS: N +53° 21' 13.67" W -6° 15' 44.70"

The historical Hotel St. George is located on Parnell Square at the top of O'Connell Street, Dublin's principal thoroughfare. Within walking distance of the Abbey & the Gate Theatre, Municipal Art Gallery, Dublin's Writers Museum, principal shopping district & other major tourist attractions. Each bedroom is en suite, individually decorated with every modern comfort, including phone, multichannel TV & tea/coffee making facilities. A computer is available for internet use & there is free WiFi throughout the hotel. Private car park, bar & restaurant. Please enquire about Facilities for Persons with Disabilities.

Member of Castle Hotel Group

Bookable on www.irelandhotels.com

Room Rate from €69.00 to €189.00

Sinéad Costello
General Manager

48

Closed 24 - 27 December

Kilronan Guesthouse

GUESTHOUSE ★★★ MAP 8 O 11

70 Adelaide Road,
Dublin 2

Tel: 01-475 5266 Fax: 01-478 2841
Email: info@kilronanhouse.com
Web: www.kilronanhouse.com
GPS: N +53° 19' 58.70" W -6° 15' 34.73"

A long standing favourite in the Dublin area, beautiful Kilronan House is perfectly positioned just around the corner from St. Stephen's Green and within walking distance of Grafton Street, Trinity College and much more. Kilronan House's 12 well appointed rooms offer the perfect escape for singles, couples and families. Rooms feature private bathrooms, televisions, phone, hairdryers and tea and coffee making facilities. All rates include our generous full Irish breakfast.

Member of Premier Guesthouses

Bookable on www.irelandhotels.com

B&B from €45.00 to €85.00

Leon Kinsella
Owner

12

Closed 23 - 27 December

B&B Rates are per Person Sharing per Night incl. Breakfast.
or Room Rates are per Room per Night - **See also Page 8**

Dublin City

La Stampa Hotel

HOTEL ★★★★ MAP 8 O 11

35/36 Dawson Street,
Dublin 2

Tel: 01-677 4444 Fax: 01-677 4411
Email: hotel@lastampa.ie
Web: www.lastampa.ie
GPS: N +53° 20' 25.34" W -6° 15' 31.48"

The 4 Star La Stampa Hotel is situated in the heart of Dublin and centrally located within easy reach of its main shopping, dining, nightspots and heritage areas, La Stampa is a perfect combination of beautifully designed interiors, exquisite surroundings with a renowned reputation for top class food and luxury accommodation. Please enquire about Facilities for Persons with Disabilities.

Member of Small Luxury Hotels

Bookable on www.irelandhotels.com

Room Rate from €120.00 to €260.00
Suites from €180.00 to €350.00

Daniel Fodor
Front of House Manager
30

Closed 25 - 27 December

Lansdowne Hotel

HOTEL ★★★ MAP 8 O 11

27-29 Pembroke Road,
Ballsbridge,
Dublin 4

Tel: 01-668 2522 Fax: 01-668 5585
Email: reception@lansdownehotel.ie
Web: www.lansdownehotel.ie
GPS: N +53° 19' 58.31" W -6° 14' 28.32"

Ideally located within 15 minutes walk of Dublin City Centre, Grafton Street & St. Stephen's Green for shopping; The new Aviva Rugby Stadium on Lansdowne Road, Royal Dublin Society (R.D.S.) & the Embassy belt in Ballsbridge. Delicious Bar Food evenings Mon - Sat. Home to the Irish House Party (Traditional Irish Music Show). Most nights experience the unique old world charm of our personal service in the Den (rugby) Bar. We aim to ensure your first class service during your stay in our cosy family run hotel.

An IHF Quality Employer

Bookable on www.irelandhotels.com

Room Rate from €59.00 to €230.00

Frank Quinn
Director
38

Activities:

Closed 23 - 29 December

Leeson Inn Downtown

GUESTHOUSE ★★★ MAP 8 O 11

24 Lower Leeson Street,
Dublin 2

Tel: 01-662 2002 Fax: 01-662 1567
Email: info@leesoninndowntown.com
Web: www.leesoninndowntown.com
GPS: N +53° 20' 3.07" W -6° 15' 19.20"

Located on the fashionable southside of Dublin city centre near St. Stephen's Green and a short stroll from the premier shopping area of Grafton Street. This guesthouse boasts to having all the major tourist attractions nearby, National Gallery, Museum, Government buildings, Trinity College, RDS and Lansdowne Stadium. There is also an abundance of restaurants, theatres and bars within walking distance. Aircoach stops 24/7 just beside the hotel for your convenience.

Bookable on www.irelandhotels.com

B&B from €45.00 to €99.00

Majella McGuane
General Manager
30

Closed 22 - 29 December

B&B Rates are per Person Sharing per Night incl. Breakfast.
or Room Rates are per Room per Night - See also Page 8

Louis Fitzgerald Hotel

HOTEL ★★★★ MAP 8 O 11

Newlands Cross,
Naas Road,
Dublin 22
Tel: 01-403 3300 Fax: 01-403 3301
Email: stay@louisfitzgeraldhotel.com
Web: www.louisfitzgeraldhotel.com
GPS: N +53° 18' 56.06'' W -6° 23' 2.51''

The 4 Star Louis Fitzgerald Hotel combines a contemporary feel with a traditional service approach. Ideally located at Newlands Cross for all national routes & adjacent to Luas park & ride. The Louis Fitzgerald Hotel is the ideal venue for business or pleasure. Boasting 190 bedrooms & suites, L.J's Bar & Restaurant and a purpose built conference facility from 2 – 350 delegates, mini gym & 300 car park spaces. Free WiFi throughout & complimentary shuttle service to all business parks. Joel's Restaurant is also part of the complex where a delicious European menu and a special children's menu is available!

Bookable on www.irelandhotels.com
Special Offer: www.irelandhotels.com/offers

B&B from €42.50 to €85.00

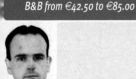

Pat Kenny
General Manager

190

Closed 23 - 29 December

Maldron Hotel Cardiff Lane

HOTEL ★★★★ MAP 8 O 11

Cardiff Lane,
Sir John Rogerson's Quay,
Dublin 2
Tel: 01-643 9500 Fax: 01-643 9510
Email: info.cardifflane@maldronhotels.com
Web: www.maldronhotels.com
GPS: N +53° 20' 42.91" W -6° 14' 28.16"

Located off the south banks of the River Liffey, close to the heart of Dublin City, the Maldron Hotel Cardiff Lane is within a short walk of city centre shopping, tourist attractions and business districts. Facilities include 304 spacious, contemporary guest rooms with complimentary broadband internet access, Stir Restaurant and Vertigo Bar. Club Vitae Health & Fitness Club incorporates a 22m swimming pool, sauna, steam room, jacuzzi, fully equipped gym and treatment suites. Please enquire about Facilities for Persons with Disabilities.

An IHF Quality Employer
Member of Maldron Hotels

Bookable on www.irelandhotels.com
Special Offer: www.irelandhotels.com/offers

Room Rate from €99.00 to €359.00

Conor O'Kane
General Manager

304

Food for Kids

Open All Year

Maldron Hotel Citywest

HOTEL ★★★ MAP 8 O 11

Kingswood Village,
Naas Road,
Dublin 22
Tel: 01-461 9900 Fax: 01-461 9910
Email: info.citywest@maldronhotels.com
Web: www.maldronhotels.com
GPS: N +53° 18' 4.37" W -6° 25' 6.24"

The Maldron Hotel Citywest is located just 9 miles from Dublin City centre and conveniently situated for guests travelling to/from the South and Dublin Airport. Comprising 129 tastefully decorated guest rooms; facilities at the Maldron Hotel Citywest include Stir Café Bar, a choice of 4 meeting rooms, free WiFi and broadband internet access and complimentary car parking. LUAS light rail transfers are available from the hotel. Please enquire about Facilities for Persons with Disabilities.

An IHF Quality Employer
Member of Maldron Hotels

Bookable on www.irelandhotels.com
Special Offer: www.irelandhotels.com/offers

Room Rate from €54.00 to €199.00

Ann Marie Traynor
General Manager

129

Food for Kids

Closed 21 - 29 December

B&B Rates are per Person Sharing per Night incl. Breakfast.
or Room Rates are per Room per Night - **See also Page 8**

Dublin City

Maldron Hotel Parnell Square

HOTEL ★★★ MAP 8 0 11

Parnell Square West,
Dublin 1

Tel: 01-871 6800 Fax: 01-871 6861
Email: info.parnellsquare@maldronhotels.com
Web: www.maldronhotels.com
GPS: N +53° 21' 18.03" W -6° 15' 44.25"

This stylish, boutique hotel is conveniently located only 2 minutes walk to O'Connell Street and is close to the city's main bus and rail terminals. All 126 guest rooms are air conditioned with complimentary broadband access in all rooms and free WiFi in all public areas. Facilities include 4 state of the art meeting rooms and Stir Café Bar. Limited underground car parking available, charges apply. Please enquire about Facilities for Persons with Disabilities.

An IHF Quality Employer

Member of Maldron Hotels

Bookable on www.irelandhotels.com
Special Offer: www.irelandhotels.com/offers

Room Rate from €79.00 to €299.00

Philip Uzice
General Manager

126

Closed 23 - 26 December

Maldron Hotel Smithfield

HOTEL ★★★ MAP 8 0 11

Smithfield,
Dublin 7

Tel: 01-485 0900 Fax: 01-485 0910
Email: info.smithfield@maldronhotels.com
Web: www.maldronhotels.com
GPS: N +53° 20' 57.72" W -6° 16' 43.04"

A modern and stylish hotel in the heart of Dublin City centre, the Maldron Hotel Smithfield comprises 92 guest rooms and suites which are furnished in a contemporary style with complimentary broadband access. Facilities include Stir Café Bar, complimentary WiFi access in public areas and 2 meeting rooms. Secure car parking is provided by Parkrite, overnight rate starting from €10. LUAS station located nearby. Please enquire about Facilities for Persons with Disabilities.

An IHF Quality Employer

Member of Maldron Hotels

Bookable on www.irelandhotels.com
Special Offer: www.irelandhotels.com/offers

Room Rate from €79.00 to €299.00

Gemma Lucey
General Manager

92

Food for Kids

Closed 24 - 26 December

Maldron Hotel Tallaght

HOTEL ★★★ MAP 8 11 0

Whitestown Way,
Tallaght,
Dublin 24
Tel: 01-468 5400 Fax: 01-468 5411
Email: info.tallaght@maldronhotels.com
Web: www.maldronhotels.com
GPS: N +53° 17' 2.21" W -6° 22' 34.69"

A newly opened modern and stylish hotel in the heart of South Dublin, the Maldron Hotel Tallaght, Dublin 24 is the perfect base for leisure visits to Ireland's Capital City. All 119 guestrooms are furnished in a contemporary style with complimentary Wi-Fi as standard. Many bedrooms feature floor to ceiling glass windows or balconies with panoramic views of the Dublin Mountains. Additional facilites include Stir Restaurant and Bar, complimentary access to Arena Leisure Centre, 9 state of the art meeting rooms and complimentary parking. Please enquire about Facilities for Persons with Disabilities.

An IHF Quality Employer

Member of Maldron Hotels

Bookable on www.irelandhotels.com
Special Offer: www.irelandhotels.com/offers

B&B from €35.00 to €139.00

Rishnoor Kaur
General Manager

119

Food for Kids

Closed 23 - 25 December

B&B Rates are per Person Sharing per Night incl. Breakfast.
or Room Rates are per Room per Night - **See also Page 8**

Maple Hotel

HOTEL ★★ MAP 8 O 11

75 Lower Gardiner Street,
Dublin 1

Tel: 01-874 0225 Fax: 01-874 5239
Email: info@maplehotel.com
Web: www.maplehotel.com
GPS: N +53° 21' 4.00" W -6° 15' 15.95"

The Maple Hotel combines small hotel charm in an elegant Georgian building with a superb location in Dublin city centre. Just two minutes walk from O'Connell Street and five minutes from Temple Bar, Dublin Castle & Trinity College. Also close to Croke Park and The O2 Arena, there is no better location for your stay in Dublin. All bedrooms en suite with colour TV, direct dial phone, hairdryer & tea/coffee facilities.

B&B from €20.00 to €125.00

Brian Moloney
Director

33

Closed 23 - 27 December

Marian Guest House

GUESTHOUSE ★ MAP 8 O 11

21 Upper Gardiner Street,
Dublin 1

Tel: 01-874 4129
Email: info@marianguesthouse.ie
Web: www.marianguesthouse.ie
GPS: N +53° 21' 28.13" W -6° 15' 37.95"

The Marian Guesthouse is owned and run by the McElroy family. It is just off Mountjoy Square and five minutes walk from the city centre and all principal shopping areas, cinemas, theatres and museums. Well appointed bedrooms some of which are en suite. Tea and coffee making facilities available and use of private car park.

B&B from €30.00 to €45.00

McElroy Family
Owners

1 5

Open All Year

Mercer Hotel

HOTEL ★★★ MAP 8 O 11

Lower Mercer Street,
Dublin 2

Tel: 01-478 2179 Fax: 01-475 6524
Email: reception@mercerhotel.ie
Web: www.mercerhotel.ie
GPS: N +53° 20' 22.03" W -6° 15' 50.58"

Luxurious, boutique style hotel located in the heart of Dublin City. Modern yet relaxed atmosphere; all rooms are beautifully appointed, en suite & fully equipped with all you need: TV, CD player, wireless internet access, a fridge. Indulge in Cusack's Bar & Restaurant. Within easy walking distance of all city centre tourist attractions, Trinity College, Grafton St., St. Stephen's Green & Temple Bar, also restaurants, cafés & bars. Free overnight parking & discounted daily rate. Book online www.mercergroup.ie. WiFi in conference rooms, lobby & bar available. Please enquire about Facilities for Persons with Disabilities.

An IHF Quality Employer

Bookable on www.irelandhotels.com

Room Rate from €69.00 to €250.00

Mark Sheridan
General Manager

41

Activities:

Closed 23 - 29 December

B&B Rates are per Person Sharing per Night incl. Breakfast.
or Room Rates are per Room per Night - **See also Page 8**

Dublin City

Merrion Hotel (The)

HOTEL ★★★★★ MAP 8 0 11

Upper Merrion Street,
Dublin 2

Tel: 01-603 0600 Fax: 01-603 0700
Email: info@merrionhotel.com
Web: www.merrionhotel.com
GPS: N +53° 20' 18.72" W -6° 15' 10.34"

Dublin's most stylish 5***** hotel, located in the city centre opposite Government Buildings and created from four restored Georgian Townhouses. Many of the 143 bedrooms and suites overlook 18th century gardens, including the luxurious Penthouse. Bars include The Cellar Bar and intimate cocktail bar, No. 23. The award-winning Cellar Restaurant serves traditional Irish cuisine, while Restaurant Patrick Guilbauds offers formal dining. Other features include an 18m pool, spa and private underground car park.

An IHF Quality Employer

Member of Leading Hotels of the World

Bookable on www.irelandhotels.com

Room Rate from €480.00 to €510.00
Suites from €960.00 to €3,000.00

Peter MacCann
General Manager

143

Food for Kids

Open All Year

Mespil Hotel

HOTEL ★★★ MAP 8 0 11

Mespil Road,
Dublin 4

Tel: 01-488 4600 Fax: 01-667 1244
Email: mespil@leehotels.com
Web: www.leehotels.com
GPS: N +53° 20' 0.17" W -6° 14' 47.05"

The Mespil boasts an ideal city centre location overlooking the banks of the Grand Canal and just 15 minutes walk to St. Stephen's Green and the city's main shopping and cultural quarters, including the RDS and Ballsbridge district. All 255 guest bedrooms are bright, modern and spacious with restful color schemes. Relax in the Terrace Bar or enjoy some tempting dishes from the Glaze Bistro. Complimentary WiFi access available in all bedrooms, meeting rooms, lobby and bar. Please enquire about Facilities for Persons with Disabilities.

An IHF Quality Employer

Member of Lee Hotels

Bookable on www.irelandhotels.com
Special Offer: www.irelandhotels.com/offers

Room Rate from €89.00 to €205.00

Martin Holohan
General Manager / Director

255

Closed 24 - 27 December

Montrose Hotel

HOTEL ★★★ MAP 8 0 11

Stillorgan Road,
Dublin 4

Tel: 01-269 3311 Fax: 01-269 3376
Email: info@montrosehotel.ie
Web: www.montrosehotel.ie
GPS: N +53° 18' 40.66" W -6° 13' 11.68"

Ideally located in Dublin 4, only ten minutes from Dublin city centre, opposite UCD and next to RTE, close to RDS, The Conference Centre, and the Aviva Stadium. Serviced by Aircoach from Dublin Airport. We have bright, spacious, relaxing bedrooms including family rooms. Delicious food and a great selection of wines, beers and spirits in our Belfield Bar and Restaurant. Lonnegans Bar is a traditional Irish bar with a pool table and large screen. Eight Meeting rooms, 100 free car park spaces, WLAN, to book go to www.montrose.ie Please enquire about Facilities for Persons with Disabilities.

An IHF Quality Employer

Member of Mercer Accommodation Group

Bookable on www.irelandhotels.com
Special Offer: www.irelandhotels.com/offers

B&B from €89.00 to €200.00

Jerry Russell
General Manager

179

Closed 23 December - 04 January

B&B Rates are per Person Sharing per Night incl. Breakfast.
or Room Rates are per Room per Night - **See also Page 8**

Mount Herbert Hotel

HOTEL ★★★ MAP 8 O 11

Herbert Road,
Lansdowne Road, Sandymount,
Dublin 4

Tel: 01-614 2000 Fax: 01-660 7077
Email: info@mountherberthotel.ie
Web: www.mountherberthotel.ie
GPS: N +53° 20' 0.26" W -6° 13' 28.09"

Exclusive location - exceptional value! Mount Herbert is a rare gem of a hotel, located in Sandymount, beside the AVIVA Stadium and within walking distance of the RDS and the O2. Easy access to the city centre by DART rail or bus. The hotels facilities include 168 modern bedrooms, Tritonville Bar, Cordyline Restaurant, 9 Conference Suites, Business Centre, free WiFi and complimentary car park. Its outstanding value has made it one of Dublin's most popular hotels for many years. Please enquire about Facilities for Persons with Disabilities.

An IHF Quality Employer

Bookable on www.irelandhotels.com

Special Offer: www.irelandhotels.com/offers

Room Rate from €69.00 to €270.00
Suites from €150.00 to €400.00

Michelle Sweeney
Sales & Marketing Manager

168

Activities:

Closed 23 - 27 December

North Star Hotel & Premier Club Suites

HOTEL ★★★ MAP 8 O 11

Amiens Street,
Dublin 1

Tel: 01-836 3136 Fax: 01-836 3561
Email: reservations@northstarhotel.ie
Web: www.northstarhotel.ie
GPS: N +53° 21' 6.45" W -6° 15' 0.44"

The North Star Hotel and Premier Club Suites, Dublin City is in short walking distance from temple Bar, O'Connell Street, Trinity College, The O2 Arena concert venue and the new Convention Centre Dublin - CCD, DART to Lansdowne road as well as shopping districts including Henry Street and Grafton Street. For all rugby and GAA Sports fans and concert goers the North Star Hotel is 10 minutes walk from Croke Park Stadium.

An IHF Quality Employer

Bookable on www.irelandhotels.com

Special Offer: www.irelandhotels.com/offers

Room Rate from €99.00 to €250.00
Suites from €150.00 to €400.00

Brian McGettigan
General Manager

175

Open All Year

Number 31

GUESTHOUSE ★★★★ MAP 8 O 11

31 Leeson Close,
Dublin 2

Tel: 01-676 5011 Fax: 01-676 2929
Email: info@number31.ie
Web: www.number31.ie
GPS: N +53° 20' 0.26" W -6° 15' 13.15"

An award-winning guesthouse right in the heart of Georgian Dublin. The former home of Ireland's leading architect Sam Stephenson, just a few minutes walk from St. Stephen's Green, museums and galleries. An oasis of tranquillity and greenery, where guests are encouraged to come back and relax and feel at home at any time of the day. Vast breakfasts are served in the dining room or in a sunny plant filled conservatory. Recommended by the Good Hotel Guide, Egon Ronay, Bridgestone 100 Best Places, Fodors and awarded Georgina Campbell's Irish Breakfast Award 2008.

Member of Hidden Ireland

B&B from €75.00 to €175.00

Noel Comer
Proprietor

21

Open All Year

Dublin City

O'Sheas Hotel

HOTEL ★ MAP 8 O 11

19 Talbot Street,
Dublin 1

Tel: 01-836 5670 Fax: 01-836 5214
Email: osheashotel@eircom.net
Web: www.osheashotel.com
GPS: N +53° 21' 2.76" W -6° 15' 17.90"

O'Sheas Hotel - renowned the world over for its close association with Irish music, song & dance - it's this that provides the theme for the hotel, with its typical Irish pub and restaurant serving the best in Irish cuisine with a healthy sprinkling of international dishes. O'Sheas Hotel has 34 recently refurbished en suite bedrooms, the hotel also has function and conference room facilities for up to 180 people and provides live entertainment seven nights. We look forward to welcoming you.

B&B from €30.00 to €80.00

John McCormack
Manager

34

Closed 24 - 25 December

Palmerstown Lodge

GUESTHOUSE ★★★ MAP 8 O 11

Palmerstown Village,
Dublin 20

Tel: 01-623 5494 Fax: 01-623 6214
Email: info@palmerstownlodge.ie
Web: www.palmerstownlodge.ie
GPS: N +53° 21' 19.01" W -6° 22' 17.25"

Prime location adjacent to all amenities and facilities this superb purpose-built property adjoins the N4/M50 motorway. Minutes from the city centre and a mere 12 minutes drive to the airport we offer all the features and standards of a hotel. Each elegant en suite bedroom has individual temperature control, ambient lighting, automated door locking system, phone, TV, etc. Separate tea/coffee and free internet area. Private car park. Golf packages available. Please enquire about Facilities for Persons with Disabilities.

Bookable on www.irelandhotels.com

B&B from €30.00 to €35.00

Gerry O'Connor
Owner

24

Open All Year

Paramount Hotel

HOTEL ★★★ MAP 8 O 11

Parliament Street & Essex Gate,
Temple Bar,
Dublin 2

Tel: 01-417 9900 Fax: 01-417 9904
Email: sales@paramounthotel.ie
Web: www.paramounthotel.ie
GPS: N +53° 20' 40.85" W -6° 16' 3.66"

Set in Temple Bar's quieter west end, Paramount Hotel is one of the city's most trendy and cosmopolitan hotels. The hotel boasts 66 en suite bedrooms, tastefully decorated in the very elegant style of the 1930s. The hotel's bar, the Turks Head, is a stylish bar renowned for its extravagant design, and vibrant colours. Bistro dishes are served daily, and the bar turns into a late bar with club at the weekend. Email: info@turkshead.ie or Web: www.turkshead.ie. Please enquire about Facilities for Persons with Disabilities.

An IHF Quality Employer

Bookable on www.irelandhotels.com

Room Rate from €70.00 to €350.00

Rita Barcoe
General Manager

66

Closed 20 - 27 December

B&B Rates are per Person Sharing per Night incl. Breakfast or Room Rates are per Room per Night - See also Page 8

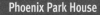

Park Plaza Tyrrelstown

HOTEL ★★★★ MAP 8 O 11

Tyrrelstown,
Dublin 15

Tel: 01-827 5600 Fax: 01-827 5601
Email: info@parkplazatyrrelstown.com
Web: www.parkplazatyrrelstown.com
GPS: N +53° 25' 12.28" W -6° 22' 38.50"

Located in close proximity to both Dublin City centre & Dublin Airport, this magnificent contemporary hotel features 155 bedrooms including suites, with each room boasting complimentary broadband & state of the art entertainment systems. A self-contained conference area houses 11 meeting rooms with a capacity for over 500 delegates. Large gym for residents. Our Time Restaurant & Hourglass Bar are tailored for your enjoyment. Complimentary extensive car parking is also provided. Please enquire about Facilities for Persons with Disabilities.

Member of Park Plaza Hotels & Resorts

Bookable on www.irelandhotels.com

Room Rate from €85.00 to €220.00
Suites from €100.00 to €320.00

Darrell Penny
General Manager

155

Activities:

Closed 25 December

Phoenix Park House

GUESTHOUSE ★★ MAP 8 O 11

38-39 Parkgate Street,
Dublin 8

Tel: 01-677 2870 Fax: 01-679 9769
Email: info@dublinguesthouse.com
Web: www.dublinguesthouse.com
GPS: N +53° 20' 53.58" W -6° 17' 41.00"

Phoenix Park House is a family-run guesthouse. All our rooms are ensuite with TV, tea and coffee facilities. Situated beside the Phoenix Park and 2 minutes walk from Heuston Station and the Luas Red Line. The 748 bus comes from the airport to Heuston Station. We are within walking distance to Guinness Storehouse, Kilmainham, Modern Art and Collins Barricks museums. Also close to the new law courts and some of Dublins best pubs and restaurants.

Bookable on www.irelandhotels.com

B&B from €30.00 to €90.00

Mary & Liam Smith
Proprietors

25

Closed 22 - 28 December

Plaza Hotel

HOTEL ★★★★ MAP 8 O 11

Belgard Road,
Tallaght,
Dublin 24

Tel: 01-462 4200 Fax: 01-462 4600
Email: info@plazahotel.ie
Web: www.plazahotel.ie
GPS: N +53° 17' 8.59" W -6° 22' 2.49"

120 bedrooms, 2 suites. Convenient location on Belgard Road, just off the M50 motorway, 8 miles from city centre. Secure underground car parking. LUAS Tallaght stop, direct tram link to the city centre is located 3 mins from the hotel. Extensive conference & banqueting facilities for up to 220 people. Floor One serving food from 9am - 10pm daily. The Playhouse Nightclub. Carvery now open daily in Grumpy McClafferty's traditional pub 12 - 2.30pm. All new evening grill from 5pm - 10pm. 20 mins from Dublin Airport. Please enquire about Facilities for Persons with Disabilities.

Bookable on www.irelandhotels.com

Room Rate from €59.00 to €189.00
Suites from €155.00 to €295.00

Jim Lavery
General Manager

122

Closed 24 - 29 December

B&B Rates are per Person Sharing per Night incl. Breakfast.
or Room Rates are per Room per Night - See also Page 8

Dublin City

Radisson Blu St Helen's Hotel

HOTEL ★★★★★ MAP 8 O 11

Stillorgan Road,
Dublin 4

Tel: 01-218 6000 Fax: 01-218 6010
Email: info.dublin@radissonblu.com
Web: www.sthelens.dublin.radissonblu.com
GPS: N +53° 18' 17.25" W -6° 12' 20.43"

One of the finest Hotels in the Irish capital, the five star Radisson Blu St. Helen's Hotel stands on 4 acres of magnificent formal gardens. The scenic setting will certainly make your stay a memorable occasion. The hotel was formerly one of Irelands most historic houses dating back to 1750, and has been meticulously restored & adapted to offer five star luxury accommodation. Dublin City Centre is easily accessible only 4 kilometres away and the hotel is serviced by Air Coach, proving easy access to and from Dublin International Airport with the newly opened Port Tunnel halving travel times.

An IHF Quality Employer

Member of Radisson Blu Hotels & Resorts

Bookable on www.irelandhotels.com

Special Offer: www.irelandhotels.com/offers

Room Rate from €109.00 to €500.00
Suites from €159.00 to €550.00

Neil Lane
General Manager

151

Food for Kids Activities:

Open All Year

Red Cow Moran Hotel

HOTEL ★★★★ MAP 8 O 11

Red Cow Complex,
Naas Road,
Dublin 22

Tel: 01-459 3650 Fax: 01-459 1588
Email: redcowres@moranhotels.com
Web: www.moranhotels.com
GPS: N +53° 19' 7.95" W -6° 21' 50.21"

4**** Red Cow Moran Hotel combines classic elegance with modern design, situated at the gateway to the provinces, minutes drive from Dublin Airport. Easy access to the city centre via the LUAS light rail service! Bedrooms are fully air conditioned with flatscreen multi channel TV, fluffy duvets, DD telephone, WiFi, hairdryer, clothes care and tea/coffee making facilities. The complex also boasts two restaurants, a choice of lively bars also serving food, conference facilities and business centre. Night Club. Free car parking. AA 4****. A Moran Hotel. Please enquire about Facilities for Persons with Disabilities.

An IHF Quality Employer

Member of Moran Hotels

Bookable on www.irelandhotels.com

B&B from €49.00 to €195.00
Suites from €150.00 to €500.00

Tom Moran
Managing Director

123

Food for Kids Activities:

Closed 24 - 26 December

RiverHouse Hotel

HOTEL ★★ MAP 8 O 11

23/24 Eustace Street,
Temple Bar,
Dublin 2

Tel: 01-670 7655 Fax: 01-670 7650
Email: reservations@riverhousehotel.com
Web: www.riverhousehotel.com
GPS: N +53° 20' 40.89" W -6° 15' 53.01"

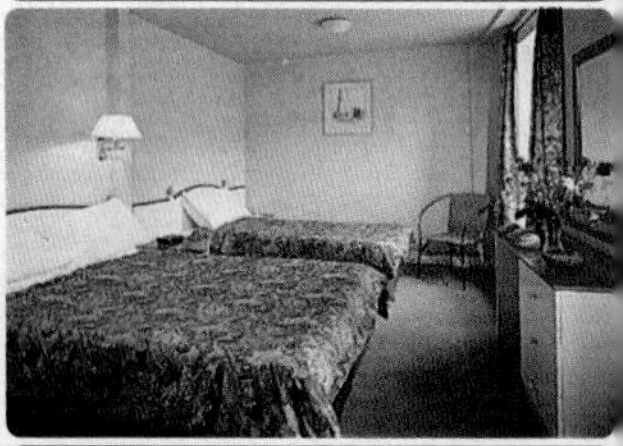

A city centre hotel located in Dublin's colourful and exciting Temple Bar area. With its cobbled streets, shops, art galleries, bars, restaurants and lively night life, Temple Bar has become a tourist attraction itself. All of our 29 bedrooms are en suite and have tea/coffee making facilities, remote control TV, radio, hairdryer and direct dial telephone. Hotel facilities include 'The Mezz' Bar and 'The Think Tank' Nightclub which is sound proofed, the best live music venues in Dublin. Family Run, friendly staff and the best breakfast in town!

Bookable on www.irelandhotels.com

B&B from €30.00 to €75.00

Sheelagh Conway
Proprietor

29

Closed 23 - 27 December

B&B Rates are per Person Sharing per Night incl. Breakfast
or Room Rates are per Room per Night - See also Page 8

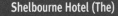

Roxford Lodge Hotel

HOTEL ★★★ MAP 8 O 11

46 Northumberland Road,
Ballsbridge,
Dublin 4

Tel: 01-668 8572 Fax: 01-668 8158
Email: reservations@roxfordlodge.ie
Web: www.roxfordlodge.ie
GPS: N +53° 20' 7.41" W -6° 14' 13.73"

Luxury family-run boutique style hotel located in Ballsbridge, Dublin's most exclusive area. Just 10 minutes walk from the city centre and all the major attractions such as Trinity College and Grafton Street. All of our en suite bedrooms have the added luxury of saunas, and most also have jacuzzi baths. All rooms have broadband internet access. Our executive suite offers the ultimate in luxury. Secure car parking. Public transport at front door. Please enquire about Facilities for Persons with Disabilities.

Room Rate from €50.00 to €160.00
Suites from €130.00 to €500.00

Desmond Killoran
Proprietor

20

Closed 24 - 27 December

Shelbourne Hotel (The)

HOTEL ★★★★★ MAP 8 O 11

27 St. Stephen's Green,
Dublin 2

Tel: 01-663 4500 Fax: 01-661 6006
Email: annemarie.whelan@renaissancehotels.com
Web: www.theshelbourne.ie
GPS: N +53° 20' 20.58" W -6° 15' 21.94"

Dublin's most distinguished address, The Shelbourne Dublin, a Renaissance Hotel, is the ultimate in 5* luxury. The Shelbourne is Dublin's most famous hotel, located in the heart of Dublin overlooking St. Stephen's Green. With 265 luxury guestrooms including 19 suites, a Heritage Lounge, the Horseshoe Bar, Lord Mayor's Lounge, the Saddle Room & No.27 bar and lounge. The food & beverage outlets are the ultimate in elegance, innovative style and luxury. Banqueting facilities to accommodate 10 to 350 guests. New luxury state of the art spa opening in 2009. Managed by Marriott International.

An IHF Quality Employer

Member of Renaissance Hotels & Resorts

Bookable on www.irelandhotels.com

Room Rate from €219.00 to €289.00
Suites from €339.00 to €2,500.00

Liam Doyle
General Manager

265

Activities:

Open All Year

Stauntons on the Green

GUESTHOUSE ★★★ MAP 8 O 11

83 St. Stephen's Green,
Dublin 2

Tel: 01-478 2300 Fax: 01-478 2263
Email: info@stauntonsonthegreen.ie
Web: www.thecastlehotelgroup.com
GPS: N +53° 20' 11.77" W -6° 15' 34.73"

Large Georgian house overlooking St. Stephen's Green, own private gardens. All rooms are en suite and fully equipped with direct dial telephone, TV and tea/coffee welcoming trays, trouser press and hairdryer. It is close to museums, galleries, Grafton Street shopping area and many other major tourist attractions. Stauntons On the Green occupies one of Dublin's most prestigious locations, close to many corporate headquarters and government buildings.

Member of Castle Hotel Group

B&B from €70.00 to €95.00

Colette Winders
Manager

45

Closed 24 - 26 December

Dublin City

Stillorgan Park Hotel

HOTEL ★★★★ MAP 8 O 11

Stillorgan Road,
Stillorgan,
Dublin 18

Tel: 01-200 1800 Fax: 01-283 1610
Email: sales@stillorganpark.com
Web: www.stillorganpark.com
GPS: N +53° 17' 41.93" W -6° 12' 10.08"

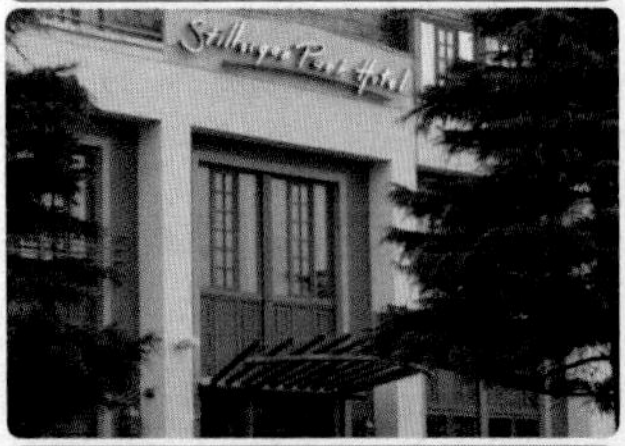

Dublin's premier city hotel, located only 3 miles from St. Stephen's Green, easily accessible from M50 motorway & all main city arteries. Boasting 150 en suite, contemporary rooms, fully air-conditioned. Outdoor courtyard. Purpose built conference area catering for 2-500 delegates & 8 new state of the art meeting rooms, video conferencing available, traditional Irish bar with AA Rosette winning restaurant, White Pebble Spa & guest gym. Complimentary shuttle service, Aircoach airport transfer available. 300 car parking spaces. AA**** & Fáilte Ireland ****. Please enquire about Facilities for Persons with Disabilities.

An IHF Quality Employer

Member of Talbot Hotel Group

Bookable on www.irelandhotels.com

Special Offer: www.irelandhotels.com/offers

Room Rate from €79.00 to €189.00

Daragh O'Neill
General Manager

150

Food for Kids *Activities:*

Closed 24 - 26 December

Tara Towers Hotel

HOTEL ★★★ MAP 8 O 11

Merrion Road,
Dublin 4

Tel: 01-269 4666 Fax: 01-269 1027
Email: reservations@taratowers.com
Web: www.taratowers.com
GPS: N +53° 18' 44.44" W -6° 12' 8.86"

The Tara Towers Hotel is a well-established favourite, beside the sea on Merrion Road, just 3km south of Dublin City centre. Situated along the sweeping curves of Dublin Bay you can experience breathtaking views of sea & shore. Rooms are spacious, fully appointed & cater for comfort. You can relax & unwind in PJ Branagan's Pub or have a sumptuous dinner in Ocras Restaurant. Guests also have the bonus of ample free parking. Located close to UCD, RDS and RTE, a 10 minute drive to the city centre & within easy distance of Lansdowne Road. Book online at www.taratowers.com.

An IHF Quality Employer

Bookable on www.irelandhotels.com

Special Offer: www.irelandhotels.com/offers

B&B from €45.00 to €200.00

Catherine McGrath
General Manager

111

Activities:

Closed 21 December - 04 January

Temple Bar Hotel

HOTEL ★★★ MAP 8 O 11

Fleet Street,
Temple Bar,
Dublin 2

Tel: 01-677 3333 Fax: 01-677 3088
Email: reservations@tbh.ie
Web: www.TempleBarHotel.com
GPS: N +53° 20' 45.00" W -6° 15' 37.49"

Located in the heart of the cultural quarter - An FBD Hotel - Temple Bar Hotel is the ideal base from which to explore Dublin. The Hotel features 129 bedrooms and is near all transport links. The Terrace Restaurant with its distinctive glass roof offers a unique dining experience. There are 5 meeting rooms accommodating up to 70 guests. Buskers Bar has an adjoining sun terrace. WiFi access is complimentary. Special online offers available www.templebarhotel.com. Please enquire about Facilities for Persons with Disabilities.

An IHF Quality Employer

Bookable on www.irelandhotels.com

Special Offer: www.irelandhotels.com/offers

Room Rate from €35.00 to €85.00

Finbar Gethins
General Manager

129

Activities:

Closed 23 - 25 December

B&B Rates are per Person Sharing per Night incl. Breakfast.
or Room Rates are per Room per Night - **See also Page 8**

Trinity Capital Hotel

HOTEL ★★★ MAP 8 O 11

Pearse Street,
Dublin 2

Tel: 01-648 1000 Fax: 01-648 1222
Email: info@trinitycapital-hotel.com
Web: www.trinitycapitalhotel.com
GPS: N +53° 20' 42.70" W -6° 15' 15.04"

The Trinity Capital Hotel is a contemporary styled property located in the heart of Dublin City centre, opposite Trinity College and only paces from entertainment and cultural attractions. Each of our beautifully designed guest rooms provides everything to suit your requirements including WiFi internet access, welcome trays & interactive TVs. Café Cairo, the hotel's bar & restaurant, offers an extensive cocktail selection & a dining menu sure to satisfy any palate. Please enquire about Facilities for Persons with Disabilities.

An IHF Quality Employer

Bookable on www.irelandhotels.com
Special Offer: www.irelandhotels.com/offers

Room Rate from €89.00 to €275.00
Suites from €129.00 to €325.00

Denyse Campbell
General Manager
195

Closed 24 - 27 December

Uppercross House

HOTEL ★★★ MAP 8 O 11

26-30 Upper Rathmines Road,
Rathmiines,
Dublin 6

Tel: 01-497 5486 Fax: 01-497 5361
Email: reservations@uppercrosshousehotel.com
Web: www.uppercrosshousehotel.com
GPS: N +53° 19' 15.00" W -6° 15' 54.82"

Uppercross House is a hotel providing 49 bedrooms of the highest standard of comfort. All with direct dial phone, TV, free WiFi internet access, tea/coffee maker, central heating and all bedrooms are en suite. Uppercross House has its own secure parking (free to guests) and is ideally situated in Dublin's south side 2km from St. Stephen's Green and R.D.S., with excellent public transport from directly outside the door. A fully licensed restaurant and bar opens nightly with a warm and friendly atmosphere.

An IHF Quality Employer

Bookable on www.irelandhotels.com
Special Offer: www.irelandhotels.com/offers

B&B from €44.50 to €79.00

David Mahon
Proprietor
49

Closed 23 - 30 December

Waterloo House

GUESTHOUSE ★★★★ MAP 8 O 11

8-10 Waterloo Road,
Ballsbridge,
Dublin 4

Tel: 01-660 1888 Fax: 01-667 1955
Email: waterloohouse@eircom.net
Web: www.waterloohouse.ie
GPS: N +53° 19' 53.67" W -6° 14' 36.62"

A warm welcome awaits you at this luxury guesthouse, in the heart of Georgian Dublin. It comprises 2 Georgian houses, refurbished to superb standard, retaining original features, offering unique atmosphere, style, elegance. Minutes from RDS, St. Stephen's Green, Grafton Street & city centre. Delicious breakfast is served in the dining room / conservatory on garden level. Lift & car park. Courtesy Irish Times & computer WiFi available free of charge. Recommended: Bridgestone 100 Best Places, Alister Sawday's, Michelin Guide, Lonely Planet, Frommers & Karen Brown.

Bookable on www.irelandhotels.com

B&B from €49.00 to €100.00
Suites from €110.00 to €220.00

Evelyn Corcoran
Proprietor
17

Closed 23 - 28 December

B&B Rates are per Person Sharing per Night incl. Breakfast.
or Room Rates are per Room per Night - **See also Page 8**

Dublin City

West County Hotel

HOTEL ★★ MAP 8 O 11

Chapelizod,
Dublin 20

Tel: 01-626 4011 Fax: 01-623 1378
Email: info@westcountyhotel.ie
Web: www.westcountyhotel.ie
GPS: N +53° 21' 5.41" W -6° 21' 21.92"

An established family-run hotel, located in the picturesque village of Chapelizod, just off the N4, close to M50 & Dublin International Airport, is convenient to Liffey Valley & Blanchardstown shopping centres. It comprises 50 en suite bedrooms equipped to 2* standards (AA). Secure & free car parking. Extensive conference and banqueting facilities. The West County is also fully Wi-Fi enabled with coverage in all bedrooms & conference rooms. Part of the Colgan Group Hotels and sister of The Lucan Spa Hotel. Special offers available Tel. 01 626 4647.

Member of The Colgan Group

Bookable on www.irelandhotels.com

B&B from €50.00 to €100.00

Gary Spain
Manager

50

Closed 25 - 27 December

Westbury Hotel (The)

HOTEL ★★★★★ MAP 8 O 11

Grafton Street,
Dublin 2

Tel: 01-679 1122 Fax: 01-679 7078
Email: westbury@doylecollection.com
Web: www.doylecollection.com
GPS: N +53° 20' 29.25" W -6° 15' 42.02"

With an unrivalled location just off Grafton Street, The Westbury Hotel is a true landmark of luxury in the very heart of the city. Recently refurbished to the highest standards, the hotel features 205 of the city's most luxurious bedrooms and showcases some of the most opulent surroundings in the city including the contemporary Marble Bar, the luxurious Gallery and Wilde - The Restaurant, a market leading dining experience.

An IHF Quality Employer

Member of Leading Hotels of the World

Bookable on www.irelandhotels.com

Room Rate from €179.00 to €499.00

Glenn Valentine
General Manager

205

Open All Year

Westin Dublin

HOTEL ★★★★★ MAP 8 O 11

Westmoreland Street,
Dublin 2

Tel: 01-645 1000 Fax: 01-645 1234
Email: reservations.dublin@westin.com
Web: www.thewestindublin.com
GPS: N +53° 20' 44.31" W -6° 15' 32.05"

Situated in the heart of the city, steps away from Grafton Street, overlooking Trinity College. One of Dublin's most luxurious five star hotels offers an ambience of warmth & Irish hospitality. Guestrooms feature the acclaimed Heavenly Bed and include 16 luxurious suites. A unique array of dining experiences awaits from the stylish Exchange Restaurant to the elegant Atrium Lounge or the popular Mint Bar. Flexible air-conditioned meeting rooms offer the latest in AV technology. The Banking Hall has been restored to its original magnificent 19th century glory. Please enquire about Facilities for Persons with Disabilities.

An IHF Quality Employer

Bookable on www.irelandhotels.com
Special Offer: www.irelandhotels.com/offers

Room Rate from €179.00 to €489.00
Suites from €299.00 to €2,600.00

Andrew R. Henning
General Manager

163

Activities:

Open All Year

B&B Rates are per Person Sharing per Night incl. Breakfast. or Room Rates are per Room per Night - **See also Page 8**

Rochestown Lodge Hotel & Replenish Day Spa

HOTEL ★★★ MAP 8 O 11

Rochestown Avenue,
Killiney, Dun Laoghaire,
Co. Dublin

Tel: 01-285 3555 Fax: 01-285 3914
Email: info@rochestownlodge.com
Web: www.rochestownlodge.com
GPS: N +53° 16' 9.63" W -6° 8' 30.66"

Whether you are staying for business or for leisure, Rochestown Lodge Hotel & Day Spa provides the perfect stylish modern setting to work or relax in complete comfort. Rochestown Lodge Hotel & Day Spa, 90 executive rooms, suites and spacious family rooms, a stylish café, lounge and bistro restaurant. A luxurious day spa, with 9 treatment rooms, manicure and pedicure suite. Fully equipped gym and 15m deck level pool. Ample car parking. Please enquire about Facilities for Persons with Disabilities.

Bookable on www.irelandhotels.com

Special Offer: www.irelandhotels.com/offers

B&B from €65.00 to €90.00
Suites from €149.00 to €189.00

Ken Fetherston
Proprietor

90

Activities:

Closed 24 - 26 December

Royal Marine Hotel

HOTEL ★★★★ MAP 8 O 11

Marine Road,
Dun Laoghaire,
Co. Dublin

Tel: 01-230 0030 Fax: 01-230 0029
Email: sales@royalmarine.ie
Web: www.royalmarine.ie
GPS: N +53° 17' 32.07" W -6° 8' 2.13"

The Royal Marine Hotel re-opened on the 22nd of June 2007 after undergoing extensive re-development. This superior Hotel has been fully restored to its former Victorian glory. This 4* hotel boasts 228 superior rooms, comprising of executive rooms and suites, a business centre, 14 conference rooms, conference suite with a maximum capacity of 500 delegates. The Hotel dining facilities include Hardys Bar, Dún Bistro & Bay Lounge. Relax, revive and retreat in the Hotel luxury Sansana Spa and The Pier Health Club. Please enquire about Facilities for Persons with Disabilities.

An IHF Quality Employer

Bookable on www.irelandhotels.com

Special Offer: www.irelandhotels.com/offers

Room Rate from €99.00 to €379.00
Suites from €199.00 to €1,999.00

Aidan Ryan
General Manager

228

Activities:

Open All Year

Deer Park Hotel Golf & Spa

HOTEL ★★★ MAP 12 P 11

Howth,
Co. Dublin

Tel: 01-832 2624 Fax: 01-839 2405
Email: sales@deerpark.iol.ie
Web: www.deerpark-hotel.ie
GPS: N +53° 22' 49.93" W -6° 4' 41.36"

14km from Dublin City/Airport on a quiet hillside overlooking the bay, Deer Park enjoys spectacular elevated sea views. Featuring Ireland's largest golf complex (5 courses), 18m swimming pool, sauna and steam room and two all-weather tennis courts. Whether on a golfing holiday or a visit to Dublin, you will find Deer Park the ideal choice. Easy access to Dublin city via DART rapid rail link. New spa and gym open. New 8 seater courtesy bus available for local pick up and drop off.

Bookable on www.irelandhotels.com

Special Offer: www.irelandhotels.com/offers

B&B from €49.00 to €90.00

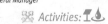

David & Antoinette Tighe
Managers

69

Activities:

Open All Year

B&B Rates are per Person Sharing per Night incl. Breakfast.
or Room Rates are per Room per Night - **See also Page 8**

Killiney / Lucan

Fitzpatrick Castle Dublin

HOTEL ★★★★ MAP 8 P 10

Killiney,
Co. Dublin

Tel: 01-230 5400 Fax: 01-230 5466
Email: info@fitzpatricks.com
Web: www.fitzpatrickhotels.com
GPS: N +53° 16' 9.62" W -6° 6' 47.10"

Fitzpatrick Castle Dublin is located in the fashionable suburbs of Killiney and Dalkey, overlooking Dublin Bay. Over 30 years of tradition in excellence has helped to create the perfect atmosphere at this family owned 18th century castle. Dining includes our award-winning restaurants, PJ's and Dungeon Bar & Grill. Full Leisure facilities including 20m pool and gym. Luxurious bedrooms, some with sea views and our recently renovated Castle Wing with sumptuous suites and authentic décor.

An IHF Quality Employer

Bookable on www.irelandhotels.com
Special Offer: www.irelandhotels.com/offers

Room Rate from €120.00 to €340.00
Suites from €220.00 to €600.00

Nicholas Logue
General Manager/Director

113

Open All Year

Finnstown Country House Hotel

HOTEL ★★★ MAP 8 N 11

Newcastle Road,
Lucan,
Co. Dublin

Tel: 01-601 0700 Fax: 01-621 4059
Email: manager@finnstown-hotel.ie
Web: www.finnstown-hotel.ie
GPS: N +53° 20' 22.75" W -6° 27' 41.05"

One of County Dublin's finest country house hotels. Set on 45 acres of private grounds it offers privacy, peace and seclusion yet is only thirty five minutes drive from the bustling city centre of Dublin. If it's good old-fashioned hospitality you're after, great food and drink, a relaxed atmosphere and stylish surroundings, you're in the right place! Leisure facilities include gym, turkish bath, tennis court and indoor heated swimming pool. Please enquire about Facilities for Persons with Disabilities.

An IHF Quality Employer

Bookable on www.irelandhotels.com
Special Offer: www.irelandhotels.com/offers

B&B from €50.00 to €95.00
Suites from €178.00 to €250.00

Nora Wyse
General Manager

82

Food for Kids Activities:

Closed 24 - 27 December

Lucan Spa Hotel

HOTEL ★★ MAP 8 N 11

Lucan,
Co. Dublin

Tel: 01-628 0494 Fax: 01-628 0841
Email: info@lucanspahotel.ie
Web: www.lucanspahotel.ie
GPS: N +53° 21' 19.41" W -6° 27' 49.66"

Situated on the road to the West (N4) and close to the M50 and Dublin Airport, this elegant hotel offers its guests comfort and convenience in a country setting. All 70 bedrooms are equipped to 3 star standards (AA). Dine in the award-winning Honora D Restaurant (evenings daily & Sunday lunch) or The Earl Bistro (7.30am - 9.45pm). All conference and weddings catered for. The hotel is also WiFi enabled. Special Offers available on 01-628 0494.

An IHF Quality Employer

Member of The Colgan Group

Bookable on www.irelandhotels.com
Special Offer: www.irelandhotels.com/offers

B&B from €40.00 to €80.00
Suites from €100.00 to €150.00

Frank Colgan
Propietor

70

Activities:

Closed 24 - 26 December

B&B Rates are per Person Sharing per Night incl. Breakfast,
or Room Rates are per Room per Night - **See also Page 8**

Moat Lodge

GUESTHOUSE ★★ MAP 8 N 11

Adamstown Road,
Lucan,
Co. Dublin

Tel: 01-624 1584 Fax: 01-628 1356
Email: info@moatlodge.ie
Web: www.moatlodge.ie
GPS: N +53° 21' 16.29" W -6° 26' 58.89"

Exclusive 17th century house, convenient to buses for city centre, 200m walk to shops/pubs in the quaint Lucan Village. Ideal base for golf. Courses nearby include the K-Club, Carton House, Luttrellstown Castle, Hermitage and Lucan Golf Club. Off N4, near N7, N3 and M50. Private secure parking. Please enquire about Facilities for Persons with Disabilities.

B&B from €35.00 to €39.00

Astrid Scott

10

Open All Year

Grand Hotel

HOTEL ★★★★ MAP 12 O 12

Malahide,
Co. Dublin

Tel: 01-845 0000 Fax: 01-845 0987
Email: booking@thegrand.ie
Web: www.thegrand.ie
GPS: N +53° 27' 2.71" W -6° 8' 50.73"

The Grand Hotel is situated by the sea in the village of Malahide. Just 10 minutes drive from Dublin Airport and 30 minutes from the city centre, the hotel is ideally situated for guests staying for business or leisure. The conference and business centre is one of Ireland's largest and most successful. All 203 bedrooms have tea/coffee making facilities and fax/broadband lines. Most bedrooms have spectacular sea views. Leisure centre includes a 21 metre swimming pool, jacuzzi, fully equipped gymnasium, sauna and steam room. Please enquire about Facilities for Persons with Disabilities.

An IHF Quality Employer

Bookable on www.irelandhotels.com

Special Offer: www.irelandhotels.com/offers

B&B from €57.50 to €125.00
Suites from €130.00 to €800.00

Matthew Ryan
Managing Director

203

Food for Kids Activities:

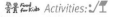

Closed 24 - 26 December

Forge Guesthouse (The)

GUESTHOUSE ★★ MAP 8 N 11

Saggart Village,
Saggart,
Co. Dublin

Tel: 01-458 9226 Fax: 01-458 7592
Email: info@theforge.ie
Web: www.theforge.ie
GPS: N +53° 16' 50.64" W -6° 26' 42.37"

This beautiful property has been newly approved to offer the best in luxurious guesthouse accommodation. This boutique style guesthouse is the perfect place to combine business with pleasure. In close proximity to Citywest Business Park and Citywest Hotel/Golf Course. At the Forge Guesthouse you are guaranteed a warm welcome and comfortable surroundings. Please enquire about Facilities for Persons with Disabilities.

Room Rate from €45.00 to €55.00

Linda Halnon Burns
Manager

10

Open All Year

B&B Rates are per Person Sharing per Night incl. Breakfast.
or Room Rates are per Room per Night - **See also Page 8**

Skerries / Sutton

Carroll's Pierhouse Hotel

HOTEL ★★ MAP 12 P 12

The Harbour,
Skerries,
Co. Dublin
Tel: 01-849 1033 Fax: 01-849 4695
Email: info@pierhousehotel.ie
Web: www.pierhousehotel.ie
GPS: N +53° 35' 6.83" W -6° 6' 18.23"

Carroll's Pierhouse Hotel is a family-run hotel, delightfully furnished & elegant in style. Situated on the Harbour Road of Skerries, a quaint fishing town about 15 mins from Dublin Airport & 30 mins from Dublin City centre. The idyllic location provides its guests with a wonderful panoramic view of the Irish Sea. Each of the hotel's executive en suite rooms has teletext TV, trouser press & tea/coffee making facilities. The restaurant provides Irish cuisine & an array of international dishes & in the main bar meals of similar content are available daily from 10am until 10pm. Our nightclub "Club Ocean" is open at weekends.

B&B from €40.00 to €60.00

Mary & Michael Carroll
Proprietors

10

Closed 24 - 27 December

Redbank House Guesthouse & Restaurant

GUESTHOUSE ★★★★ MAP 12 P 12

5 - 7 Church Street,
Skerries,
Co. Dublin
Tel: 01-849 1005 Fax: 01-849 1598
Email: info@redbank.ie
Web: www.redbank.ie
GPS: N +53° 34' 47.24" W -6° 6' 33.35"

Enjoy the extended hospitality of the McCoy's in Redbank House. The world famous seafood restaurant is the dining room of Redbank House. The 18 en suite rooms have the McCoys sense of style and elegance. The area is particularly rich in golf courses and a wide variety of leisure activities includes sea fishing, boat trips, sailing and horse riding. The Chef Proprietor Terry McCoy cooks the catch of the day landed at Skerries Pier specialising in the world famous Dublin Bay prawns. Just 20 minutes from Dublin Airport on the new M1. On-street parking Pay & Display, Mon - Sat: 8am - 6pm.

An IHF Quality Employer

Member of Premier Guesthouses

Bookable on www.irelandhotels.com

Special Offer: www.irelandhotels.com/offers

B&B from €50.00 to €75.00

Terry McCoy
Proprietor

18

Activities:

Open All Year

Marine Hotel

HOTEL ★★★ MAP 12 P 11

Sutton Cross,
Dublin 13
Tel: 01-839 0000 Fax: 01-839 0442
Email: info@marinehotel.ie
Web: www.marinehotel.ie
GPS: N +53° 23' 19.42" W -6° 6' 37.63"

The Marine Hotel overlooks the north shore of Dublin Bay with its lawn sweeping down to the sea shore. All bedrooms are en suite and have trouser press, TV, direct dial phone and tea/coffee facilities. The city centre is 6km away and the airport 25 minutes drive. Close by is the DART rapid rail system. The hotel has a heated indoor swimming pool and sauna. Nearby are the Royal Dublin and Portmarnock championship golf courses. Please enquire about Facilities for Persons with Disabilities.

An IHF Quality Employer

Bookable on www.irelandhotels.com

Room Rate from €50.00 to €200.00

Matthew Ryan
Managing Director

48

Food for Kids

Closed 24 - 26 December

B&B Rates are per Person Sharing per Night incl. Breakfast. or Room Rates are per Room per Night - **See also Page 8**

Carnegie Court Hotel

HOTEL ★★★ MAP 12 O 12

North Street,
Swords,
Co. Dublin
Tel: 01-840 4384 Fax: 01-840 4505
Email: info@carnegiecourt.com
Web: www.carnegiecourt.com
GPS: N +53° 27' 44.91" W -6° 13' 4.32"

The Carnegie Court Hotel is a luxury accommodation hotel ideally situated in the town of Swords, 5 mins from Dublin Airport and 20 mins from the city centre. The hotel comprises 36 beautifully decorated and spacious bedrooms. A warm welcoming atmosphere makes it the perfect place of rest, be it business or pleasure. Enjoy our award-winning Courtyard Restaurant or indulge in a night out in one of our five bars. Other facilities include conference & banqueting services and an extensive secure car park. Please enquire about Facilities for Persons with Disabilities.

An IHF Quality Employer

B&B from €65.00 to €120.00

Allen Harrington
General Manager

36

Activities:

Closed 25 - 27 December

Kettles Country House Hotel

HOTEL ★★★ MAP 12 O 9

Lispopple Cross,
Swords,
Co. Dublin
Tel: 01-813 8511 Fax: 01-813 8510
Email: info@kettleshotel.ie
Web: www.kettleshotel.ie
GPS: N +53° 28' 56.77" W -6° 17' 17.83"

Where once stood the Kettle family home and their thriving public house, then known as the Rolestown Inn since 1978, now stands Kettles Country House which opened its doors to the public on Thursday 25th January 2007 and is now run by their elder sons. In this stunning new hotel you will find a host of luxuries, from a choice of lounge & bars, to the ever so decedent Leys Brazeel Restaurant. If it is a home from home where you can lay your head that you are looking for, then look no further than our 25 stylishly decorated bedrooms.

Bookable on www.irelandhotels.com

B&B from €49.00 to €109.00
Suites from €189.00 to €380.00

Patrick Lernihan
General Manager

25

Closed 25 - 26 December

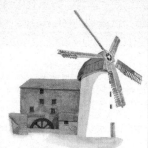

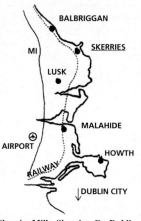

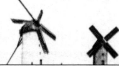

B&B Rates are per Person Sharing per Night incl. Breakfast.
or Room Rates are per Room per Night - See also Page 8

Athy / Clane

Carlton Abbey Hotel & C-Spa

HOTEL ★★★★ MAP 7 M 9

Town Centre,
Athy,
Co. Kildare

Tel: 059-863 0100 Fax: 059-863 0101
Email: reservations.abbey@carlton.ie
Web: www.carlton.ie/abbey
GPS: N +52° 59' 37.74" W -6° 58' 56.96"

The 4**** hotel, leisure club & C-Spa. Carlton Abbey Hotel is situated in the heart of Athy, Co. Kildare. 50 minutes from Dublin. 49 luxurious bedrooms including junior/family suites along with conference & banqueting facilities for 200 guests. The Abbey Bar & Bistro, formerly an old church, is the centre piece of this restoration with Benedicts Restaurant offering an intimate dining experience. State of the art leisure club with 21m pool, sauna, jacuzzi, steam room & modern gym. C-Spa with 6 treatment rooms is an oasis of calm for all guests to enjoy. Room Reservations LoCall 1890 288 288.

Bookable on www.irelandhotels.com

Special Offer: www.irelandhotels.com/offers

B&B from €49.00 to €129.00

Ted Egan
General Manager

49

Closed 24 - 27 December

Clanard Court Hotel

HOTEL ★★★★ MAP 7 M 9

Dublin Road,
Athy,
Co. Kildare

Tel: 059-864 0666 Fax: 059-864 0888
Email: sales@clanardcourt.ie
Web: www.clanardcourt.ie
GPS: N +52° 59' 55.48" W -6° 57' 35.58"

Clanard Court Hotel is a delightful, boutique style 4**** hotel with beautiful gardens situated just 1 hour from Dublin and 1km from Athy Town. It boasts 38 superbly appointed guest rooms complete with all modern conveniences including interactive TV and unlimited broadband. It is family-run with strong emphasis on customer service. Clanard Court specialises in tailor made banqueting and events. There is a choice of banqueting and conference rooms accommodating up to 450 pax. The ideal choice for superb food and genuine, warm hospitality - a leading wedding venue in Leinster.

Bookable on www.irelandhotels.com

Special Offer: www.irelandhotels.com/offers

B&B from €50.00 to €130.00

Mary Fennin Byrne
Managing Director

38

Food for Kids Activities:

Closed 23 - 26 December

Westgrove Hotel

HOTEL ★★★★ MAP 8 N 11

Clane,
Co. Kildare

Tel: 045-989900 Fax: 045-989911
Email: reservations@westgrovehotel.com
Web: www.westgrovehotel.com
GPS: N +53° 17' 25.01" W -6° 40' 53.70"

Nestling in the outskirts of Clane Village, this contemporary and glamourous hotel is easily accessible, only 10 minutes from both the M7 or M4 motorways. Providing an array of facilities to pamper the most discerning guest, there is a choice of bars and restaurants, a designer roof top garden, extensive leisure centre and dedicated Elemis Spa. With Mondello on the doorstep and Punchestown under 15 minutes away, the hotel can be a haven for sporting enthusiasts. Golfers of all levels are catered for with 7 courses within 20 minutes. Modern, light-filled conference suites provide the perfect working environment.

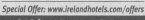

Member of Select Hotels of Ireland

Bookable on www.irelandhotels.com

Special Offer: www.irelandhotels.com/offers

B&B from €75.00 to €160.00
Suites from €200.00 to €470.00

Ian Hyland
General Manager

99

Activities:

Closed 24 - 26 December

B&B Rates are per Person Sharing per Night incl. Breakfast or Room Rates are per Room per Night - See also Page 8

Derby House Hotel

HOTEL ★★ MAP 7 M 10

Dublin Road,
Kildare Town,
Co. Kildare
Tel: 045-522144 Fax: 045-521247
Email: enquiries@derbyhousehotel.ie
Web: www.derbyhousehotel.ie
GPS: N +53° 9' 19.95" W -6° 54' 26.24"

A friendly and warm welcome awaits you at the Derby House Hotel. Conveniently located in the town centre, the hotel now incorporates Kingsland Restaurant offering Chinese and European cuisine. This 20 bedroomed hotel is conveniently located for racing, angling and numerous golf courses including the renowned K Club. Many attractions, including the Japanese Gardens, Irish National Stud and Kildare Village, are also nearby. Please enquire about Facilities for Persons with Disabilities.

Bookable on www.irelandhotels.com

B&B from €50.00 to €85.00
Suites from €120.00 to €150.00

KINGSLAND

Sarah Chan
Proprietor

20

Activities:

Open All Year

Opening times:
12th February to Christmas
7 days a week
9 a.m. - 5 p.m.
Irish national stud
est. 1946
The Irish National Stud
Japanese Gardens, St. Fiachra's Garden & Horse Museum
• Location: 45 mins South of Dublin off the M7 Exit 13 onto R 415
• Access By Road, By Bus from Dublin or Rail to Kildare Town (Shuttle Bus from Rail station to Kildare Village Chic outlet shopping & Irish National Stud)
• The only Stud farm in Ireland open to the public offering daily guided tours
• World Famous Japanese Gardens
• Award winning St. Fiachra's Garden
• Horse Museum
• Gift shop and Restaurant
• Free car and coach park
Tel: +353 (0)45 521617
Irish National Stud,
Tully, Kildare, Ireland.
Email: japanesegardens@eircom.net
Japanese Gardens Celebrating 100 Years Centenary 2010
ONE ADMISSION CHARGE COVERS ALL 4 ATTRACTIONS
Bookable on line at: www.irish-national-stud.ie

B&B Rates are per Person Sharing per Night incl. Breakfast.
or Room Rates are per Room per Night - See also Page 8

Leixlip / Maynooth / Monasterevin

Courtyard Hotel Leixlip

HOTEL ★★★★ MAP 8 N 11

Main Street,
Leixlip,
Co. Kildare
Tel: 01-629 5100 Fax: 01-629 5111
Email: info@courtyard.ie
Web: www.courtyard.ie
GPS: N +53° 21' 50.48" W -6° 29' 19.78"

"Pure perfection takes time" - Arthur Guinness, 1756. Arthur Guinness created the perfect pint in Leixlip 250 years ago and a quarter of a millennium later, Luke Moriarty & the Moriarty Group strive to keep that perfection alive here at the Courtyard Hotel. Built on the site where Arthur Guinness created his brewing empire, the hotel offers old world charm, beautiful original stone work with contemporary design in an idyllic setting. Arthur Guinness is legendary for his pint & the Courtyard Hotel is legendary for its 4* comfort, exquisite dining, the famous courtyard & of course 'The Black Stuff' in Arthurs Bar.

Member of The Moriarty Group

Bookable on www.irelandhotels.com

Special Offer: www.irelandhotels.com/offers

B&B from €55.00 to €75.00
Suites from €150.00 to €220.00

Luke Moriarty
Owner

40

Activities:

Closed 25 - 26 December

Glenroyal Hotel (The)

HOTEL ★★★ MAP 8 N 11

Straffan Road,
Maynooth,
Co. Kildare
Tel: 01-629 0909 Fax: 01-629 0919
Email: info@glenroyal.ie
Web: www.glenroyal.ie
GPS: N +53° 22' 47.30" W -6° 35' 17.26"

Located 20 minutes from Dublin convenient to the M4 with National rail and bus links on our doorstep. Ideally located for the business or leisure traveller, the Glenroyal Hotel has a well earned reputation for friendliness, informality and hospitality. All bedrooms are well equipped and comfortable. the atmosphere in Saints Bar & Bistro is relaxed. Our facilites also include a leisure club baosting two 20m pools, Sauna, Jacuzzi, Steam room & Gymnasium. Ealu Spa, extensive conference and banquetting facilities with free car parking. For golf enthusiasts, Carton & The K Club are minutes away.

Bookable on www.irelandhotels.com

Special Offer: www.irelandhotels.com/offers

B&B from €39.50 to €75.00

Helen Courtney
General Manager

113

Food for Kids Activities:

Closed 25 - 26 December

Hazel Hotel

HOTEL ★★★ MAP 7 N 10

Dublin Road,
Monasterevin,
Co. Kildare
Tel: 045-525373 Fax: 045-525810
Email: sales@hazelhotel.com
Web: www.hazelhotel.com
GPS: N +53° 8' 9.22" W -7° 4' 11.13"

The Hazel Hotel is a family-run country hotel on the main Dublin/Cork/Limerick road (N7). All bedrooms have bath/shower, colour TV and international direct dial telephone. The hotel's restaurant has extensive à la carte and table d'hôte menus. Ample car parking. Entertainment is provided. Ideal base for going to the Curragh, Naas or Punchestown racecourses. Several golf courses close by. National Stud and Japanese Gardens only 7 miles from hotel. No service charge. Please enquire about Facilities for Persons with Disabilities.

An IHF Quality Employer

B&B from €50.00 to €70.00
Suites from €130.00 to €150.00

Margaret Kelly
Proprietor

24

Closed 23 - 26 December

B&B Rates are per Person Sharing per Night incl. Breakfast or Room Rates are per Room per Night - **See also Page 8**

Harbour Hotel & Restaurant

HOTEL ★★ MAP 8 N 10

Limerick Road,
Naas,
Co. Kildare
Tel: 045-879145 Fax: 045-874002
Email: mary@harbourhotel.ie
Web: www.harbourhotel.ie
GPS: N +53° 12' 58.26" W -6° 40' 4.02"

Looking after the needs of our guests and providing quality service is a priority in this family-run hotel. All rooms have colour TV, direct dial telephone, hairdryer and teasmaid. We offer superb home-cooked food, extensive à la carte and table d'hôte menus and excellent wine list. Relax and enjoy a drink in our comfortable lounge. Conveniently situated to Dublin City, ferry, airport, Punchestown Racecourse, The Curragh and Mondello Park.

Bookable on www.irelandhotels.com

B&B from €60.00 to €110.00

Mary Monaghan
Proprietor

10

Closed 24 - 26 December

Maudlins House Hotel

HOTEL ★★★★ MAP 8 N 10

Exit 9, M7,
Dublin Road, Naas,
Co. Kildare
Tel: 045-896999 Fax: 045-906411
Email: info@maudlinshousehotel.ie
Web: www.maudlinshousehotel.ie
GPS: N +53° 13' 54.01" W -6° 38' 25.13"

Maudlins House Hotel is a 4**** luxury country house hotel, located just off the M7, easily accessible from the south, conveniently located 1km from Naas town centre. 25km from Dublin city centre, 20km from Dublin Airport and ideal for those travelling to the West. The hotel comprises 19 luxury rooms, 5 private coach rooms and 1 Nás na Rí suite. The double AA rosette winning Virginia Restaurant, Maudlins Bar, conference & banqueting facilities. Local amenities include golf, horse racing, Goffs horse sales, Japanese Gardens and National Stud, Whitewater Shopping Centre & Kildare Village Outlet Centre. A place to indulge yourself.

B&B from €79.00 to €95.00
Suites from €200.00 to €250.00

David Fagan
Director

1 24

Food for Kids Activities:

Closed 25 - 26 December

Osprey Hotel & Spa

HOTEL ★★★★ MAP 8 N 10

Devoy Quarter,
Naas,
Co. Kildare
Tel: 045-881111 Fax: 045-881112
Email: info@osprey.ie
Web: www.osprey.ie
GPS: N +53° 12' 47.55" W -6° 40' 12.65"

The Osprey Complex, located in the heart of Kildare, is only 35 minutes from Dublin City and close to all major routes. It includes the Osprey Hotel, Osprey Spa, Life: health & leisure, Time: venue, Osprey Conference Centre, and Osprey Business Campus. Osprey Hotel is of contemporary style with 104 bedrooms including two penthouse suites & has a dramatic foyer, glazed atria, Mash: Restaurant, Statler Bar and Waldorf Lounge and ballroom. It has been designed to cater for an entirely new lifestyle. Complimentary wireless connectivity throughout. Suites available up to €1,000 per night.

Bookable on www.irelandhotels.com
Special Offer: www.irelandhotels.com/offers

B&B from €69.50 to €167.50
Suites from €319.00 to €1,000.00

Aundrea Tallon
General Manager

104

Activities:

Closed 24 - 30 December

B&B Rates are per Person Sharing per Night incl. Breakfast.
or Room Rates are per Room per Night - **See also Page 8**

Newbridge / Straffan

Gables Guesthouse & Leisure Centre

GUESTHOUSE ★★★ MAP 7 M 10

Ryston,
Newbridge,
Co. Kildare
Tel: 045-435330 Fax: 045-435355
Email: gablesguesthse@ireland.com

GPS: N +53° 10' 30.15" W -6° 47' 34.95"

Set on the banks of the Liffey, our family-run guesthouse has 25 bedrooms with bath/shower, multi channel TV, direct dial telephone, hairdryer and teas maid. Our leisure centre includes a 20 metre indoor swimming pool, jacuzzi, steam room, large sauna, thermium, plunge pool and fully equipped gym. Horse racing, greyhound racing, golf and fishing are well catered for locally. A warm and friendly welcome awaits you at the Gables. Brochures available on request.

B&B from €45.00 to €80.00

Ray Cribbin
Proprietor

25

Closed 24 December - 02 January

Keadeen Hotel

HOTEL ★★★★ MAP 7 M 10

Curragh Road,
Newbridge,
Co. Kildare
Tel: 045-431666 Fax: 045-434402
Email: info@keadeenhotel.ie
Web: www.keadeenhotel.ie

GPS: N +53° 10' 13.65" W -6° 48' 51.70"

Kildare's longest family-run hotel, the Keadeen is ideally located on 7 acres of magnificent landscaped gardens, just 30 minutes from Dublin off the M7. This charming 4**** hotel offers unrivalled standards of service and facilities with a variety of 75 luxurious spacious bedrooms, a superb indoor health and fitness complex and 18 metre pool. An extensive range of conference/banqueting suites for up to 1000 delegates. Dining facilities include the award-winning Derby Restaurant, the sophisticated 'Club Bar', the Drawing Room Lounge. Please enquire about Facilities for Persons with Disabilities.

An IHF Quality Employer

B&B from €125.00 to €140.00

Rose O'Loughlin
Proprietor

75

Activities:

Closed 24 December - 04 January

Kildare Hotel, Spa and Country Club - The K Club

HOTEL ★★★★★ MAP 8 N 11

At Straffan,
Co. Kildare
Tel: 01-601 7200 Fax: 01-601 7297
Email: resortsales@kclub.ie
Web: www.kclub.ie

GPS: N +53° 18' 26.21" W -6° 37' 29.88"

The K Club is Ireland's premier AA 5 Red Star resort, located 40 minutes from Dublin City Centre & Airport. Both river fishing & course fishing are available, the magnificent K Spa offers a chance to pamper yourself in style or work out before dining in one of our sumptuous restaurants. The Palmer Course was the host venue of the 2006 Ryder Cup Matches and The Smurfit Course was Home of The Smurfit Kappa European Open. The Kids Club allows you to relax while your children are well looked after & have fun while learning. Each weekend we offer tours of the wine cellar and art & history. Meeting facilities for up to 400 people.

An IHF Quality Employer

Member of Preferred Hotel Group

Bookable on www.irelandhotels.com

Special Offer: www.irelandhotels.com/offers

B&B from €195.00 to €550.00
Suites from €515.00 to €7,000.00

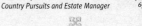

Mick Casey
Country Pursuits and Estate Manager

69

Open All Year

B&B Rates are per Person Sharing per Night incl. Breakfast
or Room Rates are per Room per Night - See also Page 8

Durrow / Killenard / Portlaoise

Castle Arms Hotel

HOTEL ★ MAP 7 L 8

The Square,
Durrow,
Co. Laois
Tel: 057-873 6117 Fax: 057-873 6566
Email: info@castlearmshotel.ie
Web: www.castlearmshotel.ie
GPS: N +52° 50' 43.25" W -7° 23' 46.33"

The Castle Arms Hotel is a family-run hotel situated in the award-winning picturesque village of Durrow. Situated 1.5 hours from Dublin, two hours from Cork and three hours from Belfast. Our reputation is for good food, service & friendliness. Local amenities include fishing. Granstown Lake is described as being the best coarse fishing lake in Europe. Trout can be fished from the local Rivers Erkina and Nore, horse trekking & many golf courses within easy reach. Brand Central designer outlet is 10 mins drive away. Ideal for a weekend away shopping. Please enquire about Facilities for Persons with Disabilities.

B&B from €50.00 to €60.00

Seosamh Murphy
General Manager

14

Open All Year

Heritage Golf & Spa Resort (The)

HOTEL ★★★★★ MAP 7 L 10

Killenard,
Co. Laois
Tel: 057-864 5500 Fax: 057-864 2350
Email: info@theheritage.com
Web: www.theheritage.com
GPS: N +53° 7' 59.39" W -7° 9' 5.98"

The Heritage Golf & Spa Resort is Ireland's most comprehensive leisure & lifestyle development. Situated in the village of Killenard just off the main Dublin - Cork motorway. We are just 40 miles from Dublin. A 98 guest room hotel, 20 therapy room resort Spa, the renowned Heritage Golf Course designed by Seve Ballesteros, Health Club, Walking & Jogging track, Ballesteros 'Natural' Golf School, Thatch Pub and Sol Oriens Italian Restaurant & Steakhouse, all provide a most comprehensive set of leisure & corporate offers at the highest quality. Superior, Junior & Penthouse Suites available.

An IHF Quality Employer

Member of Preferred Hotels & Resorts

Bookable on www.irelandhotels.com

Special Offer: www.irelandhotels.com/offers

B&B from €60.00 to €115.00
Suites from €220.00 to €500.00

Donagh Davern
Resort General Manager

98

Food for Kids Activities:

Closed 23 - 28 December

Killeshin (The)

HOTEL ★★★★ MAP 7 L 9

Dublin Road,
Portlaoise,
Co. Laois
Tel: 057-863 1200 Fax: 057-863 1205
Email: info@thekilleshin.com
Web: www.thekilleshin.com
GPS: N +53° 2' 24.81" W -7° 16' 20.20"

The Killeshin Hotel, Portlaoise opened in May 2007. This 87 bedroomed contemporary styled property is situated at the edge of Portlaoise town, ideally located in the centre of Ireland, only 1/2 km from M7, N7, N8. Facilities include the Cedar Rooms - Bar and Restaurant, Forum at the Killeshin - offering 12 multi purpose meeting rooms, the Walnut Room - Banqueting venue and Zest - our health & fitness club, The Killeshin Hotel, Portlaoise, where making you feel welcome and well looked after is at the heart of everythiing we do. Please enquire about Facilities for Persons with Disabilities.

Bookable on www.irelandhotels.com

Special Offer: www.irelandhotels.com/offers

B&B from €60.00 to €100.00

Mary Staunton
General Manager

87

Activities:

Closed 24 - 26 December

B&B Rates are per Person Sharing per Night incl. Breakfast or Room Rates are per Room per Night - See also Page 8

Maldron Hotel Portlaoise

HOTEL ★★★ MAP 7 L 9

Midway, Abbeyleix Road,
Portlaoise,
Co. Laois

Tel: 057-869 5900 Fax: 057-869 5901

Email: info.portlaoise@maldronhotels.com

Web: www.maldronhotels.com

GPS: N +53° 0' 55.99" W -7° 18' 3.50"

This superior 90 bedroom hotel is conveniently situated off exit 17 on the Dublin N7/Cork N8 junction and only 2km from Portlaoise town centre. All rooms are en suite with power showers, tea/coffee making facilities, broadband internet access and satellite television. Guests can also avail of the hotel's Stir Restaurant & Bar, meeting suites & Club Vitae Health & Fitness Club with a 20m pool, treatment rooms and a gym. Extensive complimentary parking on-site. Please enquire about Facilities for Persons with Disabilities.

An IHF Quality Employer

Member of Maldron Hotels

Bookable on www.irelandhotels.com

Special Offer: www.irelandhotels.com/offers

Room Rate from €49.00 to €229.00

Michael Lally
General Manager

90

Food for Kids

Closed 20 - 28 December

Portlaoise Heritage Hotel

HOTEL ★★★★ MAP 7 L 9

Town Centre,
Portlaoise,
Co. Laois

Tel: 057-867 8588 Fax: 057-867 8577

Email: info@theheritagehotel.com

Web: www.theheritagehotel.com

GPS: N +53° 2' 5.68" W -7° 18' 11.02"

The Portlaoise Heritage Hotel has earned itself the reputation of being one of the most sought after hotels in Ireland. Nestled in the heart of Portlaoise Town, it is the most accessible central location in Ireland, only 1 hour from Dublin with excellent rail & road network to any part of the country. The hotel boasts 110 bedrooms including de luxe & executive rooms, facilities include 3 bars, 3 restaurants, 5* health & fitness club and Ealu Medical Therapy Spa. With lots of activities, it is the perfect location to explore the heart of Ireland. Please enquire about Facilities for Persons with Disabilities.

An IHF Quality Employer

Bookable on www.irelandhotels.com

Special Offer: www.irelandhotels.com/offers

B&B from €69.00 to €120.00
Suites from €250.00 to €375.00

Jacinta Naughton
General Manager

2 108

Food for Kids

Closed 22 - 27 December

B&B Rates are per Person Sharing per Night incl. Breakfast.
or Room Rates are per Room per Night - See also Page 8

Clondra / Longford Town

Richmond Inn Guesthouse

GUESTHOUSE ★★★ MAP 11 J 13

Clondra,
Co. Longford

Tel: 043-332 6126 Fax: 043-332 6166
Email: therichmondinn@eircom.net
Web: www.richmondinnireland.com
GPS: N +53° 43' 52.78" W -7° 54' 17.20"

A family-run guesthouse and pub in the picturesque village of Clondra. 7km from Longford Town. The Richmond Inn occupies a prime position in this pretty village, standing on the banks of the Royal Canal overlooking the harbour. Your hosts are Des & Frances McPartland who assure their patrons of a warm welcome and fine home cooking. All rooms are en suite with TV, direct dial phone, tea/coffee making facilities. Local amenities include fishing, horse riding, golf, walking and cycling.

Bookable on www.irelandhotels.com

B&B from €40.00 to €70.00

Des & Frances McPartland
Owners 5

Closed 12 December - 12 January

Annaly Hotel

HOTEL ★★ MAP 11 J 13

57 Main Street,
Longford Town

Tel: 043-334 2058 Fax: 043-334 6244
Email: info@annalyhotel.ie
Web: www.annalyhotel.ie
GPS: N +53° 43' 42.65" W -7° 48' 3.18"

Modern hotel located in the centre of Longford. Café bar in comfortable surroundings. Very competitive rates with a host of entertainment on site. 30 fully serviced stylish bedrooms. Full conference facilities and large function room. Food available from 7:30am - 9pm including lunch and dinner.

B&B from €55.00 to €75.00

Jim Reynolds
Proprietor 30

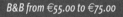

Activities:

Closed 24 - 26 December

Longford Arms Hotel

HOTEL ★★★ MAP 11 J 13

Main Street,
Longford Town,
Co. Longford

Tel: 043-334 6296 Fax: 043-334 6244
Email: longfordarms@eircom.net
Web: www.longfordarms.ie
GPS: N +53° 43' 43.46" W -7° 48' 6.34"

Ideally located in the heart of the Midlands, this comfortable hotel, renovated to exacting standards, has a vibrant and relaxing atmosphere. The hotel boasts a state of the art conference centre, health and leisure centre, excellent restaurant and award-winning coffee shop where you can be assured of fine food, service and a warm welcome in relaxed, convivial surroundings. Free WiFi available to guests staying in executive bedrooms, also available in lobby & bar area. Available locally: 18 hole golf course, angling, equestrian centre and watersports on the Shannon.

Bookable on www.irelandhotels.com

B&B from €40.00 to €100.00

Jim Reynolds
Proprietor 57

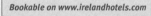

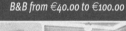

Activities:

Closed 24 - 27 December

B&B Rates are per Person Sharing per Night incl. Breakfast.
or Room Rates are per Room per Night - See also Page 8

Viewmount House

GUESTHOUSE MAP 11 J 13

Dublin Road,
Longford

Tel: 043-334 1919 Fax: 043-334 2906
Email: info@viewmounthouse.com
Web: www.viewmounthouse.com
GPS: N +53° 43' 17.26" W -7° 46' 14.83"

Built to a 4**** specification. Beautiful Georgian house offering luxury accommodation, 1km from Longford town centre. Set in 4 acres of magnificent gardens adjoining Longford Golf Course. Bedrooms are individually styled with antique furniture. Wonderful freshly cooked breakfast is served in the beautiful Georgian blue dining room with its vaulted ceilings. Chef Gary O'Hanlon offers sensational food in the VM Restaurant. The exposed stonework and an abundance of candles give a cosy atmosphere at night.

B&B from €60.00 to €75.00
Suites from €150.00 to €200.00

James & Beryl Kearney
Proprietors

13

Open All Year

Beaufort House

GUESTHOUSE ★★★★ MAP 12 O 15

Ghan Road,
Carlingford,
Co. Louth

Tel: 042-937 3879 Fax: 042-937 3878
Email: michaelcaine@beauforthouse.net
Web: www.beauforthouse.net
GPS: N +54° 2' 25.77" W -6° 10' 35.88"

Beaufort House, Co. Louth's only 4* guesthouse, listed in Bridgestone, Michelin BIB Hotel Award, Georgina Campbell, a magnificent shoreside residence with glorious sea & mountain views in mediaeval Carlingford Village. Your hosts, Michael & Glynnis Caine, Failte Ireland Award winners of Excellence, will ensure the highest standards. In-house activities include sailing school & yacht charter. Golfing arranged in any of 5 golf courses within 20 mins of Beaufort House. Private car parking. Dinner by prior arrangement. Small business conference facilities. Please enquire about Facilities for Persons with Disabilities.

B&B from €40.00 to €60.00

Michael & Glynnis Caine

5

Open All Year

McKevitt's Village Hotel

HOTEL ★★ MAP 12 O 15

Market Square,
Carlingford,
Co. Louth

Tel: 042-937 3116 Fax: 042-937 3144
Email: mckevittshotel@yahoo.com
Web: www.mckevittshotel.com
GPS: N +54° 2' 25.41" W -6° 11' 13.98"

McKevitt's Village Hotel is family owned and personally supervised by Kay & Terry McKevitt. At the hotel, pride of place is taken in the personal attention given to guests by owners and staff. Carlingford is one of Ireland's oldest and most interesting medieval villages. Beautifully situated on the shores of Carlingford Lough and half way between Dublin and Belfast.

B&B from €65.00 to €85.00

Dermot O'Farrell
Manager

17

Open All Year

B&B Rates are per Person Sharing per Night incl. Breakfast.
or Room Rates are per Room per Night - **See also Page 8**

Drogheda

d (The)

HOTEL ★★★★ MAP 12 O 13

Scotch Hall,
Drogheda,
Co. Louth
Tel: 041-987 7700 Fax: 041-987 7702
Email: info@thedhotel.com
Web: www.thedhotel.com
GPS: N +53° 42' 50.39" W -6° 20' 42.39"

The stylish 4 star d hotel is located on the banks of the River Boyne in the historic town of Drogheda, only 25 minutes from Dublin Airport. The d has 104 luxurious bedrooms, many with river views, family rooms & balcony rooms as well as two penthouse suites with rooftop terraces. The hotel has six meeting & event suites and the viaduct suite on the waterfront is Drogheda's premier wedding venue. The d hotel is the official players' hotel of the European Tour 3 Irish Open.

Bookable on www.irelandhotels.com

Special Offer: www.irelandhotels.com/offers

Room Rate from €79.00 to €299.00
Suites from €250.00 to €1,000.00

Rory Scott
General Manager

104

Activities:

Closed 24 - 29 December

Glenside Hotel

HOTEL ★★ MAP 12 O 13

Dublin Road,
Drogheda,
Co. Louth
Tel: 041-982 9185 Fax: 041-982 9049
Email: info@glensidehotel.ie
Web: www.glensidehotel.ie
GPS: N +53° 41' 17.53" W -6° 18' 0.83"

The Glenside Hotel is situated 2km south of Drogheda and 20 mins from Dublin Airport on the N1. With 16 en suite rooms fitted to an exceptionally high standard, one master suite, à la carte restaurant and lounge bar, banquet facilities for up to 200 guests. The perfect setting for a special wedding day. Ideal base for golfing enthusiasts and touring Co. Louth/Meath. Ample car parking.

B&B from €30.00 to €60.00
Suites from €100.00 to €200.00

Ronan McAuley
Proprietor

16

Closed 24 - 26 December

Westcourt Hotel

HOTEL ★★★ MAP 12 O 13

West Street,
Drogheda,
Co. Louth
Tel: 041-983 0965 Fax: 041-983 0970
Email: reservations@westcourt.ie
Web: www.westcourt.ie
GPS: N +53° 42' 53.74" W -6° 21' 13.88"

Just 25 minutes from Dublin Airport, in the heart of Drogheda and the historical Boyne Valley, Westcourt Hotel is close to great shopping centres, top golf courses, Newgrange and many other historical sites. The hotel is central for a lively or quiet weekend getaway, suitable for family and business travel. Well connected by road and rail, featuring modern rooms and high speed internet access. We can accommodate meetings, conventions and weddings for 300. We have secure parking. Enjoy a pint in our Barroco Bar and dance the night away in Earth Nightclub.

B&B from €50.00 to €65.00

Valerie Sherlock
General Manager

27

Activities:

Closed 25 - 26 December

B&B Rates are per Person Sharing per Night incl. Breakfast.
or Room Rates are per Room per Night - **See also Page 8**

Ballymascanlon House Hotel

HOTEL ★★★★ MAP 12 O 14

Carlingford Road (R173),
Dundalk,
Co. Louth
Tel: 042-935 8200 Fax: 042-937 1598
Email: info@ballymascanlon.com
Web: www.ballymascanlon.com
GPS: N +54° 1' 52.82" W -6° 21' 8.14"

Ballymascanlon House is a Fáilte Ireland, AA 4**** country house hotel just 45 mins by motorway from Dublin & Belfast. Just 8 miles from medieval Carlingford, it is set on 130 acres of parkland with its own Ruddy & Craddock designed 18 hole golf course. The beautifully appointed bedroom accommodation, award-winning Restaurant and Terrace Bar are complemented by modern leisure facilities including 20m deck level pool, sauna, jacuzzi, steam room, outdoor Canadian hot tub, gym and tennis courts. The perfect short break destination. New Function/Conference Centre now open.

An IHF Quality Employer

Bookable on www.irelandhotels.com

Special Offer: www.irelandhotels.com/offers

B&B from €80.00 to €95.00
Suites from €200.00 to €250.00

Oliver Quinn
Managing Director

90

Activities:

Open All Year

Lismar Guesthouse & Serviced Apartments

GUESTHOUSE ★★★ MAP 12 O 14

8-9 Stapleton Place,
Dundalk,
Co. Louth
Tel: 042-935 7246 Fax: 042-935 7247
Email: lismar@iol.ie
Web: www.lismar.ie
GPS: N +53° 59' 55.66" W -6° 24' 24.98"

Lismar is a superb family-run guesthouse only an hour from major airports and ferries, easily accessible from the M1 and within walking distance of bus and train stations. Situated on a quiet street, only minutes walk to Dundalk town centre and all amenities. Lismar is the ideal base for trips to the Cooley Peninsula, Carlingford, the Mournes, the Tain Trail, golf and race courses. Short let self-catering apartments and studio apartments also available. Michael and Elizabeth welcome you to enjoy all modern facilities and maximum comfort in their proudly refurbished Edwardian property.

Bookable on www.irelandhotels.com

B&B from €45.00 to €45.00

Michael & Elizabeth Smyth

8

Closed 24 - 28 December

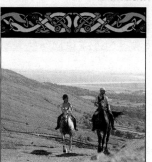

B&B Rates are per Person Sharing per Night incl. Breakfast.
or Room Rates are per Room per Night - **See also Page 8**

Ashbourne / Athboy

Aisling Guest House

GUESTHOUSE ★★ MAP 12 O 12

Dublin Road,
Baltrasna, Ashbourne,
Co. Meath
Tel: 01-835 0359 Fax: 01-835 1135
Email: info@aislingguesthouse.ie
Web: www.aislingguesthouse.ie
GPS: N +53° 29' 49.96" W -6° 23' 4.67"

Aisling Guest House has been Catering for Guests the last 25 years & Renowned Worldwide, as you can see from the Testimonial Page. We are 2 minutes from the Main street of Ashbourne, 5 minutes from M50, 5 minutes from Fairyhouse Race Course & Tattersalls Horse Sales. Croke Park & Dublin Airport are just 10 minutes away. The bus stops outside our gate which is a 20 minutes journey to the Dublin City centre. Aisling is one of the largest guesthouses in the Meath/Dublin area. With 20 rooms and apartments. We pride ourselves in providing top class accommodation & service.

B&B from €30.00 to €35.00
Suites from €90.00 to €130.00

Rod Cosgrave
Proprietor
20

Open All Year

Ashbourne Marriott Hotel

HOTEL ★★★★ MAP 12 O 12

The Rath,
Ashbourne,
Co. Meath
Tel: 01-835 6800 Fax: 01-835 6801
Email: info@marriottashbourne.com
Web: www.marriottashbourne.com
GPS: N +53° 31' 38.35" W -6° 24' 55.04"

Ashbourne Marriott Hotel brings a new concept in luxury, ideally located in Ashbourne, Co.Meath, within close proximity to Dublin. Designed to an exceptionally high four star standard, this contemporary hotel offers 148 luxurious bedrooms and 8 meeting rooms featuring over 9,000 sq ft of meeting space. This property boasts a modern contemporary restaurant Grill Twenty One, funky upbeat lounge and bar, Red and Clann, fitness and leisure centre. Please enquire about Facilities for Persons with Disabilities.

Bookable on www.irelandhotels.com
Special Offer: www.irelandhotels.com/offers

Room Rate from €99.00 to €169.00
Suites from €189.00 to €249.00

Gabriele Molari
General Manager
148

Closed 24 - 26 December

Old Darnley Lodge Hotel

HOTEL ★★ MAP 11 M 12

Main Street,
Athboy,
Co. Meath
Tel: 046-943 2283 Fax: 046-943 2255
Email: info@olddarnley.com
Web: www.olddarnley.com
GPS: N +53° 37' 18.39" W -6° 55' 14.15"

The Old Darnley Lodge Hotel is steeped in heritage, charm and character. A warm, friendly welcome awaits you, offering traditional hospitality in one of the most historic areas of Ireland. The Old Darnley Lodge Hotel is the ideal location for Weddings and Functions. The Hotel is close to Meath's finest Golf Clubs, which makes it the ideal retreat for a leisurely short break.

B&B from €65.00 to €70.00

Sean Mangan
General Manager
14

Closed 25 - 26 December

B&B Rates are per Person Sharing per Night incl. Breakfast.
or Room Rates are per Room per Night - **See also Page 8**

Bettystown Court Conference & Leisure Hotel

HOTEL ★★★★ MAP 12 O 13

Bettystown,
Co. Meath

Tel: 041-981 2900 Fax: 041-981 2939
Email: info@bettystowncourthotel.com
Web: www.bettystowncourthotel.com
GPS: N +53° 41' 47.43" W -6° 14' 59.88"

4**** property in the coastal town of Bettystown. Bettystown Court is located within walking distance of the stunning beach and Laytown Golf Course, only 25 minutes from Dublin Airport & 10 minutes from Drogheda. The hotel has a cool modern stylish feel - with guest comfort paramount. Extensive free car parking, a full leisure centre is available at the hotel with sauna, steam room, pool, jacuzzi, bar, restaurant, conference and banqueting for up to 450 people. Member of Brennan Hotels Dublin, Clonmel, Kilkenny, Arklow and Meath. Please enquire about Facilities for Persons with Disabilities.

An IHF Quality Employer

Member of Brennan Hotels

Bookable on www.irelandhotels.com

Special Offer: www.irelandhotels.com/offers

B&B from €50.00 to €110.00
Suites from €110.00 to €290.00

Philip Murphy
General Manager

120

Open All Year

Dunboyne Castle Hotel & Spa

HOTEL ★★★★ MAP 12 N 11

Dunboyne,
Co. Meath

Tel: 01-801 3500 Fax: 01-436 6801
Email: info@dunboynecastlehotel.com
Web: www.dunboynecastlehotel.com
GPS: N +53° 25' 1.73" W -6° 28' 38.88"

Set in the historical village of Dunboyne, you will find Dunboyne Castle Hotel & Spa, a 4**** hotel with 145 bedrooms, magnificent gardens, large conference and banquet facilities for up to 500 delegates. In addition, Seoid, our state of the art spa, is spread over 3 floors with 18 treatment rooms. Dunboyne Castle Hotel is just 12 miles from Dublin Airport and 10 miles from Dublin City centre. The "Heritage Capital" is just on your doorstep with tours to historical Newgrange and Hill of Tara. Please enquire about Facilities for Persons with Disabilities.

An IHF Quality Employer

Member of Great Hotels Organisation

Bookable on www.irelandhotels.com

Special Offer: www.irelandhotels.com/offers

B&B from €60.00 to €170.00
Suites from €300.00 to €1,500.00

Shane Cookman
Group Director

145

Activities:

Open All Year

Marriott Johnstown House Hotel, Spa, Residences & Training Pitches

HOTEL ★★★★ MAP 11 M 11

Enfield,
Co. Meath

Tel: 046-954 0000 Fax: 046-954 0001
Email: info@johnstownhouse.com
Web: www.marriottjohnstownhouse.com
GPS: N +53° 24' 18.49" W -6° 50' 15.15"

Located off the M4, 40 mins from Dublin and set on 120 acres of parkland. Dine at the Pavilion Restaurant, Atrium Brasserie, Coachouse Bar or Juice Bar. Up to 1000 delegates catered for in fully equipped meeting rooms. Home to an exclusive 18 treatment room Elemis Spa, Leisure Centre, Thermal Suite and 20m Swimming Pool. 40 two bedroom residences and state of the art training pitches complete the resort. Please enquire about Facilities for Persons with Disabilities.

An IHF Quality Employer

Bookable on www.irelandhotels.com

Special Offer: www.irelandhotels.com/offers

B&B from €47.50 to €85.00
Suites from €145.00 to €230.00

David Hennessy
General Manager

126

Activities:

Open All Year

B&B Rates are per Person Sharing per Night incl. Breakfast.
or Room Rates are per Room per Night - **See also Page 8**

Gormanston / Johnstownbridge / Kells

City North Hotel

HOTEL ★★★★ MAP 12 O 13

Gormanston,
Co. Meath

Tel: 01-690 6666 Fax: 01-690 6677
Email: info@citynorthhotel.com
Web: www.citynorthhotel.com
GPS: N +53° 38' 17.90" W -6° 15' 26.14"

Located on the Belfast to Dublin M1 motorway 20 mins north of Dublin Airport, M50 & Dublin port tunnel, this stylish new hotel is close to several bustling towns with their quaint craft shops, stylish boutiques, superb restaurants & bars, famed Boyne Valley region, Newgrange. Enjoy a relaxing coastal stroll, golf, horse racing, hill walking, karting, falconry, clay pigeon shooting - all nearby. Superb conference facilities for 650. Regular coach services to Dublin, Drogheda, Dundalk, Dublin Airport – calling at City North Hotel. Please enquire about Facilities for Persons with Disabilities.

Member of Select Hotels

Bookable on www.irelandhotels.com

Special Offer: www.irelandhotels.com/offers

Room Rate from €49.50 to €120.00
Suites from €90.00 to €160.00

Aogan Dunne
General Manager

128

Food for Kids Activities:

Closed 24 - 26 December

Hamlet Court Hotel

HOTEL ★★★ MAP 11 M 11

Johnstownbridge,
Enfield,
Co. Meath

Tel: 046-954 1200 Fax: 046-954 1704
Email: info@thehamlet.ie
Web: www.thehamlet.ie
GPS: N +53° 24' 6.30" W -6° 51' 19.35"

Nestled in the village of Johnstownbridge, 1km from Enfield, 30 minutes from Dublin on the new M4. This contemporary hotel was designed to provide you with all the latest features that modern Irish hotels have to offer. Winner of The Best Irish Wedding Venue and our award-winning Chef, Mr. John Conmy, are just a taste of what the Hamlet Court has to offer. Where "Customer Service" was invented before the word. Please enquire about Facilities for Persons with Disabilities.

Bookable on www.irelandhotels.com

Special Offer: www.irelandhotels.com/offers

B&B from €70.00 to €140.00
Suites from €180.00 to €280.00

John O'Neill
Owner

30

Food for Kids

Open All Year

Headfort Arms

HOTEL ★★★ MAP 11 M 13

Headfort Place,
Kells,
Co. Meath

Tel: 0818-222 800 Fax: 046-924 0587
Email: info@headfortarms.ie
Web: www.headfortarms.ie
GPS: N +53° 43' 37.20" W -6° 52' 29.33"

A regional landmark, the Headfort Arms Hotel has been run and managed by the Duff family for the past 35 years. Located in the Heritage Town of Kells, only one hour from Dublin City centre on the main route to Donegal. 45 bedrooms with de luxe facilities, Wellness Spa and private guest car park. Adjoining is the award-winning Vanilla Pod Restaurant. Sporting packages are a speciality, Headfort Golf Club is on the doorstep, with equestrian, fishing and heritage trips all close by. Alternative Tel No: 046 9240063. Please enquire about Facilities for Persons with Disabilities.

Member of Irish Country Hotels

Bookable on www.irelandhotels.com

B&B from €45.00 to €99.00
Suites from €179.00 to €299.00

Peggy, Vincent & Olivia Duff
Proprietors

45

Food for Kids Activities:

Closed 25 December

B&B Rates are per Person Sharing per Night incl. Breakfast.
or Room Rates are per Room per Night - **See also Page 8**

Station House Hotel and Signal Restaurant

HOTEL ★★★ MAP 12 N 12

Kilmessan,
Co. Meath

Tel: 046-902 5239 Fax: 046-902 5588
Email: info@thestationhousehotel.com
Web: www.thestationhousehotel.com
GPS: N +53° 33' 50.03" W -6° 40' 1.17"

Step off the fast track into a relaxed rural setting, where peace and tranquillity exude. Set on 12 acres of landscaped gardens & woodlands, this first class hotel offers many amenities we appreciate today, not forgetting yesterday's charm. The Signal Suite is a unique, exclusive haven with four poster bed & whirlpool bath. The Signal Restaurant, which has won numerous awards, is open daily for breakfast, lunch & fine dining. Bar food served daily. 20 miles from Dublin. This is the perfect retreat with talior made packages from beauty to golf. Special offers online: www.thestationhousehotel.com.

Bookable on www.irelandhotels.com

Special Offer: www.irelandhotels.com/offers

B&B from €30.00 to €140.00
Suites from €100.00 to €300.00

Denise Slattery
Manager

20

Activities:

Open All Year

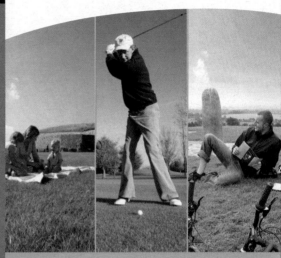

B&B Rates are per Person Sharing per Night incl. Breakfast.
or Room Rates are per Room per Night - See also Page 8

Navan

Ardboyne Hotel

HOTEL ★★★ MAP 12 N 13

Dublin Road,
Navan,
Co. Meath

Tel: 046-902 3119 Fax: 046-902 2355
Email: info@ardboynehotel.com
Web: www.ardboynehotel.com
GPS: N +53° 38' 25.47" W -6° 40' 18.56"

The Ardboyne Hotel Navan is set amidst a treasure trove of Irish historical sites in County Meath. Our warm and comfortable atmosphere coupled with our extensive gardens make the Ardboyne Hotel a perfect haven to unwind after an eventful day. Located just 2 minutes outside Navan Town, and just 40 minutes from Dublin. The hotel offers guests a wide range of facilities, including 29 tastefully decorated bedrooms. The Kells Bar, La Mezzanine Restaurant and extensive conference and banqueting facilities for up to 500 people. Excellent golf courses nearby, including Knightsbrook.

An IHF Quality Employer

Bookable on www.irelandhotels.com

Special Offer: www.irelandhotels.com/offers

B&B from €50.00 to €95.00

Michael Power
General Manager

29

Food for Kids Activities:

Closed 24 - 26 December

Bellinter House

HOTEL ★★★★ MAP 12 N 13

Navan,
Co. Meath

Tel: 046-903 0900 Fax: 046-903 1373
Email: reservations@bellinterhouse.com
Web: www.bellinterhouse.com
GPS: N +53° 35' 38'' W -6° 39' 54''

Standing majestically on the banks of the River Boyne in the rolling landscape of County Meath, Bellinter House exudes period glamour. The house meticulously preserves its classic Georgian heritage whole enhancing it with the best of modern Irish design, Individually designed bedrooms, a fine dining experience at Eden and the ultimate in pamper at the Bathhouse Spa. Located just under an hour from Dublin City and Dublin Airport.

Member of Manor House Hotels

Bookable on www.irelandhotels.com

Special Offer: www.irelandhotels.com/offers

Room Rate from €140.00 to €180.00
Suites from €200.00 to €240.00

Patrick Hanley
General Manager

34

Activities:

Open All Year

Ma Dwyers Guesthouse

GUESTHOUSE ★★★ MAP 12 N 13

Dublin Road,
Navan,
Co. Meath

Tel: 046-907 7992 Fax: 046-907 7995
Email: info@olddarnley.com
Web: www.olddarnley.com
GPS: N +53° 38' 37.98" W -6° 40' 23.83"

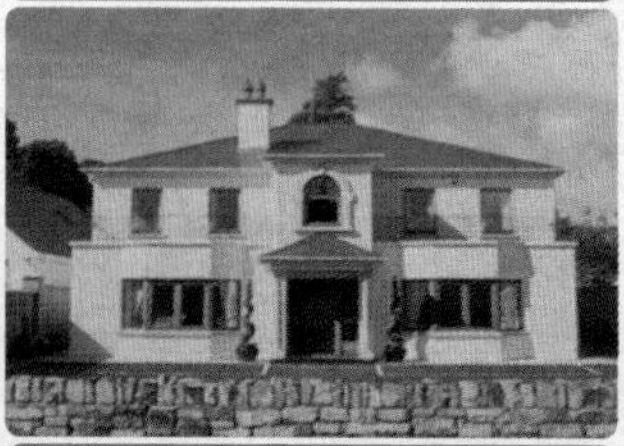

Ma Dwyers Guesthouse possesses many of the qualities of a high class hotel, along with a cosy homely feel which is so vitally important. 9 beautiful en suite rooms with a direct dial telephone, TV, hairdryer and tea/coffee facilities with fax and photocopying services available. Ideally located just minutes walk from the town centre and plenty of historic landmarks to see and activities to enjoy including golf, fishing, boating and horse riding. 13 new bedrooms will open during 2008. Please enquire about Facilities for Persons with Disabilities.

B&B from €50.00 to €50.00

Joan O'Brien

25

Open All Year

B&B Rates are per Person Sharing per Night incl. Breakfast.
or Room Rates are per Room per Night - **See also Page 8**

Newgrange Hotel

HOTEL ★★★ MAP 12 N 13

Bridge Street,
Navan,
Co. Meath

Tel: 046-907 4100 Fax: 046-907 3977
Email: info@newgrangehotel.ie
Web: www.newgrangehotel.ie
GPS: N +53° 39' 6.79" W -6° 40' 58.70"

Centrally located in Navan town only 40 mins from Dublin, The Newgrange is a modern hotel, designed and inspired by the ancient history of the area. In addition to 62 elegantly decorated en suite bedrooms, the hotel boasts extensive conference and banqueting facilities, 3 bars, a fine dining restaurant, café and daily lunchtime carvery. Local attractions include The Hill of Tara, Newgrange & Trim Castle. Activities in the area include salmon fishing, golfing, horse racing and horse riding. Championship Golf available at Knightsbrook. Please enquire about Facilities for Persons with Disabilities.

An IHF Quality Employer

Member of Cusack Hotels

Bookable on www.irelandhotels.com

Special Offer: www.irelandhotels.com/offers

B&B from €50.00 to €95.00

Mary Murphy
General Manager

62

Food for Kids Activities:

Closed 24 - 26 December

Brogan's

GUESTHOUSE ★★★ MAP 11 M 12

High Street,
Trim,
Co. Meath

Tel: 046-943 1237 Fax: 046-943 7648
Email: info@brogans.ie
Web: www.brogans.ie
GPS: N +53° 33' 27.11" W -6° 47' 21.56"

Brogans was built nearly two centuries ago using much of the original stone from Trim Castle. It boasts 18 tastefully decorated, modern en suite guestrooms. Our Bar and Beacon Restaurant rests right in the centre of an 19th century woollen mill. Whatever your taste Brogans Guesthouse & Bar has a little something special to offer everyone who passes through its historic doors. Located in town centre.

B&B from €40.00 to €60.00

Gary Britton

18

Open All Year

Castle Arch Hotel

HOTEL ★★★ MAP 11 M 12

Trim,
Co. Meath

Tel: 046-943 1516 Fax: 046-943 6002
Email: info@castlearchhotel.com
Web: www.castlearchhotel.com
GPS: N +53° 33' 3.52" W -6° 47' 42.15"

Located in the heart of Trim, Co. Meath, just 30 miles from Dublin. The Castle Arch Hotel is a charming boutique style hotel with 23 beautifully decorated bedrooms. Locally renowned for traditional home cooked foods with daily carvery and bar food. The hotel is minutes walk from the historically famous Trim Castle and a short drive from Kells, Newgrange and the Hill of Tara. Other local attractions include angling, horse racing and horse riding. There are also 9 local golf courses with special discounted packages available, including Christy O'Connor Jnr designed championship golf course at Knightsbrook.

An IHF Quality Employer

Member of Cusack Hotels

Bookable on www.irelandhotels.com

Special Offer: www.irelandhotels.com/offers

B&B from €49.00 to €95.00

Patrick Curran
General Manager

23

Closed 24 - 26 December

B&B Rates are per Person Sharing per Night incl. Breakfast.
or Room Rates are per Room per Night - **See also Page 8**

Trim / Carrickmacross

Knightsbrook Hotel Spa & Golf Resort

HOTEL ★★★★ MAP 11 M 12

Dublin Road,
Trim,
Co. Meath

Tel: 046-948 2100 Fax: 046-948 2056
Email: info@knightsbrook.com
Web: www.knightsbrook.com
GPS: N +53° 32' 55.87" W -6° 45' 55.48"

Built to an exceptionally high 4**** standard, this hotel offers a unique experience in luxury and opulence combined with modern sophistication. 131 de luxe rooms with all the facilities a discerning guest requires. Guests will enjoy an extensive leisure centre with swimming pool, jacuzzi, sauna, steam room and River Spa has established itself as one of the Leading Spas in the Country. 18 hole championship golf course designed by Christy O'Connor Jnr on site. Conference facilities for up to 1,000 delegates.

An IHF Quality Employer

Bookable on www.irelandhotels.com

Special Offer: www.irelandhotels.com/offers

B&B from €55.00 to €100.00
Suites from €185.00 to €370.00

Patrick Curran
General Manager

131

Activities:

Closed 24 - 25 December

Trim Castle Hotel

HOTEL ★★★★ MAP 11 M 12

Trim,
Co. Meath

Tel: 046-948 3000 Fax: 046-948 3077
Email: info@trimcastlehotel.com
Web: www.trimcastlehotel.com
GPS: N +53° 33' 14.05" W -6° 47' 27.90"

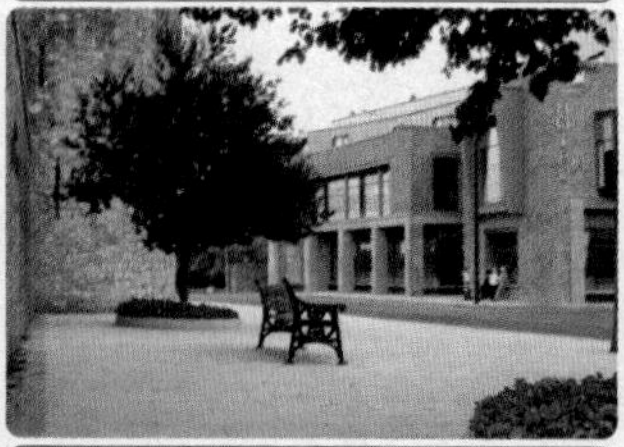

Overlooking the mystical Trim Castle, our hotel features 68 luxury guest rooms, The Bailey Bar, Barista Café and Jules Restaurant. Trim Castle Hotel is just 40 minutes from Dublin and is an ideal touring base for the Boyne Valley. Golf, angling, and equestrian activities together with a wonderful heritage tour can be booked at the hotel. Excellent accommodation and dinner packages available. Please enquire about Facilities for Persons with Disabilities.

Bookable on www.irelandhotels.com

B&B from €55.00 to €100.00
Suites from €125.00 to €200.00

Noel Comer
General Manager

68

Activities:

Closed 24 - 26 December

Nuremore Hotel & Country Club

HOTEL ★★★★ MAP 12 N 14

Carrickmacross,
Co. Monaghan

Tel: 042-966 1438 Fax: 042-966 1853
Email: info@nuremore.com
Web: www.nuremore.com
GPS: N +53° 57' 46.56" W -6° 41' 41.96"

Set in tranquil and beautiful surroundings, amidst a championship 18-hole golf course, the Nuremore offers unrivalled standards of service and sporting, leisure and conference facilities. The Country Club boasts an 18m swimming pool, whirlpool, sauna, steam room, gym, tennis courts & a beauty treatment spa. There is a wide range of spacious rooms and demi-suites on offer and our award-winning 3 AA Rosette restaurant serves superb cuisine in idyllic surroundings, cooked by Ireland's Chef of the Year 2005 and Ulster's Chef of the Year 2006, Raymond McArdle. Only 1 hour from Dublin, take the M1 & then the N2.

An IHF Quality Employer

Bookable on www.irelandhotels.com

Special Offer: www.irelandhotels.com/offers

B&B from €100.00 to €160.00

Julie Gilhooly
Proprietor

70

Activities:

Open All Year

B&B Rates are per Person Sharing per Night incl. Breakfast.
or Room Rates are per Room per Night - **See also Page 8**

Shirley Arms Hotel

HOTEL ★★★★ MAP 12 N 14

Lower Main Street,
Carrickmacross,
Co. Monaghan

Tel: 042-967 3100 Fax: 042-967 3177
Email: reception@shirleyarmshotel.ie
Web: www.shirleyarmshotel.ie
GPS: N +53° 58' 40.59" W -6° 43' 11.96"

Nestled in the heart of Patrick Kavanagh country & the home of Carrickmacross Lace, the Shirley Arms Hotel has undergone a total transformation & has been recently approved 4* hotel by Failte Ireland. A chic Manor House hotel, the Shirley Arms Hotel was constructed in the early 19th Century & is an important part of the architechtural heritage of Carrickmacross. We offer 25 rooms & have our own private parking & banqueting facilities for up to 150 guests. Located close to Dundalk, Monaghan Town, Ardee & Cavan. Approx. 1hr from Belfast & Dublin. Ideal for leisure & golf breaks, weddings & conferences.

B&B from €70.00 to €110.00
Suites from €200.00 to €300.00

Jim & Colm McBride
Proprietors

25

Activities:

Closed 24 - 26 December

Castle (The) at Castle Leslie Estate

GUESTHOUSE MAP 11 M 16

Glaslough,
Co. Monaghan

Tel: 047-88100 Fax: 047-88256
Email: info@castleleslie.com
Web: www.castleleslie.com
GPS: N +54° 18' 57.77" W -6° 53' 45.29"

Built to a 4**** specification. Nestled on 1,000 acres, Castle Leslie Estate is dotted with ancient woodland and glittering lakes. It is a stunningly beautiful and scheduled rural escape and offers a variety of accommodation and activities. Stay at the magnificent and romantic Castle, a complete respite from the world. Explore the estate on horseback, enjoy coarse fishing on the lake, take in a movie at our cinema or luxuriate in a treatment at the Victorian Treatment Rooms. These are just some of the choices that await you in the hidden corner of Ireland.

B&B from €105.00 to €125.00

Brian Baldwin
Estate General Manager

20

Closed 23 - 27 December

Lodge (The) at Castle Leslie Estate

HOTEL ★★★★ MAP 11 M 16

Glaslough,
Co. Monaghan

Tel: 047-88100 Fax: 047-88256
Email: info@castleleslie.com
Web: www.castleleslie.com
GPS: N +54° 19' 7.86" W -6° 53' 36.00"

Nestled on 1,000 acres, Castle Leslie Estate is dotted with ancient woodland and glittering lakes. It is a stunningly beautiful and scheduled rural escape and offers a variety of accommodation and activities. Stay at the magnificent and romantic Castle, the charming and social lodge or the Old Stable Mews, perfect for guests that want the convenience of hotel living combined with private self catering. Explore the estate on horseback, enjoy coarse fishing on the lake, take in a movie at our cinema or luxuriate in a treatment at the Victorian Treatment Rooms. These are just some of the choices that await you in the hidden corner of Ireland.

B&B from €75.00 to €110.00

Brian Baldwin
Estate General Manager

30

Food for Kids

Closed 23 - 27 December

Monaghan Town / Birr

Hillgrove Hotel Leisure & Spa

HOTEL ★★★★ MAP 11 M 16

Old Armagh Road,
Monaghan,
Co. Monaghan
Tel: 047-81288 Fax: 047-84951
Email: info@hillgrovehotel.com
Web: www.hillgrovehotel.com
GPS: N +54° 14' 47.35" W -6° 57' 18.13"

A majestic and magical setting awaits you, minutes walk from Monaghan Town. Luxurious bedrooms, including suites with jacuzzis. Exquisite restaurant and bars. State of the art conference centre. Leisure club with swimming pool, jacuzzi, steam room, sauna, gym, hot tub, tanning rooms & hair salon. Spa & wellness centre with rasul, herbal sauna, hydrotherapy pool, floatation bed, pedi spas, relaxation room. Murder Mysteries & CSI packages, spa pamper & girlie packages. Over 55's discounts. Please enquire about Facilities for Persons with Disabilities.

An IHF Quality Employer

Bookable on www.irelandhotels.com
Special Offer: www.irelandhotels.com/offers

B&B from €35.00 to €100.00
Suites from €100.00 to €250.00

Colm & Audri Herron
Proprietors
87

Food for Kids Activities:

Open All Year

Aaron House

GUESTHOUSE ★★★ MAP 7 J 9

Kinnitty,
Birr,
Offaly
Tel: 057-913 7040 Fax: 057-913 7040
Email: mail@aaronhouse.ie
Web: www.aaronhouse.ie
GPS: N +53° 5' 58.09" W -7° 42' 49.02"

We offer award-winning accommodation with old style hospitality. Situated close to the Slieve Bloom Mountains in the beautiful village of Kinnitty. Within walking distance of Kinnitty Castle, only 10 minutes from Birr. Purpose built spacious rooms with club class 6 beds! DD phones, TV, power showers, hairdryer, iron/ ironing board, guest TV Lounge, tea/coffee making facilities. Breakfast menu available, traditional & buffet style breakfast served. Easy to find, hard to leave - Be our Guest! Please enquire about Facilities for Persons with Disabilities.

Bookable on www.irelandhotels.com
Special Offer: www.irelandhotels.com/offers

B&B from €40.00 to €40.00

Betty Grimes
Proprietor
5

Open All Year

County Arms Hotel & Leisure Club

HOTEL ★★★★ MAP 7 J 9

Moorpark,
Birr,
Co. Offaly
Tel: 057-912 0791 Fax: 057-912 1234
Email: info@countyarmshotel.com
Web: www.countyarmshotel.com
GPS: N +53° 5' 26.33" W -7° 54' 21.30"

One of Ireland's finest family-run hotels. Unwind at the Springs Leisure Club & Wellness Suites with luxurious spa treatments. Stay in spacious suites & bedrooms, including family rooms with bunk beds. Meet in modern conference facilities, enhanced by our central location within 90 minutes of Dublin, Galway, Limerick. Enjoy our award-winning restaurant, Georgian walled garden, lively bar & homely lounge. Book great value special offers including Golf, Walking, Spa, Murder Mystery. Please enquire about Facilities for Persons with Disabilities.

Member of www.familyhotels.ie

Bookable on www.irelandhotels.com
Special Offer: www.irelandhotels.com/offers

B&B from €45.00 to €120.00
Suites from €199.00 to €399.00

Loughnane Family Since 1962
70

Food for Kids Activities:

Open All Year

B&B Rates are per Person Sharing per Night incl. Breakfast.
or Room Rates are per Room per Night - **See also Page 8**

Bridge House Hotel

HOTEL ★★★★ MAP 7 K 10

Tullamore,
Co. Offaly

Tel: 057-932 5600 Fax: 057-932 5690
Email: info@bridgehouse.com
Web: www.bridgehouse.com
GPS: N +53° 16' 29.85" W -7° 29' 39.96"

Renowned for good food & hospitality. The Bridge House Hotel is the perfect choice for a relaxing break. Enjoy the Sanctuary Spa & leisure club, outdoor hydro pool, gym & virtual reality golf simulator. There is good shopping locally, buses are welcome and there is lots to do. Winner of best hotel bar & other awards including Michelin guide recommendations, the Bridge House offers 4 distinctive dining options & a range of live entertainment. Please enquire about Facilities for Persons with Disabilities.

An IHF Quality Employer

Bookable on www.irelandhotels.com

Special Offer: www.irelandhotels.com/offers

B&B from €50.00 to €175.00
Suites from €140.00 to €500.00

Colm McCabe
General Manager

70

Food for Kids Activities:

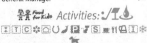

Open All Year

Grennans Country House & Cottages

GUESTHOUSE ★★★★ MAP 7 K 10

Aharney,
Tullamore,
Co. Offaly

Tel: 057-935 5893 Fax: 057-935 5893
Email: deirdregrennan5@eircom.net
Web: www.grennanscountryhouse.ie
GPS: N +53° 18' 13.02" W -7° 34' 7.72"

Situated in the heart of the Midlands, 1 mile off N.80, 1.5 hours from Dublin Airport, Grennans Country House & Cottages is a purpose built luxury guesthouse with two 4* cottages ; a golfer's paradise - 10 golf courses within 1/2 hour's drive. Rural setting, ample car parking. All rooms are en suite & tastefully furnished, with super king beds, DD phone, TV, tea/coffee facilities, spring water, clock radio, hairdryer, iron/ironing board. Guest TV lounge, home-baking. Access for wheelchair users. Ideal touring base, golfing, fishing, equestrian, walking - your choice is our pleasure.

Member of Mid East Tourism

B&B from €45.00 to €45.00

Deirdre & Pat Grennan

6

Open All Year

Sea Dew Guesthouse

GUESTHOUSE ★★★ MAP 7 K 10

Clonminch Road,
Tullamore,
Co. Offaly

Tel: 057-935 2054 Fax: 057-935 2054
Email: enquiries@seadewguesthouse.com
Web: www.seadewguesthouse.com
GPS: N +53° 16' 6.96" W -7° 29' 19.46"

Set in a mature garden of trees, just 5 mins walk from town centre, Sea Dew is a purpose-built luxury guesthouse. Conservatory breakfast room will give you a bright start to the day where there is an excellent selection of fresh produce and home baking with breakfast cooked to order. Bedrooms are en suite with TV, phone, hairdryer, iron, tea/coffee and complimentary broadband. Private car park, swimming pool (25m) and gym just 5 mins walk. Golfing, fishing, horse riding and hill walking nearby. Please enquire about Facilities for Persons with Disabilities.

Bookable on www.irelandhotels.com

Special Offer: www.irelandhotels.com/offers

B&B from €30.00 to €65.00

Claire Gilsenan
Proprietor

10

Closed 23 - 28 December

B&B Rates are per Person Sharing per Night incl. Breakfast.
or Room Rates are per Room per Night - **See also Page 8**

Tullamore / Athlone

Tullamore Court Hotel Conference & Leisure Centre

HOTEL ★★★★ MAP 7 K 10

Tullamore,
Co. Offaly

Tel: 057-934 6666 Fax: 057-934 6677
Email: res@tullamorecourthotel.ie
Web: www.tullamorecourthotel.ie
GPS: N +53° 16' 11.58" W -7° 29' 32.73"

The Tullamore Court is a contemporary 4 star hotel in the heart of the Midlands, offering an uncompromising mix of modern luxury with traditional hospitality. Luxurious accommodation complimented by fine dining, extensive leisure facilities and friendly professional staff, combine to create the perfect choice for your next short break. Tullamore itself is a vibrant town offering visitors a wide choice of restaurants, entertainment and shopping. The surrounding countryside has a whole host of activities and attractions. Check our website for the top 20 things to do and all special offers.

An IHF Quality Employer

Bookable on www.irelandhotels.com

Special Offer: www.irelandhotels.com/offers

B&B from €55.00 to €105.00
Suites from €190.00 to €290.00

Philip O'Brien
General Manager

104

Activities:

Closed 24 - 26 December

Creggan Court Hotel

HOTEL ★★★ MAP 7 J 11

N6 Centre,
Dublin Road, Athlone,
Co. Westmeath

Tel: 090-647 7777 Fax: 090-647 7111
Email: info@creggancourt.com
Web: www.creggancourt.com
GPS: N +53° 24' 37.21" W -7° 53' 39.13"

The Creggan Court Hotel is located just off junction 8 of the motorway, midway between Dublin and Galway. It is an ideal base to explore the Midlands. The Creggan Court offers spacious en suite rooms and free ample car parking. Athlone is a golfer's paradise, surrounded by championship golf courses such as Glasson, Mount Temple, Esker Hills and many more. Please enquire about Facilities for Persons with Disabilities.

B&B from €55.00 to €85.00

Catherine Daly
General Manager

70

Closed 24 - 26 December

Glasson Hotel & Golf Club

HOTEL ★★★★ MAP 11 J 11

Glasson,
Athlone,
Co. Westmeath

Tel: 090-648 5120 Fax: 090-648 5444
Email: info@glassongolf.ie
Web: www.glassongolfhotel.ie
GPS: N +53° 28' 32.38" W -7° 54' 2.68"

"Glorious Glasson, a treat for all the senses" is what C. Kinny, a past guest has to say. The views are magnificent, the welcome the warmest, the most spacious & sumptuous rooms & of course, championship Golf. Enjoy Sauna, Steam Room, Massage, Boat Trips and rural country walks during your stay. "The holes range from good to great & the setting is at every turn little short of enthralling" James W. Finegan, Golf Journalist. The hotel is suited to both the discerning golfer and those looking for peace & relaxation. Glasson has established a reputation for its food, using the very best of local produce in a range of classic dishes.

Bookable on www.irelandhotels.com

Special Offer: www.irelandhotels.com/offers

B&B from €45.00 to €110.00
Suites from €190.00 to €400.00

Gareth Jones & Fidelma Reid
Managers

65

Activities:

Closed 24 - 26 December

B&B Rates are per Person Sharing per Night incl. Breakfast. or Room Rates are per Room per Night - **See also Page 8**

Hodson Bay Hotel

HOTEL ★★★★ MAP 11 J 11

Athlone,
Co. Westmeath

Tel: 090-644 2000 Fax: 090-644 2020
Email: info@hodsonbayhotel.com
Web: www.hodsonbayhotel.com
GPS: N +53° 28' 4.25" W -7° 59' 20.67"

This luxurious hotel and spa is located on the picturesque shores of Lough Ree in the heart of Ireland. The hotel is renowned for its plush accommodation, fine cuisine and a warm, welcoming atmosphere. Leisure facilities include a 20m pool and gym with steam room and sauna, while the spa offers a superb array of pampering treatments and a unique thermal spa. The hotel is adjacent to Athlone Golf Club, Hodson Bay Sports and a marina. Complimentary broadband access in all guest bedrooms and meeting rooms. Please enquire about Facilities for Persons with Disabilities.

An IHF Quality Employer

Bookable on www.irelandhotels.com

Special Offer: www.irelandhotels.com/offers

B&B from €65.00 to €210.00
Suites from €170.00 to €460.00

Timothy Hayes
General Manager

182

Food for Kids

Open All Year

Prince of Wales Hotel

HOTEL ★★★★ MAP 11 J 11

Church Street,
Athlone,
Co. Westmeath

Tel: 090-647 6666 Fax: 090-649 1750
Email: info@theprinceofwales.ie
Web: www.theprinceofwales.ie
GPS: N +53° 25' 26.16" W -7° 56' 18.49"

The Prince of Wales Hotel, in the heart of Athlone, has offered the very highest standards of comfort & service since 1810. Redeveloped in 2004, the hotel boasts 46 stylish, modern rooms, including six de luxe rooms. Each room is a tranquil haven of understated luxury, equipped with television, DVD, complimentary WiFi & climate control. Excellent, state-of-the-art conference & meeting rooms are also available. Our lively Prince Bar offers an extensive array of food & drink and is one of the most popular bars in town. We look forward to welcoming you. Please enquire about Facilities for Persons with Disabilities.

An IHF Quality Employer

Member of Callanan Hotels

Bookable on www.irelandhotels.com

Special Offer: www.irelandhotels.com/offers

B&B from €30.00 to €120.00

Chris Vos
General Manager

46

Activities:

Closed 24 - 27 December

Radisson Blu Hotel Athlone

HOTEL ★★★★ MAP 11 J 11

Northgate Street,
Athlone,
Co. Westmeath

Tel: 090-644 2600 Fax: 090-644 2655
Email: info.athlone@radissonblu.com
Web: www.radissonblu.ie/hotel-athlone
GPS: N +53° 25' 28.37" W -7° 56' 28.89"

The Radisson Blu Hotel Athlone is centrally located overlooking the River Shannon with magnificent views of the Marina, the historical cathedral and Athlone Castle. Within walking distance of the train and bus station. 128 stylish bedrooms / suites in an urban and ocean theme. Elements Restaurant offers the finest contemporary food in a trendy environment. Quayside bar and lounge with riverside terrace is the perfect location for guests to relax and enjoy the panoramic views across the town and the river. Synergy Health and Leisure Club offers a 16.5m indoor pool, sauna, steam room and fully equipped gym. Car parking is available.

Bookable on www.irelandhotels.com

Special Offer: www.irelandhotels.com/offers

B&B from €69.00 to €105.00
Suites from €149.00 to €259.00

Shane Fitzpatrick
General Manager

128

Food for Kids Activities:

Open All Year

B&B Rates are per Person Sharing per Night incl. Breakfast.
or Room Rates are per Room per Night - **See also Page 8**

Athlone / Moate

Shamrock Lodge Hotel and Conference Centre

HOTEL ★★★ MAP 11 J 11

Clonown Road,
Athlone,
Co. Westmeath
Tel: 090-649 2601 Fax: 090-649 2737
Email: info@shamrocklodgehotel.ie
Web: www.shamrocklodgehotel.ie
GPS: N +53° 25' 17.19" W -7° 57' 2.69"

The Shamrock Lodge Country House Hotel & Conference centre is a modern & stylish hotel and welcomes you with traditional Irish hospitality. Tucked away on its own magnificent gardens with private free car parking, there is no better backdrop for your break. Ideally located in the historic town of Athlone and boasting 40 deluxe rooms and 12 two bedroom apart-hotels. The Shamrock Lodge is the heart of every great break. Please enquire about Facilities for Persons with Disabilities.

Bookable on www.irelandhotels.com

B&B from €55.00 to €85.00
Suites from €149.00 to €299.00

Mr. Paddy McCaul
Proprietor
64

Activities:

Closed 24 - 27 December

Sheraton Athlone Hotel

HOTEL ★★★★ MAP 11 J 11

Athlone,
Co. Westmeath
Tel: 090-645 1000 Fax: 090-645 1001
Email: reservations@sheratonathlonehotel.com
Web: www.sheratonathlonehotel.com
GPS: N +53° 25' 25.64" W -7° 56' 5.82"

Located in the heart of Athlone, the contemporary 12 storey Sheraton Athlone Hotel is fast becoming one of Irelands premier leisure destinations. The hotels offers 167 superbly appointed deluxe bedrooms with 2 opulent penthouse suites & 1 stunning presidential suite. The elegant La Provence restaurant offers superb french & contemporary cuisine, casual Harvest Café, lively bar, Leisure Centre & superb Sirana Spa with an urban feel offering 7 treatment rooms. Please enquire about Facilities for Persons with Disabilities.

An IHF Quality Employer

Bookable on www.irelandhotels.com
Special Offer: www.irelandhotels.com/offers

B&B from €59.00 to €199.00
Suites from €139.00 to €279.00

Mark Long
General Manager
167

Activities:

Closed 25 - 26 December

Temple Country Retreat & Spa

GUESTHOUSE ★★★★ MAP 11 J 11

Horseleap,
Moate,
Co. Westmeath
Tel: 057-933 5118 Fax: 057-933 5008
Email: reservations@templespa.ie
Web: www.templespa.ie
GPS: N +53° 24' 20.76" W -7° 36' 9.79"

An oasis of calm, Temple Country Retreat and Spa is Ireland's original destination spa for adults only. Located just over an hour from Dublin, Temple creates a total spa experience. You can join in a daily activity program of yoga, walks, fitness and relaxation classes, and with over 80 different spa treatments you're spoilt for choice, not forgetting the vitality suite with hydrotherapy pool, sauna, steam room and experience showers. 23 luxurious bedrooms, including two suites, all with panoramic countryside views. Please enquire about Facilities for Persons with Disabilities.

Bookable on www.irelandhotels.com

B&B from €75.00 to €175.00
Suites from €350.00 to €550.00

Declan & Bernadette Fagan
Owners
23

Activities:

Closed 22- 27 December

B&B Rates are per Person Sharing per Night incl. Breakfast.
or Room Rates are per Room per Night - **See also Page 8**

Annebrook House

HOTEL ★★★★ MAP 11 L 12

Austin Friar Street,
Mullingar,
Co. Westmeath
Tel: 044-935 3300 Fax: 044-935 3333
Email: info@annebrook.ie
Web: www.annebrook.ie
GPS: N +53° 31' 30.01" W -7° 20' 19.13"

Mullingar's newest 4* town centre hotel, the Annebrook House Hotel, steeped in history, is located next door to acres of town parkland with ample private parking on site. Choice of dining experiences from The Bistro, to the more relaxed Brosna Bar with daily carvery lunch and evening bar food menu. Luxurious accommodation with a mixture of classic and executive guest bedrooms and unique apart-hotel suites to cater for the leisure or business guest. Extensive conference & banqueting facilities. Please enquire about Facilities for Persons with Disabilities.

B&B from €50.00 to €90.00

Berty Dunne
General Manager

70

Activities:

Closed 25 - 26 December

North Tipperary, Laois, Offaly, Westmeath, East Galway
Mid Ireland
IT'S A KIND OF MAGIC
Belvedere
Mid Ireland
Visitors Card
www.midirelandtourism.ie
Free Visitors Card with Guide Book & Map
Dublin
Shannon
Save
up to €2000
in Discounts
& Added
Benefits
at Visitor Attractions,
Leisure Activities,
Accommodation,
Restaurants
and much more!
For a free Information Pack
including Mid Ireland Visitors Card
contact Mid Ireland Tourism at
00 353 57 91 20923
info@midirelandtourism.ie
www.midirelandtourism.ie

B&B Rates are per Person Sharing per Night incl. Breakfast.
or Room Rates are per Room per Night - **See also Page 8**

Mullingar

Bloomfield House Hotel

HOTEL ★★★ MAP 11 L 12

Belvedere,
Mullingar,
Co. Westmeath

Tel: 044-934 0894 Fax: 044-934 3767
Email: reservations@bloomfieldhouse.com
Web: www.bloomfieldhouse.com
GPS: N +53° 29' 15.47" W -7° 21' 44.96"

Located in the beautiful countryside of central Ireland, historic Bloomfield House nestles on the shores of Lough Ennell surrounded by magnificent parkland and gently sloping meadows. Easy travelling distance from all regions and just 60 minutes from Dublin, Bloomfield House blends tradition and elegance with the latest amenities. Combining comfort, hospitality and service with an excellent leisure & spa facility, neighbouring the golf club and Belvedere House, relaxation proves effortless at Bloomfield House Hotel. Please enquire about Facilities for Persons with Disabilities.

Bookable on www.irelandhotels.com

Special Offer: www.irelandhotels.com/offers

B&B from €55.00 to €120.00
Suites from €150.00 to €250.00

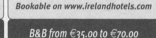

Ronan Byrne
General Manager

111

Food for Kids

Closed 24 - 25 December

Greville Arms Hotel

HOTEL ★★★ MAP 11 L 12

Mullingar,
Co. Westmeath

Tel: 044-934 8563 Fax: 044-934 8052
Email: info@grevillearmshotel.ie
Web: www.grevillearms.ie
GPS: N +53° 31' 32.62" W -7° 20' 27.50"

In the heart of Mullingar town, the Greville Arms Hotel is a home from home where customers and their comfort is our main concern. Recently refurbished, the hotel offers 39 luxuriously appointed rooms. The Greville Restaurant is renowned for its cuisine and fine wines. No visit to Mullingar would be complete without a visit to our Ulysses Bar with its life-sized wax figure of James Joyce and other memorabilia. Local attractions include Belvedere House and Gardens, golf, fishing and horse riding.

An IHF Quality Employer

B&B from €40.00 to €90.00

John Cochrane
General Manager

39

Food for Kids Activities: ✓

Closed 25 December

McCormacks Guesthouse

GUESTHOUSE ★★★ MAP 11 L 12

Old Dublin Road,
Mullingar,
Co. Westmeath

Tel: 044-934 1483
Email: info@mccormacksbandb.com
Web: www.mccormacksbandb.com
GPS: N +53° 31' 13.49" W -7° 18' 3.70"

One mile from Mullingar Town and across the road from Mullingar Park Hotel. All rooms are en suite including large family rooms. Situated in a peaceful farm setting and yet within walking distance of town. Facilities for fishermen and tennis court and picnic area on grounds. Internet broadband access available to guests. Three specially adapted wheelchair accessible rooms. Numerous golf courses and fishing lakes nearby. Located just off Mullingar bypass (N4) at junction with N52 bypass. Sauna and hot tub cabin available at reasonable rates. Please enquire about Facilities for Persons with Disabilities.

Bookable on www.irelandhotels.com

B&B from €35.00 to €70.00

Tom & Margaret Mc Cormack
Proprietors

10

Open All Year

B&B Rates are per Person Sharing per Night incl. Breakfast.
or Room Rates are per Room per Night - **See also Page 8**

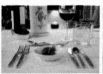

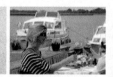

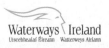

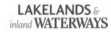

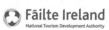

Mullingar / Rathowen

Mullingar Park Hotel

HOTEL ★★★★ MAP 11 L 12

Dublin Road,
Mullingar,
Co. Westmeath

Tel: 044-933 7500 Fax: 044-933 5937
Email: info@mullingarparkhotel.com
Web: www.mullingarparkhotel.com
GPS: N +53° 31' 22.38" W -7° 18' 12.56"

Contemporary designed hotel located on the N4, just 1 hour from Dublin with free car parking. This hotel is elegantly decorated & fully equipped to international standards. 95 superbly appointed bedrooms, award-winning Terrace Restaurant, Horseshoe Bar, Courtyard Lounge & private landscaped gardens. Large conference & banqueting facilities (AA Business Hotel of the Year 2008-09). Azure Leisure Club: 20m Indoor Pool, Sauna, Steam Room and fully equipped Gym with Beauty Treatment Suites. Please enquire about Facilities for Persons with Disabilities.

Bookable on www.irelandhotels.com
Special Offer: www.irelandhotels.com/offers

B&B from €90.00 to €150.00
Suites from €200.00 to €350.00

Josephine Hughes
Proprietor

95

Food for Kids Activities:

Closed 25 - 26 December

Newbury Hotel

HOTEL ★★★ MAP 11 L 12

Dominick Street,
Mullingar,
Co. Westmeath

Tel: 044-934 2888 Fax: 044-934 4618
Email: info@thenewburyhotel.com
Web: www.thenewburyhotel.com
GPS: N +53° 31' 27.26" W -7° 20' 49.39"

The 3* Newbury Hotel is a beautiful 26 bedroom hotel in the centre of Mullingar, beside the Railway Station & just 50 mins from Dublin. The hotel brings you the pleasure of comfort, good food & service in a relaxed & friendly environment. In our basement you will find the newly opened Chinese restaurant. Co. Westmeath has beautiful lakes, rivers & waterways offering a wide variety of water sports as well as good quality angling. Boat hire is available on our lakes. Horse riding, golf, pitch & putt, as well as horse racing in nearby Kilbeggan are in plentiful supply. Please enquire about Facilities for Persons with Disabilities.

B&B from €39.00 to €85.00

Garvan McGinley
Proprietor

26

Activities:

Open All Year

Feerick's Hotel

HOTEL ★★★ MAP 11 K 13

Rathowen,
Co. Westmeath

Tel: 043-667 6025 Fax: 043-667 6961
Email: info@feericks.ie
Web: www.feericks.ie
GPS: N +53° 39' 24.64" W -7° 31' 16.43"

Feerick's Hotel was established by John Feerick, a native of Ballinrobe, Co. Mayo. Recently, extensive renovation has transformed it into a very successful Hotel, Pub & Restaurant with 13 en suite rooms & large function/meeting rooms. Situated on the busy N4 in the village of Rathowen between Mullingar & Longford & 1 hour from Dublin, it has become a popular coach stop on the N4 with a reputation for good reasonably priced food. Food served from 7am till late, steaks a specialty but the menu contains choices for all. Please enquire about Facilities for Persons with Disabilities.

B&B from €40.00 to €60.00

John Feerick

13

Closed 25 December

B&B Rates are per Person Sharing per Night incl. Breakfast.
or Room Rates are per Room per Night - **See also Page 8**

Arklow Bay Conference, Leisure & Spa Hotel

HOTEL ★★★ MAP 8 O 8

Arklow,
Co. Wicklow

Tel: 0402-32309 Fax: 0402-32300
Email: reservations@arklowbay.com
Web: www.brennanhotels.com
GPS: N +52° 48' 11.04" W -6° 8' 36.47"

Among the hills and by the sea, Arklow is a unique destination for a leisure break. The 92 bedroomed hotel offers an elegant and comfortable setting for business or leisure. Residents can enjoy the extensive leisure facilities and the Bay Beauty & Day Spa. Sister hotels: Dublin Green Isle, Clonmel Park, Kilkenny Springhill Court, Meath Bettystown Court. Please enquire about Facilities for Persons with Disabilities.

An IHF Quality Employer

Member of Brennan Hotels

Bookable on www.irelandhotels.com
Special Offer: www.irelandhotels.com/offers

B&B from €45.00 to €95.00

Tina O'Sullivan
General Manager

92

Open All Year

Bridge Hotel

HOTEL ★★ MAP 8 O 8

Bridge Street,
Arklow,
Co. Wicklow

Tel: 0402-31666 Fax: 0402-31666
Email: hbridge@eircom.net
GPS: N +52° 47' 53.39" W -6° 9' 8.88"

The Bridge hotel is family owned and run, with 14 en suite bedrooms, TV and car parking. The hotel is situated at the bridge in Arklow Town, approximately 1 hour from Dublin and Rosslare. There is a wide choice of local golf courses as well as fine beaches nearby. Arklow is an ideal base from which to see the beautiful scenery of Wicklow.

B&B from €55.00 to €70.00

Jim Hoey
Proprietor

1 14

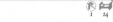

Closed 25 - 26 December

Ballyknocken House & Cookery School

GUESTHOUSE ★★★★ MAP 8 P 9

Glenealy,
Ashford,
Co. Wicklow

Tel: 0404-44627 Fax: 0404-44696
Email: reservations@ballyknocken.com
Web: www.ballyknocken.com
GPS: N +52° 58' 37.47" W -6° 8' 35.32"

1850's charming farmhouse, elegantly furnished with antiques. Individually styled bedrooms, most with claw feet baths offer lovely views over gardens and forest. Pre-dinner sherry by the Drawing Room's log fire before the splendid dinner using garden and local produce. Run by TV3 chef, Catherine Fulvio - the award winning Ballyknocken Cookery School is on site. Packages including cookery classes available. Superb breakfasts. Near to Wicklow Mountains, Glendalough, Powerscourt. Excellent golf, e.g. Druid's Glen. Lovely walks. Dublin 29 miles. Bridgestone 100 Best Places to Stay. Gift vouchers.

An IHF Quality Employer

Bookable on www.irelandhotels.com
Special Offer: www.irelandhotels.com/offers

B&B from €55.00 to €59.00

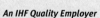

Catherine Fulvio
Chef / Proprietor

7

Closed 12 December - 10 January

B&B Rates are per Person Sharing per Night incl. Breakfast.
or Room Rates are per Room per Night - **See also Page 8**

Ashford / Blessington

Bel-Air Hotel

HOTEL ★ MAP 8 P 9

Ashford,
Co. Wicklow

Tel: 0404-40109 Fax: 0404-40188
Email: belairhotel@eircom.net
Web: www.belairhotelequestrian.com
GPS: N +53° 0' 5.49" W -6° 7' 18.61"

Bel-Air Hotel is a family-run country hotel situated in the centre of 81 hectares of parklands. The lovely gardens have a breathtaking view to the sea. The traditional family atmosphere and rich history make the hotel a popular venue, rooms en suite with tea making facilities, TV and hairdryers. Adjacent Equestrian Centre specialises in cross country riding and jumping for experienced riders. Family-run since 1937.

Member of Equestrian Holidays Ireland

B&B from €60.00 to €65.00

William Freeman
Owner

10

Closed 24 December - 15 January

Chester Beatty Inn

HOTEL ★★ MAP 8 P 9

Ashford Village,
Co. Wicklow

Tel: 0404-40206 Fax: 0404-49003
Email: hotelchesterbeatty@eircom.net
Web: www.hotelchesterbeatty.ie
GPS: N +53° 0' 39.91" W -6° 6' 31.68"

Charming Country Inn Family-run hotel with 12 luxury en suite rooms. Extensive menus of finest quality freshly cooked meals served, lounge, traditional Irish bar with open log fires. Enjoy true Irish hospitality. We are located 35 minutes south of Dublin on route N11. Ideal spot for touring Wicklow, the Garden of Ireland. Mount Usher Gardens just 3 minutes walk away. Close to Glendalough, Powerscourt and many other tourist attractions. Numerous golf courses close by including Druids Glen and the European Golf Club. 1st Class Equestrian facilities, Hill walking. Private Car Parking.

Bookable on www.irelandhotels.com
Special Offer: www.irelandhotels.com/offers

B&B from €30.00 to €80.00

Paul & Kiity Caprani

12

Activities:

Closed 24 - 26 December

Avon Rí

HOLIDAY VILLAGE MAP 8 N 10

Blessington Lakeshore,
Burgage, Blessington,
Co. Wicklow

Tel: 045-900670 Fax: 045-857756
Email: info@avonri.com
Web: www.avonri.com
GPS: N +53° 9' 41.39" W -6° 31' 59.88"

Avon Rí is a wonderfully unique holiday, sporting and event resort spectacularly located on shores of The Blessington Lakes in Co.Wicklow, only 40 minutes drive from the Centre of Dublin. Glorious views of the lake and the surrounding mountains and glens. A thrilling list of professionally organised and supervised outdoor activities and a leisure centre and restaurant and luxury accommodation amount to a truly outstanding offering of a five star standard hotel in an unforgettable location. Please enquire about Facilities for Persons with Disabilities.

Bookable on www.irelandhotels.com
Special Offer: www.irelandhotels.com/offers

Room Rate from €80.00 to €300.00

Greg Forrestal
General Manager

39

Activities:

Open All Year

B&B Rates are per Person Sharing per Night incl. Breakfast.
or Room Rates are per Room per Night - **See also Page 8**

Best Western Esplanade Hotel

HOTEL ★★★ MAP 8 P 10

Strand Road,
Bray,
Co. Wicklow
Tel: 01-286 2056 Fax: 01-286 6496
Email: info@esplanadehotel.ie
Web: www.esplanadehotel.ie
GPS: N +53° 11' 55.60" W -6° 5' 46.29"

Stylish hotel with magnificent views, 12 miles from Dublin. Located on the seafront in Bray, the hotel retains many of its splendid Victorian features whilst offering modern day luxury and comfort. Comfortable lounges, excellent menu choices and exceptional value for money. Close to Bray DART station. A member of the Strandwood Hotel Group. Please enquire about Facilities for Persons with Disabilities.

Member of Best Western

Bookable on www.irelandhotels.com
Special Offer: www.irelandhotels.com/offers

Room Rate from €79.00 to €149.00

Cormac O'Sullivan
General Manager
94

Closed 24 - 27 December

Crofton Bray Head Inn

GUESTHOUSE ★★ MAP 8 P 10

Strand Road,
Bray,
Co. Wicklow
Tel: 01-286 7182 Fax: 01-286 7182
Email: croftonbrayheadinn@hotmail.com
GPS: N +53° 11' 46.81" W -6° 5' 34.50"

This 140 year old building is situated on the seafront, under the Bray Head Mountain. A 10 minute walk away from an excellent commuter train to Dublin, but also ideally located for touring Wicklow - The Garden of Ireland. The Bray Head Inn has ample car parking and is fully licensed. It has a lift, en suite bedrooms with TV and telephone. Our prices include full Irish breakfast.

Bookable on www.irelandhotels.com

B&B from €50.00 to €50.00

Ena Regan Cummins
30

Closed 01 October - 01 June

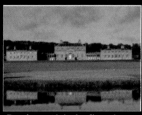

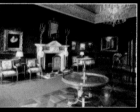

B&B Rates are per Person Sharing per Night incl. Breakfast.
or Room Rates are per Room per Night - **See also Page 8**

Martello Hotel (The)

HOTEL ★★ MAP 8 P 10

Strand Road,
Bray,
Co. Wicklow
Tel: 01-286 8000 Fax: 01-286 4254
Email: info@themartello.ie
Web: www.themartello.ie
GPS: N +53° 12' 7.18" W -6° 5' 54.07"

A family-run hotel with spectacular seaviews. Catering for the business or leisure guest, with well appointed en suite accommodation, as well as self-catering apartments. The Martello Bar offers a superb bar food menu or dine in the Tower Bistro from our select menu and fine wines. Conference and banqueting facilities. Ideally located for touring Dublin City and County Wicklow. Located 5 minutes from all public transport and N11 Motorway. Please enquire about Facilities for Persons with Disabilities.

Bookable on www.irelandhotels.com
Special Offer: www.irelandhotels.com/offers

Room Rate from €69.00 to €100.00

John Duggan
General Manager

25

Activities:

Closed 24 - 26 December

Ramada Hotel Bray

HOTEL ★★★ MAP 8 P 10

Southern Cross,
Bray,
Co. Wicklow
Tel: 01-276 0258 Fax: 01-276 0298
Email: info@woodlandcourthotel.com
Web: www.woodlandcourthotel.com
GPS: N +53° 11' 11.90" W -6° 6' 0.72"

The recently extended and refurbished 86 bedroomed hotel is situated just 12 miles south of Dublin City centre off the M11 / M50 link road. Located in private grounds with ample free parking, the Ramada Hotel Bray is the ideal base for touring County Wicklow and Dublin City. Only minutes away from both the LUAS (Sandyford) or DART (Bray), commuting to and from the hotel could not be easier. We have excellent value family rooms that can sleep up to 5/6 persons comfortably. Please enquire about Facilities for Persons with Disabilities.

An IHF Quality Employer

Member of Ramada Worldwide

Bookable on www.irelandhotels.com
Special Offer: www.irelandhotels.com/offers

Room Rate from €75.00 to €125.00

86

Food for Kids Activities:

Closed 24 - 26 December

Rathsallagh House, Golf and Country Club

GUESTHOUSE ★★★★ MAP 8 N 9

Dunlavin,
(West Wicklow),
Co. Wicklow
Tel: 045-403112 Fax: 045-403343
Email: info@rathsallagh.com
Web: www.rathsallagh.com
GPS: N +53° 1' 42.48" W -6° 43' 42.55"

Winner of the Best Restaurant in Leinster Award 2007, the Supreme Irish Breakfast Awards and the AA Five Yellow Star Award for Guest Accommodation, Rathsallagh is a large Country House on 570 acres one hour south of Dublin Airport. With its own 18 hole Championship Golf Course, rated in Irelands top 30 (John Redmond 2007), Rathsallagh is close to the K Club, home of the 2006 Ryder Cup. Rathsallagh is an ideal venue for conferences, weddings & incentive outings. It is also available for private parties & rental.

An IHF Quality Employer

Member of Ireland's Blue Book

Bookable on www.irelandhotels.com
Special Offer: www.irelandhotels.com/offers

Room Rate from €250.00 to €290.00

Catherine & Joe O'Flynn Snr
Proprietors

29

Activities:

Closed 04 January - 23 February

B&B Rates are per Person Sharing per Night incl. Breakfast.
or Room Rates are per Room per Night - See also Page 8

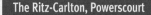

Summerhill House Hotel

HOTEL ★★★ MAP 8 O 10

Enniskerry,
Co. Wicklow

Tel: 01-286 7928 Fax: 01-286 7929
Email: info@summerhillhousehotel.com
Web: www.summerhillhousehotel.com
GPS: N +53° 11' 25.47" W -6° 9' 50.23"

This charming hotel is just a short walk to the quaint village of Enniskerry, and the famous Powerscourt Gardens. Located on the N11, 19km south of Dublin City and 15km to Dun Laoghaire Ferryport. 55 spacious bedrooms, private free car parking, traditional Irish breakfast, hill walking and nature trails, local golf courses, family rooms (2 adults and 3 children). Enjoy a rare blend of the Wicklow countryside close to Dublin City. A member of the Strandwood Hotel Group. Please enquire about Facilities for Persons with Disabilities.

An IHF Quality Employer

Member of Strandwood Hotel Group

Bookable on www.irelandhotels.com

Special Offer: www.irelandhotels.com/offers

B&B from €55.00 to €95.00

Daniel Corbett
Area General Manager

55

Activities:

Closed 24 - 25 December

The Ritz-Carlton, Powerscourt

HOTEL ★★★★★ MAP 8 O 10

Powerscourt Estate,
Enniskerry,
Co. Wicklow

Tel: 01-274 8888 Fax: 01-274 9999
Email: powerscourtinquiries@ritzcarlton.com
Web: www.ritzcarlton.com
GPS: N +53° 11' 10.22" W -6° 10' 51.20"

Nestled among the breathtaking glens and mountain foothills south of Dublin, The Ritz-Carlton, Powerscourt, offers guests a glorious golf and spa experience enriched by magnificent scenic views and historic elegance. Visitors will enjoy impeccable service and a wealth of comforting amenities including dining at Gordon Ramsay at Powerscourt, The Sugar Loaf Lounge and McGill's traditional Irish Pub. For meeting and special events, the hotel includes extensive function space and private dining facilities. Please enquire about Facilities for Persons with Disabilities.

Member of The Ritz-Carlton Hotel Company L.L.C

B&B from €92.50 to €185.00
Suites from €225.00 to €5,000.00

Allan Federer
General Manager

200

Activities:

Open All Year

Glendalough Hotel

HOTEL ★★★ MAP 8 O 9

Glendalough,
Co. Wicklow

Tel: 0404-45135 Fax: 0404-45142
Email: info@glendaloughhotel.ie
Web: www.glendaloughhotel.ie
GPS: N +53° 0' 41.01" W -6° 19' 32.79"

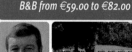

Situated in the heart of the Wicklow Mountains National Park and Ireland's most scenic valley, this family run hotel not only offers majestic views, but also serves some of the finest local and international cuisine in the tranquil setting of the Glendasan River Restaurant. Ease of access to walking trails, golf courses, outdoor persuits and yet only 45km from Dublin City centre means that The Glendalough Hotel is uniquely located to deliver the perfect break from the stresses of modern living. Please enquire about Facilities for Persons with Disabilities.

Member of Irish Welcome Tour

B&B from €59.00 to €82.00

Pat Casey
General Manager

42

Activities:

Closed 01 - 31 January

B&B Rates are per Person Sharing per Night incl. Breakfast.
or Room Rates are per Room per Night - **See also Page 8**

Glendalough / Glen-O-The-Downs / Rathnew

Lynham's Hotel

HOTEL ★★★ MAP 8 O 9

Laragh,
Glendalough,
Co. Wicklow
Tel: 0404-45345 Fax: 0404-45514
Email: info@lynhamsoflaragh.ie
Web: www.lynhamsoflaragh.ie
GPS: N +53° 0' 28.88" W -6° 17' 50.02"

Family owned Lynham's Hotel Laragh is situated in the heart of Wicklow National Park, just a few minutes from the beautiful historic Glendalough. The warm welcoming atmosphere of Jake's Bar lends a traditional air to Lynham's. Famous for its superb bar food, you can also enjoy candlelight dining in our old world restaurant. Lynham's also offer special concessions to the world famous Druids Glen and Druids Heath Golf Courses.

B&B from €50.00 to €130.00

John & Anne Lynham
Managers
14

Closed 21 - 28 December

Glenview Hotel & Leisure Cub

HOTEL ★★★★ MAP 8 O 10

Glen-O-The-Downs,
Delgany,
Co. Wicklow
Tel: 01-287 3399 Fax: 01-287 7511
Email: sales@glenviewhotel.com
Web: www.glenviewhotel.com
GPS: N +53° 8' 31.89" W -6° 7' 38.66"

Situated on a magnificent panoramic site overlooking the garden of Ireland. The Glenview Hotel offers 70 deluxe bedrooms, the unrivalled Penthouse Suite, the award-winning Woodlands Restaurant, Conservatory Bar, 8 meeting rooms for up to 220 delegates and a magnificent leisure club. From the moment you walk through the door you will experience a warm welcome, gracious hospitality and personal service. Relax and unwind in the Haven Beauty salons where calm and peace replace stress and tension. Please enquire about Facilities for Persons with Disabilities.

An IHF Quality Employer

Bookable on www.irelandhotels.com
Special Offer: www.irelandhotels.com/offers

B&B from €55.00 to €140.00

Pat Hevey
General Manager
70

Food for Kids *Activities:*

Open All Year

Tinakilly House Hotel

HOTEL ★★★★ MAP 8 P 9

Wicklow,
(Rathnew),
Co. Wicklow
Tel: 0404-69274 Fax: 0404-67806
Email: reservations@tinakilly.ie
Web: www.tinakilly.ie
GPS: N +52° 59' 46.61" W -6° 4' 1.56"

This Victorian mansion was built for Captain Halpin, who laid the world's telegraph cables. The bedrooms, some with 4 poster beds, are furnished in period style and most overlook the Irish Sea. Award-winning cuisine is prepared from garden vegetables, local fish and Wicklow lamb. The warm welcome ensures a relaxing, memorable stay. Available locally - golf, horse riding, Powerscourt, Mount Usher Gardens and Wicklow Mountains. Dublin 46km.

An IHF Quality Employer

Bookable on www.irelandhotels.com
Special Offer: www.irelandhotels.com/offers

B&B from €100.00 to €125.00
Suites from €230.00 to €320.00

Conrad Robinson
General Manager
51

Closed 24 - 27 December

B&B Rates are per Person Sharing per Night incl. Breakfast.
or Room Rates are per Room per Night - **See also Page 8**

Grand Hotel

HOTEL ★★★ MAP 8 P 9

Main Street,
Wicklow Town,
Co. Wicklow

Tel: 0404-67337 Fax: 0404-69607
Email: reservations@grandhotel.ie
Web: www.grandhotel.ie
GPS: N +52° 58' 50.28" W -6° 2' 51.92"

The Grand Hotel has been welcoming guests to the picturesque seaside town of Wicklow since 1896. Centrally located in the heart of "The Garden of Ireland", it's the perfect relaxing base for exploring Wicklow. Facilities include: 33 luxurious rooms, lively main bar and cosy lounge, food served all day, excellent conferencing and banqueting facilities and secure parking. Stunning scenery, golf, walking, historic houses and gardens all nearby. Dublin 48km. Please enquire about Facilities for Persons with Disabilities.

B&B from €40.00 to €90.00

Sean Kelly
General Manager

33

Closed 24 - 26 December

Woodenbridge Hotel

HOTEL ★★★ MAP 8 O 8

Vale Of Avoca,
Arklow,
Co. Wicklow

Tel: 0402-35146 Fax: 0402-35573
Email: info@woodenbridgehotel.com
Web: www.woodenbridgehotel.com
GPS: N +52° 49' 55.95" W -6° 14' 6.62"

Family owned and run with 23 en suite rooms, including rooms with balconies overlooking Woodenbridge golf course. Dating from 1608 the hotel is the oldest in Ireland. Our restaurant and bar serve quality Irish food: Bord Bia accredited. Tourism Menu award-winner, bar food served all day. Horse riding, fishing, golfing, fine beaches and walking available locally. Near Avoca film location for Ballykissangel. Please enquire about Facilities for Persons with Disabilities.

An IHF Quality Employer

Member of Best Western

Bookable on www.irelandhotels.com

Special Offer: www.irelandhotels.com/offers

B&B from €35.00 to €75.00

Esther O'Brien & Bill O'Brien
Proprietors

23

Open All Year

Woodenbridge Lodge

HOTEL ★★★ MAP 8 O 8

Vale Of Avoca,
Arklow,
Co. Wicklow

Tel: 0402-35146 Fax: 0402-35573
Email: info@woodenbridgehotel.com
Web: www.woodenbridgehotel.com
GPS: N +52° 49' 55.95" W -6° 14' 6.62"

Woodenbridge Lodge is sheltered by Wicklow's rolling hills and is in the picturesque Vale of Avoca. Situated on the banks of the Aughrim River, with 40 bedrooms. A perfect setting for golfing breaks, family reunions, or relaxing, peaceful weekends for two. Il Ruscello Italian restaurant is located here, with authentic Italian cuisine recommended by Paolo Tullio. Please enquire about Facilities for Persons with Disabilities.

An IHF Quality Employer

Member of Best Western

B&B from €35.00 to €75.00

Esther O'Brien & Bill O'Brien
Proprietors

40

Open All Year

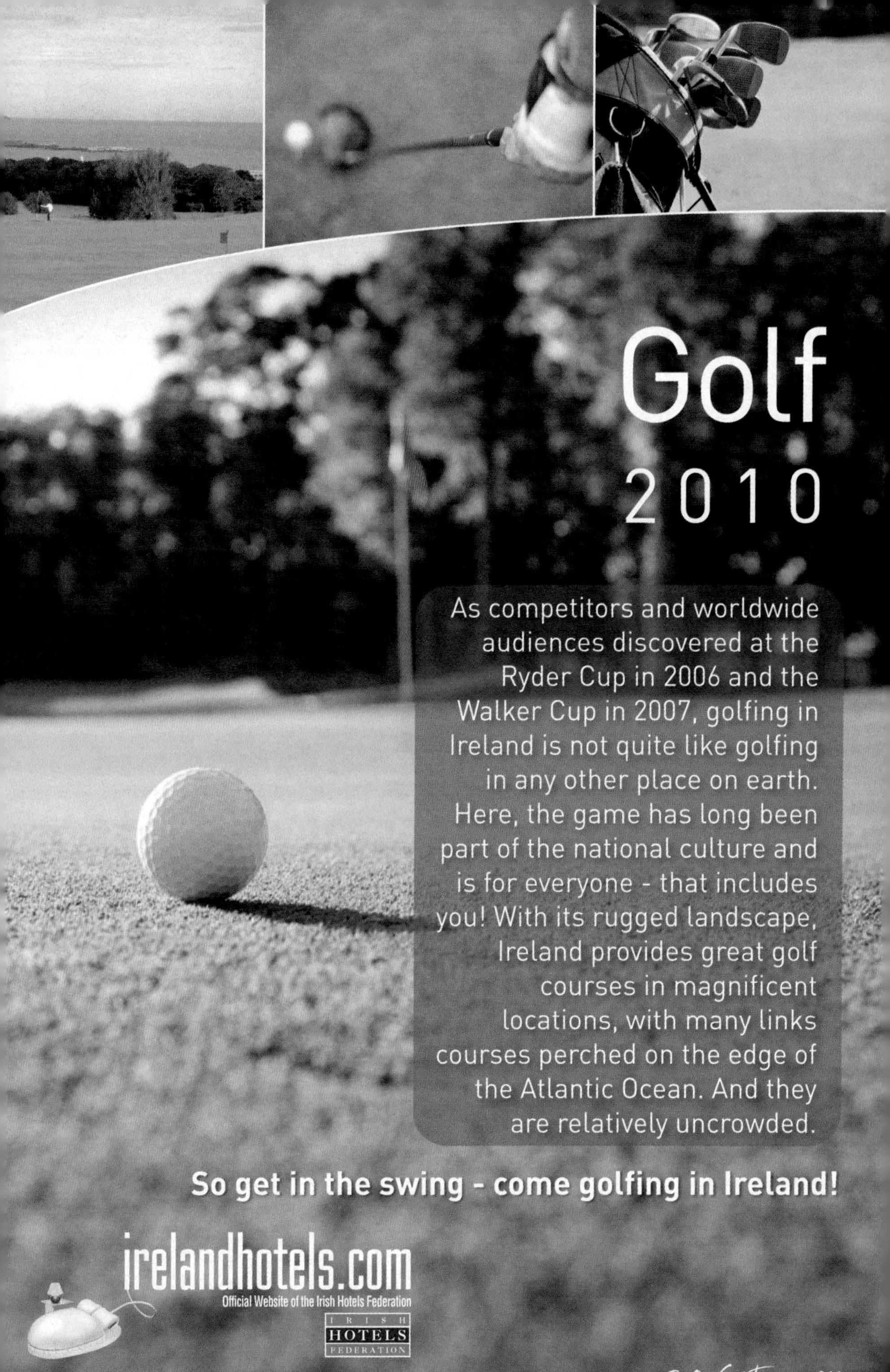
Golf
2010
As competitors and worldwide audiences discovered at the Ryder Cup in 2006 and the Walker Cup in 2007, golfing in Ireland is not quite like golfing in any other place on earth. Here, the game has long been part of the national culture and is for everyone - that includes you! With its rugged landscape, Ireland provides great golf courses in magnificent locations, with many links courses perched on the edge of the Atlantic Ocean. And they are relatively uncrowded.
So get in the swing - come golfing in Ireland!
irelandhotels.com
Official Website of the Irish Hotels Federation
IRISH HOTELS FEDERATION

We invite you to sample the golf, the countryside and the friendship of the Irish people and then to stay in some of Ireland's most charming accommodation. We have listed a range of hotels and guesthouses which are either situated on or close to a golf course. Your host will assist you if necessary in arranging your golfing requirements including tee reservations and green fee charges. A full description of the hotels and guesthouses may be seen by consulting the relevant page number below. ***Listings are by Region, County, Premises Name in alphabetical order.***

Ireland South

Co. Carlow

Mount Wolseley Hotel Spa & Country Club
Tullow, Co. Carlow
Tel: 059-918 0100 ....Page 36
Golf Course(s) On Site:
1 x 18 Hole Golf Course(s)
Green Fees from: *€40.00*
Facilities available:
GP GC AT AB CH PG HC

Talbot Hotel Carlow
Carlow Town, Co. Carlow
Tel: 059-915 3000 ....Page 35
Arrangements with Golf Courses:
Carlow Golf Club, Mount Juliet, Gowran, The Heritage
Green Fees from: *€60.00*
Facilities available:
GP TA GC AT AB CH PG HC

Co. Cork

Actons Hotel
Kinsale, Co. Cork
Tel: 021-477 9900 ....Page 56
Arrangements with Golf Courses:
Kinsale, Old Head of Kinsale, Fota Island, Bandon, Harbour Point, Little Island
Green Fees from: *€30.00*
Facilities available:
GP TA GC AT AB CH TC PG HC

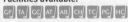

Ashlee Lodge
Blarney, Co. Cork
Tel: 021-438 5346 ....Page 40
Arrangements with Golf Courses:
Lee Valley, Harbour Point, Fota Island, Muskerry, Cork, Mallow
Green Fees from: *€30.00*
Facilities available:
GP TA GC AT AB CH TC PG HC

Blarney Castle Hotel
Blarney, Co. Cork
Tel: 021-438 5116 ....Page 40
Arrangements with Golf Courses:
Muskerry, Lee Valley, Fota Island, Harbour Point, Mallow, Monkstown, Blarney, Kinsale
Green Fees from: *€30.00*
Facilities available:
GP TA GC AT AB CH TC PG HC

Blarney Golf Resort
Blarney, Co. Cork
Tel: 021-438 4477 ....Page 40
Golf Course(s) On Site:
1 x 18 Hole Golf Course(s)
Arrangements with Golf Courses:
Lee Valley, Cork Golf Club, Fota Island, Douglas Golf Club, Bantry Golf Club
Green Fees from: *€30.00*
Facilities available:
GP TA GC AT AB CH TC PG HC

Blue Haven Kinsale (The)
Kinsale, Co. Cork
Tel: 021-477 2209 ....Page 56
Arrangements with Golf Courses:
Kinsale Golf Club, Old Head Golf Club
Green Fees from: *€50.00*
Facilities available:
GP TA GC AT AB CH TC PG HC

Celtic Ross Hotel Conference & Leisure Centre
Rosscarbery, Co. Cork
Tel: 023-884 8722 ....Page 60
Arrangements with Golf Courses:
Skibbereen, Bandon, Lisselan, Bantry, Kinsale, Dunmore
Facilities available:
GP TA GC AT AB CH TC PG HC

Commodore Hotel
Cobh, Co. Cork
Tel: 021-481 1277 ....Page 45
Arrangements with Golf Courses:
Cobh - 18 Hole Course, Water Rock Golf Course, East Cork, Midleton
Green Fees from: *€25.00*
Facilities available:
GP TA AT AB

Dunmore House Hotel
Clonakilty, Co. Cork
Tel: 023-883 3352 ....Page 43
Golf Course(s) On Site:
1 x 9 Hole Golf Course(s)
Arrangements with Golf Courses:
Macroom, Bandon, Skibbereen, Old Head of Kinsale, The Island and Fota Island
Green Fees from: *€25.00*
Facilities available:
GP GC AT AB CH TC HC

Fernhill Hotel
Carrigaline, Co. Cork
Tel: 021-437 2226 ....Page 42
Arrangements with Golf Courses:
Cork Golf Club, Fota Golf Club, Monkstown Golf Club
Green Fees from: *€20.00*
Facilities available:
GP GC AT AB CH TC PG

Fota Island Hotel & Spa
Fota Island, Co. Cork
Tel: 021-467 3000 ....Page 54
Golf Course(s) On Site:
1 x 9 Hole Golf Course(s)
1 x 18 Hole Golf Course(s)
Green Fees from: *€62.00*
Facilities available:
GP TA GC AT AB CH TC PG HC

Glengarriff Eccles Hotel
Glengarriff, Co. Cork
Tel: 027-63003 ....Page 54
Arrangements with Golf Courses:
Bantry Bay, Glengarriff, Ring of Kerry
Green Fees from: *€30.00*
Facilities available:
GP AB PG

Gresham Metropole
Cork City, Co. Cork
Tel: 021-464 3700 ....Page 49
Arrangements with Golf Courses:
Fota Island, Little Island, Harbour Point, Muskerry, Kinsale
Facilities available:
TA GC AT AB CH TC PG HC

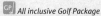

GP *All inclusive Golf Package* | TA *Tuition available* | GC *Golf Cart / Pull Cart* | AT *Arrange Tee Off Times* | HC *Hire Of Caddy*
AB *Advance Golf Booking Made* | CH *Hire Of Clubs* | TC *Transport To Course* | PG *Preferential Green Fees*

Maryborough Hotel & Spa
Cork City, Co. Cork
Tel: 021-436 5555 ....Page 52
Arrangements with Golf Courses:
Douglas, Fota Island, Cork, Kinsale Old Head, Harbour Point, Monkstown
Green Fees from: *€45.00*
Facilities available:
GP TA GC AT AB CH TC PG HC

Old Bank House (The)
Kinsale, Co. Cork
Tel: 021-477 4075 ....Page 58
Arrangements with Golf Courses:
Old Head of Kinsale, Kinsale - Farrangalway, Fota Golf Course, Cork Golf Club, Ballybunion, Waterville
Green Fees from: *€50.00*
Facilities available:
GP TA AT AB CH TC PG HC

Trident Hotel
Kinsale, Co. Cork
Tel: 021-477 9300 ....Page 58
Arrangements with Golf Courses:
Old Head Golf Links, Kinsale Golf Club, Cork Golf Club, Fota Island, Lee Valley
Green Fees from: *€30.00*
Facilities available:
GP TA GC AT AB CH TC PG HC

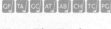

WatersEdge Hotel
Cobh, Co. Cork
Tel: 021-481 5566 ....Page 45
Arrangements with Golf Courses:
Fota Island, Harbour Point, Cobh, Water Rock, East Cork, Old Head of Kinsale, Cork
Green Fees from: *€35.00*
Facilities available:
GP TA GC AT AB CH TC PG HC

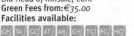

Westlodge Hotel
Bantry, Co. Cork
Tel: 027-50360 ....Page 39
Arrangements with Golf Courses:
Bantry Bay Golf Club - guaranteed times, 18 hole Championship Course
Green Fees from: *€40.00*
Facilities available:
GP TA GC AT AB CH TC PG HC

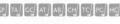

White House
Kinsale, Co. Cork
Tel: 021-477 2125 ....Page 59
Arrangements with Golf Courses:
Kinsale 18 Hole and 9 Hole, Old Head, Bandon, Carrigaline, Muskerry
Green Fees from: *€25.00*
Facilities available:
AT AB CH PG

Co. Kerry

Aghadoe Heights Hotel & Spa
Killarney, Co. Kerry
Tel: 064-663 1766 ....Page 76
Arrangements with Golf Courses:
Waterville, Ballybunion, Killarney, Beaufort, Tralee, Dooks, Old Head of Kinsale
Green Fees from: *€45.00*
Facilities available:
GP TA GC AT AB CH TC PG HC

Ard-Na-Sidhe Country House
Caragh Lake, Co. Kerry
Tel: 066-976 9105 ....Page 64
Arrangements with Golf Courses:
Dooks, Killorglin, Waterville, Beaufort, Killarney, Tralee
Green Fees from: *€70.00*
Facilities available:
GP TA GC AT AB CH TC HC

Barr na Sraide Inn
Dingle (An Daingean), Co. Kerry
Tel: 066-915 1331 ....Page 67
Arrangements with Golf Courses:
Dingle Golf Links, Ceann Sibéal, Castlegregory
Green Fees from: *€30.00*
Facilities available:
GC AT AB CH TC

Best Western Eviston House Hotel
Killarney, Co. Kerry
Tel: 064-663 1640 ....Page 77
Arrangements with Golf Courses:
Killarney, Ballybunion, Beaufort, Waterville, Dooks, Tralee
Green Fees from: *€50.00*
Facilities available:
GP TA GC AT AB CH TC PG HC

Bianconi
Killorglin, Co. Kerry
Tel: 066-976 1146 ....Page 92
Arrangements with Golf Courses:
Killarney, Beaufort, Dunloe, Killorglin, Dooks, Waterville, Tralee, Ballybunion, Dingle
Green Fees from: *€50.00*
Facilities available:
GP TA GC AT AB CH TC HC

Brehon (The)
Killarney, Co. Kerry
Tel: 064-663 0700 ....Page 77
Arrangements with Golf Courses:
Ross, Beaufort, Dooks, Mahonys, Killeen, Lackabane (Killarney)
Green Fees from: *€55.00*
Facilities available:
GP AT AB TC PG

Brookhaven Country House
Waterville, Co. Kerry
Tel: 066-947 4431 ....Page 97
Arrangements with Golf Courses:
Skellig Bay, Waterville Links Course, Ring of Kerry, Dooks, Tralee, Killarney
Green Fees from: *€70.00*
Facilities available:
GC AT CH TC HC

Butler Arms Hotel
Waterville, Co. Kerry
Tel: 066-947 4144 ....Page 98
Arrangements with Golf Courses:
Waterville, Dooks, Killarney, Tralee, Ring of Kerry, Skellig Bay
Green Fees from: *€60.00*
Facilities available:
GP TA GC AT AB CH TC PG HC

Carrig Country House
Caragh Lake, Co. Kerry
Tel: 066-976 9100 ....Page 64
Arrangements with Golf Courses:
Dooks, Killarney, Beaufort, Killorglin, Waterville, Tralee, Ring Of Kerry, Kenmare
Green Fees from: *€37.00*
Facilities available:
GP AT AB CH

Castlerosse Hotel and Golf Resort
Killarney, Co. Kerry
Tel: 064-663 1144 ....Page 79
Golf Course(s) On Site:
1 x 9 Hole Golf Course(s)
Arrangements with Golf Courses:
Killarney's Mahony's Point, Killeen, Lackabane, Dooks, Beaufort
Green Fees from: *€18.00*
Facilities available:
GP TA GC AT AB CH PG HC

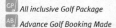

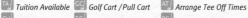

GP *All inclusive Golf Package* TA *Tuition Available* GC *Golf Cart / Pull Cart* AT *Arrange Tee Off Times*
AB *Advance Golf Booking Made* CH *Hire Of Clubs* TC *Transport To Course* PG *Preferential Green Fees* HC *Hire Of Caddy*

Co. Kerry CONTINUED

Dingle Skellig Hotel & Peninsula Spa
Dingle (An Daingean), Co. Kerry
Tel: 066-915 0200 ....Page 69
Arrangements with Golf Courses:
Dingle Golf Links, Ceann Sibéal, Castlegregory
Green Fees from: *€29.00*
Facilities available:
GP GC AT AB CH PG

Fairview Guesthouse
Killarney, Co. Kerry
Tel: 064-663 4164 ....Page 82
Arrangements with Golf Courses:
Killarney, Waterville, Tralee, Dooks, Ballybunion, Beaufort
Green Fees from: *€30.00*
Facilities available:
GP TA GC AT AB CH TC PG HC

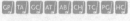

Foley's Townhouse & Restaurant
Killarney, Co. Kerry
Tel: 064-663 1217 ....Page 82
Arrangements with Golf Courses:
Killarney, Barrow, Beaufort, Dooks, Ballybunion, Waterville
Facilities available:
AT AB

Fuchsia House
Killarney, Co. Kerry
Tel: 064-663 3743 ....Page 83
Arrangements with Golf Courses:
Killarney, Tralee, Ballybunion, Waterville, Dooks, Beaufort
Green Fees from: *€50.00*
Facilities available:
TA GC AT AB CH TC PG HC

Gleann Fia Country House
Killarney, Co. Kerry
Tel: 064-663 5035 ....Page 83
Arrangements with Golf Courses:
Killarney, Beaufort, Tralee, Ballybunion, Dooks, Waterville, Ring of Kerry Golf Course, Kenmare, Old Head, Kinsale, Skellig Bay
Green Fees from: *€50.00*
Facilities available:
GP TA GC AT AB CH TC PG HC

Grand Hotel
Tralee, Co. Kerry
Tel: 066-712 1499 ....Page 96
Arrangements with Golf Courses:
Tralee, Ballybunion, Waterville, Dingle, Dooks, Killarney
Green Fees from: *€75.00*
Facilities available:
GP TA GC AT AB CH TC PG HC

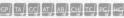

Heights Hotel - Killarney (The)
Killarney, Co. Kerry
Tel: 064-663 1158 ....Page 84
Arrangements with Golf Courses:
3 in Killarney Golf Club, Beaufort, Dooks, Killorglin
Green Fees from: *€40.00*
Facilities available:
GP AT AB CH PG HC

Hotel Dunloe Castle
Killarney, Co. Kerry
Tel: 064-664 4111 ....Page 85
Arrangements with Golf Courses:
Dunloe, Dooks, Beaufort, Killarney, Ross, Killorglin
Green Fees from: *€70.00*
Facilities available:
GP TA GC AT AB CH TC PG HC

Inveraray Farm Guesthouse
Killarney, Co. Kerry
Tel: 064-664 4224 ....Page 86
Arrangements with Golf Courses:
Beaufort, Dunloe, Killarney, Ross, Killorglin, Dooks
Green Fees from: *€35.00*
Facilities available:
TA GC AT AB CH TC HC

Killarney Lodge
Killarney, Co. Kerry
Tel: 064-663 6499 ....Page 87
Arrangements with Golf Courses:
Killarney GC, Tralee, Waterville, Dooks, Old Head, Ballybunion
Green Fees from: *€60.00*
Facilities available:
TA GC AT AB CH TC PG HC

Killarney Park Hotel
Killarney, Co. Kerry
Tel: 064-663 5555 ....Page 87
Arrangements with Golf Courses:
Killarney, Ballybunion, Tralee, Waterville, Dooks, Ring of Kerry
Green Fees from: *€70.00*
Facilities available:
TA GC AT AB CH TC PG

Killarney Plaza Hotel & Spa
Killarney, Co. Kerry
Tel: 064-662 1100 ....Page 87
Arrangements with Golf Courses:
Killarney Golf & Fishing Club, Waterville, Ballybunion, Dooks, Tralee, Old Head of Kinsale
Green Fees from: *€55.00*
Facilities available:
GP AT AB CH HC

Killarney Royal Hotel
Killarney, Co. Kerry
Tel: 064-663 1853 ....Page 88
Arrangements with Golf Courses:
Killarney, Tralee, Dooks, Waterville, Beaufort, Ross
Green Fees from: *€60.00*
Facilities available:
TA GC AT AB CH TC PG

Kingfisher Lodge Guesthouse
Killarney, Co. Kerry
Tel: 064-663 7131 ....Page 89
Arrangements with Golf Courses:
Beaufort, Killarney, Killorglin, Waterville, Ballybunion, Tralee
Green Fees from: *€20.00*
Facilities available:
GP TA GC AT AB CH TC PG HC

Lake Hotel
Killarney, Co. Kerry
Tel: 064-663 1035 ....Page 89
Arrangements with Golf Courses:
Killarney (3 courses), Beaufort, Dooks, Ballybunion, Waterville, Tralee, Ross, Castlerosse, Ring of Kerry, Skellig Bay
Green Fees from: *€30.00*
Facilities available:
GP TA GC AT AB CH TC PG HC

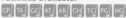

Manor West Hotel, Spa & Leisure Club
Tralee, Co. Kerry
Tel: 066-719 4500 ....Page 97
Arrangements with Golf Courses:
Tralee, Ring of Kerry, Castleisland, Ballybunion, Dooks
Green Fees from: *€35.00*
Facilities available:
GP GC AT AB CH TC PG HC

Meadowlands Hotel
Tralee, Co. Kerry
Tel: 066-718 0444 ....Page 97
Arrangements with Golf Courses:
Ballybunion, Tralee (Barrow), Killarney, Dooks, Killorglin, Waterville
Facilities available:
TA GC AT AB CH PG HC

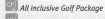

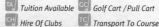

GP *All inclusive Golf Package* · TA *Tuition Available* · GC *Golf Cart / Pull Cart* · AT *Arrange Tee Off Times*
AB *Advance Golf Booking Made* · CH *Hire Of Clubs* · TC *Transport To Course* · PG *Preferential Green Fees* · HC *Hire Of Caddy*

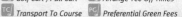

O'Donnabhain's
Kenmare, Co. Kerry
Tel: 064-664 2106 ....Page 73
Arrangements with Golf Courses:
Kenmare, Ring of Kerry, Bantry, Dooks, Waterville
Green Fees from:*€50.00*
Facilities available:
GP AT AB TC PG

Parknasilla Resort
Sneem, Co. Kerry
Tel: 064-667 5600 ....Page 93
Golf Course(s) On Site:
1 x 9 Hole Golf Course(s)
Facilities available:
AT CH PG

Scotts Hotel Killarney
Killarney, Co. Kerry
Tel: 064-663 1060 ....Page 92
Arrangements with Golf Courses:
Killarney, Ross, Beaufort, Ring of Kerry, Dooks, Ballybunion
Green Fees from:*€40.00*
Facilities available:
GP AT AB CH TC PG HC

Sheen Falls Lodge
Kenmare, Co. Kerry
Tel: 064-664 1600 ....Page 74
Arrangements with Golf Courses:
Kenmare, Ring of Kerry
Green Fees from:*€45.00*
Facilities available:
GP TA GC AT AB CH TC PG HC

Smugglers Inn
Waterville, Co. Kerry
Tel: 066-947 4330 ....Page 98
Arrangements with Golf Courses:
Waterville (2 Courses), Killarney (2 Courses), Dooks, Tralee, Ballybunion, Kenmare, Parknasilla
Green Fees from:*€65.00*
Facilities available:
GP TA GC AT AB CH TC PG HC

Sneem Hotel
Sneem, Co. Kerry
Tel: 064-667 5100 ....Page 94
Arrangements with Golf Courses:
Ring of Kerry Golf Course, Waterville, Parknasilla, Killeen & Mahonys Golf Courses Killarney, Old Head Golf Links Kinsale
Green Fees from:*€50.00*
Facilities available:
GP AT CH TC HC

Co. Kilkenny

Butler House
Kilkenny City, Co. Kilkenny
Tel: 056-776 5707 ....Page 99
Arrangements with Golf Courses:
Kilkenny, Mount Juliet, Carlow, Killerig Castle, Kilkea Castle, Gowran Park
Green Fees from:*€30.00*
Facilities available:
TA GC AT AB CH TC PG HC

Kilford Arms Hotel
Kilkenny City, Co. Kilkenny
Tel: 056-776 1018 ....Page 101
Arrangements with Golf Courses:
Mount Juliet, Kilkenny Golf Course, Castlecomer Golf Course, Callan Golf Course, Borris Golf Course
Facilities available:
GP AT AB TC

Kilkenny River Court
Kilkenny City, Co. Kilkenny
Tel: 056-772 3388 ....Page 102
Arrangements with Golf Courses:
Gowran Park, Kilkenny
Green Fees from:*€30.00*
Facilities available:
GP AT AB CH TC PG HC

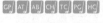

Langton House Hotel
Kilkenny City, Co. Kilkenny
Tel: 056-776 5133 ....Page 102
Arrangements with Golf Courses:
Mount Juliet, Kilkenny Golf Club, Gowran Park, Castlecomer Golf Club
Green Fees from:*€90.00*
Facilities available:
GP AT AB CH TC PG HC

Lyrath Estate Hotel, Spa & Convention Centre
Kilkenny City, Co. Kilkenny
Tel: 056-776 0088 ....Page 103
Arrangements with Golf Courses:
Gowran Park, Kilkenny
Green Fees from:*€30.00*
Facilities available:
GP AT AB CH TC PG HC

Mount Juliet
Thomastown, Co. Kilkenny
Tel: 056-777 3000 ....Page 105
Golf Course(s) On Site:
1 x 18 Hole Golf Course(s)
Green Fees from:*€70.00*
Facilities available:
GP TA GC AT AB CH TC PG HC

Co. Tipperary

Abbey Court Hotel, Lodges & Trinity Leisure Spa
Nenagh, Co. Tipperary
Tel: 067-41111..........................Page 110
Arrangements with Golf Courses:
Nenagh, Roscrea, Birr, Portumna, Thurles, Castletroy
Green Fees from:*€25.00*
Facilities available:
GP TA GC AT AB CH TC PG HC

Ach Na Sheen Guesthouse
Tipperary Town, Co. Tipperary
Tel: 062-51298 ....Page 111
Arrangements with Golf Courses:
Tipperary, Ballykisteen, Cahir, Dundrum
Green Fees from:*€30.00*
Facilities available:
TA GC AT AB CH HC

Ballykisteen Hotel & Golf Resort
Tipperary Town, Co. Tipperary
Tel: 062-33333 ....Page 111
Golf Course(s) On Site:
1 x 18 Hole Golf Course(s)
Green Fees from:*€25.00*
Facilities available:
GP TA GC AT AB CH PG HC

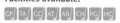

Cahir House Hotel
Cahir, Co. Tipperary
Tel: 052-744 3000 ....Page 106
Arrangements with Golf Courses:
Cahir Park, Carrick-on-Suir, Clonmel, Ballykisteen, Dundrum, Tipperary, Thurles, Mount Juliet
Green Fees from:*€30.00*
Facilities available:
GP TA GC AT AB CH TC PG HC

GP *All inclusive Golf Package* TA *Tuition Available* GC *Golf Cart / Pull Cart* AT *Arrange Tee Off Times*
AB *Advance Golf Booking Made* CH *Hire Of Clubs* TC *Transport To Course* PG *Preferential Green Fees* HC *Hire Of Caddy*

Co. Tipperary CONTINUED

Dundrum House Hotel, Golf & Leisure Resort
Cashel, Co. Tipperary
Tel: 062-71116 ....Page 107
Golf Course(s) On Site:
1 x 18 Hole Golf Course(s)
Green Fees from: *€35.00*
Facilities available:
GP TA GC AT AB CH TC PG HC

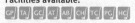

Kilcoran Lodge Hotel, Lodges & Leisure Centre
Cahir, Co. Tipperary
Tel: 052-744 1288 ....Page 106
Arrangements with Golf Courses:
Cahir GC, Clonmel GC, Tipperary GC, Mitchelstown GC, Ballykisteen GC, Dundrum GC.
Green Fees from: *€25.00*
Facilities available:
GC AT AB

Co. Waterford

Dooley's Hotel
Waterford City, Co. Waterford
Tel: 051-873531 ....Page 120
Arrangements with Golf Courses:
Waterford, Tramore, Faithlegg, Waterford Castle, Mount Juliet, Carrick-on-Suir
Green Fees from: *€55.00*
Facilities available:
GP TA GC AT AB CH TC PG HC

Faithlegg House Hotel
Faithlegg, Co. Waterford
Tel: 051-382000 ....Page 116
Golf Course(s) On Site:
1 x 18 Hole Golf Course(s)
Arrangements with Golf Courses:
Waterford Castle, Tramore, Waterford Golf Club, Faithlegg Golf Course, Mount Juliet
Green Fees from: *€50.00*
Facilities available:
GP TA GC AT AB CH PG HC

Lismore House Hotel
Lismore, Co. Waterford
Tel: 058-72966........................Page 116
Arrangements with Golf Courses:
Gold Coast Golf Club, Dungarvan Golf Club
Green Fees from: *€25.00*
Facilities available:
GP AT AB TC PG

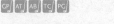

Majestic Hotel
Tramore, Co. Waterford
Tel: 051-381761 ....Page 118
Arrangements with Golf Courses:
Tramore, Waterford, Faithlegg, Waterford Castle, Mount Juliet, Dunmore East
Green Fees from: *€30.00*
Facilities available:
GP TA GC AT AB CH TC PG HC

Ocean Hotel
Dunmore East, Co. Waterford
Tel: 051-383136 ....Page 116
Arrangements with Golf Courses:
Waterford, Waterford Castle, Faithlegg, Dunmore East, Tramore
Green Fees from: *€35.00*
Facilities available:
GP AT AB CH TC PG HC

O'Shea's Hotel
Tramore, Co. Waterford
Tel: 051-381246 ....Page 118
Arrangements with Golf Courses:
Tramore, Faithlegg, Waterford Castle, Waterford, Dungarvan
Green Fees from: *€45.00*
Facilities available:
GP TA GC AT AB CH TC PG HC

Park Hotel, Leisure Centre & Holiday Homes
Dungarvan, Co. Waterford
Tel: 058-42899........................Page 114
Arrangements with Golf Courses:
Dungarvan Golf Club, West Waterford Golf Club, Gold Coast Golf Club
Green Fees from: *€25.00*
Facilities available:
GP TA GC AT AB CH TC PG

Rhu Glenn Country Club Hotel
Waterford City, Co. Waterford
Tel: 051-832242......................Page 122
Arrangements with Golf Courses:
Waterford, New Ross, Faithlegg, Waterford Castle, Tramore, Dunmore East, Mount Juliet
Green Fees from: *€40.00*
Facilities available:
GC AT AB CH

Sands Hotel (The)
Tramore, Co. Waterford
Tel: 051-381355 ....Page 118
Arrangements with Golf Courses:
Tramore
Green Fees from: *€60.00*
Facilities available:
GP TA GC AT AB CH TC PG

Tower Hotel & Leisure Centre
Waterford City, Co. Waterford
Tel: 051-862300......................Page 123
Arrangements with Golf Courses:
Waterford Castle, Waterford, Faithlegg, Tramore
Green Fees from: *€25.00*
Facilities available:
GP TA GC AT AB CH PG HC

Co. Wexford

Amber Springs Hotel & Health Spa
Gorey, Co. Wexford
Tel: 053-948 4000 ....Page 126
Arrangements with Golf Courses:
Seafield, Courtown, Coollattin, Ballymoney
Green Fees from: *€36.00*
Facilities available:
GP AT AB TC PG

Ashdown Park Hotel Conference & Leisure Centre
Gorey, Co. Wexford
Tel: 053-948 0500 ....Page 127
Arrangements with Golf Courses:
Courtown, Ballymoney, Coolattin, Enniscorthy, Woodenbridge, Seafield
Green Fees from: *€40.00*
Facilities available:
GP TA GC AT AB CH TC PG HC

Kelly's Resort Hotel & Spa
Rosslare, Co. Wexford
Tel: 053-913 2114....................Page 129
Arrangements with Golf Courses:
Rosslare Golf Club, St. Helen's Bay Golf & Country Club, Wexford Golf Club
Green Fees from: *€40.00*
Facilities available:
GP TA GC AT AB TC PG

Riverside Park Hotel and Leisure Club
Enniscorthy, Co. Wexford
Tel: 053-923 7800 ....Page 126
Arrangements with Golf Courses:
Enniscorthy Golf Club, Rosslare Golf Club, Wexford Golf Club, New Ross Golf Club, Seafield Golf Club, St. Helen's Golf Club
Green Fees from: *€40.00*
Facilities available:
GP AT AB TC PG

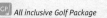

GP *All inclusive Golf Package* · TA *Tuition Available* · GC *Golf Cart / Pull Cart* · AT *Arrange Tee Off Times*
AB *Advance Golf Booking Made* · CH *Hire Of Clubs* · TC *Transport To Course* · PG *Preferential Green Fees* · HC *Hire Of Caddy*

Seafield Golf & Spa Hotel
Gorey, Co. Wexford
Tel: 053-942 4000 ....Page 128
Golf Course(s) On Site:
1 x 18 Hole Golf Course(s)
Green Fees from: *€25.00*
Facilities available:
GP TA GC AT AB CH PG HC

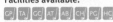

Talbot Hotel Conference and Leisure Centre
Wexford Town, Co. Wexford
Tel: 053-912 2566 ....Page 134
Arrangements with Golf Courses:
St. Helen's, Wexford, Rosslare, Enniscorthy, Courtown
Green Fees from: *€25.00*
Facilities available:
GP TA GC AT AB CH TC PG HC

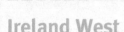

Ireland West

Co. Clare

Aran View House Hotel & Restaurant
Doolin, Co. Clare
Tel: 065-707 4061 ....Page 140
Arrangements with Golf Courses:
Lahinch Links Course, Lahinch Castle Course, Doonbeg Greg Norman Course, Woodstock, Ennis Golf Club
Green Fees from: *€150.00*
Facilities available:
AT AB CH

Dough Mor Lodge
Lahinch, Co. Clare
Tel: 065-708 2063 ....Page 148
Arrangements with Golf Courses:
Lahinch Golf Club (36 holes), Doonbeg Golf Club, Kilrush, Kilkee, East Clare, Shannon, Dromoland Castle
Facilities available:
AT AB

Greenbrier Inn Guesthouse
Lahinch, Co. Clare
Tel: 065-708 1242 ....Page 148
Arrangements with Golf Courses:
Lahinch Championship Links, Lahinch Castle Links, Doonbeg Championship Links, Woodstock (Ennis), Dromoland Castle GC
Green Fees from: *€50.00*
Facilities available:
TA GC HC

Grovemount House
Ennistymon, Co. Clare
Tel: 065-707 1431 ....Page 146
Arrangements with Golf Courses:
Lahinch, Spanish Point, Doonbeg, Ennis, Dromoland
Green Fees from: *€50.00*
Facilities available:
TA GC AT AB CH

Halpin's Townhouse Hotel
Kilkee, Co. Clare
Tel: 065-905 6032 ....Page 147
Arrangements with Golf Courses:
Ballybunion, Lahinch, Kilkee, Doonbeg, Woodstock, Shannon
Green Fees from: *€40.00*
Facilities available:
GP TA GC AT AB CH TC PG HC

Oakwood Arms Hotel
Shannon Airport, Co. Clare
Tel: 061-361500 ....Page 151
Arrangements with Golf Courses:
Shannon Golf Club, Dromoland Golf Club
Green Fees from: *€65.00*
Facilities available:
GP AT AB TC PG

Park Inn Shannon
Shannon Airport, Co. Clare
Tel: 061-471122 ....Page 152
Arrangements with Golf Courses:
Shannon Golf Course
Green Fees from: *€60.00*
Facilities available:
GP TA GC AT AB CH TC PG HC

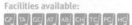

Sancta Maria Hotel
Lahinch, Co. Clare
Tel: 065-708 1041 ....Page 149
Arrangements with Golf Courses:
Lahinch Championship Golf Links, Lahinch Castle, Doonbeg, Woodstock, Dromoland, Spanish Point
Green Fees from: *€40.00*
Facilities available:
GP TA GC AT AB CH TC PG HC

Temple Gate Hotel
Ennis, Co. Clare
Tel: 065-682 3300 ....Page 145
Arrangements with Golf Courses:
Woodstock, Ennis, Lahinch, East Clare, Doonbeg, Dromoland
Green Fees from: *€20.00*
Facilities available:
GP TA GC AT AB CH TC PG HC

Vaughan Lodge and Seafood Restaurant
Lahinch, Co. Clare
Tel: 065-708 1111 ....Page 149
Arrangements with Golf Courses:
Lahinch, Doonbeg, Spanish Point, Dromoland, Kilrush, Ennis
Green Fees from: *€100.00*
Facilities available:
GP AT AB CH TC HC

Co. Donegal

Arnolds Hotel
Dunfanaghy, Co. Donegal
Tel: 074-913 6208 ....Page 158
Arrangements with Golf Courses:
Dunfanaghy 18 Hole Links, Cloughaneely 9 Hole Parkland, Rosapenna 36 Hole Links, Cruit Island 9 Hole Links, Portsalon 18 Hole Links, Letterkenny 18 Hole Parkland
Green Fees from: *€26.00*
Facilities available:
GP GC AT AB CH TC PG HC

Ballyliffin Lodge & Spa
Ballyliffin, Co. Donegal
Tel: 074-937 8200 ....Page 153
Arrangements with Golf Courses:
Ballyliffin Golf Club
Facilities available:
GP TA AT AB PG

Best Western Milford Inn Hotel
Milford, Co. Donegal
Tel: 074-915 3313 ....Page 162
Arrangements with Golf Courses:
Portsalon, Rosapenna, Letterkenny, Dunfanaghy, Ballyliffin, Letterkenny
Green Fees from: *€35.00*
Facilities available:
GP TA GC AT AB CH TC PG HC

Castle Grove Country House Hotel
Letterkenny, Co. Donegal
Tel: 074-915 1118 ....Page 160
Arrangements with Golf Courses:
Portsalon, Letterkenny, Rosapenna, Ballyliffin, Murvagh
Green Fees from: *€50.00*
Facilities available:
GP GC AT AB CH PG HC

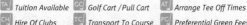

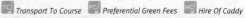

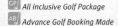

GP *All inclusive Golf Package* TA *Tuition Available* GC *Golf Cart / Pull Cart* AT *Arrange Tee Off Times*
AB *Advance Golf Booking Made* CH *Hire Of Clubs* TC *Transport To Course* PG *Preferential Green Fees* HC *Hire Of Caddy*

Co. Donegal CONTINUED

Downings Bay Hotel
Downings, Co. Donegal
Tel: 074-915 5586 ....Page 158
Arrangements with Golf Courses:
Rosapenna Links, Dunfanaghy, Portsalon, Letterkenny
Green Fees from: *€25.00*
Facilities available:
GP TA GC AT AB TC PG HC

Great Northern Hotel
Bundoran, Co. Donegal
Tel: 071-984 1204 ....Page 155
Golf Course(s) On Site:
1 x 18 Hole Golf Course(s)
Arrangements with Golf Courses:
Donegal, Strandhill, Rosses Point
Green Fees from: *€35.00*
Facilities available:
GP TA GC AT AB CH TC PG HC

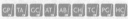

Highlands Hotel
Glenties, Co. Donegal
Tel: 074-955 1111 ....Page 159
Arrangements with Golf Courses:
Narin Portnoo Golf Club
Green Fees from: *€55.00*
Facilities available:
GP AT AB TC PG

Inishowen Gateway Hotel
Buncrana, Co. Donegal
Tel: 074-936 1144 ....Page 155
Arrangements with Golf Courses:
Buncrana, North West Golf Course, Ballyliffin Old Course, Ballyliffin Glashedy Course
Green Fees from: *€30.00*
Facilities available:
GP AT AB PG

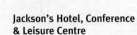

Jackson's Hotel, Conference & Leisure Centre
Ballybofey, Co. Donegal
Tel: 074-913 1021....................Page 152
Arrangements with Golf Courses:
Ballybofey and Stranorlar, Murvagh, Cruit Island, Portsalon, Dunfanaghy
Green Fees from: *€20.00*
Facilities available:
GP TA AT AB CH TC HC

Malin Hotel
Malin, Co. Donegal
Tel: 074-937 0606 ....Page 161
Arrangements with Golf Courses:
Ballyliffin Golf Club - Glashedy Links and The Old Course, Greencastle Golf Club, North West Golf Club
Green Fees from: *€70.00*
Facilities available:
GP AT AB CH PG

Solis Lough Eske Castle
Donegal Town, Co. Donegal
Tel: 074-972 5100 ....Page 158
Arrangements with Golf Courses:
Donegal (Murvagh), Narin/Portnoo, Ballyliffin
Green Fees from: *€35.00*
Facilities available:
GP TA GC AT AB CH TC PG HC

Waters Edge (The)
Rathmullan, Co. Donegal
Tel: 074-915 8182 ....Page 163
Arrangements with Golf Courses:
Portsalon, Letterkenny, Rosapenna, Dunfanaghy, Ballyliffin
Green Fees from: *€35.00*
Facilities available:
GP TA AT AB CH TC PG HC

Co. Galway

Anno Santo Hotel
Galway City, Co. Galway
Tel: 091-523011 ....Page 171
Arrangements with Golf Courses:
Glenlo, Athenry, Galway, Oughterard, Galway Bay, Barna
Facilities available:
GP TA AB CH TC PG HC

Claregalway Hotel
Galway City, Co. Galway
Tel: 091-738300......................Page 172
Arrangements with Golf Courses:
Cregmore Park Golf Course
Green Fees from: *€35.00*
Facilities available:
GP GC AT AB PG HC

Inishmore House
Galway City, Co. Galway
Tel: 091-582639......................Page 176
Arrangements with Golf Courses:
Barna, Galway Bay, Oughterard, Athenry, Galway, Gort
Green Fees from: *€35.00*
Facilities available:
GP TA GC AT AB CH TC PG HC

Lady Gregory Hotel, Conference & Leisure Club
Gort, Co. Galway
Tel: 091-632333......................Page 180
Arrangements with Golf Courses:
Gort
Green Fees from: *€30.00*
Facilities available:
GP TA GC AT AB CH TC PG HC

Shannon Oaks Hotel & Country Club
Portumna, Co. Galway
Tel: 090-974 1777 ....Page 185
Arrangements with Golf Courses:
Portumna Golf Course, Birr Golf Club, Glasson Golf Club, East Clare, Galway Bay, Athenry Golf Course
Green Fees from: *€25.00*
Facilities available:
GP AT AB PG

Westwood Hotel (The)
Galway City, Co. Galway
Tel: 091-521442 ....Page 180
Arrangements with Golf Courses:
Barna, Oughterard, Ballyconneely, Galway Bay Golf and Country Club, Galway Golf Club, Cregmore, Athenry
Facilities available:
GP AT AB PG

Co. Limerick

Courtenay Lodge Hotel
Newcastle West, Co. Limerick
Tel: 069-62244 ....Page 195
Arrangements with Golf Courses:
Newcastle West, Adare Manor Golf & Country Club, Adare Golf Club, Ballybunion, Charleville, Dingle (Ceann Sibeal)
Green Fees from: *€40.00*
Facilities available:
GP TA GC AT AB TC PG HC

GP *All inclusive Golf Package* TA *Tuition Available* GC *Golf Cart / Pull Cart* AT *Arrange Tee Off Times*
AB *Advance Golf Booking Made* CH *Hire Of Clubs* TC *Transport To Course* PG *Preferential Green Fees* HC *Hire Of Caddy*

Fitzgeralds Woodlands House Hotel & Spa
Adare, Co. Limerick
Tel: 061-605100 .... Page 190
Arrangements with Golf Courses:
Adare Manor Golf Club, Adare Golf Club, Newcastle West, Charleville, Limerick County Golf Club, Castletroy Golf Club
Green Fees from: *€32.00*
Facilities available:
GP TA GC AT AB CH TC PG HC

Rathkeale House Hotel
Rathkeale, Co. Limerick
Tel: 069-63333 .... Page 195
Arrangements with Golf Courses:
Adare, Adare Manor, Newcastle West, Charleville, Ballybunion
Green Fees from: *€50.00*
Facilities available:
GP TA GC AT AB CH TC PG HC

Co. Mayo

Ashford Castle
Cong, Co. Mayo
Tel: 094-954 6003 .... Page 200
Golf Course(s) On Site:
1 x 9 Hole Golf Course(s)
Facilities available:
TA GC CH

Castlecourt Hotel Spa, Leisure, Conference
Westport, Co. Mayo
Tel: 098-55088 .... Page 203
Arrangements with Golf Courses:
Westport, Ballinrobe, Castlebar, Belmullet, Clew Bay, Enniscrone
Green Fees from: *€30.00*
Facilities available:
GP TA GC AT AB CH TC PG HC

Courthouse (The)
Ballyhaunis, Co. Mayo
Tel: 094-963 0068 .... Page 198
Arrangements with Golf Courses:
Ballyhaunis
Green Fees from: *€20.00*
Facilities available:
GP AT AB

Downhill House Hotel & Eagles Leisure Club
Ballina, Co. Mayo
Tel: 096-21033 .... Page 197
Arrangements with Golf Courses:
Ballina, Enniscrone, Carne (Belmullet), Rosses Point, Strandhill, Westport, Claremorris, Ballinrobe, Castlebar, Tubbercurry, Swinford
Green Fees from: *€35.00*
Facilities available:
GP TA GC AT AB CH TC PG HC

Healys Restaurant & Fishing Lodge
Pontoon, Co. Mayo
Tel: 094-925 6443 .... Page 201
Arrangements with Golf Courses:
Castlebar, Ballina, Westport, Enniscrone, Carne, Swinford, Ballinrobe, Mulranny, Belmullet, Rosses Point, Strandhill
Green Fees from: *€40.00*
Facilities available:
GP TA GC AT AB CH TC PG HC

Hotel Westport
Westport, Co. Mayo
Tel: 098-25122 .... Page 204
Arrangements with Golf Courses:
Westport, Castlebar, Ballinrobe, Carne (Belmullet), Enniscrone, Clew Bay
Green Fees from: *€25.00*
Facilities available:
GP TA GC AT AB CH TC PG HC

Sea Rod Inn
Belmullet, Co. Mayo
Tel: 097-86767 .... Page 198
Arrangements with Golf Courses:
Carne, Belmullet, New Doohoma Par 3
Green Fees from: *€50.00*
Facilities available:
GP AT AB

Westport Plaza Hotel Spa, Leisure, Conference
Westport, Co. Mayo
Tel: 098-51166 .... Page 205
Arrangements with Golf Courses:
Westport, Ballinrobe, Belmullet, Clew Bay, Enniscrone, Castlebar
Green Fees from: *€30.00*
Facilities available:
GP TA GC AT AB CH TC PG HC

Westport Woods Hotel & Spa
Westport, Co. Mayo
Tel: 098-25811 .... Page 206
Arrangements with Golf Courses:
Westport, Castlebar, Ballinrobe, Clew Bay, Carne (Belmullet)
Green Fees from: *€35.00*
Facilities available:
GP TA GC AT AB CH TC PG HC

Wyatt Hotel
Westport, Co. Mayo
Tel: 098-25027 .... Page 206
Arrangements with Golf Courses:
Westport Golf Club, Castlebar Golf Club, Ballinrobe Golf Club, Carne Golf Links
Green Fees from: *€35.00*
Facilities available:
GP TA GC AT AB CH TC PG HC

Co. Sligo

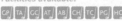

Castle Dargan Golf Hotel Wellness
Ballygawley, Co. Sligo
Tel: 071-911 8080 .... Page 207
Golf Course(s) On Site:
1 x 18 Hole Golf Course(s)
Green Fees from: *€40.00*
Facilities available:
GP TA GC AT AB CH TC PG

Radisson Blu Hotel & Spa Sligo
Sligo Town, Co. Sligo
Tel: 071-914 0008 .... Page 209
Arrangements with Golf Courses:
Co.Sligo Golf Club, Rosses Point
Green Fees from: *€40.00*
Facilities available:
GP TA GC AT AB CH PG

Yeats Country Hotel, Spa & Leisure Club
Rosses Point, Co. Sligo
Tel: 071-917 7211 .... Page 209
Arrangements with Golf Courses:
Co. Sligo, Strandhill, Enniscrone, Bundoran, Castle Dargan, Murvagh
Green Fees from: *€75.00*
Facilities available:
GP TA GC AT AB TC PG HC

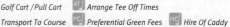

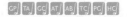

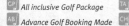

GP *All inclusive Golf Package* TA *Tuition Available* GC *Golf Cart / Pull Cart* AT *Arrange Tee Off Times*
AB *Advance Golf Booking Made* CH *Hire Of Clubs* TC *Transport To Course* PG *Preferential Green Fees* HC *Hire Of Caddy*

Northern Ireland

Co. Antrim

Bushmills Inn Hotel
Bushmills, Co. Antrim
Tel: 028-2073 3000 ....Page 216
Arrangements with Golf Courses:
Royal Portrush, Portstewart, Castlerock, Ballycastle, Bushfoot, Gracehill
Facilities available:
GP TA GC AT AB CH TC HC

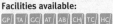

Galgorm Resort & Spa
Ballymena, Co. Antrim
Tel: 028-2588 1001..................Page 215
Arrangements with Golf Courses:
Galgorm Castle Championship Course, Full 18-Hole Course
Green Fees from: *£26.00*
Facilities available:
GP TA GC AT AB CH TC PG HC

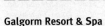

Hilton Templepatrick
Templepatrick, Co. Antrim
Tel: 028-9443 5500 ....Page 218
Golf Course(s) On Site:
1 x 18 Hole Golf Course(s)
Green Fees from: *£25.00*
Facilities available:
GP TA GC AT AB CH TC PG HC

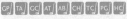

Londonderry Arms Hotel
Carnlough, Co. Antrim
Tel: 028-2888 5255 ....Page 216
Arrangements with Golf Courses:
Cairndhu GC (18 Hole, 7 miles), Galgorm GC (18 Hole, 14 miles), Ballycastle (18 Hole, 26 miles), Cushendall (9 Hole, 12 miles)
Facilities available:
AT

Ramada Portrush
Portrush, Co. Antrim
Tel: 028-7082 6100 ....Page 217
Arrangements with Golf Courses:
Royal Portrush, Portstewart, Castlerock, Ballycastle, Bushfoot, Gracehill, Galgorm Castle
Green Fees from: *£50.00*
Facilities available:
TA GC AT AB CH TC HC

Belfast City

Malone Lodge Hotel & Apartments
Belfast City
Tel: 028-9038 8000 ....Page 220
Arrangements with Golf Courses:
Malone Golf Club
Green Fees from: *£40.00*
Facilities available:
GP TA GC AT AB CH TC PG HC

Co. Derry

Radisson Blu Roe Park Resort
Limavady, Co. Derry
Tel: 028-7772 2222 ....Page 222
Golf Course(s) On Site:
1 x 18 Hole Golf Course(s)
Arrangements with Golf Courses:
Roe Park Golf Club, Radisson SAS Roe Park Resort
Green Fees from: *£25.00*
Facilities available:
GP TA GC AT AB CH TC PG HC

Co. Down

Burrendale Hotel, Country Club & Spa
Newcastle, Co. Down
Tel: 028-4372 2599 ....Page 222
Arrangements with Golf Courses:
Royal County Down, Kilkeel, Downpatrick, Ardglass, Spa, Bright
Facilities available:
AT AB

Co. Fermanagh

Mahon's Hotel
Irvinestown, Co. Fermanagh
Tel: 028-6862 1656 ....Page 224
Arrangements with Golf Courses:
Castle Hume Golf Course, Enniskillen Golf Club, Murvagh Golf Club, Nick Faldo's Course at Lough Erne Resort
Facilities available:
GP TA GC AT AB CH TC PG HC

Dublin & Ireland East

Co. Cavan

Radisson Blu Farnham Estate Hotel
Cavan Town, Co. Cavan
Tel: 049-437 7700 ....Page 232
Golf Course(s) On Site:
1 x 18 Hole Golf Course(s)
Green Fees from: *€35.00*
Facilities available:
GP GC AT AB CH TC PG

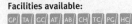

Slieve Russell Hotel Golf & Country Club
Ballyconnell, Co. Cavan
Tel: 049-952 6444 ....Page 231
Golf Course(s) On Site:
1 x 18 Hole Golf Course(s)
1 x Par 3 Golf Course(s)
Green Fees from: *€50.00*
Facilities available:
GP TA GC AT AB CH TC PG HC

Co. Dublin

Aberdeen Lodge
Dublin City, Co. Dublin
Tel: 01-283 8155 ....Page 236
Arrangements with Golf Courses:
St. Margarets, Portmarnock, K Club, Elm Park, Carton House, Druids Glen
Green Fees from: *€60.00*
Facilities available:
GP TA GC AT AB CH TC HC

Airportview Hotel & Spa
Blakes Cross, Co. Dublin
Tel: 01-843 8756 ....Page 233
Arrangements with Golf Courses:
Rush Golf Club, Skerries Golf Club, Balbriggan Golf Club, Swords Open, Donabate Golf Club, Portmarnock Links
Green Fees from: *€25.00*
Facilities available:
GP GC AT AB CH TC PG

GP *All inclusive Golf Package* TA *Tuition Available* GC *Golf Cart / Pull Cart* AT *Arrange Tee Off Times*
AB *Advance Golf Booking Made* CH *Hire Of Clubs* TC *Transport To Course* PG *Preferential Green Fees* HC *Hire Of Caddy*

Castleknock Hotel and Country Club
Dublin City, Co. Dublin
Tel: 01-640 6300 ....Page 245
Golf Course(s) On Site:
1 x 18 Hole Golf Course(s)
Arrangements with Golf Courses:
Luttrellstown, Carton House, Citywest, Castleknock Golf Course
Green Fees from:*€40.00*
Facilities available:
GP GC AT AB CH PG HC

Charleville Lodge
Dublin City, Co. Dublin
Tel: 01-838 6633 ....Page 246
Arrangements with Golf Courses:
St. Margaret's, Luttrellstown, The Links, Portmarnock, The Island Golf Links
Green Fees from:*€70.00*
Facilities available:
GP TA GC AT AB CH TC PG HC

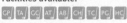

Clontarf Castle Hotel
Dublin City, Co. Dublin
Tel: 01-833 2321 ....Page 247
Arrangements with Golf Courses:
Royal Dublin, St. Margaret's, Portmarnock, St. Anne's, Clontarf, Malahide
Green Fees from:*€70.00*
Facilities available:
GP TA GC AT AB CH TC PG HC

Deer Park Hotel Golf & Spa
Howth, Co. Dublin
Tel: 01-832 2624 ....Page 269
Golf Course(s) On Site:
1 x 18 Hole Golf Course(s)
2 x 9 Hole Golf Course(s)
1 x Par 3 Golf Course(s)
Green Fees from:*€20.00*
Facilities available:
GP TA GC AT AB CH

Grand Hotel
Malahide, Co. Dublin
Tel: 01-845 0000 ....Page 271
Arrangements with Golf Courses:
Portmarnock GC, Malahide GC, The Island GC, Swords GC, St. Margarets, Royal Dublin
Green Fees from:*€60.00*
Facilities available:
AT AB TC

Gresham (The)
Dublin City, Co. Dublin
Tel: 01-874 6881 ....Page 252
Arrangements with Golf Courses:
Royal Dublin, Portmarnock, St. Margaret's, The Island, St. Anne's, Malahide
Facilities available:
GC AT AB CH

Lucan Spa Hotel
Lucan, Co. Dublin
Tel: 01-628 0494 ....Page 270
Arrangements with Golf Courses:
Lucan Golf Club
Facilities available:
AT AB PG

Redbank House Guesthouse & Restaurant
Skerries, Co. Dublin
Tel: 01-849 1005 ....Page 272
Arrangements with Golf Courses:
Skerries, Laytown, Bettystown, Baltray, Portmarnock, St. Margaret's, Donabate
Green Fees from:*€40.00*
Facilities available:
GP TA GC AT AB CH TC PG HC

Rochestown Lodge Hotel & Replenish Day Spa
Dun Laoghaire, Co. Dublin
Tel: 01-285 3555 ....Page 269
Arrangements with Golf Courses:
Powerscourt GC, Woodbrook GC, Druids Glen GC, The European GC
Green Fees from:*€95.00*
Facilities available:
GP AT AB CH PG

Waterside House Hotel & Signal Restaurant
Donabate, Co. Dublin
Tel: 01-843 6153 ....Page 234
Arrangements with Golf Courses:
Donabate, Turvey, Beaverstown, Balcarrick, The Island Links, St. Margaret's
Green Fees from:*€35.00*
Facilities available:
GP TA GC AT AB CH TC PG HC

Co. Kildare

Glenroyal Hotel (The)
Maynooth, Co. Kildare
Tel: 01-629 0909 ....Page 276
Arrangements with Golf Courses:
Knockanally, K Club, Killeen, Castlewarden, Bodenstown, Citywest, Carton
Facilities available:
GP AT AB

Maudlins House Hotel
Naas, Co. Kildare
Tel: 045-896999 ....Page 277
Arrangements with Golf Courses:
Naas Golf Club, The Heritage Killenard, Craddockstown Golf Club, Knockanally Golf Club, Palmerstown House, K-Club, Straffan
Green Fees from:*€50.00*
Facilities available:
GP TA AT AB CH TC PG HC

Westgrove Hotel
Clane, Co. Kildare
Tel: 045-989900 ....Page 274
Arrangements with Golf Courses:
Millicent GC, Killeen GC, Craddockstown GC, Knockanally GC, K Club, Carton House.
Facilities available:
GP AT AB CH PG HC

Co. Laois

Heritage Golf & Spa Resort (The)
Killenard, Co. Laois
Tel: 057-864 5500 ....Page 280
Golf Course(s) On Site:
1 x 18 Hole Golf Course(s)
1 x 9 Hole Golf Course(s)
Green Fees from:*€60.00*
Facilities available:
GP TA GC AT AB CH TC PG HC

Killeshin (The)
Portlaoise, Co. Laois
Tel: 057-863 1200 ....Page 280
Arrangements with Golf Courses:
Abbeyleix, Rathdowney, Heath, Mountrath, Portarlington
Green Fees from:*€25.00*
Facilities available:
GP AT AB TC PG

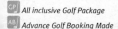

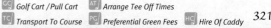

GP *All inclusive Golf Package* TA *Tuition Available* GC *Golf Cart / Pull Cart* AT *Arrange Tee Off Times*
AB *Advance Golf Booking Made* CH *Hire Of Clubs* TC *Transport To Course* PG *Preferential Green Fees* HC *Hire Of Caddy*

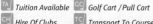

Co. Longford

Annaly Hotel
Longford Town, Co. Longford
Tel: 043-334 2058 ....Page 282
Arrangements with Golf Courses:
Longford, Ballyconnell, Glasson, Mullingar, Roscommon
Facilities available:
GP TA GC AT AB CH TC PG HC

Longford Arms Hotel
Longford Town, Co. Longford
Tel: 043-334 6296 ....Page 282
Arrangements with Golf Courses:
Longford, Glasson, Ballyconnell, Carrick-on-Shannon, Roscommon, Mullingar
Facilities available:
AT AB TC

Co. Louth

Ballymascanlon House Hotel
Dundalk, Co. Louth
Tel: 042-935 8200 ....Page 285
Golf Course(s) On Site:
1 x 18 Hole Golf Course(s)
Green Fees from: *€25.00*
Facilities available:
GP GC AT AB CH TC PG

d (The)
Drogheda, Co. Louth
Tel: 041-987 7700 ....Page 284
Arrangements with Golf Courses:
Baltray (County Louth), Seapoint, Bettystown & Laytown, Dundalk
Green Fees from: *€40.00*
Facilities available:
GP AB TC

Co. Meath

Bellinter House
Navan, Co. Meath
Tel: 046-903 0900 ....Page 290
Arrangements with Golf Courses:
Royal Tara, Headford Kells, Killeen Castle
Green Fees from: *€50.00*
Facilities available:
TA GC AT AB CH TC PG HC

Headfort Arms
Kells, Co. Meath
Tel: 0818-222 800 ....Page 288
Arrangements with Golf Courses:
Headfort Golf Course - 36 Holes, Royal Tara, Navan Race Course, Delvin Castle, Ballinlough Castle
Green Fees from: *€35.00*
Facilities available:
GP TA GC AT AB TC PG HC

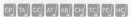

Knightsbrook Hotel Spa & Golf Resort
Trim, Co. Meath
Tel: 046-948 2100 ....Page 292
Golf Course(s) On Site:
1 x 18 Hole Golf Course(s)
Arrangements with Golf Courses:
Kileen Castle, Headfort Co. Meath, Rathcore, Royal Tara, Co. Louth
Green Fees from: *€30.00*
Facilities available:
GP TA GC AT AB CH TC PG HC

Station House Hotel and Signal Restaurant
Kilmessan, Co. Meath
Tel: 046-902 5239 ....Page 289
Arrangements with Golf Courses:
Royal Tara, Blackbush, Headfort, The K Club, The Island Links, Carton House
Green Fees from: *€35.00*
Facilities available:
GP TA GC AT AB CH PG HC

Trim Castle Hotel
Trim, Co. Meath
Tel: 046-948 3000 ....Page 292
Arrangements with Golf Courses:
Royal Tara, Headfort Old and New, Rathcore
Green Fees from: *€45.00*
Facilities available:
GP AT AB TC PG

Co. Monaghan

Nuremore Hotel & Country Club
Carrickmacross, Co. Monaghan
Tel: 042-966 1438 ....Page 292
Golf Course(s) On Site:
1 x 18 Hole Golf Course(s)
Arrangements with Golf Courses:
Baltray, Greenore, Seapoint, Dundalk, Concra Wood
Green Fees from: *€35.00*
Facilities available:
GP TA GC AT AB CH TC PG HC

Shirley Arms Hotel
Carrickmacross, Co. Monaghan
Tel: 042-967 3100 ....Page 293
Arrangements with Golf Courses:
Manann Castle Carrickmacross, Concra Wood Castleblaney
Green Fees from: *€25.00*
Facilities available:
GP TC

Co. Offaly

Bridge House Hotel
Tullamore, Co. Offaly
Tel: 057-932 5600 ....Page 295
Arrangements with Golf Courses:
Esker Hills & Tullamore Golf Club both 5 minutes away, Castle Barna Golf Club 12km away, Glasson, Virtual Reality Golf Facility on site
Green Fees from: *€35.00*
Facilities available:
GP TA GC AT AB CH TC PG HC

County Arms Hotel & Leisure Club
Birr, Co. Offaly
Tel: 057-912 0791 ....Page 294
Arrangements with Golf Courses:
Birr, Portumna, Roscrea, Esker Hills, Castle Barna, Nenagh
Green Fees from: *€20.00*
Facilities available:
GP TA GC AT AB CH TC PG HC

Tullamore Court Hotel Conference & Leisure Centre
Tullamore, Co. Offaly
Tel: 057-934 6666 ....Page 296
Arrangements with Golf Courses:
Tullamore, Esker Hills, Castle Barna, Mount Temple, Glasson, Birr, The Heritage at Killenard
Green Fees from: *€35.00*
Facilities available:
GP TA GC AT AB CH TC PG HC

Co. Westmeath

Glasson Hotel & Golf Club
Athlone, Co. Westmeath
Tel: 090-648 5120 ....Page 296
Golf Course(s) On Site:
1 x 18 Hole Golf Course(s)
Arrangements with Golf Courses:
Glasson Golf Hotel and Country Club, Athlone Golf Club, Mount Temple Golf Club, Esker Hills, Moate Golf Club, Tullamore
Green Fees from: *€60.00*
Facilities available:
GP TA GC AT AB CH TC PG HC

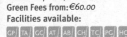

Greville Arms Hotel
Mullingar, Co. Westmeath
Tel: 044-934 8563 ....Page 300
Arrangements with Golf Courses:
Mullingar, Glasson, Mount Temple, Tullamore, Longford, Esker Hills
Green Fees from: *€30.00*
Facilities available:
GP TA GC AT AB CH TC PG HC

Prince of Wales Hotel
Athlone, Co. Westmeath
Tel: 090-647 6666 ....Page 297
Arrangements with Golf Courses:
Mount Temple, Athlone, Glasson, Esker Hills
Green Fees from: *€25.00*
Facilities available:
GP GC AT AB CH TC PG

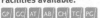

Sheraton Athlone Hotel
Athlone, Co. Westmeath
Tel: 090-645 1000 ....Page 298
Arrangements with Golf Courses:
Glasson Golf Course, Athlone Golf Course, Moate Golf Course, Mount Temple, Esker Hills
Green Fees from: *€60.00*
Facilities available:
AT AB PC

Co. Wicklow

Avon Rí
Blessington, Co. Wicklow
Tel: 045-900670 ....Page 304
Arrangements with Golf Courses:
Tulfarris, Citywest
Green Fees from: *€60.00*
Facilities available:
GP TA GC AT AB CH TC PG HC

Chester Beatty Inn
Ashford, Co. Wicklow
Tel: 0404-40206 ....Page 304
Arrangements with Golf Courses:
Druid's Glen, Woodenbridge, Blainroe, European, Powerscourt, Wicklow Golf Club
Green Fees from: *€35.00*
Facilities available:
GP TA GC AT AB CH TC PG HC

Glendalough Hotel
Glendalough, Co. Wicklow
Tel: 0404-45135 ....Page 307
Arrangements with Golf Courses:
The European Club, Woodenbridge, Charlesland, Druid's Glen, Blainroe, Roundwood
Green Fees from: *€35.00*
Facilities available:
GP GC AT AB CH TC

Martello Hotel (The)
Bray, Co. Wicklow
Tel: 01-286 8000 ....Page 306
Arrangements with Golf Courses:
Bray, Woodbrook, Old Conna, Powerscourt, Greystones, Druid's Glen
Green Fees from: *€50.00*
Facilities available:
AT AB CH TC PG

Rathsallagh House, Golf and Country Club
Dunlavin, Co. Wicklow
Tel: 045-403112......................Page 306
Golf Course(s) On Site:
1 x 18 Hole Golf Course(s)
Arrangements with Golf Courses:
Mount Juliet, Druid's Glen, Powerscourt, Portmarnock, Mount Wolseley, The Heritage
Green Fees from: *€55.00*
Facilities available:
GP TA GC AT AB CH TC PG HC

Summerhill House Hotel
Enniskerry, Co. Wicklow
Tel: 01-286 7928 ....Page 307
Arrangements with Golf Courses:
Powerscourt, Druid's Glen, Kilternan, Old Conna
Green Fees from: *€35.00*
Facilities available:
GP TA GC AT AB CH TC PG

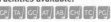

The Ritz-Carlton, Powerscourt
Enniskerry, Co. Wicklow
Tel: 01-274 8888 ....Page 307
Golf Course(s) On Site:
2 x 18 Hole Golf Course(s)
Green Fees from: *€60.00*
Facilities available:
GP TA GC AT AB CH TC PG HC

Did you know?

Year round golfing in Ireland is perfectly feasible - provided you have suitable wet weather gear! - but conditions are best between April and October.

During these months you can expect to be able to play up to 7pm in the evening at least, with many courses playable until 10pm or 11pm. During the months of June-August you may even fit two games into a single day.

For best value, aim to play as early as possible in the day and preferrably on a week day. In many golf clubs there are few if any tee times available to visitors at weekends during the summer, so if you must play at the weekend book well in advance.

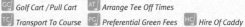

GP *All inclusive Golf Package* TA *Tuition Available* GC *Golf Cart / Pull Cart* AT *Arrange Tee Off Times*
AB *Advance Golf Booking Made* CH *Hire Of Clubs* TC *Transport To Course* PG *Preferential Green Fees* HC *Hire Of Caddy*

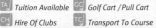

One Source
Endless Possibilities
irelandhotels.com
Official Website of the Irish Hotels Federation
IRISH
HOTELS
FEDERATION

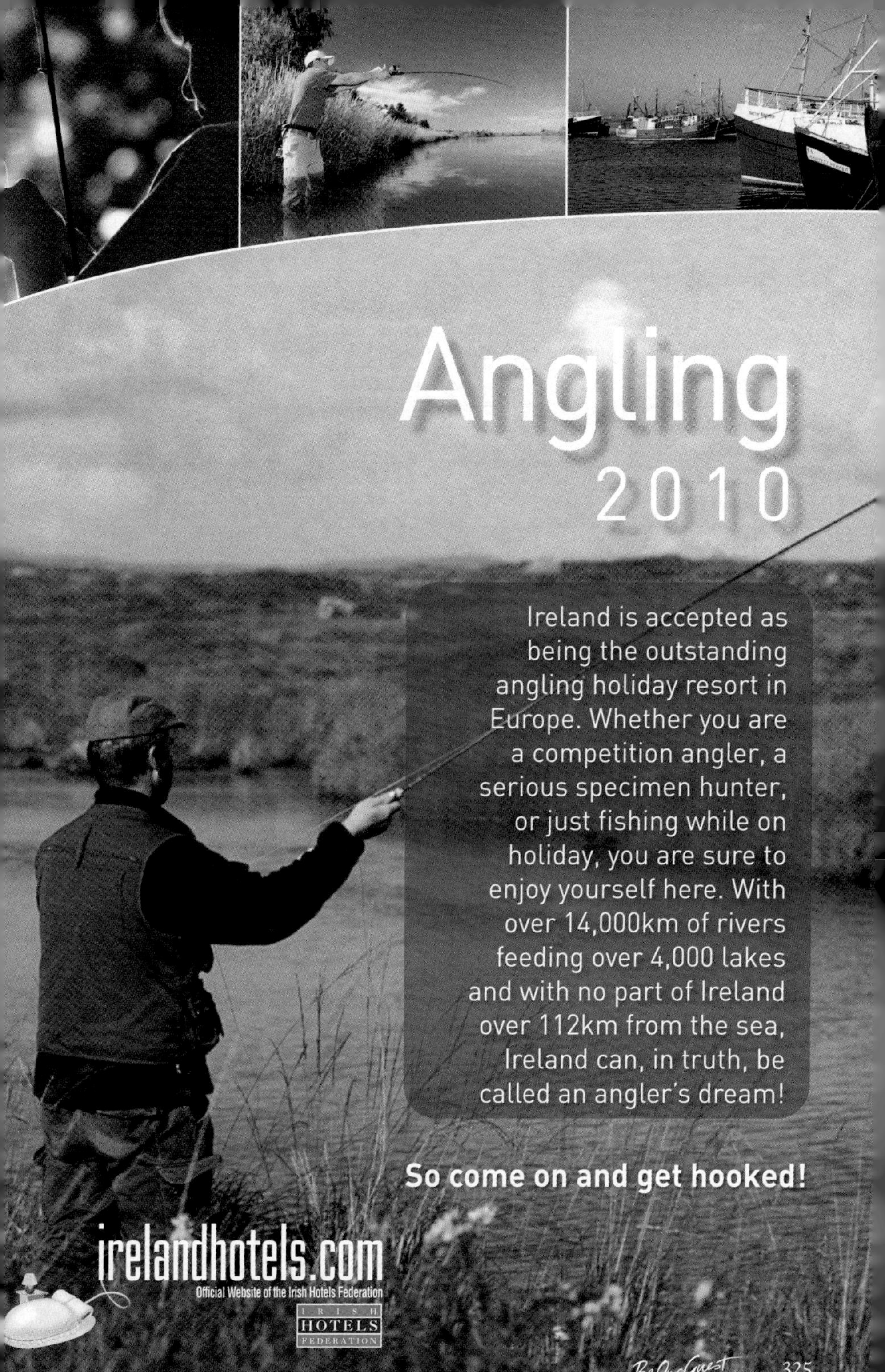
Angling
2010
Ireland is accepted as being the outstanding angling holiday resort in Europe. Whether you are a competition angler, a serious specimen hunter, or just fishing while on holiday, you are sure to enjoy yourself here. With over 14,000km of rivers feeding over 4,000 lakes and with no part of Ireland over 112km from the sea, Ireland can, in truth, be called an angler's dream!
So come on and get hooked!
irelandhotels.com
Official Website of the Irish Hotels Federation
IRISH HOTELS FEDERATION

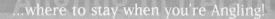

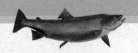

...where to stay when you're Angling!

We invite you to sample the fishing, the countryside and the friendship of the Irish people and then to stay in some of Ireland's most charming accommodation. We have listed a range of hotels and guesthouses which are either situated with or near angling facilities. Your host will assist you in arranging your angling itinerary. A full description of the hotels and guesthouses may be seen by consulting the relevant page number below.

Listings are by Region, County, Premises Name in alphabetical order.

Ireland South

Co. Cork

Bayview Hotel
Ballycotton, Co. Cork
Tel: 021-464 6746 ....Page 37
Sea Angling:
Cod, Pollock, Shark, Mackerel
Facilities available:
BH DR PL GI FR

Celtic Ross Hotel Conference & Leisure Centre
Rosscarbery, Co. Cork
Tel: 023-884 8722 ....Page 60
Coarse Angling:
Bream, Roach, Tench
Game Angling:
Trout, Salmon
Sea Angling:
Cod, Shark, Wrasse, Flat Fish
Facilities available:
BT BH DR PL GI FR PR

Commodore Hotel
Cobh, Co. Cork
Tel: 021-481 1277......................Page 45
Sea Angling:
Ling, Cod, Pollock, Conger, Blue Shark
Facilities available:
BT BH DR PL FR

Coolcower House
Macroom, Co. Cork
Tel: 026-41695..........................Page 59
Coarse Angling:
Bream, Rudd, Pike, Perch
Game Angling:
Trout
Facilities available:
BH DR PL TR FR PR

Fota Island Hotel & Spa
Fota Island, Co. Cork
Tel: 021-467 3000 ....Page 54
Sea Angling:
Blue Shark, Yellow Fin Tuna, Pollock, Wrasse, Cod, Mackerel, Conger Eel
Facilities available:
BT BH PL TR PR

Garryvoe Hotel
Shanagarry, Co. Cork
Tel: 021-464 6718 ....Page 62
Sea Angling:
Cod, Shark, Mackerel, Pollock
Facilities available:
BT BH DR PL GI TR FR PR

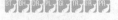

Munster Arms Hotel
Bandon, Co. Cork
Tel: 023-884 1562 ....Page 39
Game Angling:
Salmon, Sea Trout, Brown Trout
Facilities available:
DR PL GI FR PR

Trident Hotel
Kinsale, Co. Cork
Tel: 021-477 9300 ....Page 58
Game Angling:
Salmon, Brown Trout
Sea Angling:
Shark, Ling, Conger Eel, Mackerel, Pollock, Sea Trout
Facilities available:
BT BH DR PL GI FR

Walter Raleigh Hotel
Youghal, Co. Cork
Tel: 024-92011..........................Page 63
Sea Angling:
Pollock, Whiting, Ling, Cod
Facilities available:
BT BH DR PL FR PR

WatersEdge Hotel
Cobh, Co. Cork
Tel: 021-481 5566 ....Page 45
Sea Angling:
Plaice, Cod, Monkfish, Bass, Turbot
Facilities available:
BT BH PL FR

Co. Kerry

Ard-Na-Sidhe Country House
Caragh Lake, Co. Kerry
Tel: 066-976 9105 ....Page 64
Game Angling:
Salmon, Trout
Facilities available:
BT BH PL GI FR PR

Barr na Sraide Inn
Dingle (An Daingean), Co. Kerry
Tel: 066-915 1331......................Page 6
Sea Angling:
Pollock, Garfish, Blue Shark, Tope, Dogfish, Ling, Whiting, Ray
Facilities available:
BT BH

Brookhaven Country House
Waterville, Co. Kerry
Tel: 066-947 4431 ....Page 9
Game Angling:
Salmon, Sea Trout
Sea Angling:
Bass, Pollock, Cod, Shark, Mackerel, Whiting
Facilities available:
BT BH DR PL GI FR PR

Butler Arms Hotel
Waterville, Co. Kerry
Tel: 066-947 4144 ....Page 9
Game Angling:
Salmon, Trout
Sea Angling:
Bass, Pollock, Cod, Shark, Mackerel, Whiting
Facilities available:
BT BH DR PL GI FR PR

Dingle Skellig Hotel & Peninsula Spa
Dingle (An Daingean), Co. Kerry
Tel: 066-915 0200 ....Page 6
Sea Angling:
Pollock, Garfish, Blue Shark, Tope, Dogfish, Ling, Whiting, Ray
Facilities available:
BT BH DR PL FR

Harbour House & Leisure Centre
Castlegregory, Co. Kerry
Tel: 066-713 9292 ....Page 6
Game Angling:
Salmon, Brown Trout, White Trout
Sea Angling:
Cod, Ray, Mackerel, Shark, etc
Facilities available:
BT BH DR PL FR

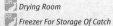

BT *Bait & Tackle* · BH *Boats For Hire* · DR *Drying Room* · PL *Packed Lunches Available On Requ*
GI *Gillie* · TR *Tackle Room* · FR *Freezer For Storage Of Catch* · PR *Permits Required*

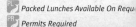

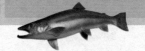

Hotel Dunloe Castle
Killarney, Co. Kerry
Tel: 064-664 4111 ....Page 85
Game Angling:
Salmon, Trout
Facilities available:
BT BH PL GI FR

Inveraray Farm Guesthouse
Killarney, Co. Kerry
Tel: 064-664 4224 ....Page 86
Game Angling:
Brown Trout, Salmon
Sea Angling:
Sea Trout
Facilities available:
BH DR PL TR FR

Killarney Royal Hotel
Killarney, Co. Kerry
Tel: 064-663 1853 ....Page 88
Game Angling:
Brown Trout, Salmon
Facilities available:
BT BH DR PL GI TR FR PR

Lake Hotel
Killarney, Co. Kerry
Tel: 064-663 1035 ....Page 89
Game Angling:
Salmon, Brown Trout
Facilities available:
BT BH DR PL GI FR PR

Sheen Falls Lodge
Kenmare, Co. Kerry
Tel: 064-664 1600 ....Page 74
Game Angling:
Salmon, Trout
Sea Angling:
Shark, Mackerel, Pollock, Skate, Conger Eel, Dogfish
Facilities available:
BT BH DR PL GI TR FR PR

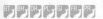

Smugglers Inn
Waterville, Co. Kerry
Tel: 066-947 4330 ....Page 98
Game Angling:
Salmon, Sea Trout, Brown Trout
Sea Angling:
Cod, Bass, Mackerel, Tuna, Plaice, Sole
Facilities available:
BT BH DR PL GI FR

Sneem Hotel
Sneem, Co. Kerry
Tel: 064-667 5100 ....Page 94
Game Angling:
Rainbow Trout, Brown Trout, Salmon
Sea Angling:
Conger, Pollock, Ray
Facilities available:
BT BH DR PL GI TR PR

Co. Kilkenny

Kilkenny River Court
Kilkenny City, Co. Kilkenny
Tel: 056-772 3388 ....Page 102
Coarse Angling:
Shad, Bream
Game Angling:
Trout, Salmon
Facilities available:
BT BH DR PL GI TR FR PR

Lyrath Estate Hotel, Spa & Convention Centre
Kilkenny City, Co. Kilkenny
Tel: 056-776 0088 ....Page 103
Coarse Angling:
Shad, Bream
Game Angling:
Salmon, Trout
Facilities available:
BT BH DR PL GI TR FR PR

Mount Juliet
Thomastown, Co. Kilkenny
Tel: 056-777 3000 ....Page 105
Game Angling:
Salmon, Trout
Facilities available:
BT DR PL GI TR FR

Waterside
Graiguenamanagh, Co. Kilkenny
Tel: 059-972 4246 ....Page 98
Coarse Angling:
Bream, Dace, Pike, Perch, Rudd, Shad, Roach
Game Angling:
Trout, Salmon
Facilities available:
PL

Co. Tipperary

Cahir House Hotel
Cahir, Co. Tipperary
Tel: 052-744 3000 ....Page 106
Coarse Angling:
Perch, Pike
Game Angling:
Trout, Salmon
Facilities available:
PL GI FR PR

Cashel Palace Hotel
Cashel, Co. Tipperary
Tel: 062-62707........................Page 107
Coarse Angling:
Perch
Game Angling:
Salmon, Brown Trout, Grilse
Facilities available:
BT BH DR PL GI TR FR PR

Kilcoran Lodge Hotel, Lodges & Leisure Centre
Cahir, Co. Tipperary
Tel: 052-744 1288 ....Page 106
Game Angling:
Salmon, Brown Trout
Facilities available:
BT BH DR PL GI PR

Co. Waterford

Lismore House Hotel
Lismore, Co. Waterford
Tel: 058-72966........................Page 116
Game Angling:
Salmon, Sea Trout
Facilities available:
BT DR PL GI FR PR

Ireland West

Co. Clare

Falls Hotel & Spa
Ennistymon, Co. Clare
Tel: 065-707 1004 ....Page 146
Coarse Angling:
Bream, Tench, Pike
Facilities available:
PL

BT *Bait & Tackle* BH *Boats For Hire* DR *Drying Room* PL *Packed Lunches Available On Request*
GI *Gillie* TR *Tackle Room* FR *Freezer For Storage Of Catch* PR *Permits Required*

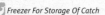

Co. Donegal

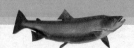

Downings Bay Hotel
Downings, Co. Donegal
Tel: 074-915 5586 .... Page 158
Sea Angling:
Pollock, Mackerel, Tuna, Ling, Skate, Cod, Haddock
Facilities available:
BH PL

Highlands Hotel
Glenties, Co. Donegal
Tel: 074-955 1111 .... Page 159
Game Angling:
Salmon, Trout
Sea Angling:
Mackerel, Pollock, Ling
Facilities available:
DR PL FR PR

Solis Lough Eske Castle
Donegal Town, Co. Donegal
Tel: 074-972 5100 .... Page 158
Coarse Angling:
Bream, Roach, Pike
Game Angling:
Salmon, Sea Trout, Grilse, Char, Brown Trout
Sea Angling:
Mackerel, Pollock
Facilities available:
BT BH DR PL GI FR PR

Co. Galway

Ballynahinch Castle Hotel
Ballynahinch, Co. Galway
Tel: 095-31006 .... Page 165
Game Angling:
Salmon, Brown Trout, Sea Trout
Sea Angling:
Charter Available
Facilities available:
BT BH DR PL GI TR FR PR

Ben View House
Clifden, Co. Galway
Tel: 095-21256 .... Page 168
Game Angling:
Salmon, Trout
Sea Angling:
Cod, Herring, Whiting, Pollock, Plaice
Facilities available:
BT BH DR FR PR

Claregalway Hotel
Galway City, Co. Galway
Tel: 091-738300 .... Page 172
Coarse Angling:
Pike
Game Angling:
Brown Trout, Salmon
Facilities available:
BT DR PL GI TR FR PR

Corrib Wave Guest House
Oughterard, Co. Galway
Tel: 091-552147 .... Page 184
Coarse Angling:
Pike, Perch
Game Angling:
Brown Trout, Salmon
Facilities available:
BT BH DR PL GI TR FR

Doonmore Hotel
Inishbofin Island, Co. Galway
Tel: 095-45814 .... Page 181
Sea Angling:
Pollock, Mackerel, Plaice
Facilities available:
BH DR PL FR

Fairhill House Hotel
Clonbur (An Fháirche), Co. Galway
Tel: 094-954 6176 .... Page 170
Coarse Angling:
Pike, Roach, Perch, Bream, Eel
Game Angling:
Salmon, Wild Brown Trout
Sea Angling:
Dogfish, Cod, Ray, Shark, Pollock
Facilities available:
BT BH DR PL GI TR FR PR

Inishbofin House Hotel
Inishbofin Island, Co. Galway
Tel: 095-45809 .... Page 181
Sea Angling:
Pollock, Ray, Plaice, Mackerel, Gurnard, Tope
Facilities available:
BT BH DR PL FR

Park Lodge Hotel
Spiddal, Co. Galway
Tel: 091-553159 .... Page 186
Sea Angling:
Mackerel, Cod, Pollock
Facilities available:
DR PL

Shannon Oaks Hotel & Country Club
Portumna, Co. Galway
Tel: 090-974 1777 .... Page 185
Game Angling:
Bream, Roach, Tench, Perch, Pike
Facilities available:
BT BH PL GI FR PR

Co. Limerick

Fitzgeralds Woodlands House Hotel & Spa
Adare, Co. Limerick
Tel: 061-605100 .... Page 190
Coarse Angling:
Pike
Game Angling:
Trout, Salmon
Facilities available:
BT BH DR PL GI FR PR

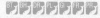

Co. Mayo

Ballina Manor Hotel
Ballina, Co. Mayo
Tel: 059-93 3243 .... Page 196
Game Angling:
Salmon, Trout
Facilities available:
BT DR PL GI TR FR PR

Castlecourt Hotel Spa, Leisure, Conference
Westport, Co. Mayo
Tel: 098-55088 .... Page 203
Coarse Angling:
Pike, Perch, Roach, Bream, Tench, Hybrids
Game Angling:
Trout, Salmon
Sea Angling:
Cod, Shark, Pollock, Plaice, Dogfish, Conger Eels, Whiting, Monkfish
Facilities available:
BT BH DR PL GI FR PR

Courthouse (The)
Ballyhaunis, Co. Mayo
Tel: 094-963 0068 .... Page 198
Coarse Angling:
Pike, Perch, Roach
Game Angling:
Salmon, Trout
Sea Angling:
Pollock, Ling, Mackerel, Shark
Facilities available:
BT PL FR

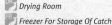

BT *Bait & Tackle* — BH *Boats For Hire* — DR *Drying Room* — PL *Packed Lunches Available On Reque*
GI *Gillie* — TR *Tackle Room* — FR *Freezer For Storage Of Catch* — PR *Permits Required*

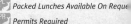

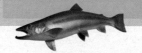

Healys Restaurant & Fishing Lodge
Pontoon, Co. Mayo
Tel: 094-925 6443 ....Page 201
Coarse Angling:
Pike, Perch
Game Angling:
Salmon, Brown Trout, Rainbow Trout, Sea Trout
Sea Angling:
Blue Shark, Pollock, Mackerel, Cod, Sole, Brill, Turbot, Plaice, Conger Eel
Facilities available:
BT BH DR PL GI TR FR PR

Hotel Westport
Westport, Co. Mayo
Tel: 098-25122.......................Page 204
Coarse Angling:
Pike, Perch, Bream, Eel, Roach, Tench
Game Angling:
Salmon, Trout
Sea Angling:
Cod, Whiting, Sea Trout, Mackerel, Monkfish
Facilities available:
BT BH DR PL GI TR FR PR

Westport Plaza Hotel Spa, Leisure, Conference
Westport, Co. Mayo
Tel: 098-51166.......................Page 205
Coarse Angling:
Pike, Perch, Roach, Bream, Tench, Hybrids
Sea Angling:
Cod, Shark, Pollock, Plaice, Dogfish, Conger Eels, Whiting, Monkfish
Facilities available:
BT BH DR PL GI FR PR

Co. Sligo

Radisson Blu Hotel & Spa Sligo
Sligo Town, Co. Sligo
Tel: 071-914 0008 ....Page 209
Coarse Angling:
Bream, Pike, Perch, Hybrids
Game Angling:
Salmon, Sea Trout, Trout
Sea Angling:
Cod, Ling, Mackerel, Pollock, Sea Bass, Shark
Facilities available:
PL

Northern Ireland

Co. Fermanagh

Killyhevlin Hotel
Enniskillen, Co. Fermanagh
Tel: 028-6632 3481 ....Page 223
Coarse Angling:
Perch, Roach, Bream, Pike
Facilities available:
PL PR

Dublin & Ireland East

Co. Cavan

Lakeside Manor Hotel
Virginia, Co. Cavan
Tel: 049-854 8200 ....Page 233
Coarse Angling:
Bream, Hybrids, Roach, Perch, Pike
Game Angling:
Trout
Facilities available:
BT BH DR PL TR FR

Co. Kildare

Maudlins House Hotel
Naas, Co. Kildare
Tel: 045-896999 ....Page 277
Coarse Angling:
Roach, Perch, Rudd, Pike, Tench
Game Angling:
Rainbow Trout, Brown Trout, Salmon
Facilities available:
PL FR PR

Co. Meath

Bellinter House
Navan, Co. Meath
Tel: 046-903 0900 ....Page 290
Coarse Angling:
Dry Fly Brown Trout
Facilities available:
BT PL GI

Co. Westmeath

Glasson Hotel & Golf Club
Athlone, Co. Westmeath
Tel: 090-648 5120 ....Page 296
Coarse Angling:
Pike, Perch, Roach, Bream
Game Angling:
Brown Trout
Facilities available:
BT BH DR PL GI FR PR

Newbury Hotel
Mullingar, Co. Westmeath
Tel: 044-934 2888 ....Page 302
Coarse Angling:
Pike, Roach, Tench, Rudd
Game Angling:
Trout
Facilities available:
BT BH DR PL GI TR FR

Prince of Wales Hotel
Athlone, Co. Westmeath
Tel: 090-647 6666 ....Page 297
Coarse Angling:
Pike,Brown Trout, Tench, Roach, Bream
Facilities available:
BT BH PL GI FR

Co. Wicklow

Avon Rí
Blessington, Co. Wicklow
Tel: 045-900670 ....Page 304
Coarse Angling:
Pike, Perch, Roach
Game Angling:
Trout
Facilities available:
BH PL GI FR PR

Did you know?

Ireland is recognised as being the outstanding angling destination in Europe. The vast variety & quality of our fishing has given the country a reputation of which we are justly proud.

The Irish climate is well suited to sport angling. It is temperate and kind to the angler with moderate summers, mild winters and adequate rainfall throughout the year.

BT *Bait & Tackle* BH *Boats For Hire* DR *Drying Room* PL *Packed Lunches Available On Request*
GI *Gillie* TR *Tackle Room* FR *Freezer For Storage Of Catch* PR *Permits Required*

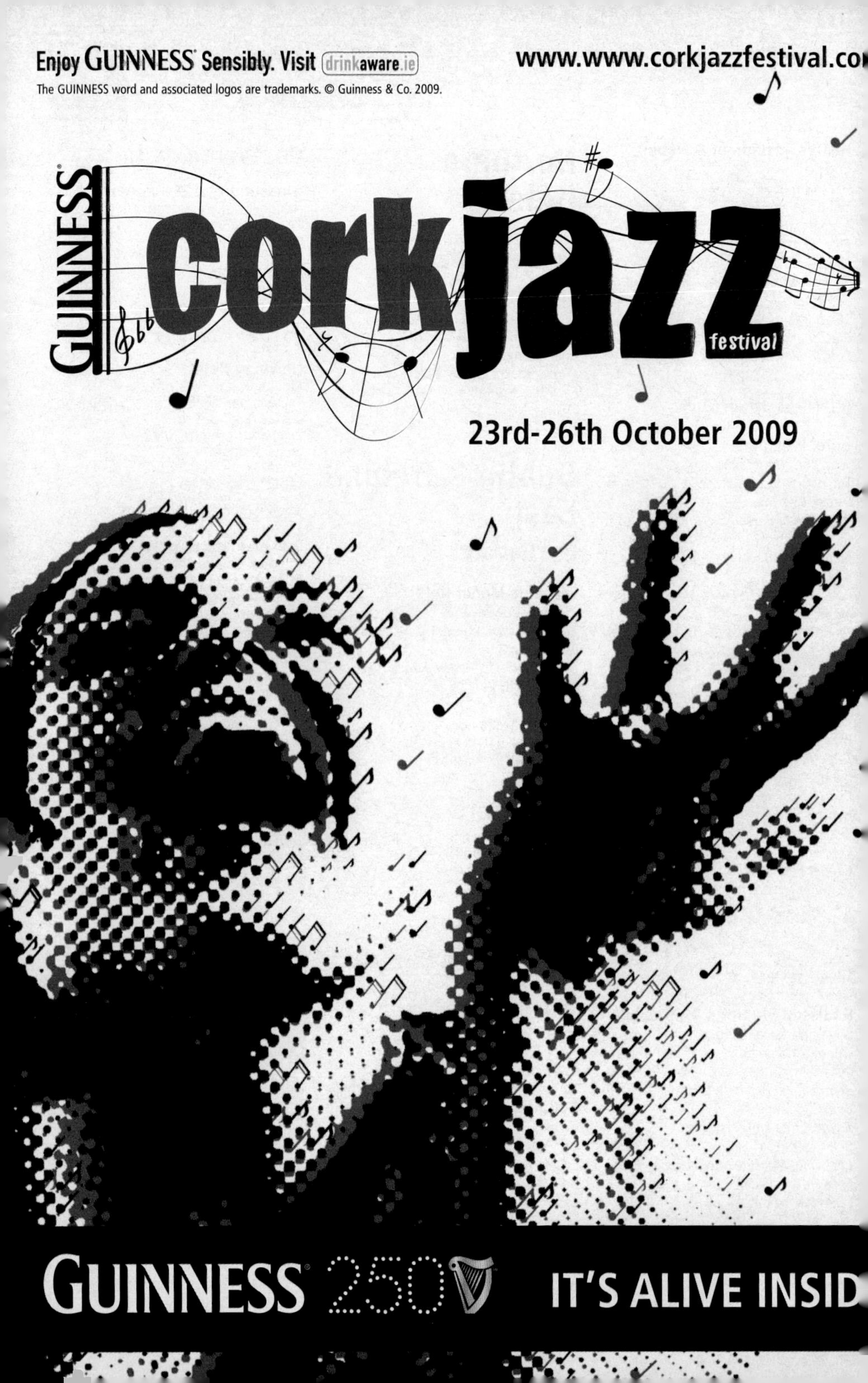
Enjoy GUINNESS Sensibly. Visit drinkaware.ie
The GUINNESS word and associated logos are trademarks. © Guinness & Co. 2009.
www.www.corkjazzfestival.co
GUINNESS
corkjazz
festival
23rd-26th October 2009
GUINNESS 250
IT'S ALIVE INSID

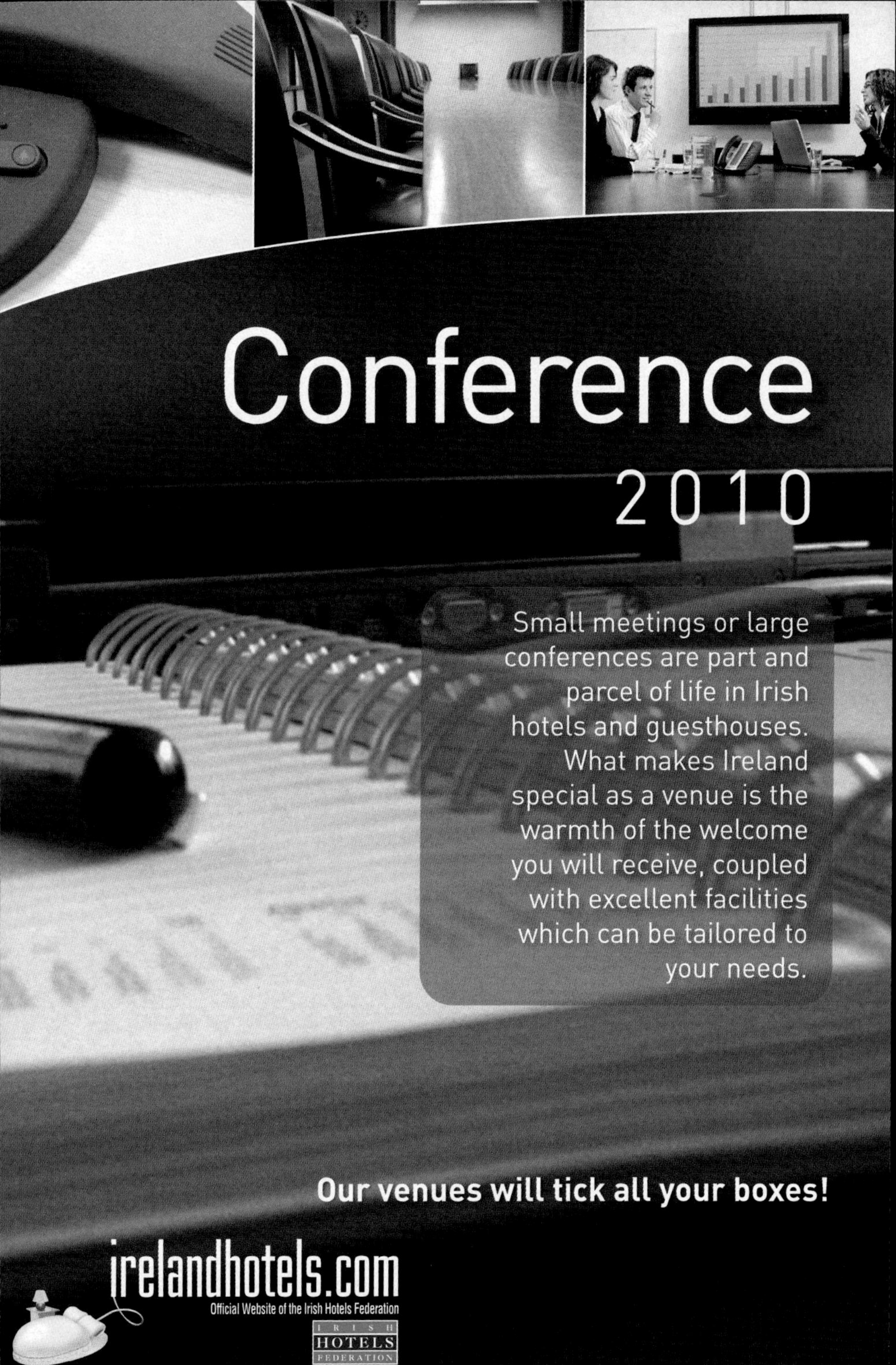
Conference
2010
Small meetings or large conferences are part and parcel of life in Irish hotels and guesthouses. What makes Ireland special as a venue is the warmth of the welcome you will receive, coupled with excellent facilities which can be tailored to your needs.
Our venues will tick all your boxes!
irelandhotels.com
Official Website of the Irish Hotels Federation
IRISH HOTELS FEDERATION

We will be glad to see you and work with you to make your meeting or conference a successful one. Choose from the wide selection of special facilities throughout the country as shown here. A full description of the hotels and guesthouses may be seen by consulting the relevant page number below.

Listings are by Region, County, Premises Name in alphabetical order.

Ireland South

Co. Carlow

Lord Bagenal Inn
Leighlinbridge, Co. Carlow
Tel: 059-977 4000 ....Page 36
Contact Person:
Sue Baldwin
Seating Capacity of Meeting Rooms:
+300: 1 -50: 4
Facilities available:
BO AC AVO

Mount Wolseley Hotel Spa & Country Club
Tullow, Co. Carlow
Tel: 059-918 0100 ....Page 36
Contact Person:
Anne Marie Hayes
Seating Capacity of Meeting Rooms:
+500: 1 +200: 1 +100: 1 +50: 2 -50: 6
Facilities available:
BO AC IEH AVO

Talbot Hotel Carlow
Carlow Town, Co. Carlow
Tel: 059-915 3000....................Page 35
Contact Person:
Niamh Whelan
Seating Capacity of Meeting Rooms:
+300: 1 +100: 1 +50: 1 -50: 2
Facilities available:
BO AC IEH AVO AVH

Co. Cork

Abbey Hotel
Ballyvourney, Co. Cork
Tel: 026-45324........................Page 38
Contact Person:
John Buckley
Seating Capacity of Meeting Rooms:
+200: 1 +50: 1 -50: 1
Facilities available:
AC AVO

Actons Hotel
Kinsale, Co. Cork
Tel: 021-477 9900....................Page 56
Contact Person:
Mary Kirby
Seating Capacity of Meeting Rooms:
+300: 1 -50: 2
Facilities available:
BO AC IEH AVH

Blarney Golf Resort
Blarney, Co. Cork
Tel: 021-438 4477....................Page 40
Contact Person:
Caroline Nyhan
Seating Capacity of Meeting Rooms:
+200: 1 +100: 1 +50: 2 -50: 5
Facilities available:
BO AC IEH AVO AVH

Celtic Ross Hotel Conference & Leisure Centre
Rosscarbery, Co. Cork
Tel: 023-884 8722 ....Page 60
Contact Person:
Steven Ward
Seating Capacity of Meeting Rooms:
+200: 1 +50: 1 -50: 1
Facilities available:
BO AC IEH AVH

Commons Inn
Cork City, Co. Cork
Tel: 021-421 0300 ....Page 48
Contact Person:
Ashley Colson
Seating Capacity of Meeting Rooms:
+300: 1 +50: 1 -50: 3
Facilities available:
BO AC AVO

Cork International Airport Hotel
Cork Airport, Co. Cork
Tel: 021-454 9800....................Page 46
Contact Person:
Carmel Lonergan
Seating Capacity of Meeting Rooms:
+300: 1 +200: 1 +100: 1 +50: 4 -50: 10
Facilities available:
BO AC AVO

Fernhill House Hotel
Clonakilty, Co. Cork
Tel: 023-883 3258 ....Page 44
Contact Person:
Teresa O'Neill
Seating Capacity of Meeting Rooms:
+300: 1 +50: 2 -50: 3
Facilities available:
BO AC IEH AVO

Fota Island Hotel & Spa
Fota Island, Co. Cork
Tel: 021-467 3000....................Page 54
Contact Person:
Jane O'Brien (Events Manager)
Seating Capacity of Meeting Rooms:
+300: 1
Facilities available:
BO AC IEH AVO AVH

BO *Black Out Facilities*
IEH *Interpreting Equipment (Can Arrange Hire)*
AC *Air Conditioning*
AVO *Audio Visual (Available On Premises)*
IEO *Interpreting Equipment (Available On Premises)*
AVH *Audio Visual (Can Arrange Hire)*

Garryvoe Hotel
Shanagarry, Co. Cork
Tel: 021-464 6718 ....Page 62
Seating Capacity of Meeting Rooms:
+400: 1 +300: 2 +200: 2 +50: 2
-50: 2
Facilities available:
BO AVO AVH

Glengarriff Eccles Hotel
Glengarriff, Co. Cork
Tel: 027-63003 ....Page 54
Contact Person:
Geraldine Owens
Seating Capacity of Meeting Rooms:
+300: 1 +50: 1 -50: 1
Facilities available:
BO AC AVH

Gresham Metropole
Cork City, Co. Cork
Tel: 021-464 3700....................Page 49
Contact Person:
Fiona Keohane
Seating Capacity of Meeting Rooms:
+500: 1 +400: 1 +300: 1 +200: 2
+100: 2 +50: 6 -50: 11
Facilities available:
BO AC IEH AVH

Hotel Isaacs
Cork City, Co. Cork
Tel: 021-450 0011 ....Page 50
Contact Person:
Paula Lynch
Seating Capacity of Meeting Rooms:
-50: 2
Facilities available:
BO AC AVH

Inchydoney Island Lodge & Spa
Clonakilty, Co. Cork
Tel: 023-883 3143....................Page 44
Contact Person:
Helen Deakin / Isobel Toft
Seating Capacity of Meeting Rooms:
+300: 1 -50: 4
Facilities available:
BO AC IEH AVO

Maryborough Hotel & Spa
Cork City, Co. Cork
Tel: 021-436 5555....................Page 52
Contact Person:
Mary Bernard
Seating Capacity of Meeting Rooms:
+400: 1 +300: 1 +100: 2 +50: 2
-50: 5
Facilities available:
BO AC IEH AVO AVH

Montenotte Hotel
Cork City, Co. Cork
Tel: 021-453 0050....................Page 52
Seating Capacity of Meeting Rooms:
+300: 1 +50: 2
Facilities available:
IEH AVH

Silver Springs Moran Hotel
Cork City, Co. Cork
Tel: 021-450 7533....................Page 53
Contact Person:
Zoe Walsh
Seating Capacity of Meeting Rooms:
+500: 2 +400: 2 +300: 4 +200: 4
+100: 4 +50: 4 -50: 7
Facilities available:
BO AC IEH AVO AVH

Springfort Hall Hotel
Mallow, Co. Cork
Tel: 022-21278 ....Page 60
Contact Person:
Paul Walsh
Seating Capacity of Meeting Rooms:
+300: 1 +200: 1 +100: 1 +50: 1
-50: 3
Facilities available:
IEH AVO

Trident Hotel
Kinsale, Co. Cork
Tel: 021-477 9300....................Page 58
Contact Person:
Hal McElroy
Seating Capacity of Meeting Rooms:
+200: 1 -50: 4
Facilities available:
BO AC IEH AVO AVH

WatersEdge Hotel
Cobh, Co. Cork
Tel: 021-481 5566 ....Page 45
Contact Person:
Paul Davidson
Seating Capacity of Meeting Rooms:
-50: 2
Facilities available:
AVO

West Cork Hotel
Skibbereen, Co. Cork
Tel: 028-21277 ....Page 62
Seating Capacity of Meeting Rooms:
+200: 1 -50: 2
Facilities available:
BO AC IEH AVH

Co. Kerry

Aghadoe Heights Hotel & Spa
Killarney, Co. Kerry
Tel: 064-663 1766....................Page 76
Contact Person:
Jacinta Prendergast
Seating Capacity of Meeting Rooms:
+100: 1 -50: 2
Facilities available:
BO AC IEH AVO

Brehon (The)
Killarney, Co. Kerry
Tel: 064-663 0700 ....Page 77
Contact Person:
Cara Fuller
Seating Capacity of Meeting Rooms:
+200: 1 +100: 1 -50: 4
Facilities available:
BO AC IEH AVO

Dingle Skellig Hotel & Peninsula Spa
Dingle (An Daingean), Co. Kerry
Tel: 066-915 0200....................Page 69
Contact Person:
Karen Byrnes
Seating Capacity of Meeting Rooms:
+200: 1 -50: 1
Facilities available:
BO AC IEH AVH

BO *Black Out Facilities*
AC *Air-Conditioning*
IEO *Interpreting Equipment (Available On Premises)*
IEH *Interpreting Equipment (Can Arrange Hire)*
AVO *Audio Visual (Available On Premises)*
AVH *Audio Visual (Can Arrange Hire)*

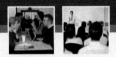

Co. Kerry CONTINUED

Europe Hotel Resort (The)
Killarney, Co. Kerry
Tel: 064-667 1300 ....Page 81
Contact Person:
Gerry Browne
Seating Capacity of Meeting Rooms:
+500: 1 +400: 1 +300: 1 +200: 2
+100: 3 +50: 6 -50: 8
Facilities available:
BO AC IEH AVO AVH

Fels Point Hotel
Tralee, Co. Kerry
Tel: 066-719 9100 ....Page 96
Contact Person:
Jacqui Dowling / Maggie Kenny
Seating Capacity of Meeting Rooms:
+300: 1 +100: 1 -50: 5
Facilities available:
BO AC IEO AVO

Gleneagle Hotel
Killarney, Co. Kerry
Tel: 064-663 6000 ....Page 84
Contact Person:
Cara Fuller
Seating Capacity of Meeting Rooms:
+500: 2 +400: 2 +300: 3 +200: 3
+100: 4 +50: 4 -50: 4
Facilities available:
BO AC IEH AVO

Grand Hotel
Tralee, Co. Kerry
Tel: 066-712 1499 ....Page 96
Contact Person:
Eileen Egan
Seating Capacity of Meeting Rooms:
+200: 1 +100: 1 +50: 6 -50: 6
Facilities available:
BO AC IEH AVH

Heights Hotel - Killarney (The)
Killarney, Co. Kerry
Tel: 064-663 1158 ....Page 84
Contact Person:
Noreen O'Leary
Seating Capacity of Meeting Rooms:
+400: 1 -50: 2
Facilities available:
AVO

International Hotel
Killarney, Co. Kerry
Tel: 064-663 1816 ....Page 85
Contact Person:
Anne Marie Collins
Seating Capacity of Meeting Rooms:
-50: 1
Facilities available:
IEO AVO

Killarney Plaza Hotel & Spa
Killarney, Co. Kerry
Tel: 064-662 1100 ....Page 87
Contact Person:
Mary Hartnett
Seating Capacity of Meeting Rooms:
+200: 1 +50: 2
Facilities available:
BO AC IEH AVO

Lake Hotel
Killarney, Co. Kerry
Tel: 064-663 1035 ....Page 89
Contact Person:
Heather MacIver / Breda Healy
Seating Capacity of Meeting Rooms:
+100: 1 +50: 1 -50: 2
Facilities available:
BO AC IEO IEH AVO AVH

Malton (The)
Killarney, Co. Kerry
Tel: 064-663 8000 ....Page 90
Contact Person:
Emer Corridan
Seating Capacity of Meeting Rooms:
+500: 1 +400: 1 +300: 1 +200: 1
+100: 1 +50: 2 -50: 2
Facilities available:
BO AC IEH AVH

Manor West Hotel, Spa & Leisure Club
Tralee, Co. Kerry
Tel: 066-719 4500....................Page 97
Contact Person:
Hazel Boyle
Seating Capacity of Meeting Rooms:
+200: 1 +50: 2 -50: 3
Facilities available:
BO AC IEH AVO

Meadowlands Hotel
Tralee, Co. Kerry
Tel: 066-718 0444....................Page 97
Contact Person:
Pamela Lucey
Seating Capacity of Meeting Rooms:
+200: 1 +100: 2 +50: 1 -50: 2
Facilities available:
BO AC IEH AVO AVH

Muckross Park Hotel & Cloisters Spa
Killarney, Co. Kerry
Tel: 064-662 3400 ....Page 90
Contact Person:
Fiona O'Doherty
Seating Capacity of Meeting Rooms:
+300: 1 +200: 1 +100: 2 +50: 4
Facilities available:
BO AC IEH AVO AVH

Parknasilla Resort
Sneem, Co. Kerry
Tel: 064-667 5600 ....Page 93
Contact Person:
Jim Feeney
Seating Capacity of Meeting Rooms:
+50: 1 -50: 1
Facilities available:
BO IEH AVH

Sneem Hotel
Sneem, Co. Kerry
Tel: 064-667 5100....................Page 94
Contact Person:
Nicola Duggan
Seating Capacity of Meeting Rooms:
+200: 1 +50: 2
Facilities available:
BO AC IEH AVO

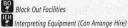

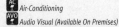

BO *Black Out Facilities*
AC *Air-Conditioning*
IEO *Interpreting Equipment (Available On Premises)*
IEH *Interpreting Equipment (Can Arrange Hire)*
AVO *Audio Visual (Available On Premises)*
AVH *Audio Visual (Can Arrange Hire)*

Co. Kilkenny

Butler House
Kilkenny City, Co. Kilkenny
Tel: 056-776 5707 ....Page 99
Contact Person:
Gabrielle Hickey
Seating Capacity of Meeting Rooms:
+100: 1 +50: 2 -50: 2
Facilities available:
IEH AVO

Hotel Kilkenny
Kilkenny City, Co. Kilkenny
Tel: 056-776 2000 ....Page 101
Contact Person:
Karen Geraghty
Seating Capacity of Meeting Rooms:
+500: 1 +400: 2 +300: 2 +200: 2 +100: 2 +50: 1 -50: 3
Facilities available:
BO AC IEH AVO

Kilkenny Ormonde Hotel
Kilkenny City, Co. Kilkenny
Tel: 056-772 3900..................Page 102
Contact Person:
Deirdre Twomey
Seating Capacity of Meeting Rooms:
+400: 1 +300: 2 +200: 2 +100: 2 +50: 4 -50: 6
Facilities available:
BO AC IEH AVO

Kilkenny River Court
Kilkenny City, Co. Kilkenny
Tel: 056-772 3388..................Page 102
Contact Person:
Kerry Foreman / Kevin Brennan
Seating Capacity of Meeting Rooms:
+200: 1 +100: 1 +50: 1 -50: 2
Facilities available:
AC IEH AVH

Langton House Hotel
Kilkenny City, Co. Kilkenny
Tel: 056-776 5133 ....Page 102
Contact Person:
Sean Reád
Seating Capacity of Meeting Rooms:
+400: 1 +50: 1 -50: 1
Facilities available:
BO AC IEH AVH

Lyrath Estate Hotel, Spa & Convention Centre
Kilkenny City, Co. Kilkenny
Tel: 056-776 0088..................Page 103
Contact Person:
Dervla / Mary Áine
Seating Capacity of Meeting Rooms:
+500: 2 +400: 3 +300: 3 +200: 3 +100: 4 +50: 6 -50: 10
Facilities available:
BO AC IEH AVO AVH

Mount Juliet
Thomastown, Co. Kilkenny
Tel: 056-777 3000..................Page 105
Contact Person:
June Aylward
Seating Capacity of Meeting Rooms:
+100: 1 +50: 3 -50: 2
Facilities available:
BO AC IEH AVO

Newpark Hotel
Kilkenny City, Co. Kilkenny
Tel: 056-776 0500..................Page 104
Contact Person:
yguilfoyle@newpark.com
Seating Capacity of Meeting Rooms:
+500: 1 +400: 1 +200: 1 +100: 1 +50: 3 -50: 7
Facilities available:
BO AC IEH AVO

Rising Sun
Mullinavat, Co. Kilkenny
Tel: 051-898173......................Page 105
Contact Person:
Kathrena O'Connor
Seating Capacity of Meeting Rooms:
+100: 1 -50: 1
Facilities available:
BO AC AVH

Co. Tipperary

Abbey Court Hotel, Lodges & Trinity Leisure Spa
Nenagh, Co. Tipperary
Tel: 067-41111 ....Page 110
Contact Person:
Imelda Connolly
Seating Capacity of Meeting Rooms:
+400: 1 +300: 1 +200: 1 +100: 3 +50: 7 -50: 4
Facilities available:
BO AC IEH AVH

Ballykisteen Hotel & Golf Resort
Tipperary Town, Co. Tipperary
Tel: 062-33333........................Page 111
Contact Person:
Sales Team
Seating Capacity of Meeting Rooms:
+200: 1 +50: 3 -50: 3
Facilities available:
BO AC IEH AVO

Cashel Palace Hotel
Cashel, Co. Tipperary
Tel: 062-62707 ....Page 107
Contact Person:
Tracy Wallace
Seating Capacity of Meeting Rooms:
+50: 1 -50: 2
Facilities available:
BO IEH AVO

Dundrum House Hotel, Golf & Leisure Resort
Cashel, Co. Tipperary
Tel: 062-71116........................Page 107
Contact Person:
Deirdre Crowe
Seating Capacity of Meeting Rooms:
+400: 1 +50: 2 -50: 3
Facilities available:
BO AC IEH AVO

BO *Black Out Facilities*
AC *Air-Conditioning*
IEO *Interpreting Equipment (Available On Premises)*
IEH *Interpreting Equipment (Can Arrange Hire)*
AVO *Audio Visual (Available On Premises)*
AVH *Audio Visual (Can Arrange Hire)*

Co. Tipperary CONTINUED

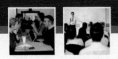

Hotel Minella & Leisure Club
Clonmel, Co. Tipperary
Tel: 052-612 2388 ....Page 109
Contact Person:
John Nallen
Seating Capacity of Meeting Rooms:
+500: 1 +400: 1 +300: 1 +200: 2 +100: 2 +50: 4 -50: 5
Facilities available:
BO AC IEH AVO AVH

Templemore Arms Hotel
Templemore, Co. Tipperary
Tel: 0504-31423......................Page 110
Contact Person:
Julie Tarrant
Seating Capacity of Meeting Rooms:
+200: 1 +50: 1 -50: 1
Facilities available:
AC AVH

Co. Waterford

Dooley's Hotel
Waterford City, Co. Waterford
Tel: 051-873531......................Page 120
Contact Person:
Clare O'Mahony
Seating Capacity of Meeting Rooms:
+300: 1 +200: 1 +100: 2 +50: 1 -50: 3
Facilities available:
BO AC IEH AVO

Faithlegg House Hotel
Faithlegg, Co. Waterford
Tel: 051-382000......................Page 116
Contact Person:
Suzanne Molloy
Seating Capacity of Meeting Rooms:
+200: 1 +50: 1 -50: 3
Facilities available:
AC IEH AVO

Lismore House Hotel
Lismore, Co. Waterford
Tel: 058-72966 ....Page 116
Contact Person:
Elaine Ahern
Seating Capacity of Meeting Rooms:
+100: 1 -50: 1
Facilities available:
BO AC IEH AVO AVH

Park Hotel, Leisure Centre & Holiday Homes
Dungarvan, Co. Waterford
Tel: 058-42899 ....Page 114
Contact Person:
David Livingstone
Seating Capacity of Meeting Rooms:
+500: 1 +400: 1 +300: 1 +200: 1 +100: 1 +50: 4 -50: 19
Facilities available:
BO AC IEH AVO AVH

Rhu Glenn Country Club Hotel
Waterford City, Co. Waterford
Tel: 051-832242 ....Page 122
Contact Person:
Anne / Rita
Seating Capacity of Meeting Rooms:
+400: 1 +300: 1 +200: 1 +100: 1 +50: 2 -50: 2
Facilities available:
AC IEH AVH

Tower Hotel & Leisure Centre
Waterford City, Co. Waterford
Tel: 051-862300 ....Page 123
Contact Person:
Catherina Hurley
Seating Capacity of Meeting Rooms:
+400: 1 +100: 3 +50: 1 -50: 2
Facilities available:
BO AC IEH AVH

Waterford Marina Hotel
Waterford City, Co. Waterford
Tel: 051-856600 ....Page 123
Contact Person:
Linda Bennett
Seating Capacity of Meeting Rooms:
-50: 3
Facilities available:
BO IEH AVH

Co. Wexford

Amber Springs Hotel & Health Spa
Gorey, Co. Wexford
Tel: 053-948 4000..................Page 126
Contact Person:
Thora O'Toole
Seating Capacity of Meeting Rooms:
+500: 1 +100: 1 -50: 6
Facilities available:
BO AC IEH AVO

Ashdown Park Hotel Conference & Leisure Centre
Gorey, Co. Wexford
Tel: 053-948 0500..................Page 127
Contact Person:
Kim Feehan
Seating Capacity of Meeting Rooms:
+500: 1 +50: 2 -50: 2
Facilities available:
BO AC IEH AVO AVH

Brandon House Hotel & Solas Croí Eco Spa
New Ross, Co. Wexford
Tel: 051-421703......................Page 128
Contact Person:
Moira Carroll
Seating Capacity of Meeting Rooms:
+300: 1 +50: 2 -50: 3
Facilities available:
AC IEH AVO

Ferrycarrig Hotel
Wexford Town, Co. Wexford
Tel: 053-912 0999 ....Page 131
Contact Person:
Áine Byrne
Seating Capacity of Meeting Rooms:
+300: 1
Facilities available:
BO AC IEH AVO

BO *Black Out Facilities*
AC *Air-Conditioning*
IEO *Interpreting Equipment (Available On Premises)*
IEH *Interpreting Equipment (Can Arrange Hire)*
AVO *Audio Visual (Available On Premises)*
AVH *Audio Visual (Can Arrange Hire)*

Marlfield House Hotel
Gorey, Co. Wexford
Tel: 053-942 1124 ....Page 127
Contact Person:
Margaret Bowe
Seating Capacity of Meeting Rooms:
-50: 1
Facilities available:
BO AVH

Riverbank House Hotel
Wexford Town, Co. Wexford
Tel: 053-912 3611 ....Page 132
Contact Person:
Caroline Byrne
Seating Capacity of Meeting Rooms:
+500: 1 +400: 1 +300: 1 +200: 1 +100: 1 +50: 1
Facilities available:
AC IEH AVO

Riverside Park Hotel and Leisure Club
Enniscorthy, Co. Wexford
Tel: 053-923 7800..................Page 126
Contact Person:
Joy Rothwell - Conference & Banqueting Manager
Seating Capacity of Meeting Rooms:
+500: 1 +200: 1 +100: 1 +50: 2 -50: 1
Facilities available:
BO AC AVO

Seafield Golf & Spa Hotel
Gorey, Co. Wexford
Tel: 053-942 4000..................Page 128
Contact Person:
Kelly Fitzgerald
Seating Capacity of Meeting Rooms:
+500: 1 +100: 1 +50: 2 -50: 2
Facilities available:
BO AC IEH AVO

Talbot Hotel Conference and Leisure Centre
Wexford Town, Co. Wexford
Tel: 053-912 2566 ....Page 134
Contact Person:
Niamh Lambert
Seating Capacity of Meeting Rooms:
+300: 1 +200: 1 +100: 2 +50: 3 -50: 8
Facilities available:
BO AC IEH AVO

Whites of Wexford
Wexford Town, Co. Wexford
Tel: 053-912 2311 ....Page 134
Contact Person:
Liz Sinnott
Seating Capacity of Meeting Rooms:
+500: 1 +400: 1 +300: 2 +200: 2 +100: 3 +50: 4 -50: 9
Facilities available:
BO AC IEH AVH

Ireland West

Co. Clare

Bunratty Castle Hotel & Angsana Spa
Bunratty, Co. Clare
Tel: 061-478700 ....Page 140
Contact Person:
Marguerite Curran
Seating Capacity of Meeting Rooms:
+100: 1 +50: 1 -50: 2
Facilities available:
BO AC IEH AVO AVH

Falls Hotel & Spa
Ennistymon, Co. Clare
Tel: 065-707 1004 ....Page 146
Contact Person:
Joanne Clancy
Seating Capacity of Meeting Rooms:
+300: 1 +50: 1 -50: 3
Facilities available:
AC IEH AVO

Oakwood Arms Hotel
Shannon Airport, Co. Clare
Tel: 061-361500 ....Page 151
Contact Person:
Yvonne McNamara
Seating Capacity of Meeting Rooms:
+300: 1 +200: 1 +100: 1 +50: 2 -50: 5
Facilities available:
BO AC IEH AVO

Temple Gate Hotel
Ennis, Co. Clare
Tel: 065-682 3300..................Page 145
Contact Person:
Paul Madden
Seating Capacity of Meeting Rooms:
+200: 1 +100: 1 +50: 2 -50: 4
Facilities available:
BO AC IEH AVO

Co. Donegal

Ballyliffin Lodge & Spa
Ballyliffin, Co. Donegal
Tel: 074-937 8200..................Page 153
Contact Person:
Breda McGonigle
Seating Capacity of Meeting Rooms:
+300: 1 +50: 1 -50: 1
Facilities available:
BO AC AVO

Downings Bay Hotel
Downings, Co. Donegal
Tel: 074-915 5586 ....Page 158
Contact Person:
Eileen Rock
Seating Capacity of Meeting Rooms:
+300: 1 +100: 1 +50: 1 -50: 1
Facilities available:
AC IEH AVO

BO *Black Out Facilities*
AC *Air-Conditioning*
IEO *Interpreting Equipment (Available On Premises)*
IEH *Interpreting Equipment (Can Arrange Hire)*
AVO *Audio Visual (Available On Premises)*
AVH *Audio Visual (Can Arrange Hire)*

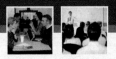

Co. Donegal CONTINUED

Great Northern Hotel
Bundoran, Co. Donegal
Tel: 071-984 1204 ....Page 155
Contact Person:
Philip McGlynn
Seating Capacity of Meeting Rooms:
+500: 1 +400: 1 +300: 1 +200: 1
+100: 1 +50: 1 -50: 1
Facilities available:
BO IEH AVO

Harvey's Point Hotel
Donegal Town, Co. Donegal
Tel: 074-972 2208................Page 157
Contact Person:
Anne-Marie McInaw
Seating Capacity of Meeting Rooms:
+500: 1 +400: 1 +300: 1 +200: 2
+100: 2 +50: 3 -50: 3
Facilities available:
AC AVO

Inishowen Gateway Hotel
Buncrana, Co. Donegal
Tel: 074-936 1144 ....Page 155
Contact Person:
Sales/Marketing Manager, Nadean Cavanagh
Seating Capacity of Meeting Rooms:
+500: 1 +100: 1
Facilities available:
BO AC IEH AVH

Jackson's Hotel, Conference & Leisure Centre
Ballybofey, Co. Donegal
Tel: 074-913 1021 ....Page 152
Contact Person:
Ankush Shingal
Seating Capacity of Meeting Rooms:
+500: 3 +200: 1 +50: 1 -50: 5
Facilities available:
BO AC IEH AVO AVH

Mill Park Hotel, Conference Centre & Leisure Club
Donegal Town, Co. Donegal
Tel: 074-972 2880................Page 157
Contact Person:
Conference & Banqueting Manager
Seating Capacity of Meeting Rooms:
+300: 1 -50: 4
Facilities available:
BO AC AVO

Solis Lough Eske Castle
Donegal Town, Co. Donegal
Tel: 074-972 5100 ....Page 158
Contact Person:
Michele McConalogue
Seating Capacity of Meeting Rooms:
+400: 1 +300: 1 +200: 1 +100: 3
+50: 3 -50: 2
Facilities available:
BO AC IEO IEH AVO AVH

Co. Galway

Best Western Flannery's Hotel
Galway City, Co. Galway
Tel: 091-755111 ....Page 172
Contact Person:
Emma Mooney
Seating Capacity of Meeting Rooms:
+50: 4 -50: 4
Facilities available:
BO AC IEH AVH

Claregalway Hotel
Galway City, Co. Galway
Tel: 091-738300 ....Page 172
Contact Person:
Tommy Normoyle
Seating Capacity of Meeting Rooms:
+500: 1 +200: 2 +100: 1 +50: 1
Facilities available:
BO AC IEH AVO

Connemara Coast Hotel
Furbo, Co. Galway
Tel: 091-592108....................Page 170
Contact Person:
Ann Downey
Seating Capacity of Meeting Rooms:
+400: 1 +300: 1 +200: 2 +100: 2
+50: 5 -50: 8
Facilities available:
BO IEH AVO

Delphi Mountain Resort
Leenane, Co. Galway
Tel: 095-42208 ....Page 182
Contact Person:
Laura Nolan
Seating Capacity of Meeting Rooms:
+50: 1 -50: 1
Facilities available:
AVO

Doonmore Hotel
Inishbofin Island, Co. Galway
Tel: 095-45814 ....Page 181
Contact Person:
Aileen Murray
Seating Capacity of Meeting Rooms:
+50: 2
Facilities available:
BO IEH AVH

g Hotel (The)
Galway City, Co. Galway
Tel: 091-865200 ....Page 174
Contact Person:
Eilish Wall
Seating Capacity of Meeting Rooms:
+100: 1 +50: 1 -50: 6
Facilities available:
BO AC IEH AVO

Inishbofin House Hotel
Inishbofin Island, Co. Galway
Tel: 095-45809 ....Page 181
Contact Person:
C&B Coordinator
Seating Capacity of Meeting Rooms:
+100: 1 +50: 2 -50: 1
Facilities available:
BO AC AVO

BO *Black Out Facilities*
IEH *Interpreting Equipment (Can Arrange Hire)*
AC *Air-Conditioning*
AVO *Audio Visual (Available On Premises)*
IEO *Interpreting Equipment (Available On Premises)*
AVH *Audio Visual (Can Arrange Hire)*

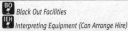

Kilmurvey House
Aran Islands, Co. Galway
Tel: 099-61218 ....Page 164
Contact Person:
Treasa Joyce
Seating Capacity of Meeting Rooms:
+50: 1
Facilities available:
BO IEH AVH

Lady Gregory Hotel, Conference & Leisure Club
Gort, Co. Galway
Tel: 091-632333 ....Page 180
Contact Person:
Brian Morrissey
Seating Capacity of Meeting Rooms:
+300: 1 -50: 2
Facilities available:
BO AC IEH AVO AVH

Meadow Court Hotel
Loughrea, Co. Galway
Tel: 091-841051......................Page 184
Contact Person:
Tom Corbett Jnr
Seating Capacity of Meeting Rooms:
+300: 1 -50: 1
Facilities available:
BO AC AVO

Park Lodge Hotel
Spiddal, Co. Galway
Tel: 091-553159......................Page 186
Contact Person:
Jane Marie Foyle
Seating Capacity of Meeting Rooms:
+50: 1 -50: 1
Facilities available:
AC AVO

Twelve (The)
Galway City, Co. Galway
Tel: 091-597000 ....Page 179
Contact Person:
Fergus O'Halloran
Seating Capacity of Meeting Rooms:
+100: 1 +50: 1 -50: 4
Facilities available:
BO AC IEH AVO

Victoria Hotel
Galway City, Co. Galway
Tel: 091-567433 ....Page 179
Contact Person:
Reception
Seating Capacity of Meeting Rooms:
-50: 1
Facilities available:
AC IEH AVH

Westwood Hotel (The)
Galway City, Co. Galway
Tel: 091-521442......................Page 180
Contact Person:
David Kelly
Seating Capacity of Meeting Rooms:
+300: 1 +200: 1 +100: 1 +50: 3 -50: 3
Facilities available:
BO AC IEH AVO

Co. Leitrim

Bush Hotel
Carrick-on-Shannon, Co. Leitrim
Tel: 071-967 1000 ....Page 188
Contact Person:
Joseph Dolan
Seating Capacity of Meeting Rooms:
+300: 1 +100: 2 +50: 3 -50: 5
Facilities available:
BO AC IEH AVO

Co. Limerick

Absolute Hotel & Spa
Limerick City, Co. Limerick
Tel: 061-463600......................Page 191
Contact Person:
Joanne Hickey
Seating Capacity of Meeting Rooms:
+100: 1 -50: 5
Facilities available:
BO AC IEH AVO AVH

Deebert House Hotel
Kilmallock, Co. Limerick
Tel: 063-31200 ....Page 191
Contact Person:
Margaret Atalla
Seating Capacity of Meeting Rooms:
+50: 1 -50: 1
Facilities available:
BO AC IEH AVO

Dunraven Arms Hotel
Adare, Co. Limerick
Tel: 061-605900 ....Page 190
Contact Person:
Louis Murphy
Seating Capacity of Meeting Rooms:
+300: 1 +200: 1 +100: 2 +50: 3 -50: 4
Facilities available:
BO AC IEH AVO AVH

Fitzgeralds Woodlands House Hotel & Spa
Adare, Co. Limerick
Tel: 061-605100......................Page 190
Contact Person:
David or Bríd
Seating Capacity of Meeting Rooms:
+400: 1 +300: 1 +200: 1 +100: 2 +50: 3 -50: 3
Facilities available:
BO AC IEH AVH

Radisson Blu Hotel & Spa
Limerick City, Co. Limerick
Tel: 061-456200 ....Page 193
Contact Person:
Suzanne O'Dwyer
Seating Capacity of Meeting Rooms:
+500: 1 +100: 1 -50: 4
Facilities available:
BO AC IEH AVO AVH

Rathkeale House Hotel
Rathkeale, Co. Limerick
Tel: 069-63333 ....Page 195
Contact Person:
Gerry O'Connor
Seating Capacity of Meeting Rooms:
+300: 1 +100: 1 -50: 1
Facilities available:
BO AC IEH AVO

BO *Black Out Facilities*
AC *Air-Conditioning*
IEO *Interpreting Equipment (Available On Premises)*
IEH *Interpreting Equipment (Can Arrange Hire)*
AVO *Audio Visual (Available On Premises)*
AVH *Audio Visual (Can Arrange Hire)*

Co. Mayo

Ashford Castle
Cong, Co. Mayo
Tel: 094-954 6003 ....Page 200
Contact Person:
Monica Feeney
Seating Capacity of Meeting Rooms:
+100: 1
Facilities available:
BO IEH AVH

Ballina Manor Hotel
Ballina, Co. Mayo
Tel: 01-808 0500 ....Page 196
Contact Person:
Sinead Costello
Seating Capacity of Meeting Rooms:
+200: 1 +100: 1 +50: 1 -50: 1
Facilities available:
BO AC IEH AVH

Castlecourt Hotel Spa, Leisure, Conference
Westport, Co. Mayo
Tel: 098-55088 ....Page 203
Contact Person:
Sinead Hopkins
Seating Capacity of Meeting Rooms:
+500: 1 +400: 1 +300: 2 +200: 3
+100: 4 +50: 6 -50: 8
Facilities available:
BO AC IEH AVO

Days Hotel Castlebar
Castlebar, Co. Mayo
Tel: 094-928 6200..................Page 198
Contact Person:
Caroline Leonard
Seating Capacity of Meeting Rooms:
+100: 2 +50: 2 -50: 4
Facilities available:
BO AC IEH AVO

Hotel Westport
Westport, Co. Mayo
Tel: 098-25122 ....Page 204
Contact Person:
Gerry Walshe / Eithne Cosgrove / Rhona Chambers
Seating Capacity of Meeting Rooms:
+500: 1 +400: 1 +300: 1 +200: 2
+100: 2 +50: 5 -50: 1
Facilities available:
BO AC IEH AVO AVH

Knock House Hotel
Knock, Co. Mayo
Tel: 094-938 8088 ....Page 200
Contact Person:
Brian Crowley
Seating Capacity of Meeting Rooms:
+100: 1 +50: 1 -50: 1
Facilities available:
AVO

Mill Times Hotel
Westport, Co. Mayo
Tel: 098-29200 ....Page 205
Contact Person:
Irene Cannon
Seating Capacity of Meeting Rooms:
+200: 1
Facilities available:
AC AVH

Park Hotel Kiltimagh
Kiltimagh, Co. Mayo
Tel: 094-937 4922 ....Page 200
Contact Person:
Conference Sales Manager
Seating Capacity of Meeting Rooms:
+300: 1 -50: 2
Facilities available:
BO AC IEH AVO

Westport Plaza Hotel Spa, Leisure, Conference
Westport, Co. Mayo
Tel: 098-51166 ....Page 205
Contact Person:
Sinead Hopkins
Seating Capacity of Meeting Rooms:
+50: 1
Facilities available:
BO AC IEH AVO

Westport Woods Hotel & Spa
Westport, Co. Mayo
Tel: 098-25811 ....Page 206
Contact Person:
Michelle McKenna
Seating Capacity of Meeting Rooms:
+200: 1 +100: 2 +50: 1 -50: 2
Facilities available:
BO AC IEH AVO AVH

Wyatt Hotel
Westport, Co. Mayo
Tel: 098-25027 ....Page 206
Contact Person:
Barney Clarke
Seating Capacity of Meeting Rooms:
+400: 1 +100: 2 +50: 3
Facilities available:
BO AC IEH AVO AVH

Co. Roscommon

Abbeyfield Hotel Conference and Leisure Centre
Ballaghaderreen, Co. Roscommon
Tel: 094-986 2100..................Page 206
Contact Person:
Liz McAvoy
Seating Capacity of Meeting Rooms:
+300: 1 +200: 1 +100: 2 +50: 2
-50: 2
Facilities available:
BO AC

Co. Sligo

Radisson Blu Hotel & Spa Sligo
Sligo Town, Co. Sligo
Tel: 071-914 0008 ....Page 209
Contact Person:
Denise Meenaghan
Seating Capacity of Meeting Rooms:
+500: 1 +400: 1 +300: 1 +200: 3
+100: 4 +50: 6 -50: 11
Facilities available:
BO AC IEH AVH

BO Black Out Facilities
AC Air-Conditioning
IEO Interpreting Equipment (Available On Premises)
IEH Interpreting Equipment (Can Arrange Hire)
AVO Audio Visual (Available On Premises)
AVH Audio Visual (Can Arrange Hire)

Sligo Park Hotel & Leisure Club
Sligo Town, Co. Sligo
Tel: 071-919 0400 ....Page 210
Contact Person:
Bernadette Coffey, Sales Manager
Seating Capacity of Meeting Rooms:
+500: 1 +400: 1 +300: 1 +200: 1
+100: 3 +50: 3 -50: 5
Facilities available:
BO AC IEH AVO AVH

Northern Ireland

Co. Antrim

Dunsilly Hotel
Antrim, Co. Antrim
Tel: 028-9446 2929................Page 215
Contact Person:
Laura Kiely
Seating Capacity of Meeting Rooms:
+200: 1 +100: 1 +50: 3 -50: 4
Facilities available:
BO AC IEH AVO AVH

Galgorm Resort & Spa
Ballymena, Co. Antrim
Tel: 028-2588 1001 ....Page 215
Contact Person:
Beth Swindlehurst
Seating Capacity of Meeting Rooms:
+500: 2 +50: 1 -50: 4
Facilities available:
BO AC AVO AVH

Hilton Templepatrick
Templepatrick, Co. Antrim
Tel: 028-9443 5500................Page 218
Seating Capacity of Meeting Rooms:
+400: 1 +50: 8 -50: 1
Facilities available:
BO AC IEH AVO AVH

Londonderry Arms Hotel
Carnlough, Co. Antrim
Tel: 028-2888 5255................Page 216
Contact Person:
Frank O'Neill & Maureen Morrow
Seating Capacity of Meeting Rooms:
+100: 1 +50: 2 -50: 2
Facilities available:
BO IEH AVH

Ramada Portrush
Portrush, Co. Antrim
Tel: 028-7082 6100 ....Page 217
Contact Person:
Mary O'Neill
Seating Capacity of Meeting Rooms:
+100: 1 +50: 1 -50: 3
Facilities available:
BO AC IEH AVH

Belfast City

Hilton Belfast
Belfast City
Tel: 028-9027 7000................Page 219
Seating Capacity of Meeting Rooms:
+400: 1 +50: 8 -50: 1
Facilities available:
BO AC IEH AVO AVH

La Mon Hotel & Country Club
Belfast City
Tel: 028-9044 8631 ....Page 219
Contact Person:
Denise Maghie (Duty Manager)
Seating Capacity of Meeting Rooms:
+500: 1 +400: 2 +300: 2 +200: 2
+100: 5 +50: 12 -50: 17
Facilities available:
BO AC AVH

Malone Lodge Hotel & Apartments
Belfast City
Tel: 028-9038 8000 ....Page 220
Contact Person:
Conference Co-Ordinator
Seating Capacity of Meeting Rooms:
+100: 1 +50: 1 -50: 4
Facilities available:
BO AC IEH AVO AVH

Co. Derry

Radisson Blu Roe Park Resort
Limavady, Co. Derry
Tel: 028-7772 2222 ....Page 222
Seating Capacity of Meeting Rooms:
+400: 1 +100: 3 +50: 2 -50: 1
Facilities available:
AVH

Co. Down

Burrendale Hotel, Country Club & Spa
Newcastle, Co. Down
Tel: 028-4372 2599 ....Page 222
Contact Person:
Fiona O'Hare
Seating Capacity of Meeting Rooms:
+200: 1 +100: 1 -50: 6
Facilities available:
BO AC IEH AVO

Canal Court Hotel
Newry, Co. Down
Tel: 028-3025 1234................Page 222
Contact Person:
Conference & Banqueting Office
Seating Capacity of Meeting Rooms:
+400: 1 +300: 1 +200: 2 +100: 3
+50: 5 -50: 4
Facilities available:
AC IEH AVO

Co. Fermanagh

Killyhevlin Hotel
Enniskillen, Co. Fermanagh
Tel: 028-6632 3481................Page 223
Contact Person:
Mandy Vance
Seating Capacity of Meeting Rooms:
+500: 1 +200: 1 +100: 2 +50: 3
Facilities available:
IEH AVH

BO *Black Out Facilities*
AC *Air-Conditioning*
IEO *Interpreting Equipment (Available On Premises)*
IEH *Interpreting Equipment (Can Arrange Hire)*
AVO *Audio Visual (Available On Premises)*
AVH *Audio Visual (Can Arrange Hire)*

Co. Fermanagh CONTINUED

Manor House Resort Hotel
Enniskillen, Co. Fermanagh
Tel: 028-6862 2211 ....Page 223
Contact Person:
Sinead Stewart
Seating Capacity of Meeting Rooms:
+400: 1 +300: 1 +200: 1 +100: 3 +50: 3 -50: 6
Facilities available:
AC AVO

Co. Tyrone

Bank House Hotel
Dungannon, Co. Tyrone
Tel: 028-8772 8080 ....Page 225
Contact Person:
Karen Campbell
Seating Capacity of Meeting Rooms:
+50: 2
Facilities available:
AC IEH AVO

Dublin & Ireland East

Co. Cavan

Hotel Kilmore
Cavan Town, Co. Cavan
Tel: 049-433 2288 ....Page 232
Contact Person:
Roisín McFadden
Seating Capacity of Meeting Rooms:
+500: 1 +200: 2 +100: 2 +50: 3 -50: 4
Facilities available:
BO AC IEH AVO

Lakeside Manor Hotel
Virginia, Co. Cavan
Tel: 049-854 8200 ....Page 233
Contact Person:
Breda Traynor
Seating Capacity of Meeting Rooms:
+400: 1 +200: 1 +50: 1 -50: 2
Facilities available:
BO AC AVO

Radisson Blu Farnham Estate Hotel
Cavan Town, Co. Cavan
Tel: 049-437 7700 ....Page 232
Contact Person:
Patsy Mooney
Seating Capacity of Meeting Rooms:
+300: 1 +100: 4 +50: 7 -50: 8
Facilities available:
BO AC IEH AVO AVH

Slieve Russell Hotel Golf & Country Club
Ballyconnell, Co. Cavan
Tel: 049-952 6444..................Page 231
Contact Person:
Órlaith Donohoe
Seating Capacity of Meeting Rooms:
+500: 2 +400: 2 +300: 3 +200: 4 +100: 4 +50: 4 -50: 7
Facilities available:
BO AC IEH AVO

Co. Dublin

Airportview Hotel & Spa
Blakes Cross, Co. Dublin
Tel: 01-843 8756....................Page 233
Contact Person:
Gerry / Annie
Seating Capacity of Meeting Rooms:
+50: 1 -50: 2
Facilities available:
BO IEH AVH

Ashling Hotel
Dublin City, Co. Dublin
Tel: 01-677 2324....................Page 239
Contact Person:
Conference Coordinator
Seating Capacity of Meeting Rooms:
+200: 1 +50: 1 -50: 8
Facilities available:
BO AC IEH AVH

Ballsbridge Inn & Towers
Dublin City, Co. Dublin
Tel: 01-668 4468....................Page 239
Contact Person:
Lisa Courtney
Seating Capacity of Meeting Rooms:
+500: 1 +400: 1 +100: 3 +50: 1 -50: 8
Facilities available:
BO AC IEH AVO

Best Western Premier Academy Plaza Hotel
Dublin City, Co. Dublin
Tel: 01-817 4141 ....Page 240
Contact Person:
Conor Dean (tel: 01 - 817 4161)
Seating Capacity of Meeting Rooms:
+100: 1 +50: 2 -50: 7
Facilities available:
BO AC IEH AVO

Bewley's Hotel Ballsbridge
Dublin City, Co. Dublin
Tel: 01-668 1111......................Page 240
Contact Person:
Barbara Dunne
Seating Capacity of Meeting Rooms:
+200: 1 -50: 7
Facilities available:
AC IEH AVO AVH

Bewley's Hotel Dublin Airport
Dublin Airport, Co. Dublin
Tel: 01-871 1000 ....Page 234
Contact Person:
Grace Callely
Seating Capacity of Meeting Rooms:
+200: 1 +100: 1 +50: 3 -50: 16
Facilities available:
AC IEH AVO AVH

Bewley's Hotel Leopardstown
Dublin City, Co. Dublin
Tel: 01-293 5000....................Page 240
Contact Person:
Helen Ryan
Seating Capacity of Meeting Rooms:
-50: 13
Facilities available:
BO AC AVO AVH

BO *Black Out Facilities* | AC *Air-Conditioning* | IEO *Interpreting Equipment (Available On Premises)*
IEH *Interpreting Equipment (Can Arrange Hire)* | AVO *Audio Visual (Available On Premises)* | AVH *Audio Visual (Can Arrange Hire)*

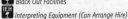

Bewley's Hotel Newlands Cross
Dublin City, Co. Dublin
Tel: 01-464 0140 ....Page 242
Contact Person:
Grainne McKeown
Seating Capacity of Meeting Rooms:
-50: 10
Facilities available:
AC AVO AVH

Blakes Hotel & Spa
Dublin City, Co. Dublin
Tel: 01-668 8324....................Page 242
Contact Person:
Pat Halpin
Seating Capacity of Meeting Rooms:
+50: 1 -50: 2
Facilities available:
BO AC IEH AVO

Bracken Court Hotel
Balbriggan, Co. Dublin
Tel: 01-841 3333 ....Page 233
Contact Person:
Helga Duffy
Seating Capacity of Meeting Rooms:
+300: 1 +200: 1 +100: 1 +50: 4 -50: 6
Facilities available:
BO AC IEH AVH

Brooks Hotel
Dublin City, Co. Dublin
Tel: 01-670 4000....................Page 242
Contact Person:
Mark O'Sullivan/Lisa Moore
Seating Capacity of Meeting Rooms:
+50: 1 -50: 2
Facilities available:
BO AC IEH AVH

Burlington (The)
Dublin City, Co. Dublin
Tel: 01-618 5600 ....Page 243
Contact Person:
Richard Huggard
Seating Capacity of Meeting Rooms:
+500: 1 +400: 3 +300: 3 +200: 3 +100: 4 +50: 4 -50: 9
Facilities available:
BO AC IEH AVO

Buswells Hotel
Dublin City, Co. Dublin
Tel: 01-614 6500 ....Page 243
Seating Capacity of Meeting Rooms:
+50: 1 -50: 5
Facilities available:
AC IEH AVO

Camden Court Hotel
Dublin City, Co. Dublin
Tel: 01-475 9666....................Page 244
Contact Person:
Denise Corboy
Seating Capacity of Meeting Rooms:
+200: 1 +100: 5 +50: 8 -50: 12
Facilities available:
BO AC IEH AVH

Carnegie Court Hotel
Swords, Co. Dublin
Tel: 01-840 4384....................Page 273
Contact Person:
Teresa Long
Seating Capacity of Meeting Rooms:
+200: 1 +100: 1 +50: 1 -50: 2
Facilities available:
BO AC IEH AVO

Cassidys Hotel
Dublin City, Co. Dublin
Tel: 01-878 0555....................Page 244
Contact Person:
Maeve Sankey
Seating Capacity of Meeting Rooms:
+50: 2 -50: 4
Facilities available:
BO AC IEH AVO

Castleknock Hotel and Country Club
Dublin City, Co. Dublin
Tel: 01-640 6300....................Page 245
Contact Person:
Dearbhla Sheridon, Events Manager
Seating Capacity of Meeting Rooms:
+500: 1 +400: 1 +300: 1 +200: 2 +100: 4 +50: 4 -50: 6
Facilities available:
BO AC IEH AVO AVH

Charleville Lodge
Dublin City, Co. Dublin
Tel: 01-838 6633....................Page 246
Contact Person:
Paul Stenson
Seating Capacity of Meeting Rooms:
-50: 1
Facilities available:
AVH

Clarence (The)
Dublin City, Co. Dublin
Tel: 01-407 0800....................Page 246
Contact Person:
Denise Bevan
Seating Capacity of Meeting Rooms:
+50: 1 -50: 3
Facilities available:
BO AC IEH AVH

Clontarf Castle Hotel
Dublin City, Co. Dublin
Tel: 01-833 2321 ....Page 247
Contact Person:
Nadiene Sheridan
Seating Capacity of Meeting Rooms:
+500: 1 +400: 1 +300: 1 +200: 1 +100: 3 +50: 2 -50: 5
Facilities available:
BO AC IEH AVH

Conrad Dublin
Dublin City, Co. Dublin
Tel: 01-602 8900....................Page 247
Contact Person:
Pamela McGrath
Seating Capacity of Meeting Rooms:
+200: 1 +100: 1 +50: 4 -50: 9
Facilities available:
BO AC IEH AVH

Crowne Plaza Dublin Northwood
Dublin Airport, Co. Dublin
Tel: 01-862 8888....................Page 235
Contact Person:
Judith Graham
Seating Capacity of Meeting Rooms:
+500: 1 +400: 1 +300: 2 +200: 3 +100: 4 +50: 5 -50: 25
Facilities available:
BO AC IEH AVO AVH

BO *Black Out Facilities*
AC *Air-Conditioning*
IEO *Interpreting Equipment (Available On Premises)*
IEH *Interpreting Equipment (Can Arrange Hire)*
AVO *Audio Visual (Available On Premises)*
AVH *Audio Visual (Can Arrange Hire)*

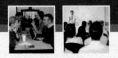

Co. Dublin CONTINUED

D4 Berkeley
Dublin City, Co. Dublin
Tel: 01-668 4468....................Page 248
Contact Person:
Lisa Courtney
Seating Capacity of Meeting Rooms:
+400: 1 +300: 1 +200: 1 +100: 2 +50: 2 -50: 9
Facilities available:
BO AC IEH AVO

Finnstown Country House Hotel
Lucan, Co. Dublin
Tel: 01-601 0700 ....Page 270
Contact Person:
Edwina King
Seating Capacity of Meeting Rooms:
+200: 1 +100: 1 +50: 1 -50: 4
Facilities available:
AC AVO AVH

Grand Hotel
Malahide, Co. Dublin
Tel: 01-845 0000 ....Page 271
Contact Person:
Hilary Fogarty
Seating Capacity of Meeting Rooms:
+400: 1 +200: 1 +100: 1 +50: 6 -50: 6
Facilities available:
BO AC IEH AVO

Gresham (The)
Dublin City, Co. Dublin
Tel: 01-874 6881 ....Page 252
Contact Person:
Michelle Costelloe
Seating Capacity of Meeting Rooms:
+300: 1 +200: 2 +100: 3 +50: 8 -50: 22
Facilities available:
BO AC IEH AVH

Hilton Dublin
Dublin City, Co. Dublin
Tel: 01-402 9988....................Page 254
Contact Person:
Natasha Sevrugina
Seating Capacity of Meeting Rooms:
+400: 1 +300: 1 +200: 2 +100: 4 +50: 4 -50: 5
Facilities available:
BO AC AVO AVH

Hilton Dublin Airport
Dublin Airport, Co. Dublin
Tel: 01-866 1800 ....Page 235
Contact Person:
events.dublinairport@hilton.com
Seating Capacity of Meeting Rooms:
+300: 1 +100: 2 -50: 9
Facilities available:
BO AC IEH AVH

Hotel Isaacs
Dublin City, Co. Dublin
Tel: 01-813 4700 ....Page 255
Contact Person:
Jeannette Mee
Seating Capacity of Meeting Rooms:
+100: 1 -50: 6
Facilities available:
BO AC IEH AVO AVH

Lansdowne Hotel
Dublin City, Co. Dublin
Tel: 01-668 2522....................Page 256
Contact Person:
Michael Quinn
Seating Capacity of Meeting Rooms:
+100: 1 +50: 1
Facilities available:
BO AVO

Lucan Spa Hotel
Lucan, Co. Dublin
Tel: 01-628 0494....................Page 270
Contact Person:
Stephen Foran
Seating Capacity of Meeting Rooms:
+500: 1 +100: 1 -50: 2
Facilities available:
AC AVO

Mercer Hotel
Dublin City, Co. Dublin
Tel: 01-478 2179 ....Page 259
Contact Person:
Mark Sheridan
Seating Capacity of Meeting Rooms:
+50: 1 -50: 1
Facilities available:
AC IEH AVO

Mount Herbert Hotel
Dublin City, Co. Dublin
Tel: 01-614 2000 ....Page 261
Contact Person:
Michelle Sweeney
Seating Capacity of Meeting Rooms:
+50: 2 -50: 7
Facilities available:
BO AC IEH AVO

Park Plaza Tyrrelstown
Dublin City, Co. Dublin
Tel: 01-827 5600....................Page 263
Contact Person:
Katerina Forejtkova
Seating Capacity of Meeting Rooms:
+500: 1 +400: 1 +300: 1 +200: 1 +100: 13 +50: 5 -50: 11
Facilities available:
BO AC IEH AVO

Radisson Blu St Helen's Hotel
Dublin City, Co. Dublin
Tel: 01-218 6000 ....Page 264
Contact Person:
Laura Shurie
Seating Capacity of Meeting Rooms:
+300: 1 +50: 7 -50: 5
Facilities available:
BO AC IEH AVH

Red Cow Moran Hotel
Dublin City, Co. Dublin
Tel: 01-459 3650....................Page 264
Contact Person:
Zoe Walsh
Seating Capacity of Meeting Rooms:
+500: 1 +400: 1 +300: 1 +200: 2 +100: 5 +50: 10 -50: 16
Facilities available:
BO AC IEH AVO AVH

BO *Black Out Facilities* · AC *Air-Conditioning* · IEO *Interpreting Equipment (Available On Premises)*
IEH *Interpreting Equipment (Can Arrange Hire)* · AVO *Audio Visual (Available On Premises)* · AVH *Audio Visual (Can Arrange Hire)*

Rochestown Lodge Hotel & Replenish Day Spa
Dun Laoghaire, Co. Dublin
Tel: 01-285 3555 .... Page 269
Contact Person:
Reservations
Seating Capacity of Meeting Rooms:
+50: 1 -50: 4
Facilities available:
BO AC IEH AVO AVH

Royal Marine Hotel
Dun Laoghaire, Co. Dublin
Tel: 01-230 0030 .... Page 269
Contact Person:
Brenda Killeen
Seating Capacity of Meeting Rooms:
+500: 1 +100: 5 +50: 6 -50: 12
Facilities available:
BO AC IEH AVO AVH

Shelbourne Hotel (The)
Dublin City, Co. Dublin
Tel: 01-663 4500 .... Page 265
Contact Person:
Anne-Marie Whelan
Seating Capacity of Meeting Rooms:
+400: 1 +100: 2 +50: 2 -50: 6
Facilities available:
BO AC IEH AVH

Stillorgan Park Hotel
Dublin City, Co. Dublin
Tel: 01-200 1800 .... Page 266
Contact Person:
Lorna Lambert
Seating Capacity of Meeting Rooms:
+500: 1 +400: 1 +300: 1 +200: 3 +100: 6 +50: 7 -50: 19
Facilities available:
BO AC IEO IEH AVO AVH

Tara Towers Hotel
Dublin City, Co. Dublin
Tel: 01-269 4666 .... Page 266
Contact Person:
Alice Papazian
Seating Capacity of Meeting Rooms:
+300: 1 +200: 1 +100: 1 +50: 3 -50: 4
Facilities available:
BO AC IEH AVO

Temple Bar Hotel
Dublin City, Co. Dublin
Tel: 01-677 3333 .... Page 266
Contact Person:
Olive Santry
Seating Capacity of Meeting Rooms:
+50: 1 -50: 4
Facilities available:
BO IEH AVH

Waterside House Hotel & Signal Restaurant
Donabate, Co. Dublin
Tel: 01-843 6153 .... Page 234
Contact Person:
Paul Slattery
Seating Capacity of Meeting Rooms:
+300: 1 +200: 1 +100: 1 +50: 2 -50: 3
Facilities available:
AC IEH AVO AVH

Westin Dublin
Dublin City, Co. Dublin
Tel: 01-645 1000 .... Page 268
Contact Person:
Marlene Buckridge
Seating Capacity of Meeting Rooms:
+200: 1 +100: 2 +50: 2 -50: 8
Facilities available:
BO AC IEH AVO AVH

Co. Kildare

Clanard Court Hotel
Athy, Co. Kildare
Tel: 059-864 0666 .... Page 274
Contact Person:
Sandra Foy / Clare Dunne
Seating Capacity of Meeting Rooms:
+400: 1 +200: 1 +100: 1 +50: 1 -50: 3
Facilities available:
BO AC IEH AVO

Courtyard Hotel Leixlip
Leixlip, Co. Kildare
Tel: 01-629 5100 .... Page 276
Contact Person:
Ashley Reddin
Seating Capacity of Meeting Rooms:
+100: 2 +50: 4 -50: 4
Facilities available:
BO AC IEH AVO AVH

Derby House Hotel
Kildare Town, Co. Kildare
Tel: 045-522144 .... Page 275
Contact Person:
Cecilia Lau
Seating Capacity of Meeting Rooms:
+200: 1 -50: 1
Facilities available:
IEH AVH

Glenroyal Hotel (The)
Maynooth, Co. Kildare
Tel: 01-629 0909 .... Page 276
Contact Person:
Kate Voice
Seating Capacity of Meeting Rooms:
+500: 1 +400: 2 +300: 4 +200: 4 +100: 6 +50: 6 -50: 12
Facilities available:
BO AC IEH AVO

Keadeen Hotel
Newbridge, Co. Kildare
Tel: 045-431666 .... Page 278
Contact Person:
Pauline Barry
Seating Capacity of Meeting Rooms:
+500: 1 +400: 1 +300: 1 +200: 1 +100: 3 +50: 4 -50: 7
Facilities available:
BO AC IEH AVO

Maudlins House Hotel
Naas, Co. Kildare
Tel: 045-896999 .... Page 277
Contact Person:
David Fagan
Seating Capacity of Meeting Rooms:
+50: 1 -50: 4
Facilities available:
BO AC IEH AVO

BO *Black Out Facilities*
AC *Air-Conditioning*
IEO *Interpreting Equipment (Available On Premises)*
IEH *Interpreting Equipment (Can Arrange Hire)*
AVO *Audio Visual (Available On Premises)*
AVH *Audio Visual (Can Arrange Hire)*

Co. Kildare CONTINUED

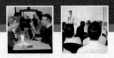

Osprey Hotel & Spa
Naas, Co. Kildare
Tel: 045-881111 ....Page 277
Contact Person:
Sharon Deegan
Seating Capacity of Meeting Rooms:
+300: 1 +200: 1 +100: 2 +50: 3
-50: 12
Facilities available:
BO AC AVH

Westgrove Hotel
Clane, Co. Kildare
Tel: 045-989900 ....Page 274
Contact Person:
Clodagh McDonnell
Seating Capacity of Meeting Rooms:
+500: 1 +400: 2 +50: 4 -50: 5
Facilities available:
BO AC IEH AVO

Co. Laois

Heritage Golf & Spa Resort (The)
Killenard, Co. Laois
Tel: 057-864 5500 ....Page 280
Contact Person:
David Haniffy
Seating Capacity of Meeting Rooms:
+400: 1 +50: 2 -50: 4
Facilities available:
BO AC IEH AVO

Killeshin (The)
Portlaoise, Co. Laois
Tel: 057-863 1200 ....Page 280
Contact Person:
Jane Hughes
Seating Capacity of Meeting Rooms:
+100: 1 +50: 2 -50: 10
Facilities available:
BO AC IEH AVO

Co. Longford

Annaly Hotel
Longford Town, Co. Longford
Tel: 043-334 2058 ....Page 282
Contact Person:
Duty Manager
Seating Capacity of Meeting Rooms:
+200: 1
Facilities available:
BO IEH AVO AVH

Longford Arms Hotel
Longford Town, Co. Longford
Tel: 043-334 6296 ....Page 282
Contact Person:
Duty Manager
Seating Capacity of Meeting Rooms:
+500: 1 +400: 1 +300: 1 +200: 1
+100: 2 +50: 3 -50: 3
Facilities available:
BO AC IEH AVO AVH

Co. Louth

Ballymascanlon House Hotel
Dundalk, Co. Louth
Tel: 042-935 8200 ....Page 285
Contact Person:
Chris Brayden
Seating Capacity of Meeting Rooms:
+400: 1 +100: 1 -50: 6
Facilities available:
BO AC IEH AVO

d (The)
Drogheda, Co. Louth
Tel: 041-987 7700 ....Page 284
Contact Person:
Elaine Carolan
Seating Capacity of Meeting Rooms:
+300: 1
Facilities available:
BO AC IEH AVO AVH

Westcourt Hotel
Drogheda, Co. Louth
Tel: 041-983 0965 ....Page 284
Contact Person:
Thomas Gavan
Seating Capacity of Meeting Rooms:
+400: 1 +300: 1 +200: 1 +100: 1
+50: 2
Facilities available:
AC AVO AVH

Co. Meath

Ardboyne Hotel
Navan, Co. Meath
Tel: 046-902 3119 ....Page 290
Contact Person:
Susan Horgan
Seating Capacity of Meeting Rooms:
+500: 1 +400: 1 +300: 1 +200: 1
+100: 2 -50: 3
Facilities available:
BO AC

Bellinter House
Navan, Co. Meath
Tel: 046-903 0900 ....Page 290
Contact Person:
Heather Chandler
Seating Capacity of Meeting Rooms:
-50: 1
Facilities available:
BO AVO

City North Hotel
Gormanston, Co. Meath
Tel: 01-690 6666 ....Page 288
Contact Person:
Susan Roddy
Seating Capacity of Meeting Rooms:
+500: 1 +100: 1 -50: 12
Facilities available:
BO AC AVO

BO *Black Out Facilities*
IEH *Interpreting Equipment (Can Arrange Hire)*
AC *Air-Conditioning*
AVO *Audio Visual (Available On Premises)*
IEO *Interpreting Equipment (Available On Premises)*
AVH *Audio Visual (Can Arrange Hire)*

Dunboyne Castle Hotel & Spa
Dunboyne, Co. Meath
Tel: 01-801 3500 ....Page 287
Contact Person:
Sinead Codd
Seating Capacity of Meeting Rooms:
+400: 1 +300: 1 -50: 8
Facilities available:
BO AC IEH AVH

Knightsbrook Hotel Spa & Golf Resort
Trim, Co. Meath
Tel: 046-948 2100..................Page 292
Contact Person:
Conference & Banqueting Manager
Seating Capacity of Meeting Rooms:
+500: 2 +400: 2 +300: 2 +200: 4
+100: 4 +50: 5 -50: 10
Facilities available:
BO AC IEH AVO AVH

Marriott Johnstown House Hotel, Spa, Residences & Training Pitches
Enfield, Co. Meath
Tel: 046-954 0000 ....Page 287
Contact Person:
Antonia McCormack
Seating Capacity of Meeting Rooms:
+500: 1 +400: 1 +300: 2 +200: 2
+100: 2 +50: 2 -50: 13
Facilities available:
BO AC IEH AVO

Newgrange Hotel
Navan, Co. Meath
Tel: 046-907 4100 ....Page 291
Contact Person:
Caroline Hegarty
Seating Capacity of Meeting Rooms:
+500: 1 +400: 1 +300: 1 +200: 4
-50: 3
Facilities available:
BO AC AVH

Station House Hotel and Signal Restaurant
Kilmessan, Co. Meath
Tel: 046-902 5239 ....Page 289
Contact Person:
Denise Slattery
Seating Capacity of Meeting Rooms:
+300: 1 +200: 1 +100: 1 +50: 1
-50: 1
Facilities available:
BO AC IEH AVO

Trim Castle Hotel
Trim, Co. Meath
Tel: 046-948 3000 ....Page 292
Contact Person:
Chanel Malone
Seating Capacity of Meeting Rooms:
+500: 1 +400: 1 +300: 1 +200: 1
+100: 2 +50: 3 -50: 6
Facilities available:
BO AC IEH AVO AVH

Co. Monaghan

Hillgrove Hotel Leisure & Spa
Monaghan Town, Co. Monaghan
Tel: 047-81288 ....Page 294
Contact Person:
Mike Nolan
Seating Capacity of Meeting Rooms:
+500: 2 +400: 2 +300: 3 +200: 3
+100: 5 +50: 8 -50: 15
Facilities available:
BO AC IEO IEH AVO AVH

Nuremore Hotel & Country Club
Carrickmacross, Co. Monaghan
Tel: 042-966 1438..................Page 292
Contact Person:
Sinéad Rock
Seating Capacity of Meeting Rooms:
+500: 1 +400: 1 +300: 1 +200: 2
+100: 3 +50: 3 -50: 6
Facilities available:
BO AC IEH AVO

Co. Offaly

Bridge House Hotel
Tullamore, Co. Offaly
Tel: 057-932 5600 ....Page 295
Contact Person:
Colm McCabe
Seating Capacity of Meeting Rooms:
+500: 1 +400: 3 +300: 4 +200: 2
+100: 3 +50: 4 -50: 9
Facilities available:
BO AC IEH AVO

County Arms Hotel & Leisure Club
Birr, Co. Offaly
Tel: 057-912 0791 ....Page 294
Contact Person:
Peter Loughnane
Seating Capacity of Meeting Rooms:
+500: 1 +400: 1 +300: 1 +200: 1
+100: 3 +50: 6 -50: 12
Facilities available:
BO AC IEH AVO

Tullamore Court Hotel Conference & Leisure Centre
Tullamore, Co. Offaly
Tel: 057-934 6666 ....Page 296
Contact Person:
Michelle Peake
Seating Capacity of Meeting Rooms:
+500: 1 +400: 1 +300: 2 +200: 2
+100: 4 +50: 8 -50: 15
Facilities available:
BO AC IEH AVO

Co. Westmeath

Annebrook House
Mullingar, Co. Westmeath
Tel: 044-935 3300 ....Page 299
Contact Person:
Bernie McHugh
Seating Capacity of Meeting Rooms:
+200: 1 +100: 1 +50: 3 -50: 4
Facilities available:
BO AC IEH AVO

BO *Black Out Facilities*
AC *Air-Conditioning*
IEO *Interpreting Equipment (Available On Premises)*
IEH *Interpreting Equipment (Can Arrange Hire)*
AVO *Audio Visual (Available On Premises)*
AVH *Audio Visual (Can Arrange Hire)*

Co. Westmeath CONTINUED

Glasson Hotel & Golf Club
Athlone, Co. Westmeath
Tel: 090-648 5120..................Page 296
Contact Person:
Gareth Jones / Fidelma Reid
Seating Capacity of Meeting Rooms:
+100: 1 +50: 1 -50: 3
Facilities available:
BO AC IEH AVO

Mullingar Park Hotel
Mullingar, Co. Westmeath
Tel: 044-933 7500 ....Page 302
Contact Person:
Ita Kerrigan
Seating Capacity of Meeting Rooms:
+500: 2 +400: 2 +300: 3 +200: 4
+100: 7 +50: 14 -50: 9
Facilities available:
BO AC IEH AVO AVH

Prince of Wales Hotel
Athlone, Co. Westmeath
Tel: 090-647 6666 ....Page 297
Contact Person:
Chris Vos
Seating Capacity of Meeting Rooms:
+100: 1 +50: 2 -50: 2
Facilities available:
BO AC IEH AVO AVH

Radisson Blu Hotel Athlone
Athlone, Co. Westmeath
Tel: 090-644 2600 ....Page 297
Contact Person:
Meetings and Events Department
Seating Capacity of Meeting Rooms:
+500: 1 +400: 1 +300: 1 +200: 2
+100: 4 +50: 4 -50: 6
Facilities available:
BO AC IEH AVO

Shamrock Lodge Hotel and Conference Centre
Athlone, Co. Westmeath
Tel: 090-649 2601..................Page 298
Contact Person:
Pamela Egan/Deborah Conroy
Seating Capacity of Meeting Rooms:
+200: 1 +100: 2 +50: 3 -50: 3
Facilities available:
AC AVH

Sheraton Athlone Hotel
Athlone, Co. Westmeath
Tel: 090-645 1000..................Page 298
Contact Person:
Joanna Hannick
Seating Capacity of Meeting Rooms:
+500: 1 +400: 1 +300: 1 +200: 2
+100: 4 +50: 10 -50: 11
Facilities available:
BO AC IEH AVO AVH

Co. Wicklow

Avon Rí
Blessington, Co. Wicklow
Tel: 045-900670 ....Page 304
Contact Person:
Siobhan Kendrick / Greg Forrestal
Seating Capacity of Meeting Rooms:
+200: 1 +50: 2 -50: 1
Facilities available:
BO AC IEH AVH

Glendalough Hotel
Glendalough, Co. Wicklow
Tel: 0404-45135 ....Page 307
Contact Person:
Alan Groarke / Nuala Kinsella
Seating Capacity of Meeting Rooms:
+100: 1 -50: 2
Facilities available:
BO AC IEH AVO

Glenview Hotel & Leisure Cub
Glen-O-The-Downs, Co. Wicklow
Tel: 01-287 3399....................Page 308
Contact Person:
Deirdre Flanagan
Seating Capacity of Meeting Rooms:
+200: 1 +100: 1 +50: 2 -50: 4
Facilities available:
BO AC IEH AVO

Martello Hotel (The)
Bray, Co. Wicklow
Tel: 01-286 8000....................Page 306
Contact Person:
Frances Lamb / Donal Byrne
Seating Capacity of Meeting Rooms:
+50: 1
Facilities available:
BO AVH

Ramada Hotel Bray
Bray, Co. Wicklow
Tel: 01-276 0258....................Page 306
Contact Person:
Michelle McHugh
Seating Capacity of Meeting Rooms:
+200: 1 +100: 1 +50: 5 -50: 1
Facilities available:
BO AC IEH AVO

The Ritz-Carlton, Powerscourt
Enniskerry, Co. Wicklow
Tel: 01-274 8888....................Page 307
Contact Person:
Tobias Schoch
Seating Capacity of Meeting Rooms:
+400: 1 +300: 1 +200: 3 +100: 2
+50: 6 -50: 6
Facilities available:
BO AC IEH AVO AVH

BO Black Out Facilities · *AC Air-Conditioning* · *IEO Interpreting Equipment (Available On Premises)*
IEH Interpreting Equipment (Can Arrange Hire) · *AVO Audio Visual (Available On Premises)* · *AVH Audio Visual (Can Arrange Hire)*

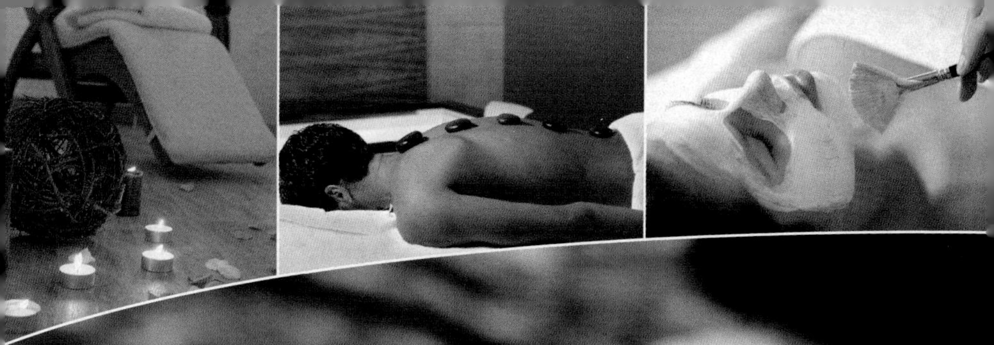

Spa & Leisure 2010

Ireland is rapidly developing its spa market, with a selection of destination, day, health and resort spas to choose from, as well as superb leisure facilities - all in the wonderful surroundings that make Ireland a unique holiday destination. The following pages will provide a flavour of some of the facilities and treatments on offer in many of the hotels and guesthouses featured in this guide.

So come on and get pampered!

We invite you to Ireland to enhance your precious leisure time. Relax in the perfect sanctuary of the oasis that is Ireland! Our philosophy is to enable you to leave us fully refreshed and restored by experiencing some of the wonderful spa & leisure treatments available in the unique and warm facilities on offer in the hotels and guesthouses listed in this section. A full description of the hotels and guesthouses can be had by looking up the appropriate page number.

Listings are by Region, County, Premises Name in alphabetical order.

Ireland South

Co. Carlow

Mount Wolseley Hotel Spa & Country Club
Tullow, Co. Carlow
Tel: 059-918 0100 ....Page 36
Name of Spa:
Sanctuary Spa
Type of Spa:
Resort Spa
No. of Treatments: 56
No. of Treatment Rooms: 14
Treatments Offered:
Facials: De Luxe Collagen Face, Eyes & Neck Treatment, Total Rehydration Treatment
Body Therapies: Total Body Polish, Balneotherapy, Cellutox Ocean Wrap
Specialist Therapies: Thalgomince Pregnancy Therapy. Elemis & Thalgo products used in our treatments, Hot & Cold Stone Massage
Facilities available:
Oval Spa Pool with Waterfalls, Experience Showers, Rasul Room, Steam Room & Dry Air Room, Floatation Chambers, Sabiamed Light Treatment, Relaxation Room

Talbot Hotel Carlow
Carlow Town, Co. Carlow
Tel: 059-915 3000 ....Page 35
Name of Spa:
Classic Beauty at the Talbot Hotel
No. of Treatments: 25
No. of Treatment Rooms: 4
Treatments Offered:
Bodywraps, Aromatherapy Massage, Manicure, Pedicure, Mens Skincare Treatment, Intensive Moisture Facial, Revitalising Eye Rescue Treatment, Teeth Whitening, Reflexology
Facilities available:
Treatment Rooms, Nail Bar, Make Up Room, Sauna, Spa Pool, Steam Room

Co. Cork

Blarney Golf Resort
Blarney, Co. Cork
Tel: 021-438 4477 ....Page 40
Name of Spa:
Blarney Golf Resort and Spa
Type of Spa:
Hotel with Leisure Club Spa
No. of Treatments: 40
No. of Treatment Rooms: 5
Treatments Offered:
Hot Stone Massage, Deep Pore Cleansing Facial, Eye Crystal Treatment, De Luxe Manicure, Seaweed Wrap, Yonka & Matis Products
Facilities available:
Sauna, 20m Swimming Pool, Gym, Jacuzzi, Steam Room, Childrens' Pool

Fota Island Hotel & Spa
Fota Island, Co. Cork
Tel: 021-467 3000 ....Page 54
Name of Spa:
Fota Island Spa
Type of Spa:
Resort Spa
No. of Treatments: 60
No. of Treatment Rooms: 18
Treatments Offered:
Cold Marine Leg Wrap, Spa Packages, Hot Stones, Marine Body Polish, Chocolate Sensualite Wrap, Green Tea Silhouette Therapy, Lushly Polynesian Hand/Foot Ritual, Comfort Zone Facials
Facilities available:
Fitness Suite, Indoor Swimming Pool, 18 Treatment Rooms, Hydrotherapy Area, Thermal Area, Juice Bar, Relaxation Area, Garden

Garryvoe Hotel
Shanagarry, Co. Cork
Tel: 021-464 6718 ....Page 62
Name of Spa:
Garyvoe Health Club
Treatments Offered:
Wide Variety of Treatments
Facilities available:
25 metre Pool, Gymnasium, Outdoor Hot Tub, Sauna, Steam Room

Inchydoney Island Lodge & Spa
Clonakilty, Co. Cork
Tel: 023-883 3143 ....Page 44
Name of Spa:
Island Spa
Type of Spa:
Thalassotherapy Resort
No. of Treatments: 25
No. of Treatment Rooms: 17
Treatments Offered:
Island Spa Tropical Ritual (new), Rasul, Slimming Algotherapy, Spa Manicure, Facial, Cryotherapy, Chocolate Ritual, Aroma Stone Massage
Facilities available:
Thalassotherapy Pool, Hammam, Sauna, Relaxation Room, Gymnasium, Seawater Pool

Maryborough Hotel & Spa
Cork City, Co. Cork
Tel: 021-436 5555 ....Page 52
Name of Spa:
Maryborough Spa
Type of Spa:
Hotel with Comprehensive Spa
No. of Treatments: 38
No. of Treatment Rooms: 10
Treatments Offered:
Hot Stone Therapy, Massage, Ayurvedic Rituals, Facials, Body Wraps, Full & 1/2 Day Programmes
Facilities available:
Relaxation Rooms, Vitality (Male & Female), Thermal Suites, 10 Treatment Rooms, Spa Café, Finishing Touches Studio

Westlodge Hotel
Bantry, Co. Cork
Tel: 027-50360 ....Page 39
No. of Treatments: 7
No. of Treatment Rooms: 2
Treatments Offered:
Reflexology, Full Body Massage, Aromatherapy Massage, Indian Head Massage, Sports Massage, Reiki, Top'n'Tail, Hot Stones Massage
Facilities available:
Heated Swimming Pool, Sauna, Steam Room, Jacuzzi, Fully equipped Gym, Squash Court

Co. Kerry

Aghadoe Heights Hotel & Spa
Killarney, Co. Kerry
Tel: 064-663 1766 .... Page 76
Name of Spa:
The Spa at The Heights
Type of Spa:
Resort Spa
No. of Treatments: 58
No. of Treatment Rooms: 10
Treatments Offered:
Futuresse Face & Body Treatments, Biodroga Wraps, Aveda Face & Body Treatments, Manicure, Pedicure, Indian Head Massage, Reflexology & Thermal Suite, Natural Magic Treatments.
Facilities available:
Hammam, Rock Sauna, Laconium, Aroma Grotto, Tropical Rain Shower, Cold Fog Shower, Heated Loungers, Relaxation Room, Slipper Bath, Serail, Swimming Pool, Jacuzzi, Fitness Suite, Tennis Court, Yoga, Pilates, Hair Salon

Ballygarry House Hotel & Spa
Tralee, Co. Kerry
Tel: 066-712 3322 .... Page 95
Name of Spa:
Nádúr
Type of Spa:
Hotel with Extensive Spa
No. of Treatments: 40
No. of Treatment Rooms: 7
Treatments Offered:
Hydrotherapy, Bamboo & Ginseng Body Polish, USPA Concept Facial Treatments, Holistic Therapy, Herbal & Mud Body Wrap, Hot Stone Massage, Ritual Body Massage, Beauty, many other treatments available
Facilities available:
Beauty Suite, Relaxing Room, Glass Sauna, Crystal Steam Room, Outdoor Canadian Hot Tub, Vitality Showers, Tanning Suite, Hydrotherapy Suite

Brehon (The)
Killarney, Co. Kerry
Tel: 064-663 0700 .... Page 77
Name of Spa:
Angsana Spa
Type of Spa:
Hotel with Comprehensive Spa
No. of Treatments: 23
No. of Treatment Rooms: 9
Treatments Offered:
Rain Shower, Massage, Body Polish, Facial, Foot Soak, Rasul, Indian Head Massage, Skin Enhancer, Signature Angsana Massage, Manicure
Facilities available:
Herb Sauna, Crystal Steam Room, Rasul, Foot Spa, Tropical Shower, Ice Fountain, Kubeldusche, Vitality Pool, Hot & Cold Spa

Castlerosse Hotel and Golf Resort
Killarney, Co. Kerry
Tel: 064-663 1144 .... Page 79
Type of Spa:
Hotel with Leisure Club Spa
No. of Treatments: 21
No. of Treatment Rooms: 2
Treatments Offered:
The non-surgical face lift, Opus Belle Facial, Hydro Lypio, Dr Grandle A.C.E., Eye Lift Rejuvenation Treatment, Clinical Facials, Variety of Body Treatments, Hot Stone Massage, Swedish Massage, Indian Head Massage, Reflexology, Ear Candling, Manicure, Pedicure

Dingle Skellig Hotel& Peninsula Spa
Dingle (An Daingean), Co. Kerry
Tel: 066-915 0200 .... Page 69
Name of Spa:
The Peninsula Spa
Type of Spa:
Hotel with Selective Spa
No. of Treatments: 55
No. of Treatment Rooms: 7
Treatments Offered:
Yon-ka Aroma Stone, Yon-ka Face & Body Treatments, Peninsula Spa Face & Body Treatments, Massage, Hydrotherapy, Body Wraps, Sports Injury, Tanning, Nail Treatments, Makeovers, Selection of unique "Irish" treatments from local Organic Products & Ingredients
Facilities available:
Outdoor Hot Tub overlooking Dingle Harbour, Relaxation Suite with Refreshments Bar, Hydrotherapy Suite, Sauna, Steam Room, Beauty Salon, Outdoor Relaxation Balcony, 17m Pool, Childrens' pool, Jacuzzi in Leisure Club

Europe Hotel Resort (The)
Killarney, Co. Kerry
Tel: 064-667 1300 .... Page 81
Name of Spa:
ESPA at the Europe
Type of Spa:
Resort Spa
No. of Treatments: 30
No. of Treatment Rooms: 16
Treatments Offered:
Espa Total Luxury, Espa Total Balance, Espa Purely Holistic, Espa New Beginnings, Espa Total Relaxation, Espa Body Cleansing Programme, Espa Ritual, Espa Face, Espa Body, Espa Mini Rituals
Facilities available:
Treatment Rooms, Couples Suite, Express Suites, Indoor / Outdoor Pools, Saunas, Gymnasium, Relaxation Rooms, Thermal Suites, Tai Chi Studio, Spa Café

Did you know?

Rasul:
An Oriental ceremony for body care involving a cleansing seaweed soap shower, medicinal muds and an invigorating herbal steam bath.

Reflexology
The physical act of applying pressure to the feet & hands without the use of oil or lotion. It is based on a system of zones & reflex areas that reflect an image of the body on the feet and hands with a premise that such work effects a physical change to the body.

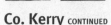

Co. Kerry CONTINUED

Killarney Park Hotel
Killarney, Co. Kerry
Tel: 064-663 5555....................Page 87
Name of Spa:
The Spa at the Killarney Park Hotel
Type of Spa:
Hotel with Extensive Spa
No. of Treatments: 45
No. of Treatment Rooms: 8
Treatments Offered:
Eve Lom Facial, Elemis Aroma Stone Therapy, Elemis Japanese Silk Booster Facial, Elemis Well Being Massage, Elemis Fennel Cleansing Cellulite and Colon Therapy, Healing Bath Ceremony, Elemis Aromapure Facial, Reflexology, Elemis Musclease Aroma Spa Ocean Wrap
Facilities available:
8 Custom-built Private Treatment Suites, A specially designed Relaxation Room, Hydrotherapy Suite, Caldarium, Couples Suite, Juice Bar

Killarney Plaza Hotel & Spa
Killarney, Co. Kerry
Tel: 064-662 1100 ....Page 87
Name of Spa:
Molton Brown Spa
No. of Treatments: 20
No. of Treatment Rooms: 8
Treatments Offered:
Selection of Molton Brown Body & Facial, Hand & Feet Therapies
Facilities available:
Private Leisure Club with Pool, Sauna, Gym, Molton Brown Spa

Lake Hotel
Killarney, Co. Kerry
Tel: 064-663 1035 ....Page 89
Name of Spa:
Muckross Fitness Centre
No. of Treatments: 14
No. of Treatment Rooms: 3
Treatments Offered:
Massages, Facials, Manicures, Pedicures
Facilities available:
Gym, Sauna, Steam Room, Outdoor Hot Tub overlooking Lake, Spa Sensations Treatment Centre

Malton (The)
Killarney, Co. Kerry
Tel: 064-663 8000....................Page 90
Name of Spa:
Innisfallen Health & Beauty Rooms
Type of Spa:
Hotel with Leisure Club Spa
No. of Treatments: 20
No. of Treatment Rooms: 3
Treatments Offered:
Hydrotherapy Bath, Facials, Manicures, Pedicures, Hot Stone Massage, Lomi Lomi Massage, Body Treatments, Waxing and Tinting
Facilities available:
Indoor Heated Swimming Pool, Jacuzzi, Steam Room, Gym, Sauna, Tennis Courts, Hydrotherapy Bath

Manor West Hotel, Spa & Leisure Club
Tralee, Co. Kerry
Tel: 066-719 4500 ....Page 97
Name of Spa:
Harmony Wellness Suites & Leisure Club
No. of Treatments: 20
No. of Treatment Rooms: 2
Treatments Offered:
Treatments & therapies from the Phytomer range. Call today for full list of treatments and packages
Facilities available:
18m Swimming Pool, Therapy Pool, Underwater Loungers, Swan Jets, Sauna, Steam Room, Jacuzzi, state-of-the-art Gymnasium, 2 Wellness Suites

Muckross Park Hotel & Cloisters Spa
Killarney, Co. Kerry
Tel: 064-662 3400....................Page 90
Name of Spa:
Cloisters Spa
Type of Spa:
Hotel with Comprehensive Spa
No. of Treatments: 50
No. of Treatment Rooms: 12
Treatments Offered:
Massage, Facials, Microdermabrasion, Manicure, Pedicure, Hot Shaves, Hydrotherapy Baths, Energy Healing, Reflexology
Facilities available:
Thermal Suite, Vitality Pool, Herb Sauna, Ice Fountain, Salt Grotto, Eucalyptus Mist, Mud Rasul, Relaxation Suite, Heated Loungers, UV Sonacare Camera

Park Hotel Kenmare
Kenmare, Co. Kerry
Tel: 064-664 1200 ....Page 74
Name of Spa:
SAMAS
Type of Spa:
Destination Spa
No. of Treatments: 30
No. of Treatment Rooms: 8
Treatments Offered:
Full Spa Facilities with Treatments - Ayurvedic, Deep Tissue, Aromatherapy, etc.
Facilities available:
Laconium, Rock Sauna, Steam, Tropical Mist Showers, Vitality Pool, Relaxation Rooms, Tai Chi, Chi Kung Pilates

Parknasilla Resort
Sneem, Co. Kerry
Tel: 064-667 5600....................Page 93
Type of Spa:
Hotel with Leisure Club Spa
No. of Treatments: 52
No. of Treatment Rooms: 12
Treatments Offered:
Exotic Ritual for Hands, Indian Head Massage, Exotic Ginger & Lime Salt Glow, Aroma Stone Massage, Skin IQ Facial, Elemis Skin Special Facial
Facilities available:
Aromatherapy Steam Room, Hydrotherapy Foot Spas, Heated Lounges, Pool, Laconium, Herb Sauna, Salt Inhalation Steam Cabin

Co. Kilkenny

Hotel Kilkenny
Kilkenny City, Co. Kilkenny
Tel: 056-776 2000 ....Page 101
Name of Spa:
Lilac Lodge Spa
No. of Treatments: 40
No. of Treatment Rooms: 4
Treatments Offered:
Dermalogica Facial Treatments, Yon-ka Facial Treatments, Aroma Hot Stone Massage, Phyto-Marine Slimming Treatment, Reflexology, Sports Therapy Massage, Waxing, Tanning, Body Treatments
Facilities available:
Luxury Relaxation Room, 4 Treatment Rooms, Complimentary off-street Parking

Kilkenny Ormonde Hotel
Kilkenny City, Co. Kilkenny
Tel: 056-772 3900 ....Page 102
Name of Spa:
KO Spa
No. of Treatments: 38
No. of Treatment Rooms: 7
Treatments Offered:
Elemis Advanced Anti-Ageing Facials, Pro-Collagen Quartz Lift Facial, SOS Purifying Facial, Absolute Spa Ritual, Deep Tissue Muscle Massage, Solo Delight Grooming for Feet, Exotic Lime & Ginger Salt Glow, Exotic Coconut Rub and Milk Ritual Wrap, Exotic Frangipani Body Nourish Wrap, Solar Oil Mini Manicure
Facilities available:
21m Swimming Pool, Kids Pool, Extensive Gym Area, Aerobics Studio, Children's Crèche Facility, Sauna, Jacuzzi, Steam Room, 7 Spa Treatment Rooms, Relaxation Room

Kilkenny River Court
Kilkenny City, Co. Kilkenny
Tel: 056-772 3388 ....Page 102
Type of Spa:
Hotel with Leisure Club Spa
No. of Treatments: 10
No. of Treatment Rooms: 3
Treatments Offered:
Aromatherapy, Massage, Sports Massage, Reiki, Reflexology
Facilities available:
Treatment Rooms, Gymnasium, 17m Swimming Pool, Geyser Pool, Jacuzzi, Steam Room

Lyrath Estate Hotel, Spa & Convention Centre
Kilkenny City, Co. Kilkenny
Tel: 056-776 0088 ....Page 103
Name of Spa:
Oasis Spa
Type of Spa:
Hotel with Comprehensive Spa
No. of Treatments: 47
No. of Treatment Rooms: 10
Treatments Offered:
European Deep Cleanse Facial, Spirulina Wrap, Bora Body Mud Wrap, Reflexology, Reiki, Caviar Facial, Indian Head Massage, Rasul, Hot Stones
Facilities available:
Male Relaxation Area, Female Relaxation Area, Hydro Pool - both indoor & outdoor, Sauna, Steam Room, Gym, Tropical Showers, Couples Suite, 17m infinity Swimming Pool, Treatment Rooms

Mount Juliet
Thomastown, Co. Kilkenny
Tel: 056-777 3000 ....Page 105
Name of Spa:
The Spa at Mount Juliet
Type of Spa:
Hotel with Selective Spa
No. of Treatments: 70
No. of Treatment Rooms: 7
Treatments Offered:
Reiki, La Stone Therapy, Floatation Therapy Treatment, Reflexology, Radiance Facial, Body Polish, Deep Cleansing Back Treatment, ESPA Facials, SpaFind Treatments
Facilities available:
Swimming Pool, Steam Room, Sauna, Gym, Relaxation Room

Newpark Hotel
Kilkenny City, Co. Kilkenny
Tel: 056-776 0500 ....Page 104
Name of Spa:
Escape Health Club & Spa
No. of Treatments: 40
No. of Treatment Rooms: 4
Treatments Offered:
Carribean Glow Body Scrub, Pure Focus Facial, Elemental Nature Massage, Aveda Luxury Spa Pedicure, Carribean Therapy Hand Treatment, Revitalizing Eye Treatment, Green Science Anti Ageing Facial
Facilities available:
Relaxation Suite, Outdoor Infinity Pool

Co. Tipperary

Abbey Court Hotel, Lodges & Trinity Leisure Spa
Nenagh, Co. Tipperary
Tel: 067-41111 ....Page 110
Name of Spa:
Trinity Leisure Spa
No. of Treatments: 20
No. of Treatment Rooms: 8
Treatments Offered:
Swedish Massage, Decleor Facials, Jessica Pedicure, Manicure, Make-up, Waxing, Self-Tan, Universal Contour Wrap
Facilities available:
Balneotherapy Bath, Sun Room

Baileys of Cashel
Cashel, Co. Tipperary
Tel: 062-61937 ....Page 107
Name of Spa:
The Gate Health & Leisure Centre
Facilities available:
20 meter Swimming Pool, State-of-the-Art Gym, Sauna, Steam Room, Jacuzzi

Ballykisteen Hotel & Golf Resort
Tipperary Town, Co. Tipperary
Tel: 062-33333.......................Page 111
Name of Spa:
Serenity Day Spa
No. of Treatments: 38
No. of Treatment Rooms: 5
Treatments Offered:
Hot Stone Massage, Matis Crystal Eye Treatment, Creative Manicure, Zen Spa Pedicure, Indian Head Massage, California Spray Tan, Vita Liberata Make-up, Matis Signature Facial
Facilities available:
Swimming Pool, Sauna, Jacuzzi, Steam Room, Gym

Cahir House Hotel
Cahir, Co. Tipperary
Tel: 052-744 3000 ....Page 106
Name of Spa:
Cahir House Hotel Health & Beauty Spa
No. of Treatments: 36
No. of Treatment Rooms: 4
Treatments Offered:
Facials, Manicure, Pedicure, Reflexology, Hydrotherapy Bath, Body Treatments, Sunbeds, Indian Head Massage, Pamper Days
Facilities available:
Steam Room, Sauna, Sun Beds

Hotel Minella & Leisure Club
Clonmel, Co. Tipperary
Tel: 052-612 2388 ....Page 109
Name of Spa:
Club Minella
No. of Treatments: 14
No. of Treatment Rooms: 2
Treatments Offered:
Massage, Reflexology, Micronized Marine Algae Wrap, Toning Body Wrap, Marine Facial, Waxing, Manicure, Body Polish
Facilities available:
Treatment Rooms, Jacuzzi, Relaxation Room, Outdoor Hot Tub, 20m Pool, Outdoor Tennis Court, Sauna, Steam Room, Gym, Gardens

Co. Waterford

Faithlegg House Hotel
Faithlegg, Co. Waterford
Tel: 051-382000......................Page 116
Name of Spa:
Estuary Club
No. of Treatments: 40
No. of Treatment Rooms: 5
Treatments Offered:
Aromatherapy Massage, Reflexology, Reiki, Deep Sea Mud Treatment, Facials
Facilities available:
Swimming Pool, Jacuzzi, Steam Room, Gym, Sauna

Park Hotel, Leisure Centre & Holiday Homes
Dungarvan, Co. Waterford
Tel: 058-42899 ....Page 114
Name of Spa:
The Park Hotel & Leisure Centre
No. of Treatments: 5
No. of Treatment Rooms: 2
Treatments Offered:
Swedish & Deep Tissue Massage, Reflexology, Therapeutic Massage
Facilities available:
20m Swimming Pool, Gym, Sauna, Steam Room, Whirlpool, Jacuzzi, Kids Pool, Chartered Physiotherapist, Kids Club

Co. Wexford

Amber Springs Hotel & Health Spa
Gorey, Co. Wexford
Tel: 053-948 4000..................Page 126
Name of Spa:
Cocoon Health & Beauty Spa
Type of Spa:
Hotel with Extensive Spa
No. of Treatment Rooms: 11
Treatments Offered:
Massage, Facials, Waxing, Manicure, Body Wraps, Balneo Treatment, Dry Floatation, Relaxation Room
Facilities available:
18m Indoor Pool, Jacuzzi, Steam Room, Sauna, Hydro Therapy Pool, Fitness Centre, Kiddies Pool & Games Room, Supervised playzone.

Ashdown Park Hotel Conference & Leisure Centre
Gorey, Co. Wexford
Tel: 053-948 0500..................Page 127
Name of Spa:
Ashdown Club & Beauty Studio
No. of Treatments: 8
No. of Treatment Rooms: 1
Treatments Offered:
Massage Treatments
Facilities available:
18m Swimming Pool, Kids' Pool, Jacuzzi, Steam Room, Sauna, Gym

Brandon House Hotel & Solas Croí Eco Spa
New Ross, Co. Wexford
Tel: 051-421703......................Page 128
Name of Spa:
Solas Croí Eco Spa
No. of Treatments: 70
No. of Treatment Rooms: 10
Treatments Offered:
Complete Tri-Dosha Ayurvedic Treatments, Reflexology, Hot Stone Massage, Full Beauty Treatments, Elemis Products
Facilities available:
20m Swimming Pool, Swimming Lessons, Sauna, Aerobics, Gym, Hydro Therapy Grotto, Kids Swimming Pool

Ferrycarrig Hotel
Wexford Town, Co. Wexford
Tel: 053-912 0999 ....Page 131
Name of Spa:
Health & Beauty at The Lodge
No. of Treatments: 45
No. of Treatment Rooms: 4
Treatments Offered:
Facials, Aromatherapy, Massage, Reflexology, Hot Stone Therapy, Indian Head Massage, Manicures & Pedicures, Makeovers, Body Treatments, Pamper Days, Bridal Packages
Facilities available:
Intense Pulsed Light, Platinum Detox, Relaxation and Reception Area

Kelly's Resort Hotel & Spa
Rosslare, Co. Wexford
Tel: 053-913 2114 ....Page 129
Name of Spa:
SeaSpa
Type of Spa:
Resort Spa
No. of Treatments: 34
No. of Treatment Rooms: 12
Treatments Offered:
Aromatherapy & Holistic Massages, Body Wraps, Facials, Ayurvedic Hot Stone Treatments, Reflexology, Reiki, Sports Therapy Massage, Manicure & Pedicure, Candling
Facilities available:
Serail Mud Room, Seaweed Baths, Rock Sauna, Heated Loungers, Sea Water Vitality Pool, Rain Forest Showers, Pebble Walk Way, Salt Infused Steam Rooms, Relaxation Rooms, Laconium Sauna

Seafield Golf & Spa Hotel
Gorey, Co. Wexford
Tel: 053-942 4000..................Page 128
Name of Spa:
Oceo Spa
Type of Spa:
Hotel with Comprehensive Spa
No. of Treatments: 66
No. of Treatment Rooms: 16
Treatments Offered:
Payot Renewing Youth Smooth Facial, Firm Facial, Hot Stone Massage, Back Massage, Resource Mineral Body Wrap & Exfoliation Fitness Wrap, Aroma Algae Detox Wrap, Oceo Spa Manicure & Pedicure
Facilities available:
16 Metre Hydrotherapy Pool, Outdoor Vitality Pool, Rasul Suite, Hammam Table, Sauna, Saunarium, Ice Grotto, Couples Suite, Spa Café, Aromatherapy Room, Kaiser Gym

Did you know?

Hammam
It means "spreader of warmth". It is the word given to the sensual bathing retreat that evolved over thousands of years and traces its roots back to the Roman Thermae.

Whites of Wexford
Wexford Town, Co. Wexford
Tel: 053-912 2311 ....Page 134
Name of Spa:
Tranquillity Spa
Type of Spa:
Hotel with Extensive Spa
No. of Treatments: 45
No. of Treatment Rooms: 9
Treatments Offered:
Massages, Facials, Thermal mud therapy, Body Wraps, Holisitc Radiance, Reflexology, Manicure/Pedicure, Anit cellulite treatments, Eye contour treatments
Facilities available:
9 treatment rooms, St. Tropez spray tan booth, make-up room, thermal suite (incl.hyrodtherapy spa pool)

Ireland West

Co. Clare

Bunratty Castle Hotel & Angsana Spa
Bunratty, Co. Clare
Tel: 061-478700 ....Page 140
Name of Spa:
Angsana Spa
No. of Treatments: 20
No. of Treatment Rooms: 5
Treatments Offered:
Massage, Body Polish, Facial, Indian Head Massage, Skin Enhancer, Hands Paraffin, Feet Paraffin, 1/2 Day & Full Day Pamper Packages
Facilities available:
Sauna, Steam Room, Vitality Pool, Relaxation Balcony, Relaxation Suite, Jacuzzi, Fully Equipped Gym, Personal Training Facilities

Falls Hotel & Spa
Ennistymon, Co. Clare
Tel: 065-707 1004 ....Page 146
Name of Spa:
River Spa
Type of Spa:
Hotel with Selective Spa
No. of Treatments: 50
No. of Treatment Rooms: 12
Treatments Offered:
Facials, Body Massage, Men's Treatments, Dry Floats, Wraps, Mud Treatments, Couples Treatments, Body Polish, 1/2 and Full Day Packages and much more
Facilities available:
20m Swimming Pool, Outdoor Hot Tub, Jacuzzi, Steam Room, Sauna, Gymnasium, Jet Pool and Childrens Pool

Kilkee Thalassotherapy Centre & Guesthouse
Kilkee, Co. Clare
Tel: 065-905 6742 ....Page 147
Name of Spa:
Kilkee Thalassotherapy Centre
Type of Spa:
Seaweed Baths
No. of Treatments: 18
No. of Treatment Rooms: 6
Treatments Offered:
Natural Seaweed Baths, Balneotherapy, Swedish Massage, Body Scrub, Seaweed Body Wrap, Frigi-Thalgo, Facials, Manicures, Pedicures, Aromatherapy, Massage, Reflexology, Hot Stone Massage
Facilities available:
Sauna, Steam Room, Manicure/Pedicure room, 6 Treatment rooms. Relaxation area. Winner, Best Day Spa 2004 (Irish Beauty Industry)

Co. Donegal

Ballyliffin Lodge & Spa
Ballyliffin, Co. Donegal
Tel: 074-937 8200 ....Page 153
Name of Spa:
The Rock Crystal Spa
Type of Spa:
Hotel with Leisure Club Spa
No. of Treatments: 30
No. of Treatment Rooms: 8
Treatments Offered:
Massage (Hot Stone), Facial (Thalgo & USPA), Hand & Foot Care, Beauty Treatments, Male Grooming, 1/2 Day Packages, Full Day Packages, Dry Floatation
Facilities available:
Relaxation Room, 17m Pool, Steam Room, Sauna, Jacuzzi, Gym, Children's Pool, Aerobics Studio

Inishowen Gateway Hotel
Buncrana, Co. Donegal
Tel: 074-936 1144 ....Page 155
Name of Spa:
Seagrass Wellbeing Centre
No. of Treatments: 50
No. of Treatment Rooms: 6
Treatments Offered:
Aroma Stone Massage, Body Wraps, Hydrotherapy, Indian Head Massage, Reiki, Aromatherapy Massage, Facials, Pedicures, Manicures, Reflexology
Facilities available:
Relaxation Room, Herbal Teas & Juice Bar, Showers & Changing Rooms, Towelling Robes and Slippers provided, Hydrotherapy Bath

Jackson's Hotel, Conference & Leisure Centre
Ballybofey, Co. Donegal
Tel: 074-913 1021 ....Page 152
Name of Spa:
Health Suite
No. of Treatments: 10
No. of Treatment Rooms: 3
Treatments Offered:
Full Body Massage, Indian Head Massage, Reflexology, Facials, Manicures, Pedicures, Yoga
Facilities available:
22m Swimming Pool, Jacuzzi, Steam Cabin, Sauna, Massage Rooms, Spa Bath, Sun Beds, Hot Tub, Aqua Lounger

Did you know?

Hot Stone Massage
Is a specialty massage that uses smooth, heated stones. They are often basalt, a black volcanic rock that absorbs and retains heat well. It is a deeply soothing, relaxing form of massage. The heat helps tight muscles release.

Hammam
It means "spreader of warmth". It is the word given to the sensual bathing retreat that evolved over thousands of years and traces its roots back to the Roman Thermae.

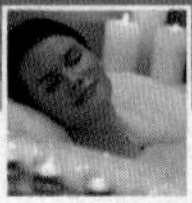

Co. Donegal CONTINUED

Mill Park Hotel, Conference Centre & Leisure Club
Donegal Town, Co. Donegal
Tel: 074-972 2880 ....Page 157
Name of Spa:
The Wellness Centre
No. of Treatments: 20
No. of Treatment Rooms: 4
Treatments Offered:
Massage, Waxing, Make up, Manicure, Pedicure, Facials, Body Wraps, Holistic Treatments, Hopi Candle, Hot Stone Therapy Treatments
Facilities available:
Massage Room, Beauty Treatment Room, Nail Bar, Heated Swimming Pool, Fitness Room, Steam Room, Jacuzzi, Solarium

Silver Tassie Hotel
Letterkenny, Co. Donegal
Tel: 074-912 5619 ....Page 161
Name of Spa:
Seascape Spa
No. of Treatments: 30
No. of Treatment Rooms: 4
Treatments Offered:
Seaweed Bath, Massage Treatments, Facials, Beauty Treatments, Pedicure, Make-Up, Spray Tan
Facilities available:
Treatment Rooms, Aroma Steam Room, Cocoon Meditation Room, Seaweed Bath, Spray Tanning Room, Hair Salon

Solis Lough Eske Castle
Donegal Town, Co. Donegal
Tel: 074-972 5100 ....Page 158
Name of Spa:
Spa Solis
No. of Treatments: 40
No. of Treatment Rooms: 7
Treatments Offered:
Facial Therapy, Bodycare Therapy, Massage Therapy, Pregnancy Therapy, Ultimate Rituals, Hand Therapy, Foot Therapy
Facilities available:
Hydrotherapy Pool, Sanarium, Tropical Rain Showers, Swimming Pool, Ice Fountain, Couples Suites, Singles Suites, Relaxation Room, Fitness Centre

Co. Galway

Abbeyglen Castle Hotel
Clifden, Co. Galway
Tel: 095-21201........................Page 167
Name of Spa:
Abbeyglen Beauty & Relaxation Centre
No. of Treatments: 16
No. of Treatment Rooms: 3
Treatments Offered:
Escale Beauté, Le Grand Classique, Optimiser, Pamper Package, De luxe Jessica Manicure, Jessica Zen Spa Pedicure, Spray Tanning
Facilities available:
Sauna, Jacuzzi, Pedicure Station, Relaxation Room, Nail Bar

Clifden Station House Hotel
Clifden, Co. Galway
Tel: 095-21699 ....Page 168
Name of Spa:
Renew Spa
Type of Spa:
Hotel with Leisure Club Spa
No. of Treatments: 18
No. of Treatment Rooms: 4
Treatments Offered:
Body Scrubs, Mud Wraps, Facials, Massages, Reflexology, Deep Cleanse, Retreat Ritual

Courtyard Marriott Galway
Galway City, Co. Galway
Tel: 091-513200......................Page 173
Name of Spa:
the Spa
No. of Treatments: 60
No. of Treatment Rooms: 7
Treatments Offered:
Signature Baths & Scrubs, Facials, Thermal Therapies, Body, Mens, IPL Rejuvenation
Facilities available:
Thermal Suite, Relaxation Loungers, Relaxation Room, Finnish Sauna, Aroma Steam Cabin, Feature Showers, Glass Ice Cave

Delphi Mountain Resort
Leenane, Co. Galway
Tel: 095-42208 ....Page 182
Name of Spa:
Delphi Mountain Resort Spa
Type of Spa:
Resort Spa
No. of Treatments: 20
No. of Treatment Rooms: 4
Treatments Offered:
Facials, Seaweed Baths, Wraps, Massages, Manicure, Pedicure
Facilities available:
Sauna, Steamroom, Jacuzzi

Inishbofin House Hotel
Inishbofin Island, Co. Galway
Tel: 095-45809 ....Page 181
No. of Treatments: 12
No. of Treatment Rooms: 7
Treatments Offered:
Variety of Treatments and Beauty Therapy available

Lady Gregory Hotel, Conference & Leisure Club
Gort, Co. Galway
Tel: 091-632333 ....Page 180
No. of Treatments: 36
No. of Treatment Rooms: 5
Treatments Offered:
Massage, Facials, Pedicures, Manicures, Tanning, Body Wraps, Waxing, Tinting, Ear Candling, Lazer Teeth Whitening
Facilities available:
Hydro Bath, Dry Floatation Bed, Foam Bath, Manicure Table, Tanning Room, 2 Bathrooms, 3 Showers, Pedicure Chair

Lough Rea Hotel & Spa
Loughrea, Co. Galway
Tel: 091-880088 ....Page 183
Name of Spa:
Shore Island Spa
No. of Treatments: 40
No. of Treatment Rooms: 10
Treatments Offered:
Massage, Hot Stone, Reflexology, Indian Head Massage, Facial
Facilities available:
Sauna, Steamroom, Sanarium, Jacuzzi, Light & Dark Relaxation Room

Did you know?

Rasul: An Oriental ceremony for body care involving a cleansing seaweed soap shower, medicinal muds and an invigorating herbal steam bath.

Raheen Woods Hotel Tranquillity Spa & Kardio Kids
Athenry, Co. Galway
Tel: 091-875888 ....Page 165
Name of Spa:
Tranquillity
No. of Treatments: 50
No. of Treatment Rooms: 6
Treatments Offered:
Germaine De Cappucini Facials, Dermalogica Facial, Body Wraps including Chocolate Wrap, Massage, Waxing, Pedicures, Manicures, Spa Days, Spray Tan, Make Up
Facilities available:
20m Heated Indoor Pool, Gymnasium, Sauna and Steam Room, Hydrotherapy Bath, Jacuzzi, Kiddies Pool, Crèche

Co. Leitrim

Ramada Hotel & Suites at Lough Allen
Drumshanbo, Co. Leitrim
Tel: 071-964 0100 ....Page 189
Name of Spa:
Oshadi
Type of Spa:
Hotel with Extensive Spa
No. of Treatments: 25
No. of Treatment Rooms: 4
Treatments Offered:
Manicure, Salt & Oil Body Scrub, Back, Neck & Shoulder Massage, Indian Head Massage, Aromatherapy Facial Massage, Sports & Fitness Massage, etc.
Facilities available:
15m Indoor Pool, Gym, Steam Room, Sauna, Outdoor Hot Tub, Kiddies' Pool

Co. Limerick

Absolute Hotel & Spa
Limerick City, Co. Limerick
Tel: 061-463600......................Page 191
Name of Spa:
Escape Spa
Type of Spa:
Hotel with Extensive Spa
No. of Treatments: 20
No. of Treatment Rooms: 6
Treatments Offered:
Active Glow Facial, Total Indulgence Facial, Absolute Harmony Facial, Inchwrap, White Chocolate Body Wrap, Yummy Mummy Body Wrap, Hot Stone Massage
Facilities available:
6 Treatment Rooms, Thermal Suite which includes Jacuzzi, Sauna, Steam Room, Ice Drench, Feature Showers, Heated Loungers, Gem Stone Room, Relaxation Area, Male/Female changing Rooms

Fitzgeralds Woodlands House Hotel & Spa
Adare, Co. Limerick
Tel: 061-605100......................Page 190
Name of Spa:
Revas Hair Salon, Beauty & Relaxation Spa
Type of Spa:
Hotel with Extensive Spa
No. of Treatments: 100
No. of Treatment Rooms: 18
Treatments Offered:
Hot Stone Massage Therapy, Body Polish, Platinum Detox, Non-Surgical Lyposculpture, Ocean Chleir Seaweed Envelopment Wrap, Genesis Inch Loss Wrap, Stimulating & Oxygenerating Facial, GM Collin Skin Care
Facilities available:
Thermal Suite, Herb Sauna, Crystal Steam Room, Experience Showers, Rasul Mud Chamber, Foot Baths, Relaxation Area, Rock Pool, Hair Salon, Balneotherapy Bath

No 1 Pery Square, Hotel & Spa
Limerick City, Co. Limerick
Tel: 061-402 402 ....Page 193
Name of Spa:
The Spa @ No1
No. of Treatments: 30
No. of Treatment Rooms: 8
Treatments Offered:
Voya Facial, Voya Massage, Pre Natal & Post Natal Massage, Mom & Me Treatments , Seaweed Bathing Ritual, Body Wraps, Couples Treatments, Manicure & Pedicure, Make Up
Facilities available:
Full Thermal Suite, Herbal Cocoon, Aroma Steam, Sauna with Coals, Foot Pools, Snooze Room, Zen Garden, Irish Mist Showers

Radisson Blu Hotel & Spa
Limerick City, Co. Limerick
Tel: 061-456200 ....Page 193
Name of Spa:
Rain Spa & Wellness Clinic
Type of Spa:
Hotel with Extensive Spa
No. of Treatments: 71
No. of Treatment Rooms: 9
Treatments Offered:
Hot Stone, Reflexology, Elemis Tahitian Bloom, Elemis Bathing Experiences, Elemis Skin Specific Facials, Exotic Lime & Ginger Salt Glow, Sole Delight Foot Treatment, Elemis Massage Therapies
Facilities available:
Hydrotherapy Bath, Beauty Suite, Thermal Suite, Outdoor Canadian Hot Tub, Relaxation Suite, Swimming Pool, Saunas

Co. Mayo

Castlecourt Hotel Spa, Leisure, Conference
Westport, Co. Mayo
Tel: 098-55088 ....Page 203
Name of Spa:
Spa Sula
No. of Treatments: 32
No. of Treatment Rooms: 10
Treatments Offered:
Rasul Mud Treatment, Dry Floatation Bath, Hydrotherapy Bath, Aromatherapy, Reflexology & Indian Head Massage, Body Treatments, Facials
Facilities available:
Thermal Suites, Rasul Mud Chamber, Dry Floatation, Outdoor Hot Tub, Rock Sauna, Relaxation Area

Did you know?

Body Wraps
Improve elimination of toxins in the body while remineralizing the body with the nutrients it needs. Wraps can have toning, relaxing, or stimulating effects and can provide relief from pain due to improper removal of metabolic waste products.

Co. Mayo CONTINUED

Hotel Westport
Westport, Co. Mayo
Tel: 098-25122 ....Page 204
Name of Spa:
Ocean Spirit Spa
Type of Spa:
Hotel with Selective Spa
No. of Treatments: 130
No. of Treatment Rooms: 10
Treatments Offered:
Aromatherapy Massage, Body Exfoliant Treatments, Body Moisturising Peels & Wraps, Facials, Pedicure/Manicure, Turkish Hammam Massage & Body Treatments, Hot Stone Massage, Homeopathic Aromatherapy Massage, Golfers Tonic, Combined Treatments / Orange Zest, Chocolate Dream Wraps
Facilities available:
Cleopatra Bath, Serail Mud Chamber, Relaxation Suite, Swimming Pools, Jacuzzi, Steam Room, Sauna, Hammam Heated Ceramic Table, Pedicure & Manicure Room, California Spray Tan Room

Westport Plaza Hotel Spa, Leisure, Conference
Westport, Co. Mayo
Tel: 098-51166 ....Page 205
Name of Spa:
Spa Sula
No. of Treatments: 32
No. of Treatment Rooms: 9
Treatments Offered:
Rasul Mud Treatment, Dry Floatation Bath, Hydrotherapy Bath, Aromatherapy, Reflexology & Indian Head Massage, Body Treatments, Facials
Facilities available:
Thermal Suites, Rasul Mud Chamber, Dry Floatation, Outdoor Hot Tub, Rock Sauna, Relaxation Area

Did you know?

Reflexology

The physical act of applying pressure to the feet & hands without the use of oil or lotion. It is based on a system of zones & reflex areas that reflect an image of the body on the feet and hands with a premise that such work effects a physical change to the body.

Westport Woods Hotel & Spa
Westport, Co. Mayo
Tel: 098-25811 ....Page 206
Name of Spa:
Westport Woods Hotel & Spa
Type of Spa:
Hotel with Selective Spa
No. of Treatments: 36
No. of Treatment Rooms: 5
Treatments Offered:
Swedish Massage, Aromatherapy Massage, Reflexology, Indian Head Massage, Le Grand Classique Facial, Hydralessence Visage Facial, Mud & Seaweed Body Polishes, Jessica Nails, St. Tropez Tanning, Hot Stone Massage
Facilities available:
Sauna, Steam Room, Jacuzzi, Relaxation Suite, Outdoor Hot Tub

Wyatt Hotel
Westport, Co. Mayo
Tel: 098-25027 ....Page 206
Name of Spa:
Wellness Suite
No. of Treatments: 12
No. of Treatment Rooms: 1
Treatments Offered:
Therapeutic Massage, Indian Head Massage, De-Stress Pamper Package, Anti-Ageing Facial Treatment, Acne/Purifying Facial, Eyelash Tinting, Manicure & Pedicure
Facilities available:
Wellness Suite

Co. Roscommon

Abbeyfield Hotel Conference and Leisure Centre
Ballaghaderreen, Co. Roscommon
Tel: 094-986 2100 ....Page 206
Name of Spa:
GAEA Spa
No. of Treatments: 30
No. of Treatment Rooms: 4
Treatments Offered:
Facial Rituals, Body Scrubs & Rubs, Cocoon Body Wraps, Hand & Feet, St. Tropez Tanning, GAEA Spa packages, Waxing, Eye treatments
Facilities available:
15mtr Pool, Steam Room, Sauna, Spa Bath, Fitness Suite

Kilronan Castle Estate & Spa
Ballyfarnon, Co. Roscommon
Tel: 071-961 8000 ....Page 207
Name of Spa:
Kilronan Castle Estate & Spa
No. of Treatments: 75
No. of Treatment Rooms: 10
Treatments Offered:
Kimia Perfection Facial, SPC Soothing Eyes Treatment, Body Therapy Massage, Hot Stone Therapy, Rasul Treatment, Floatation Treatment, Pregnancy Treatments, Scrubs & Wraps, Waxing, Manicures, Pedicures
Facilities available:
17m Pool, Sauna, Steam Room, Jacuzzi, Gym, Fitness Studio, Nail Bar, Relaxation Room, Juice Bar

Co. Sligo

Castle Dargan Golf Hotel Wellness
Ballygawley, Co. Sligo
Tel: 071-911 8080 ....Page 207
Name of Spa:
Icon Spa
Type of Spa:
Hotel with Comprehensive Spa
No. of Treatments: 47
No. of Treatment Rooms: 8
Treatments Offered:
Venus Beauty Med Medi-Spa & Aesthetic Treatments, Kerstin Florian Facials, Body Wraps & Scrubs, Microdermabrasion, Balneotherapy, Floatation Therapy, Beauty Treatments, Men's Treatments, Touch Therapies, Mother-To-Be Treatments, Venus Beauty Med.
Facilities available:
HydroSpa, Oxygen Steam Room, Ice Fountain, Herb Sauna, Hydrotherapy Pool/Suite, Relaxation Suite, Touch Therapy Suite, Nail Bar

Did you know?

'CACI' Quantum: Non-Surgical Face & Body Lifts

The CACI Quantum is the most advanced face and body treatment system available. Using specific facial techniques in conjunction with a combination of slimming and toning applications, it restores and re-defines facial muscles, reducing lines and wrinkles while simultaneously tightening body muscles.

Pier Head Hotel, Spa and Leisure Centre
Mullaghmore, Co. Sligo
Tel: 071-916 6171 ....Page 208
Name of Spa:
Pier Head Spa & Leisure Centre
No. of Treatment Rooms: 2
Treatments Offered:
Hot Stone Therapy, Reflexology, Swedish Massage, Full Range of Dermalogical Facials available, Waxing, Manicures and many other beauty treatments
Facilities available:
Seaweed Bath & Steam Showers, Outdoor Canadian Hot Tub, Indoor Heated Swimming Pool, Sea-Facing Gym, Sauna & Massage Room

Radisson Blu Hotel & Spa Sligo
Sligo Town, Co. Sligo
Tel: 071-914 0008 ....Page 209
Name of Spa:
Solas Spa
Type of Spa:
Hotel with Extensive Spa
No. of Treatments: 50
No. of Treatment Rooms: 7
Treatments Offered:
Thermal Suite & Rasul, ESPA facials, Body Massage, Body Wraps, Pre & Post Natal Treatments, Reflexology, Holistic Treatments, Manicure & Pedicure, Full & Half Day Package.
Facilities available:
Balenotherapy Bath, Thermal Suite & Rasul, 7 Treatment Rooms, Dry Flotation Tank, Relaxation Suite

Yeats Country Hotel, Spa & Leisure Club
Rosses Point, Co. Sligo
Tel: 071-917 7211 ....Page 209
Name of Spa:
Eros Health Spa
Type of Spa:
Hotel with Selective Spa
No. of Treatments: 35
No. of Treatment Rooms: 6
Treatments Offered:
Seaweed Baths, Hydrotherapy Bath, Reiki, Reflexology, Aromatherapy, Swedish Massage, Hot Stone Treatments, Yon-ka Paris Beauty Treatments, Manicure, Waxing
Facilities available:
Relaxation Suite, Double Treatment Room, Single Treatment Room, Double Seaweed Bath Suite, Single Seaweed Bath Suite, Hydrotherapy Suite, Day Packages & Vouchers available

Northern Ireland

Co. Antrim

Galgorm Resort & Spa
Ballymena, Co. Antrim
Tel: 028-2588 1001 ....Page 215
Name of Spa:
Galgorm Spa
No. of Treatments: 40
No. of Treatment Rooms: 11
Treatments Offered:
Facials, Massage, Manicure, Pedicure, Wraps, Heat Treatments, Scrubs, Reflexology, Tanning, Make-up, Waxing
Facilities available:
Ooutdoor Hot Tub, Hydrotherapy Pool, fitness Suite, Laconium, Herb Caldarium, Aroma Grotto, Ice Fountain, Sauna, Experience Shower, Lounge

Co. Derry

Radisson Blu Roe Park Resort
Limavady, Co. Derry
Tel: 028-7772 2222................Page 222
Name of Spa:
Roe Spa
No. of Treatments: 50
No. of Treatment Rooms: 12
Treatments Offered:
Hot Stone Massage, Seaweed Body Wraps, Skin Specific Facials, Anti-Ageing & Advanced Performance Facials, Jessana Spa Pedicure & Manicure, Elemis Bathing Ceremonies, Exotic Rasul, Aqua Veda Exfoliation Treatment, Specific Men's Treatments, Glow Minerals Make Up
Facilities available:
Champagne Bath, Rasul Mud Chamber, Aqua Veda Exfoliation Table, Aromatherapy Steam Shower, Pedicure Suite & Nail Clinic, Aqua Meditation Chamber, Relaxation Suite, Refreshment Centre & Leisure Facilities

Co. Down

Burrendale Hotel, Country Club & Spa
Newcastle, Co. Down
Tel: 028-4372 2599................Page 222
Name of Spa:
Burrendale Spa
No. of Treatments: 50
No. of Treatment Rooms: 8
Treatments Offered:
Facial, Massage, Make Up, Body Wrap, Reflexology, Manicure, Pedicure, Waxing, Nail Art, Hot Stone Therapy, Full Body Treatments, Reiki, Aromatherapy, Floatation Treatment, Body Exfoliation, Treatments for Men, Full Spa, Day & Weekend Pampering Packages
Facilities available:
Hairdressers, Relaxation Room, Treatment Rooms, Swimming Pool, Spa Bath, Sauna, Solarium, Gym & Fitness Suite

Co. Fermanagh

Killyhevlin Hotel
Enniskillen, Co. Fermanagh
Tel: 028-6632 3481 ....Page 223
Name of Spa:
The Spa
No. of Treatments: 37
No. of Treatment Rooms: 4
Treatments Offered:
Elemis Deep Tissue Back Massage, Indian Head Massage, Reflexology, Elemis Oxygen Calm Facial, Elemis Pro-Collagen Marine Facial, Elemis Exotic Moisture Dew
Facilities available:
Indoor Swimming Pool, Spa Pool, Hydrotherapy Area, Jacuzzi, Outdoor Hot Tub, Sauna, Steam Room, Changing Facilities with Robes

Did you know?

Aromatherapy
Aromatherapy is a form of alternative medicine that uses volatile liquid plant materials, known as essential oils (EOs), and other scented compounds from plants for the purpose of affecting a person's mood or health.

Dublin & Ireland East

Co. Cavan

Radisson Blu Farnham Estate Hotel
Cavan Town, Co. Cavan
Tel: 049-437 7700.................Page 232
Name of Spa:
Farnham Estate Health Spa
Type of Spa:
Resort Spa
No. of Treatments: 100
No. of Treatment Rooms: 19
Treatments Offered:
Renew Rose Facial, Specialised Prescription Facial, Caviar Facial, Farnham Estate Cure, The Real Aromatherapy Experience, Trilogy Lavender Dreams
Facilities available:
Gymnasium, Indoor/Outdoor Infinity Pool, Thermal Suite, 19 Treatment Rooms, 7km of Walkways, Relaxation Rooms, Yoga Studio

Slieve Russell Hotel Golf & Country Club
Ballyconnell, Co. Cavan
Tel: 049-952 6444.................Page 231
Name of Spa:
Ciúin Spa and Wellness Centre
Type of Spa:
Resort Spa
No. of Treatments: 44
No. of Treatment Rooms: 17
Treatments Offered:
Full Range Of Elemis Treatments - Elemis Mothers To Be Massage, Elemis Body Sculpting Cellulite & Colon Therapy, Elemis Aromastone Therapy. Along with Ciúin Signature Body Treatment. Full And Half Day Rituals. O.P.I. and Bare Mineral Make-up for finishing touches, Holistic Therapy, Microdermabrasion.
Facilities available:
Hammam (Traditional Turkish Bath), Herb Sauna, Salt Grotto, Floatation Tank, Relaxation Room, Rasul, Adventure and Health Showers, Hydrotherapy Pool, 17 Treatment rooms

Co. Dublin

Airportview Hotel & Spa
Blakes Cross, Co. Dublin
Tel: 01-843 8756...................Page 233
Name of Spa:
Secrets Spa
No. of Treatments: 35
No. of Treatment Rooms: 10
Treatments Offered:
Massages, Facial, Beauty Therapy, Body Treatments, Hydro Bath
Facilities available:
Pool, Saunas, Steam Room, Small Gym Area

Blakes Hotel & Spa
Dublin City, Co. Dublin
Tel: 01-668 8324...................Page 242
Name of Spa:
Blakes Spa
No. of Treatments: 10
No. of Treatment Rooms: 4
Treatments Offered:
Full Body Massage, Manual Lymphatic Drainage, Feet Reflexology Massage, Oil-Seasalt Massage, Shiatsu, La Stone-Therapy, Indian Head Massage, Beauty Treatments, Ayurvedic Treatment
Facilities available:
Aroma Steam Bath, Herbal Bath, Finnish Sauna, Laconium, Ice Fountain, Crystal Sound Meditation Room, Relaxation Area, Jacuzzi, Colour Therapy, Feet Reflexology Walk

Castleknock Hotel and Country Club
Dublin City, Co. Dublin
Tel: 01-640 6300...................Page 245
Name of Spa:
Tonic Health & Day Spa
No. of Treatments: 19
No. of Treatment Rooms: 4
Treatments Offered:
Facials, Massage, Reflexology, Body Treatments, Manicures, Pedicures, Waxing, False Tan Application, Beauty Treatments
Facilities available:
Sauna, Steam Room, Spa Jacuzzi, 18m Swimming Pool, Gymnasium, Aerobics Studio, Childrens' Pool

Clarence (The)
Dublin City, Co. Dublin
Tel: 01-407 0800...................Page 246
Name of Spa:
Therapy Treatment Room
No. of Treatments: 5
No. of Treatment Rooms: 1
Treatments Offered:
1 Hour Body Massage, Aromatherapy Massage 1.5 hours, Swedish Massage 1.5 hours. Pre-Natal Massage 1 hour, Facial Massage 1 hour
Facilities available:
Fitness Room with running machine, cross-trainer & cycling machine

Deer Park Hotel Golf & Spa
Howth, Co. Dublin
Tel: 01-832 2624...................Page 269
Name of Spa:
DP Spa
Type of Spa:
Hotel with Selective Spa
No. of Treatments: 65
No. of Treatment Rooms: 6
Treatments Offered:
Hot Stone Massage, Balneotherapy Bath, Hydro Lifting Facial, Moor Mud Body Mask, Full Body Spray Tan, Full Body Massage
Facilities available:
Single Treatment Rooms, Double Treatment Rooms, Relaxation Room, Balneotherapy Bath Room, Spray Tan Room

Rochestown Lodge Hotel & Replenish Day Spa
Dun Laoghaire, Co. Dublin
Tel: 01-285 3555...................Page 269
Name of Spa:
Replenish Day Spa
No. of Treatments: 60
No. of Treatment Rooms: 9
Treatments Offered:
Aroma Stone Therapy, Skin Specific Facials, Massage Rituals, Aroma Spa Wraps, Luxurious Manicures / Pedicures, Tinting, Waxing, Make Up
Facilities available:
9 Multi-functional Treatment Rooms, Hydrotherm Facilities, Consultation Area, Relaxation Suite, Pedicure / Manicure Suite, Ladies / Gents Changing Area, Juice Bar, Retail Area

Royal Marine Hotel
Dun Laoghaire, Co. Dublin
Tel: 01-230 0030 .... Page 269
Name of Spa:
Sansanaspa
Type of Spa:
Hotel with Comprehensive Spa
No. of Treatments: 50
No. of Treatment Rooms: 9
Treatments Offered:
Uspa Face & Body Rituals, Dry Floatation, Hydrotherapy, Razul, Massage, Hot Stone Therapy, Tanning, Manicure & Pedicure, Body Wraps, Body Scrubs
Facilities available:
18m Infinity Pool, Jacuzzi, Treatment Rooms, Gymnasium, Rock Sauna, Aroma Steam, Drench Shower, Experience Shower, Ice Font, Aqua Relaxation Room

Stillorgan Park Hotel
Dublin City, Co. Dublin
Tel: 01-200 1800 .... Page 266
Name of Spa:
White Pebble Spa
Type of Spa:
Hotel with Extensive Spa
No. of Treatments: 30
No. of Treatment Rooms: 7
Treatments Offered:
8 Facials including Le Grand Classique & Alpha Vital, Tanning, Eyes, Hands & Feet, Reflexology, Body Treatments, Waxing, Stone Massage
Facilities available:
Relaxation Room, Steam Room, Changing Rooms, Gym

Co. Kildare

Glenroyal Hotel (The)
Maynooth, Co. Kildare
Tel: 01-629 0909 .... Page 276
Name of Spa:
Ealú Spa
No. of Treatments: 25
No. of Treatment Rooms: 6
Treatments Offered:
Body Wraps, Hot Stone Massage, Waxing, Facials, Manicures, Pedicures, Spray Tans, Indian Head Massage, Tinting, Make up
Facilities available:
2 x 20m Pools, Sauna, Jacuzzi, Steam Room, Solariums, Hydro Spa, Gymnasium, Aerobics Studio, Spinning Room

Maudlins House Hotel
Naas, Co. Kildare
Tel: 045-896999 .... Page 277
Name of Spa:
Maudlins Hair Salon
No. of Treatments: 34
No. of Treatment Rooms: 2
Treatments Offered:
Full Hair Salons
Facilities available:
Massaging Chairs for Hair Treatments

Osprey Hotel & Spa
Naas, Co. Kildare
Tel: 045-881111 .... Page 277
Name of Spa:
Osprey Spa
No. of Treatments: 75
No. of Treatment Rooms: 8
Treatments Offered:
Hydrofloat, Rasul Bath, Reflexology, Sports Massage, Hot Stone Massage, Aromatherapy, La Phyto Facial, Pedicure, Hammam Hot Massage, Tranquillity Face & Body Treatment, Maternity Massage
Facilities available:
Swimming Pool, Foot Baths, Sanarium, Relaxation Room, Salt Grotto, Snow Paradise, Hydro Jet Pool, Fitness Studio, Steam Room, Family Changing Room

Westgrove Hotel
Clane, Co. Kildare
Tel: 045-989900 .... Page 274
Name of Spa:
Spa Haven
Type of Spa:
Hotel with Extensive Spa
No. of Treatments: 20
No. of Treatment Rooms: 7
Treatments Offered:
Elemis Facials, Deep Tissue Massage, Hot Stone Therapy, Elemis Body Wraps, Hydrotherapy Bath, Rasul Mud Chamber, Hammam Body Cleansing
Facilities available:
Fully Equipped Gym, 20m Pool, Sauna, Steam Room, Jacuzzi, Kids Pool, Aerobics Suite

Co. Laois

Heritage Golf & Spa Resort (The)
Killenard, Co. Laois
Tel: 057-864 5500 .... Page 280
Name of Spa:
The Spa at the Heritage
Type of Spa:
Resort Spa
No. of Treatments: 70
No. of Treatment Rooms: 20
Treatments Offered:
Massage, Wraps, Hydrotherapy, Facials, Mud Wraps, Stone Therapy, Manicure, Sports & Body Therapy, Mens Treatments, Eye/Lip Treatments
Facilities available:
Sanarium, Tepidarium, Hydrotherapy Pool, Tropical Showers, Hammam, Steam Bath, Sauna, Foot Bath, Mud Chamber, Ice Fountain

Co. Longford

Longford Arms Hotel
Longford Town, Co. Longford
Tel: 043-334 6296 .... Page 282
Name of Spa:
Life Health & Fitness
No. of Treatments: 15
No. of Treatment Rooms: 3
Treatments Offered:
Indian Head Massage, Swedish/Maternity/Infant Deep Tissue Massage, Hot Stone Massage, Aromatherapy, Manicures & Pedicures
Facilities available:
Sauna, Steam Room, Jacuzzi, 22 Metre Salt Pool, Large Gym

Did you know?

Body Wraps
Improve elimination of toxins in the body while remineralizing the body with the nutrients it needs. Wraps can have toning, relaxing, or stimulating effects and can provide relief from pain due to improper removal of metabolic waste products.

Co. Meath

Bellinter House
Navan, Co. Meath
Tel: 046-903 0900..................Page 290
Name of Spa:
The Bathhouse Spa
Type of Spa:
Hotel with Extensive Spa
No. of Treatments: 55
No. of Treatment Rooms: 6
Treatments Offered:
Mums to Be Ritual, Stress Reliever, Relaxation Ritual, Voya Detoxifying Package, Uspa Body Ritual, Reiki, Aromatherapy Massage, Seaweed Oil Special Massage, Swedish Massage, Voya Seaweed Bath, Uspa Eye Contour Wrap, USPA Facials
Facilities available:
Indoor Swimming Pool, Sauna, Steam Room, Hot Tub

Dunboyne Castle Hotel & Spa
Dunboyne, Co. Meath
Tel: 01-801 3500 ....Page 287
Name of Spa:
Seoid
Type of Spa:
Hotel with Comprehensive Spa
No. of Treatments: 80
No. of Treatment Rooms: 18
Treatments Offered:
Balneotherapy, Dry Floatation, Hydrojet Water Massage Bed, Rasul, Anne Sémonin product range, Voya product range
Facilities available:
18 Treatment Rooms including Hydrotherapy Pool, Heat Rooms, Experience Showers, Fitness Suite, Outdoor Hot Tub, Relaxation Rooms

Knightsbrook Hotel Spa & Golf Resort
Trim, Co. Meath
Tel: 046-948 2100 ....Page 292
Name of Spa:
The River Spa
Type of Spa:
Hotel with Extensive Spa
No. of Treatments: 8
No. of Treatment Rooms: 17
Treatments Offered:
Holistic Therapies, Facials, Body Treatments, Rasul, Massage
Facilities available:
Gym, 16m Swimming Pool, Herb Sauna, Rasul Bath, Salt Grotto, Steam Room, Jacuzzi, Foot Spas, Spa Treatment Rooms

Marriott Johnstown House Hotel, Spa, Residences & Training Pitches
Enfield, Co. Meath
Tel: 046-954 0000.................Page 287
Name of Spa:
The Spa at Marriott Johnstown House
Type of Spa:
Hotel with Comprehensive Spa
No. of Treatments: 55
No. of Treatment Rooms: 18
Treatments Offered:
Serail Mud / Milk Chamber, Hammam Therapies, Precious Stone Therapy, Floatation Room, Elemis Full Body Deep Tissue Muscle Massage, Elemis Aroma Hot Stone Therapy, Elemis Visible Brilliance Facial, Elemis Exotic Frangipani Body Nourish Wrap, Elemis Nurturing Massage for Mother-To-Be, The Male Must Have
Facilities available:
Indoor Heated Swimming Pool, Gymnasium, Hot Thermal Suite, Outdoor Hot Tub, Pilates Studio, 18 Spa Therapy Rooms

Co. Monaghan

Hillgrove Hotel Leisure & Spa
Monaghan Town, Co. Monaghan
Tel: 047-81288 ....Page 294
Name of Spa:
Lir Spa & Wellness Centre
Type of Spa:
Hotel with Comprehensive Spa
No. of Treatments: 85
No. of Treatment Rooms: 8
Treatments Offered:
Facials, Massage, Body Wraps, Exfoliation, Water Treatments, Alternative Therapies, Tanning Treatments, Beauty Treatments, Nail Bar & Hair Salon
Facilities available:
Thermal Spa Area, Rasul, Floatation Bed, Hydrotherapy Pool, Herbal Sauna, Pedi Spas, Ice Fountain, Monsoon Showers, Relaxation Room, Hair Salon

Co. Offaly

Bridge House Hotel
Tullamore, Co. Offaly
Tel: 057-932 5600.................Page 295
Name of Spa:
Sanctuary Spa
Type of Spa:
Hotel with Selective Spa
No. of Treatments: 50
No. of Treatment Rooms: 7
Treatments Offered:
Swedish Holistic Massage, Spray Tan, Sports Massage, Indian Head Massage, Facials, Hot Stone Therapy, Reflexology, Seaweed Treatments, Nail Bar, Hydrotherapy Treatments, Relaxation Chambers
Facilities available:
Sauna, Steam Room, Jacuzzi, Outdoor Hydrotherapy Pool, Swimming Pool, State of the Art Health Club, Fitness/ Aerobic Studio, Power Plate Vibration Training System, Cardio Theatre, Spinning, Boxercise, Personal Trainers, Virtual Golf

County Arms Hotel & Leisure Club
Birr, Co. Offaly
Tel: 057-912 0791 ....Page 294
Name of Spa:
Springs Wellness Suites
No. of Treatments: 30
No. of Treatment Rooms: 7
Treatments Offered:
Decleor Spa Treatments. Mónamuir Therapy Peat Products & Treatments. Aromamassage, Aroma Expert Facials, Aroma Body Wraps, Localised Aroma Treatments Including Perfect Legs, Perfect Bust & Tranquility Hair & Scalp, Spray Tanning, Pedicure, Manicure
Facilities available:
Jacuzzi, Kids Pool, Sauna, Steam Room, 20m Pool, Hydrotherapy Pool, Air-Conditioned Gym, Whirlpool

Did you know?

Body Wraps
Improve elimination of toxins in the body while remineralizing the body with the nutrients it needs. Wraps can have toning, relaxing, or stimulating effects and can provide relief from pain due to improper removal of metabolic waste products.

Co. Westmeath

Sheraton Athlone Hotel
Athlone, Co. Westmeath
Tel: 090-645 1000 ....Page 298
Name of Spa:
Sirana Spa
Type of Spa:
Hotel with Comprehensive Spa
No. of Treatments: 50
No. of Treatment Rooms: 7
Treatments Offered:
Body Wraps, Aromatherapy, Massage, Hot Stone Treatments, Full Body Polish, Head Massage, Facials, Hand & Foot Treatments, Sirana Fresh Facial, Bamboo Massage, Coconut Rub & Milk Ritual by Elemis, Leighton Denny Manicures & Pedicures
Facilities available:
Swimming Pool, Sauna, Steam Room, Relaxation Suite, Rasul, Laconium, Hair & Beauty Studios, Jacuzzi, Tepidarium & Serenity Area, Sheraton Fitness offering the latest life fitness technology

Temple Country Retreat & Spa
Moate, Co. Westmeath
Tel: 057-933 5118 ....Page 298
Name of Spa:
Temple Country Retreat & Spa
Type of Spa:
Destination Spa
No. of Treatments: 80
No. of Treatment Rooms: 18
Treatments Offered:
Massage, Reflexology, Hot Stone Massage, Detox Herbal Massage, Chocotherapy, Vinotherapy, Jessana Manicure, Jessana Pedicure, Floatation, Organic Facials
Facilities available:
Vitality Pool, Sauna, Steam Room, Experience Showers, Foot Spa, Yoga Studio, Gym, Juice Bar, Tranquillity Room, Daily Programme of Yoga, Walking, Fitness & Relaxation Classes, Pilates & Chi-Kung Classes, One-to-One Personal Training, Nutritionist & Lifestyle Coach by Appointment

Co. Wicklow

Glenview Hotel & Leisure Cub
Glen-O-The-Downs, Co. Wicklow
Tel: 01-287 3399 ....Page 308
Name of Spa:
The Haven Beauty Salons
No. of Treatments: 26
No. of Treatment Rooms: 3
Treatments Offered:
Luxurious Chocolate & Cinnamon Body Sculpting Soufflé. Fresh Menthol De-stress Leg Ritual, Citrus Cellutox Body Blitz, Mediterranean Olive Moisture Dew Facial, Full Body Hot Stone Massage, Reflexology
Facilities available:
Swimming Pool, Sauna, Steam Room, Jacuzzi, Outdoor Hot Tub, Fully Equipped Gymnasium

The Ritz-Carlton, Powerscourt
Enniskerry, Co. Wicklow
Tel: 01-274 8888 ....Page 307
Name of Spa:
ESPA at The Ritz-Carlton, Powerscourt
Type of Spa:
Hotel with Comprehensive Spa
No. of Treatments: 50
No. of Treatment Rooms: 22
Treatments Offered:
ESPA at Ritz-Carlton Treatments Rituals, ESPA Ayurvedic influenced Treatments, ESPA Advanced Facials
Facilities available:
Fitness Suite includes Technologym, Chi Studio, Indoor Swimming Pool, Spa Café, 22 Treatment Rooms

Did you know?

Thalassotherapy
This is a traditional, holistic marine-based therapy that uses natural ocean elements to restore wellness and to unveil one's pure, natural beauty.

Pressotherapy
This is an exclusive detoxifying treatment, which through effective lymphatic drainage, helps to promote the body's natural toxin clearing functions. The revitalization and oxygenation of the tissue helps to slim and redefine the legs, stomach and arms while enhancing skin tone.

Reiki
Reiki practitioners channel energy in a particular pattern to heal and harmonize. Unlike other healing therapies based on the premise of a human energy field, Reiki seeks to restore order to the body whose vital energy has become unbalanced. It brings about deep relaxation, destroys energy blockages, detoxifies the system.

Abhyanga
Abhyanga massage is a gentle but firm whole body massage from head to toe using warm medicated oils. Oils are chosen according to the prakruti (psychosomatic constitution) and the illness.
The massage is done in a soft rhythmic way with one or two persons massaging at the same time for forty five to sixty minutes.

Hammam
It means "spreader of warmth". It is the word given to the sensual bathing retreat that evolved over thousands of years and traces its roots back to the Roman Thermae.

Westport House, Co.Ma

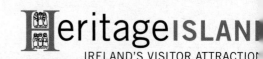

Dalkey Castle

Foynes Flying Boat Museum

Somme Heritage Centre

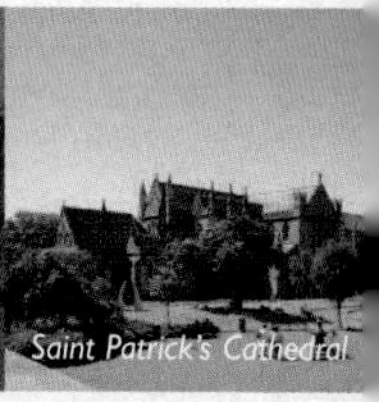

Saint Patrick's Cathedral

KEY TO MAPS

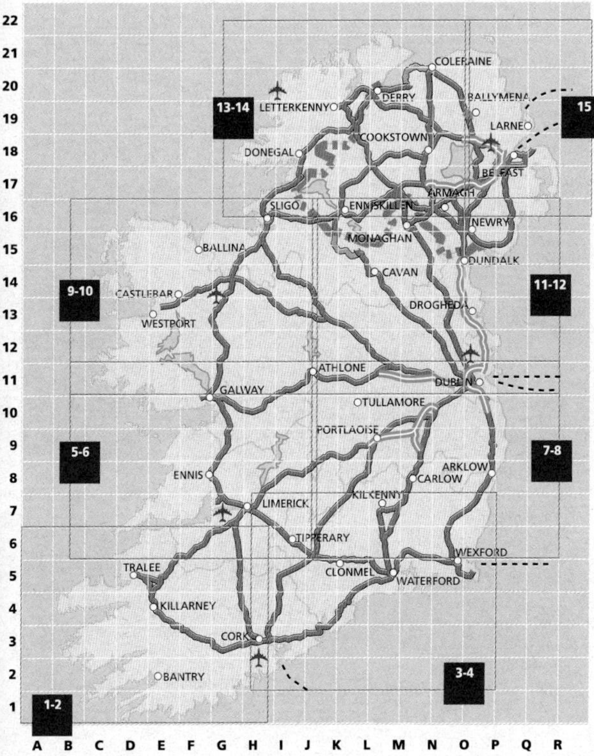

LEGEND

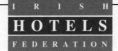

- M50 Motorway
- N7 Dual Carriageway
- N2 National Primary Routes
- N69 National Secondary Routes
- Regional Routes
- Other Roads
- 14 Distances Between Centres (in Kilometres)
- County Boundary
- Northern Ireland/ Republic of Ireland Border
- SHANNON AIRPORT Airports
- Ferries
- Holyhead

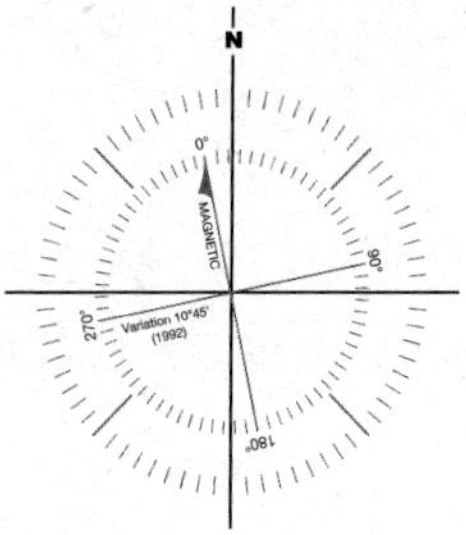

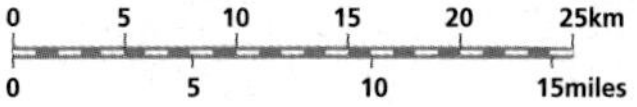

SCALE 1 : 625 000

DISTANCE CHART

in Kilometres

	ARMAGH	ATHLONE	BELFAST	CARLOW	CLIFDEN	CORK	DERRY	DUBLIN	DUNDALK	ENNISKILLEN	GALWAY	KILKENNY	KILLARNEY	LARNE	LIMERICK	PORTLAOISE	ROSSLARE HARBOUR	SHANNON AIRPORT	SLIGO	TRALEE	WATERFORD	WEXFORD
ATHLONE	159																					
BELFAST	66	224																				
CARLOW	211	108	248																			
CLIFDEN	316	171	370	256																		
CORK	380	219	423	187	287																	
DERRY	114	225	118	309	303	460																
DUBLIN	129	124	167	82	296	256	233															
DUNDALK	45	142	82	166	314	340	158	84														
ENNISKILLEN	81	127	135	240	237	346	98	175	101													
GALWAY	238	92	303	177	79	206	277	216	233	192												
KILKENNY	245	121	282	39	248	148	335	114	200	242	169											
KILLARNEY	388	229	430	235	295	89	480	303	348	356	214	196										
LARNE	105	264	40	287	411	462	122	206	121	174	343	320	470									
LIMERICK	279	119	320	138	184	101	369	192	238	245	105	114	109	356								
PORTLAOISE	208	71	250	37	229	174	287	82	167	192	150	50	221	285	109							
ROSSLARE HARBOUR	282	201	320	93	348	206	385	151	237	324	269	100	272	356	204	130						
SHANNON AIRPORT	293	134	345	163	172	126	357	216	261	261	93	138	134	380	24	134	229					
SLIGO	148	116	203	224	167	336	134	213	171	68	142	237	345	240	235	187	319	224				
TRALEE	382	222	423	242	288	121	472	296	341	349	208	216	32	460	103	213	291	127	338			
WATERFORD	285	167	324	74	296	126	383	156	240	290	217	48	192	359	124	97	81	148	283	211		
WEXFORD	264	184	301	76	330	187	365	132	219	306	250	81	254	338	187	113	19	209	299	272	61	
WICKLOW	185	138	222	61	311	256	293	56	140	221	232	100	303	259	193	82	118	216	238	296	135	100

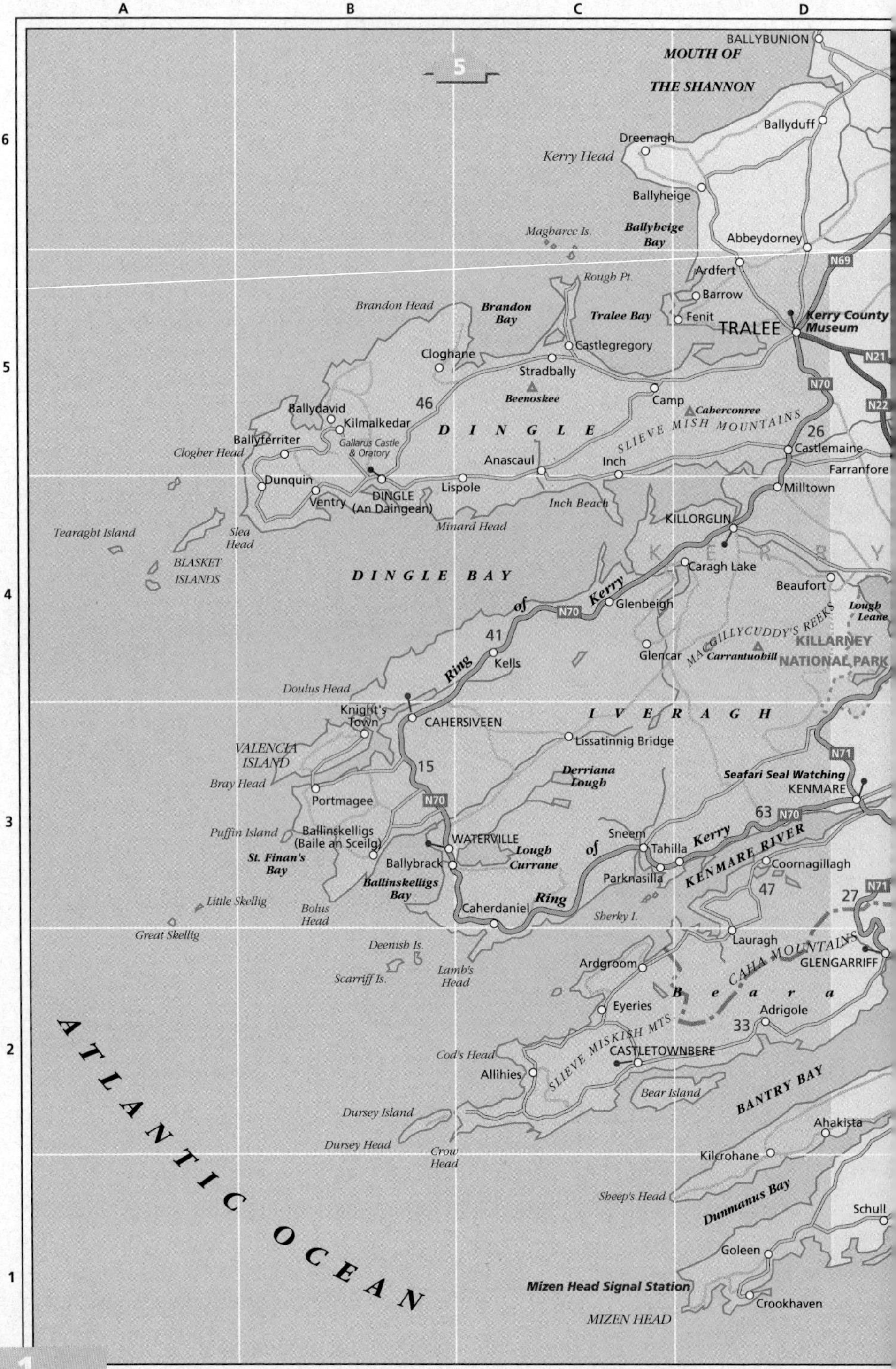
A
B
C
D
6
5
4
3
2
1
5
BALLYBUNION
MOUTH OF THE SHANNON
Ballyduff
Dreenagh
Kerry Head
Ballyheige
Magharee Is.
Ballyheige Bay
Abbeydorney
N69
Ardfert
Rough Pt.
Barrow
Brandon Head
Brandon Bay
Tralee Bay
Fenit
TRALEE
Kerry County Museum
Castlegregory
Cloghane
Stradbally
N21
Camp
N70
Beenoskee
46
Caherconree
N22
Ballydavid
Kilmalkedar
D I N G L E
SLIEVE MISH MOUNTAINS
26
Ballyferriter
Gallarus Castle & Oratory
Castlemaine
Clogher Head
Anascaul
Inch
Farranfore
Dunquin
Lispole
Milltown
Ventry
DINGLE (An Daingean)
Inch Beach
Minard Head
KILLORGLIN
Tearaght Island
Slea Head
K E R R Y
BLASKET ISLANDS
Caragh Lake
D I N G L E B A Y
Beaufort
Kerry
Glenbeigh
Lough Leane
of
N70
MACGILLYCUDDY'S REEKS
41
Glencar
Carrantuohill
KILLARNEY NATIONAL PARK
Kells
Ring
Doulus Head
Knight's Town
CAHERSIVEEN
I V E R A G H
Lissatinnig Bridge
VALENCIA ISLAND
N71
15
Derriana Lough
Seafari Seal Watching
Bray Head
KENMARE
Portmagee
N70
63
N70
Puffin Island
Ballinskelligs (Baile an Sceilg)
WATERVILLE
Sneem
Tahilla
Kerry
KENMARE RIVER
St. Finan's Bay
Ballybrack
Lough Currane
of
Coornagillagh
Parknasilla
Ballinskelligs Bay
47
N71
Little Skellig
Bolus Head
Caherdaniel
Ring
Sherky I.
27
Great Skellig
Lauragh
Deenish Is.
CAHA MOUNTAINS
GLENGARRIFF
Ardgroom
Scarriff Is.
Lamb's Head
B e a r a
Eyeries
Adrigole
33
SLIEVE MISKISH MTS.
Cod's Head
CASTLETOWNBERE
Allihies
Bear Island
BANTRY BAY
Dursey Island
Ahakista
Dursey Head
Crow Head
Kilcrohane
Sheep's Head
Dunmanus Bay
Schull
ATLANTIC OCEAN
Goleen
Mizen Head Signal Station
Crookhaven
MIZEN HEAD
1

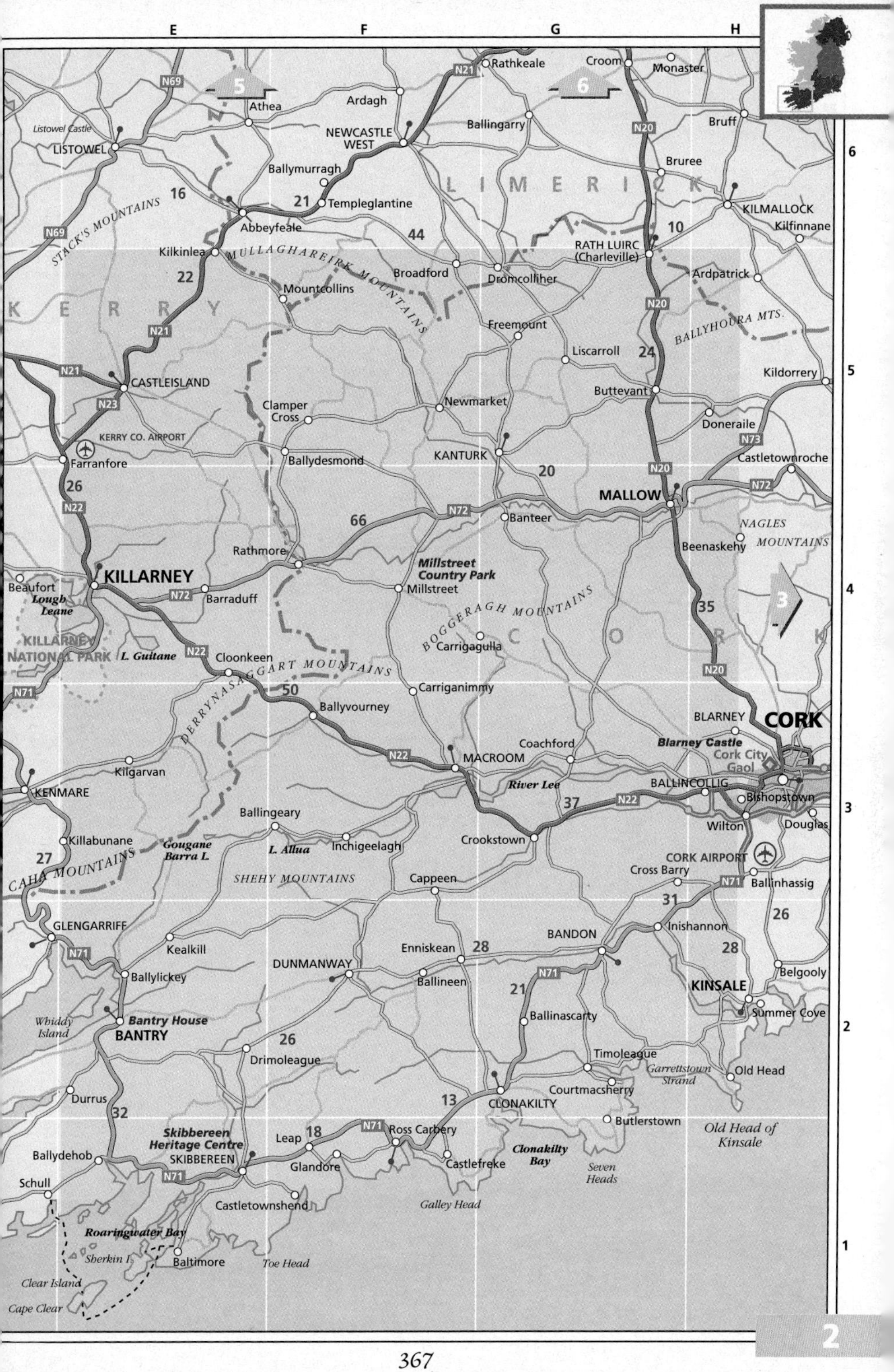

E
F
G
H
6
5
4
3
2
1
5
6
3
2
LIMERICK
KERRY
CORK
Rathkeale
Croom
Monaster
Athea
Ardagh
Listowel Castle
LISTOWEL
NEWCASTLE WEST
Ballingarry
Bruff
Bruree
Ballymurragh
Templeglantine
KILMALLOCK
Kilfinnane
STACK'S MOUNTAINS
Abbeyfeale
Kilkinlea
MULLAGHAREIRK MOUNTAINS
Broadford
Dromcolliher
RATH LUIRC (Charleville)
Ardpatrick
Mountcollins
BALLYHOURA MTS.
Freemount
Liscarroll
CASTLEISLAND
Kildorrery
Buttevant
Clamper Cross
Newmarket
Doneraile
KERRY CO. AIRPORT
Farranfore
Ballydesmond
KANTURK
Castletownroche
MALLOW
Banteer
NAGLES MOUNTAINS
Beenaskehy
Rathmore
Millstreet Country Park
Millstreet
KILLARNEY
Beaufort
Lough Leane
Barraduff
BOGGERAGH MOUNTAINS
Carrigagulla
KILLARNEY NATIONAL PARK
L. Guitane
Cloonkeen
DERRYNASAGGART MOUNTAINS
Carriganimmy
Ballyvourney
BLARNEY
CORK
Blarney Castle
Cork City Gaol
Coachford
MACROOM
River Lee
BALLINCOLLIG
Bishopstown
Kilgarvan
KENMARE
Ballingeary
Wilton
Douglas
Crookstown
Killabunane
Gougane Barra L.
L. Allua
Inchigeelagh
CORK AIRPORT
CAHA MOUNTAINS
SHEHY MOUNTAINS
Cappeen
Cross Barry
Ballinhassig
GLENGARRIFF
Inishannon
BANDON
Kealkill
Enniskean
DUNMANWAY
Ballineen
Belgooly
Ballylickey
KINSALE
Ballinascarty
Summer Cove
Whiddy Island
Bantry House
BANTRY
Drimoleague
Timoleague
Garrettstown Strand
Old Head
Courtmacsherry
Durrus
CLONAKILTY
Butlerstown
Skibbereen Heritage Centre
SKIBBEREEN
Leap
Ross Carbery
Old Head of Kinsale
Ballydehob
Glandore
Castlefreke
Clonakilty Bay
Seven Heads
Schull
Castletownshend
Galley Head
Roaringwater Bay
Sherkin I.
Baltimore
Toe Head
Clear Island
Cape Clear
N21
N69
N20
N23
N22
N72
N73
N71
16
21
44
10
22
24
26
20
66
35
50
37
27
31
28
21
26
32
13
18

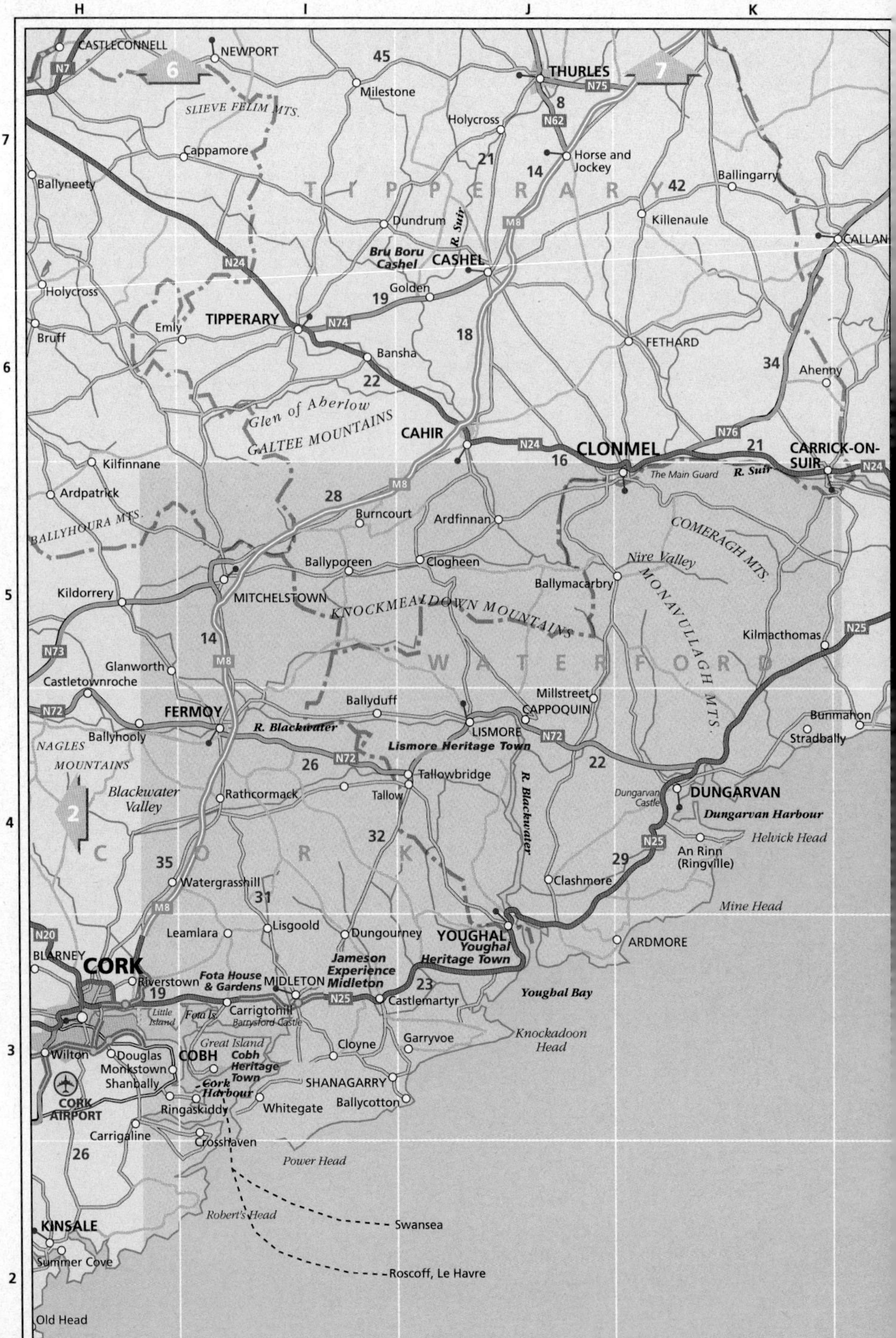

H
I
J
K
7
6
5
4
3
2
CASTLECONNELL
NEWPORT
N7
6
45
THURLES
7
N75
Milestone
SLIEVE FELIM MTS.
8
N62
Holycross
Horse and Jockey
Cappamore
21
14
Ballyneety
TIPPERARY
42
Ballingarry
Killenaule
CALLAN
Dundrum
R. Suir
M8
Bru Boru Cashel
CASHEL
N24
Holycross
Golden
19
TIPPERARY
N74
Emly
Bruff
18
FETHARD
Bansha
34
Ahenny
22
Glen of Aherlow
GALTEE MOUNTAINS
CAHIR
N76
21
N24
CLONMEL
CARRICK-ON-SUIR
Kilfinnane
16
The Main Guard
R. Suir
N24
M8
Ardpatrick
28
Burncourt
Ardfinnan
COMERAGH MTS.
BALLYHOURA MTS.
Ballyporeen
Clogheen
Nire Valley
Ballymacarbry
MONAVULLAGH MTS.
Kildorrery
MITCHELSTOWN
KNOCKMEALDOWN MOUNTAINS
N25
Kilmacthomas
14
N73
M8
WATERFORD
Glanworth
Castletownroche
Millstreet
CAPPOQUIN
N72
FERMOY
Ballyduff
Bunmahon
LISMORE
Ballyhooly
R. Blackwater
N72
Stradbally
NAGLES MOUNTAINS
Lismore Heritage Town
22
26
N72
Tallowbridge
R. Blackwater
Blackwater Valley
2
Rathcormack
Tallow
Dungarvan Castle
DUNGARVAN
Dungarvan Harbour
32
N25
An Rinn (Ringville)
Helvick Head
CORK
29
35
Watergrasshill
Clashmore
31
M8
Mine Head
N20
Leamlara
Lisgoold
Dungourney
YOUGHAL
Youghal Heritage Town
ARDMORE
BLARNEY
CORK
Jameson Experience Midleton
Riverstown
Fota House & Gardens
MIDLETON
23
19
N25
Castlemartyr
Youghal Bay
Little Island
Fota Is.
Carrigtohill
Barryscourt Castle
Knockadoon Head
Great Island
Cobh Heritage Town
Garryvoe
Wilton
Douglas
COBH
Cloyne
Monkstown
Shanbally
Cork Harbour
SHANAGARRY
CORK AIRPORT
Ringaskiddy
Whitegate
Ballycotton
Carrigaline
Crosshaven
26
Power Head
Robert's Head
Swansea
KINSALE
Summer Cove
Roscoff, Le Havre
Old Head
3

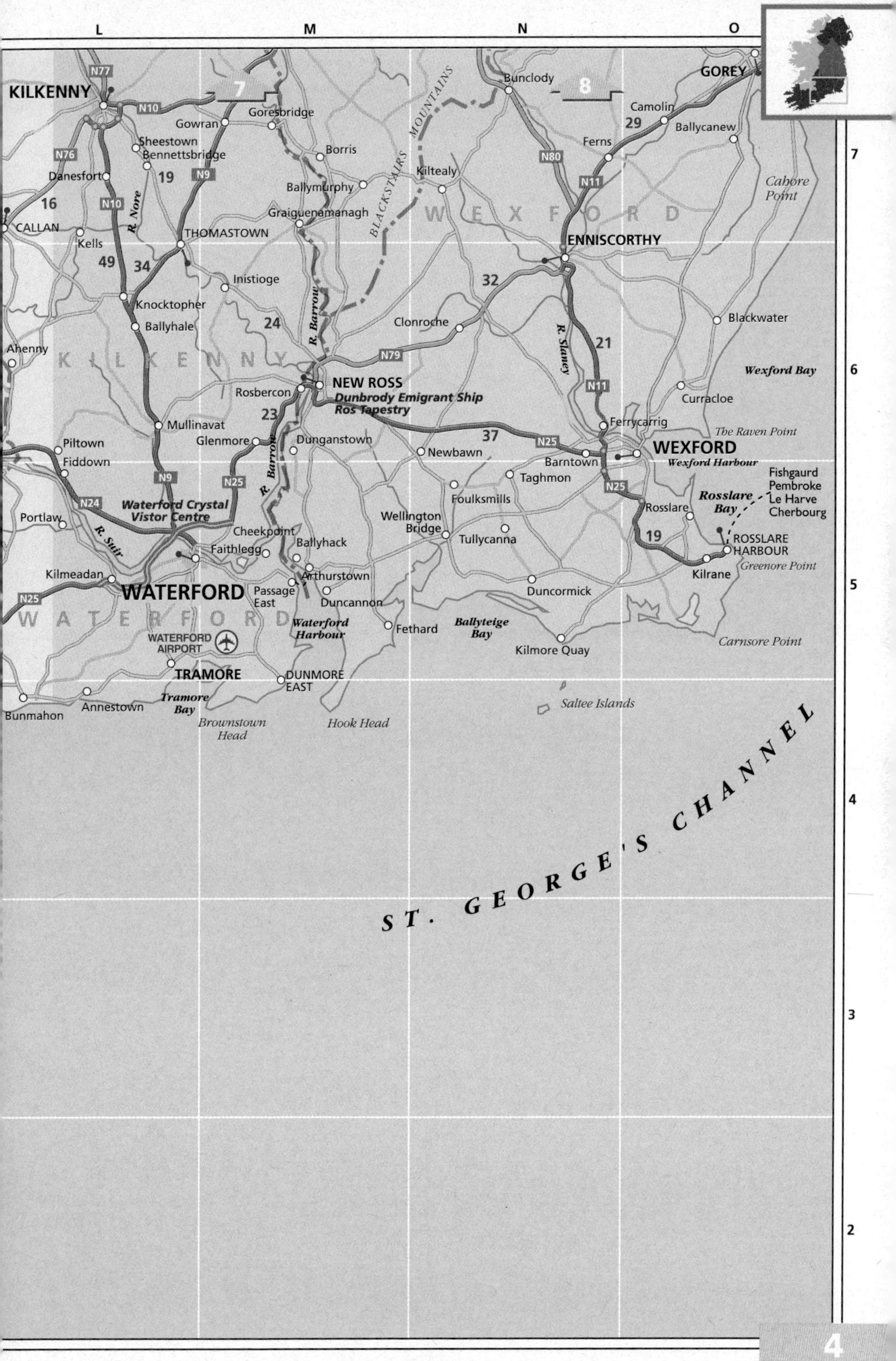
L
M
N
O
7
6
5
4
3
2
4
7
8
KILKENNY
N77
N10
Gowran
Goresbridge
Sheestown
Bennettsbridge
N76
Danesfort
19
N9
Borris
Ballymurphy
Kiltealy
BLACKSTAIRS MOUNTAINS
Bunclody
GOREY
Camolin
29
Ballycanew
Ferns
N80
N11
Cahore Point
16
N10
R. Nore
CALLAN
Kells
THOMASTOWN
Graiguenamanagh
WEXFORD
ENNISCORTHY
49
34
Inistioge
32
Knocktopher
24
Clonroche
Blackwater
Ballyhale
R. Barrow
R. Slaney
21
Ahenny
KILKENNY
N79
Wexford Bay
NEW ROSS
N11
Rosbercon
Dunbrody Emigrant Ship
Ros Tapestry
Curracloe
23
Mullinavat
37
Ferrycarrig
The Raven Point
Glenmore
Dunganstown
N25
WEXFORD
Piltown
Newbawn
Barntown
Wexford Harbour
Fiddown
N9
N25
Taghmon
Fishgaurd
Pembroke
Le Harve
Cherbourg
Foulksmills
N25
Rosslare
Rosslare Bay
Waterford Crystal
Vistor Centre
N24
Wellington Bridge
Portlaw
R. Suir
Cheekpoint
Tullycanna
19
ROSSLARE HARBOUR
Faithlegg
Ballyhack
Greenore Point
Kilmeadan
Arthurstown
Kilrane
N25
WATERFORD
Passage East
Duncannon
Duncormick
WATERFORD
Waterford Harbour
Fethard
Ballyteige Bay
WATERFORD AIRPORT
Kilmore Quay
Carnsore Point
TRAMORE
DUNMORE EAST
Saltee Islands
Bunmahon
Annestown
Tramore Bay
Brownstown Head
Hook Head
ST. GEORGE'S CHANNEL

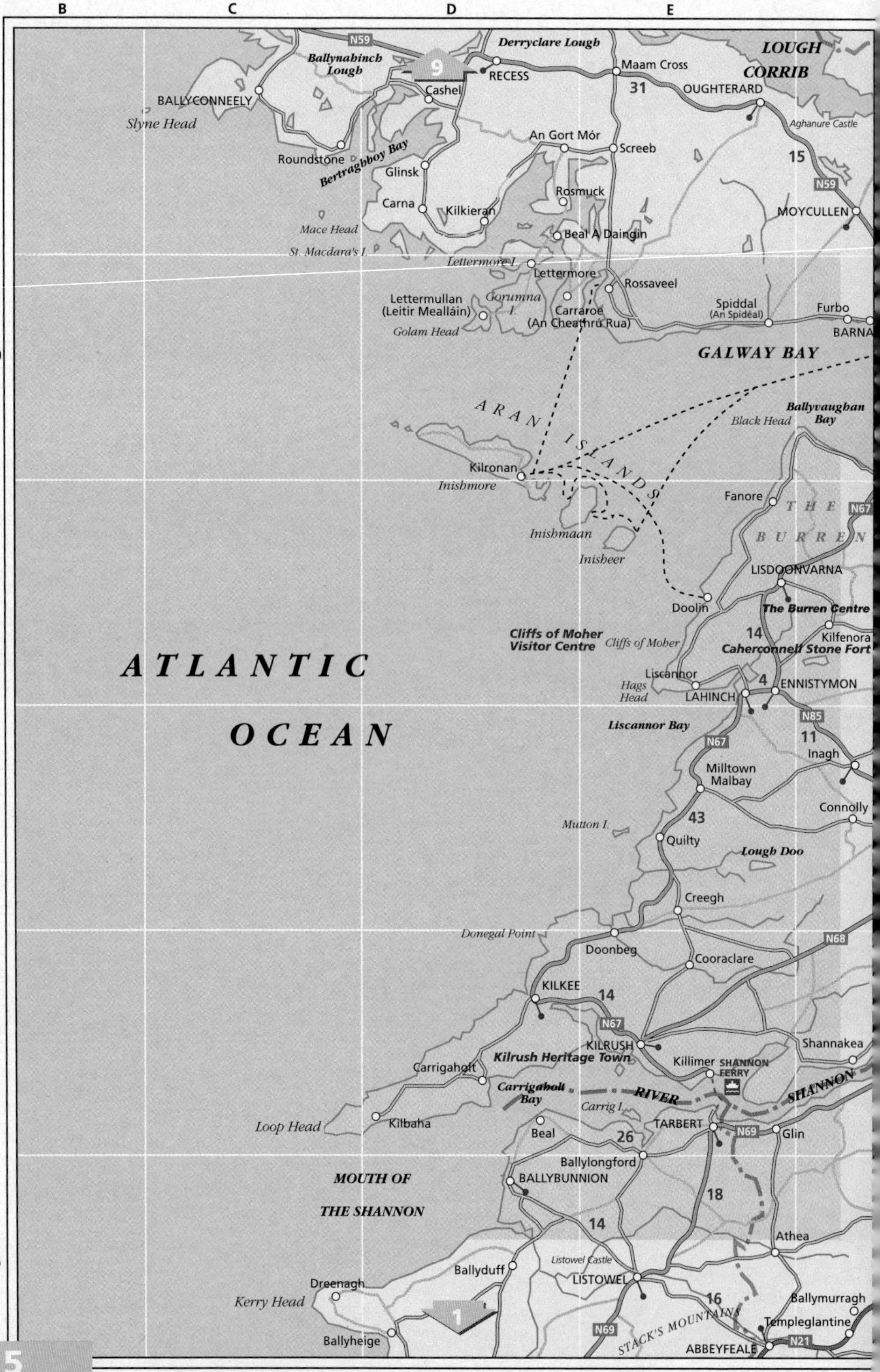
B
C
D
E
11
10
9
8
7
6
N59
Derryclare Lough
LOUGH
CORRIB
Ballynahinch
Lough
9
RECESS
Maam Cross
31
OUGHTERARD
BALLYCONNEELY
Cashel
Aghanure Castle
Slyne Head
An Gort Mór
Screeb
15
Roundstone
Bertraghboy Bay
Glinsk
N59
Rosmuck
MOYCULLEN
Carna
Kilkieran
Mace Head
Beal A Daingin
St. Macdara's I.
Lettermore I.
Lettermore
Rossaveel
Lettermullan
(Leitir Mealláin)
Gorumna
I.
Carraroe
(An Cheathrú Rua)
Spiddal
(An Spidéal)
Furbo
BARNA
Golam Head
GALWAY BAY
ARAN ISLANDS
Ballyvaughan
Bay
Black Head
Kilronan
Inishmore
Fanore
THE BURREN
N67
Inishmaan
Inisheer
LISDOONVARNA
Doolin
The Burren Centre
Cliffs of Moher
Visitor Centre
Cliffs of Moher
14
Kilfenora
Caherconnell Stone Fort
ATLANTIC
OCEAN
Liscannor
Hags
Head
LAHINCH
4
ENNISTYMON
Liscannor Bay
N85
N67
11
Inagh
Milltown
Malbay
Connolly
43
Mutton I.
Quilty
Lough Doo
Creegh
Donegal Point
N68
Doonbeg
Cooraclare
KILKEE
14
N67
KILRUSH
Shannakea
Kilrush Heritage Town
Killimer
SHANNON
FERRY
Carrigaholt
Carrigaholt
Bay
RIVER
SHANNON
Carrig I.
Loop Head
Kilbaha
Beal
TARBERT
N69
Glin
26
Ballylongford
MOUTH OF
THE SHANNON
BALLYBUNNION
18
14
Athea
Listowel Castle
Ballyduff
LISTOWEL
Dreenagh
Kerry Head
16
Ballymurragh
1
STACK'S MOUNTAINS
Templeglantine
N69
Ballyheige
ABBEYFEALE
N21

5

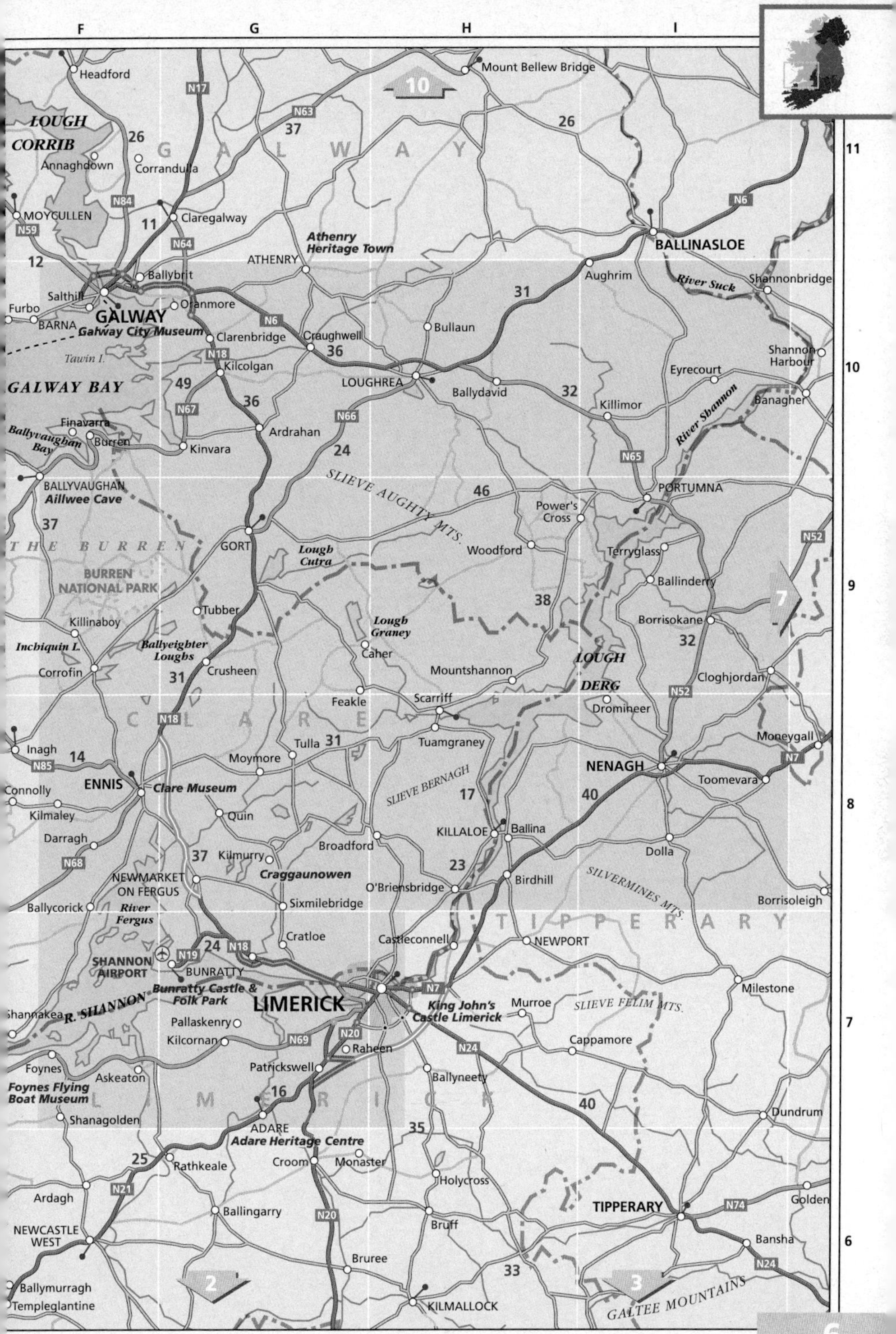

F
G
H
I
11
10
9
8
7
6
Headford
Mount Bellew Bridge
N17
10
N63
37
26
LOUGH CORRIB
26
G A L W A Y
Annaghdown
Corrandulla
N6
N84
MOYCULLEN
N59
11
Claregalway
Athenry Heritage Town
BALLINASLOE
N64
12
ATHENRY
Aughrim
Ballybrit
River Suck
Shannonbridge
Salthill
31
Furbo
Oranmore
GALWAY
BARNA
Galway City Museum
N6
Clarenbridge
Bullaun
Craughwell
36
Tawin I.
N18
Shannon Harbour
Kilcolgan
Eyrecourt
GALWAY BAY
49
LOUGHREA
Ballydavid
32
36
Killimor
Banagher
N67
N66
River Shannon
Finavarra
Ardrahan
Ballyvaughan Bay
Burren
Kinvara
24
N65
SLIEVE AUGHTY MTS.
BALLYVAUGHAN
PORTUMNA
Aillwee Cave
46
Power's Cross
37
N52
T H E   B U R R E N
GORT
Woodford
Lough Cutra
Terryglass
BURREN NATIONAL PARK
Ballinderry
38
7
Tubber
Killinaboy
Lough Graney
Borrisokane
Inchiquin L.
Ballyeighter Loughs
Caher
32
LOUGH
Corrofin
Crusheen
Mountshannon
Cloghjordan
31
DERG
Scarriff
Feakle
Dromineer
N52
C   L   A   R   E
N18
Tuamgraney
Tulla
31
Moneygall
Inagh
14
Moymore
N7
N85
NENAGH
ENNIS
Clare Museum
Toomevara
Connolly
SLIEVE BERNAGH
17
40
Kilmaley
Quin
KILLALOE
Ballina
Darragh
Broadford
Dolla
37
Kilmurry
23
N68
NEWMARKET ON FERGUS
Craggaunowen
SILVERMINES MTS.
Birdhill
O'Briensbridge
Ballycorick
River Fergus
Sixmilebridge
Borrisoleigh
T I P P E R A R Y
Cratloe
Castleconnell
NEWPORT
24
N18
SHANNON AIRPORT
N19
BUNRATTY
Milestone
Bunratty Castle & Folk Park
N7
Shannakea
R. SHANNON
LIMERICK
King John's Castle Limerick
Murroe
SLIEVE FELIM MTS.
Pallaskenry
N20
Kilcornan
N69
Raheen
N24
Cappamore
Foynes
Patrickswell
Askeaton
Ballyneety
Foynes Flying Boat Museum
16
L I M E R I C K
40
Shanagolden
Dundrum
ADARE
35
Adare Heritage Centre
25
Rathkeale
Croom
Monaster
Holycross
Ardagh
N21
Golden
Ballingarry
N20
TIPPERARY
N74
Bruff
NEWCASTLE WEST
Bansha
Bruree
33
N24
2
3
Ballymurragh
GALTEE MOUNTAINS
Templeglantine
KILMALLOCK
6

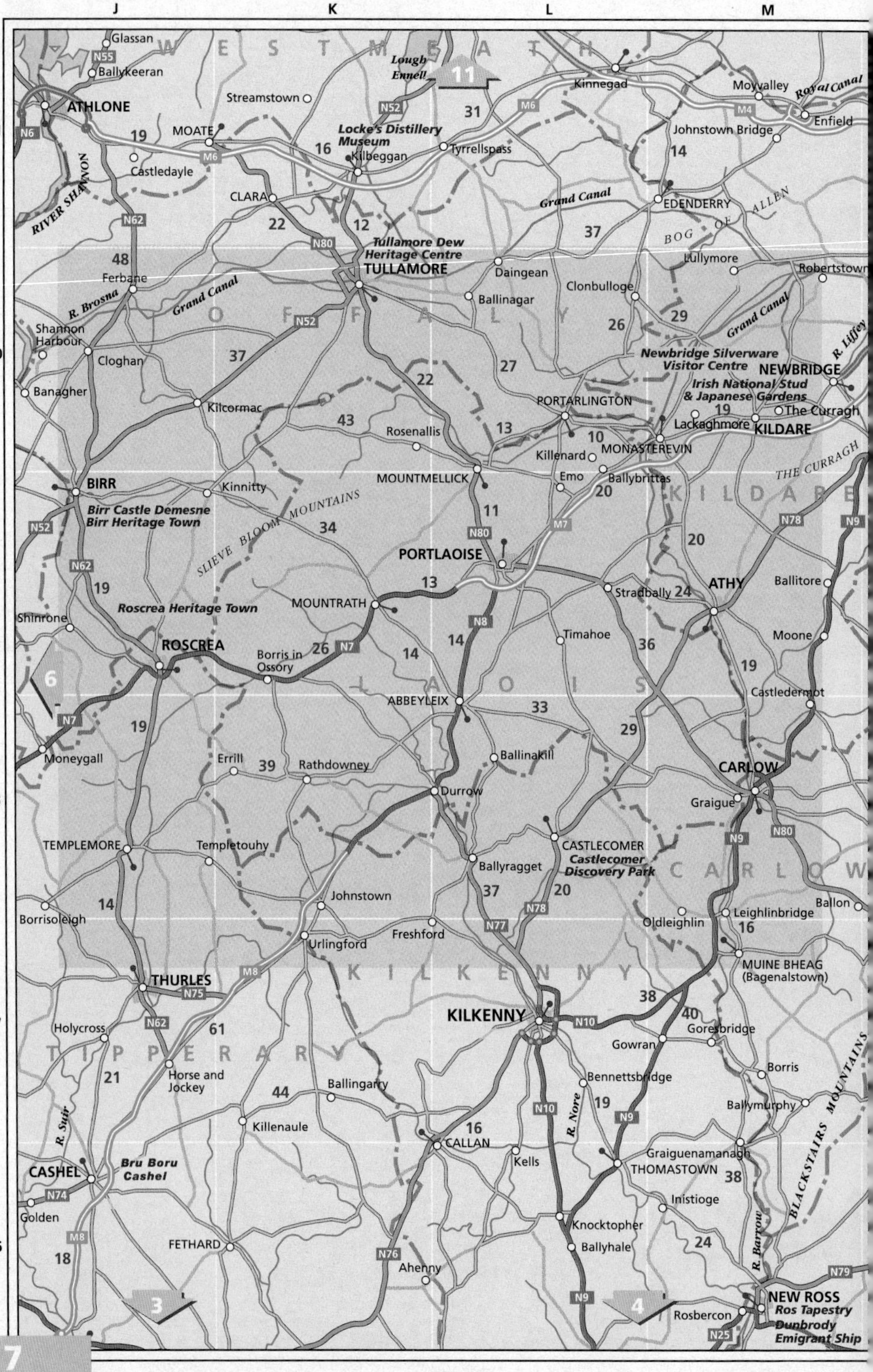
J
K
L
M
11
10
9
8
7
6
WESTMEATH
Glassan
N55
Ballykeeran
Lough Ennell
11
Kinnegad
Moyvalley
Royal Canal
Enfield
ATHLONE
Streamstown
N52
31
M6
M4
N6
19
MOATE
Locke's Distillery Museum
16
Kilbeggan
Tyrrellspass
Johnstown Bridge
14
RIVER SHANNON
Castledayle
M6
CLARA
Grand Canal
EDENDERRY
BOG OF ALLEN
N62
22
12
37
Tullamore Dew Heritage Centre
N80
48
TULLAMORE
Daingean
Lullymore
Robertstown
Ferbane
Clonbulloge
R. Brosna
Grand Canal
Ballinagar
OFFALY
N52
26
29
Grand Canal
R. Liffey
Shannon Harbour
Cloghan
37
Newbridge Silverware Visitor Centre
27
NEWBRIDGE
Banagher
22
Irish National Stud & Japanese Gardens
Kilcormac
PORTARLINGTON
19
The Curragh
43
Lackaghmore
KILDARE
Rosenallis
13
10
MONASTEREVIN
Killenard
THE CURRAGH
MOUNTMELLICK
Emo
Ballybrittas
BIRR
Kinnitty
20
KILDARE
Birr Castle Demesne
Birr Heritage Town
SLIEVE BLOOM MOUNTAINS
11
N52
34
M7
N78
N9
N80
20
N62
PORTLAOISE
19
13
Stradbally
24
ATHY
Ballitore
Roscrea Heritage Town
MOUNTRATH
Shinrone
N8
Timahoe
Moone
ROSCREA
14
36
Borris in Ossory
26
N7
14
19
6
LAOIS
Castledermot
ABBEYLEIX
33
N7
19
29
Moneygall
Ballinakill
CARLOW
Errill
39
Rathdowney
Durrow
Graigue
TEMPLEMORE
Templetouhy
CASTLECOMER
Castlecomer Discovery Park
N9
N80
Ballyragget
CARLOW
14
37
20
Johnstown
Ballon
Borrisoleigh
N78
Leighlinbridge
Freshford
Oldleighlin
N77
16
Urlingford
MUINE BHEAG (Bagenalstown)
KILKENNY
THURLES
M8
N75
38
40
KILKENNY
N10
Goresbridge
Holycross
N62
61
Gowran
TIPPERARY
Horse and Jockey
Bennettsbridge
Borris
21
44
Ballingarry
19
R. Nore
Ballymurphy
N10
N9
BLACKSTAIRS MOUNTAINS
R. Suir
Killenaule
16
CALLAN
Bru Boru Cashel
Graiguenamanagh
CASHEL
Kells
THOMASTOWN
38
N74
Inistioge
Golden
Knocktopher
Ballyhale
24
FETHARD
R. Barrow
M8
18
N76
Ahenny
N79
NEW ROSS
3
N9
4
Ros Tapestry
Dunbrody Emigrant Ship
Rosbercon
N25
7

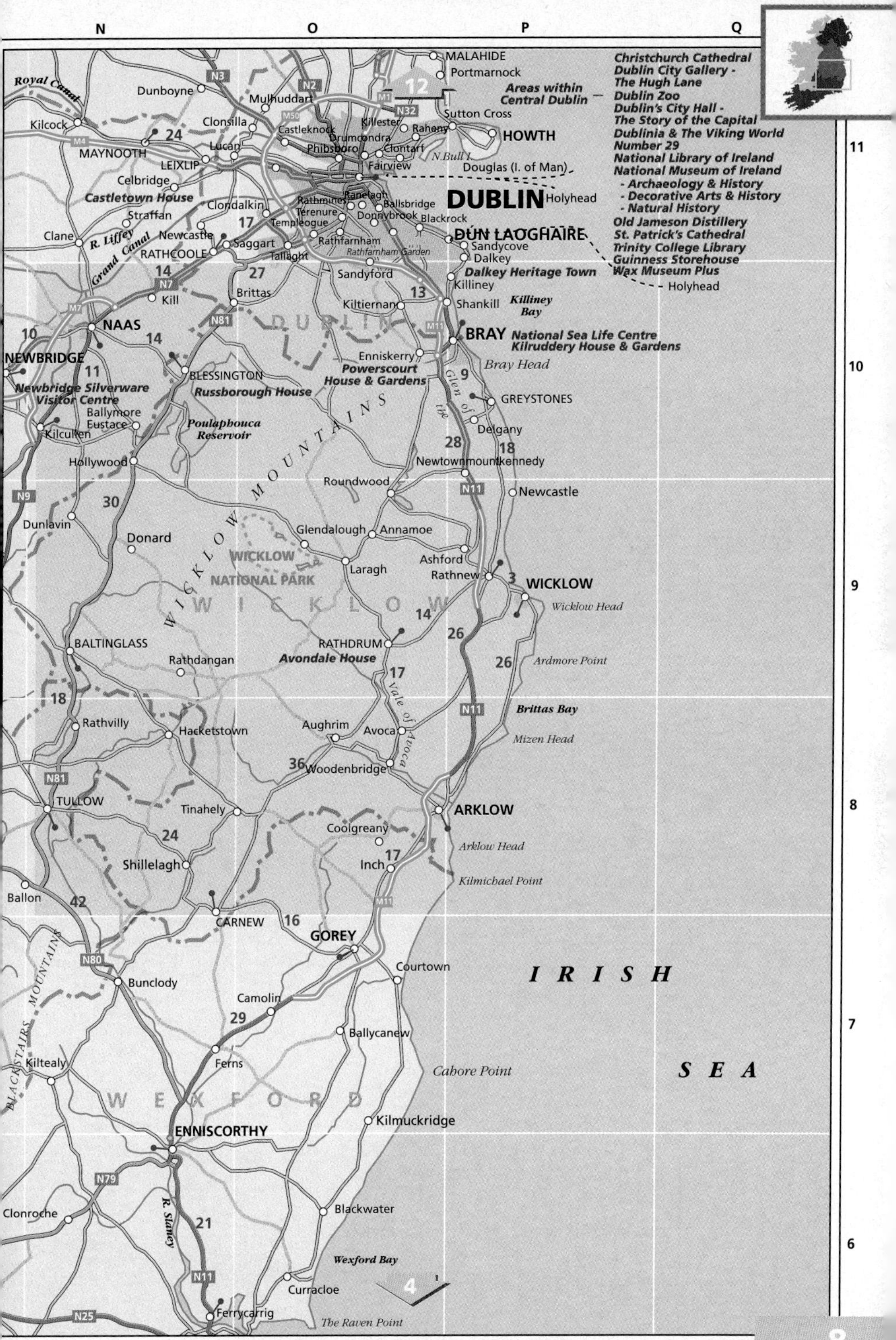

N
O
P
Q
11
10
9
8
7
6
Christchurch Cathedral
Dublin City Gallery - The Hugh Lane
Dublin Zoo
Dublin's City Hall - The Story of the Capital
Dublinia & The Viking World
Number 29
National Library of Ireland
National Museum of Ireland
- Archaeology & History
- Decorative Arts & History
- Natural History
Old Jameson Distillery
St. Patrick's Cathedral
Trinity College Library
Guinness Storehouse
Wax Museum Plus
Areas within Central Dublin
MALAHIDE
Portmarnock
Sutton Cross
HOWTH
Royal Canal
Dunboyne
Mulhuddart
Kilcock
Clonsilla
Castleknock
Killester
Raheny
Drumcondra
Phibsboro
Clontarf
MAYNOOTH
Lucan
LEIXLIP
Fairview
N.Bull I.
Douglas (I. of Man)
Celbridge
Castletown House
DUBLIN
Holyhead
Clondalkin
Rathmines
Ranelagh
Ballsbridge
Terenure
Donnybrook
Blackrock
Straffan
Templeogue
DÚN LAOGHAIRE
Clane
R. Liffey
Newcastle
Rathfarnham
Grand Canal
Saggart
Rathfarnham Garden
Sandycove
RATHCOOLE
Tallaght
Dalkey
Sandyford
Dalkey Heritage Town
Holyhead
Killiney
Kill
Brittas
Kiltiernan
Shankill
Killiney Bay
NAAS
DUBLIN
BRAY
National Sea Life Centre
Kilruddery House & Gardens
NEWBRIDGE
Enniskerry
Bray Head
BLESSINGTON
Powerscourt House & Gardens
Newbridge Silverware Visitor Centre
Russborough House
Glen of the
GREYSTONES
Ballymore Eustace
Kilcullen
Poulaphouca Reservoir
WICKLOW MOUNTAINS
Delgany
Hollywood
Newtownmountkennedy
Roundwood
Newcastle
Dunlavin
Glendalough
Annamoe
Donard
WICKLOW NATIONAL PARK
Ashford
Laragh
Rathnew
WICKLOW
Wicklow Head
WICKLOW
BALTINGLASS
RATHDRUM
Rathdangan
Avondale House
Ardmore Point
Vale of Avoca
Brittas Bay
Rathvilly
Aughrim
Avoca
Hacketstown
Mizen Head
Woodenbridge
TULLOW
Tinahely
ARKLOW
Coolgreany
Arklow Head
Shillelagh
Inch
Kilmichael Point
Ballon
CARNEW
GOREY
BLACKSTAIRS MOUNTAINS
Courtown
Bunclody
IRISH
Camolin
Ballycanew
Ferns
Kiltealy
Cahore Point
SEA
WEXFORD
Kilmuckridge
ENNISCORTHY
Clonroche
R. Slaney
Blackwater
Wexford Bay
Curracloe
Ferrycarrig
The Raven Point

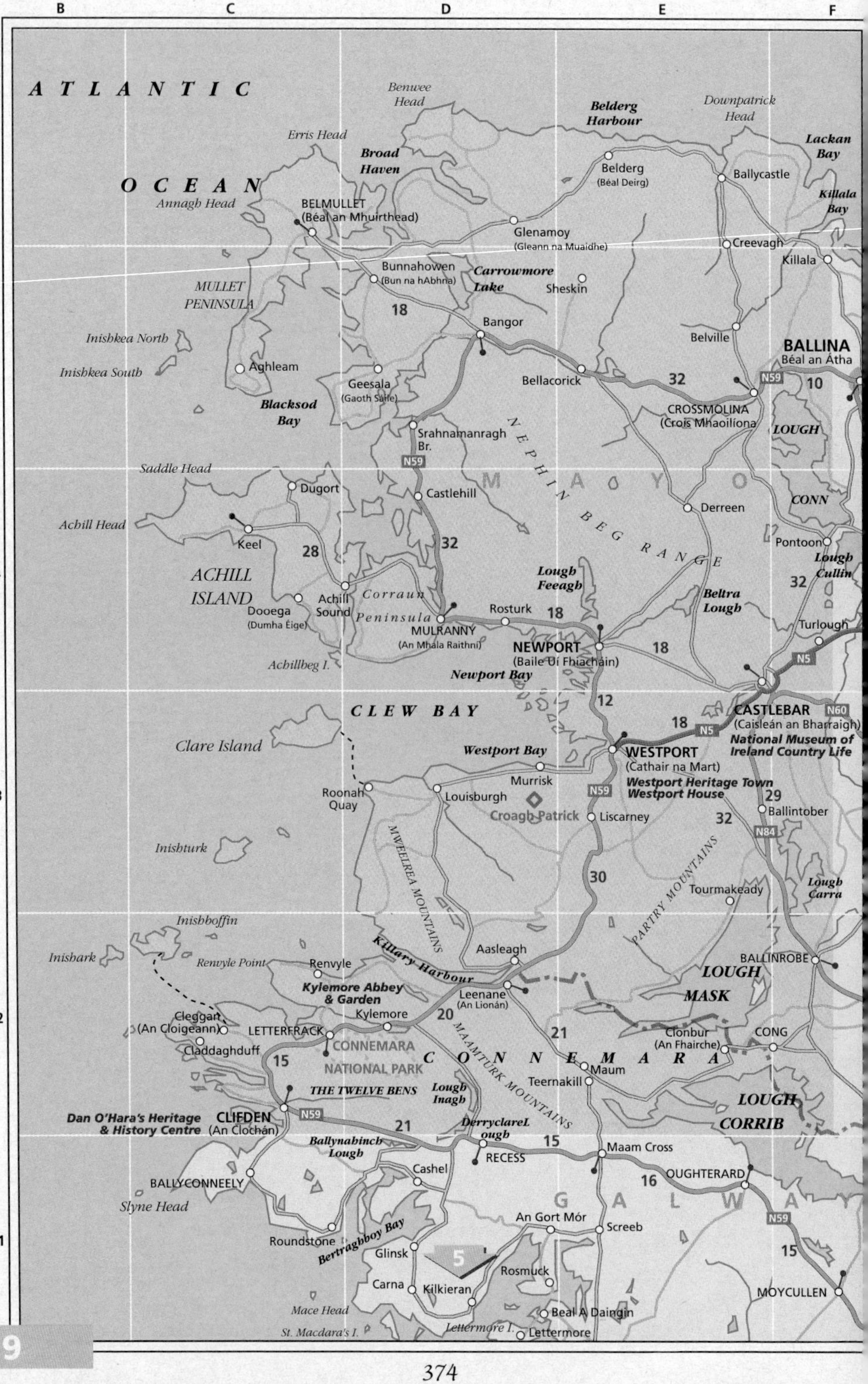
B
C
D
E
F
16
15
14
13
12
11
ATLANTIC
OCEAN
Benwee Head
Belderg Harbour
Downpatrick Head
Lackan Bay
Erris Head
Broad Haven
Belderg
(Béal Deirg)
Ballycastle
Killala Bay
Annagh Head
BELMULLET
(Béal an Mhuirthead)
Glenamoy
(Gleann na Muaidhe)
Creevagh
Killala
Bunnahowen
(Bun na hAbhna)
Carrowmore Lake
Sheskin
MULLET PENINSULA
18
Bangor
Belville
BALLINA
Béal an Átha
Inishkea North
Inishkea South
Aghleam
Geesala
(Gaoth Sáile)
Bellacorick
32
N59
10
Blacksod Bay
CROSSMOLINA
(Crois Mhaoilíona)
LOUGH
Srahnamanragh Br.
N59
NEPHIN BEG RANGE
MAYO
Saddle Head
Dugort
Castlehill
Derreen
CONN
Achill Head
Keel
28
32
Pontoon
Lough Cullin
ACHILL ISLAND
Lough Feeagh
32
Dooega
(Dumha Éige)
Achill Sound
Corraun Peninsula
Rosturk
18
Beltra Lough
MULRANNY
(An Mhala Raithní)
NEWPORT
(Baile Uí Fhiacháin)
18
Turlough
N5
Achillbeg I.
Newport Bay
12
CLEW BAY
CASTLEBAR
(Caisleán an Bharraigh)
N60
18
N5
Clare Island
National Museum of Ireland Country Life
Westport Bay
WESTPORT
(Cathair na Mart)
Murrisk
Westport Heritage Town
Westport House
Roonah Quay
Louisburgh
N59
29
Ballintober
Croagh Patrick
Liscarney
32
N84
Inishturk
MWEELREA MOUNTAINS
30
PARTRY MOUNTAINS
Lough Carra
Tourmakeady
Inishboffin
Inishark
Renvyle Point
Renvyle
Killary Harbour
Aasleagh
BALLINROBE
LOUGH MASK
Kylemore Abbey & Garden
Leenane
(An Lionán)
Cleggan
(An Cloigeann)
Kylemore
20
LETTERFRACK
21
Clonbur
(An Fhairche)
CONG
Claddaghduff
CONNEMARA NATIONAL PARK
15
CONNEMARA
MAAMTURK MOUNTAINS
Maum
THE TWELVE BENS
Lough Inagh
Teernakill
LOUGH CORRIB
Dan O'Hara's Heritage & History Centre
CLIFDEN
(An Clochán)
N59
21
DerryclareLough
Ballynabinch Lough
15
RECESS
Maam Cross
Cashel
16
OUGHTERARD
BALLYCONNEELY
Slyne Head
GALWAY
An Gort Mór
Screeb
N59
Roundstone
Bertraghboy Bay
Glinsk
5
15
Rosmuck
Carna
Kilkieran
MOYCULLEN
Mace Head
Beal A Daingin
St. Macdara's I.
Lettermore I.
Lettermore

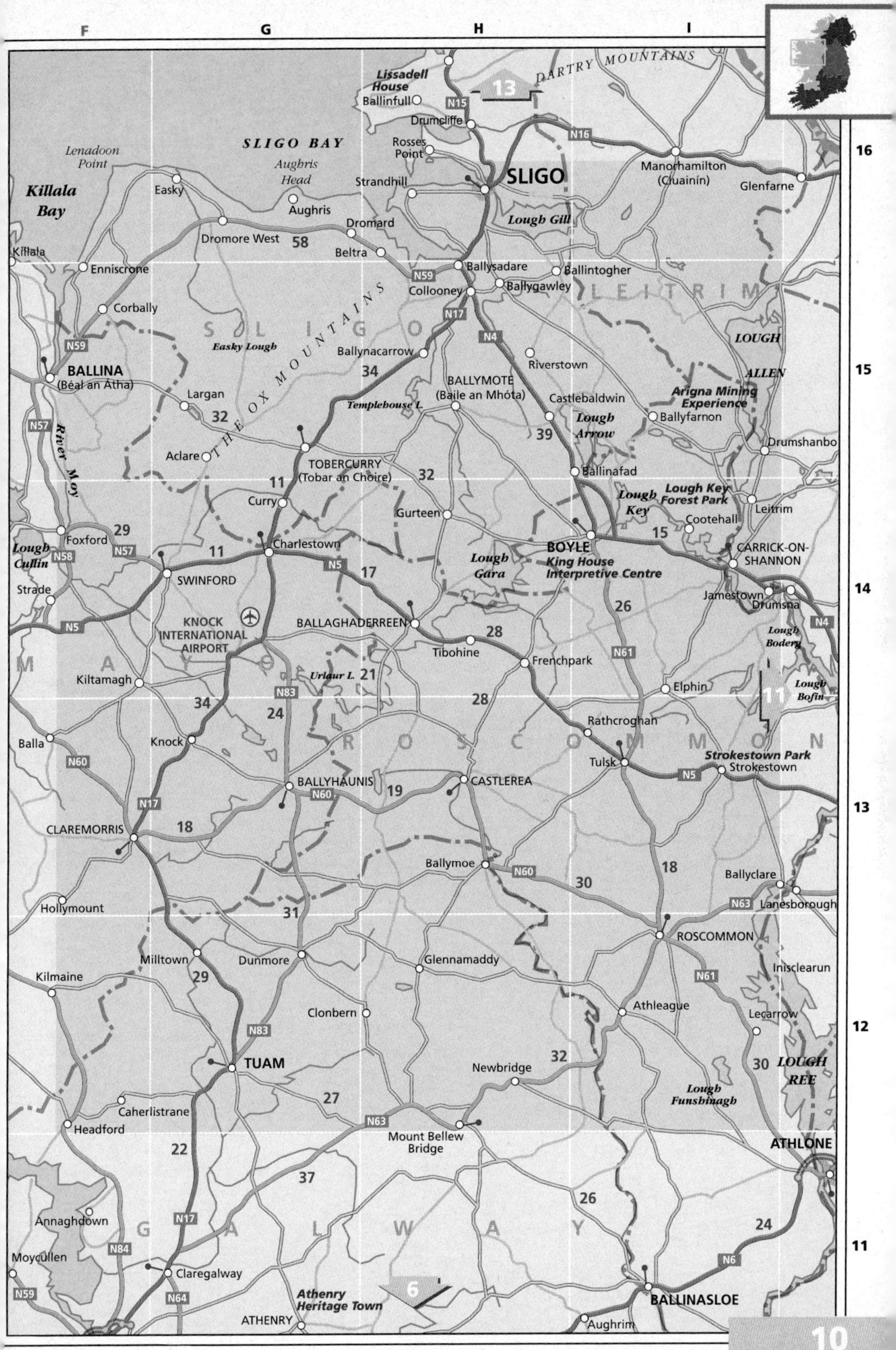

F
G
H
I
16
15
14
13
12
11
10
Lissadell House
Ballinfull
Drumcliffe
DARTRY MOUNTAINS
13
N15
N16
SLIGO BAY
Lenadoon Point
Killala Bay
Aughris Head
Aughris
Easky
Rosses Point
Strandhill
SLIGO
Manorhamilton (Cluainín)
Glenfarne
Lough Gill
Dromore West
58
Dromard
Beltra
Killala
Enniscrone
Ballysadare
Ballintogher
N59
Collooney
Ballygawley
LEITRIM
Corbally
N17
SLIGO
THE OX MOUNTAINS
Easky Lough
N4
LOUGH ALLEN
N59
Ballynacarrow
Riverstown
BALLINA
(Béal an Átha)
34
BALLYMOTE
(Baile an Mhóta)
Largan
Castlebaldwin
Arigna Mining Experience
Templehouse L.
32
Lough Arrow
Ballyfarnon
N57
River Moy
39
Drumshanbo
Aclare
TOBERCURRY
(Tobar an Choire)
32
Ballinafad
11
Lough Key
Lough Key Forest Park
Curry
Gurteen
Leitrim
Cootehall
Foxford
29
15
Lough Cullin
N58
N57
11
Charlestown
BOYLE
King House Interpretive Centre
CARRICK-ON-SHANNON
N5
17
Lough Gara
Strade
SWINFORD
Jamestown
Drumsna
26
KNOCK INTERNATIONAL AIRPORT
N5
BALLAGHADERREEN
28
N4
Lough Boderg
Tibohine
MAYO
Frenchpark
N61
Kiltamagh
Urlaur L.
21
Elphin
Lough Bofin
11
N83
28
34
24
Rathcroghan
Balla
Knock
ROSCOMMON
Tulsk
Strokestown Park
Strokestown
N60
BALLYHAUNIS
CASTLEREA
N5
N60
19
N17
CLAREMORRIS
18
Ballymoe
N60
30
18
Ballyclare
Hollymount
N63
Lanesborough
31
ROSCOMMON
Milltown
Dunmore
Glennamaddy
Inisclearun
Kilmaine
29
N61
Athleague
Clonbern
Lecarrow
N83
TUAM
Newbridge
32
30
LOUGH REE
Lough Funshinagh
27
Caherlistrane
Headford
N63
Mount Bellew Bridge
ATHLONE
22
37
26
Annaghdown
GALWAY
N17
24
N84
Moycullen
N6
Claregalway
N59
N64
Athenry Heritage Town
6
BALLINASLOE
ATHENRY
Aughrim

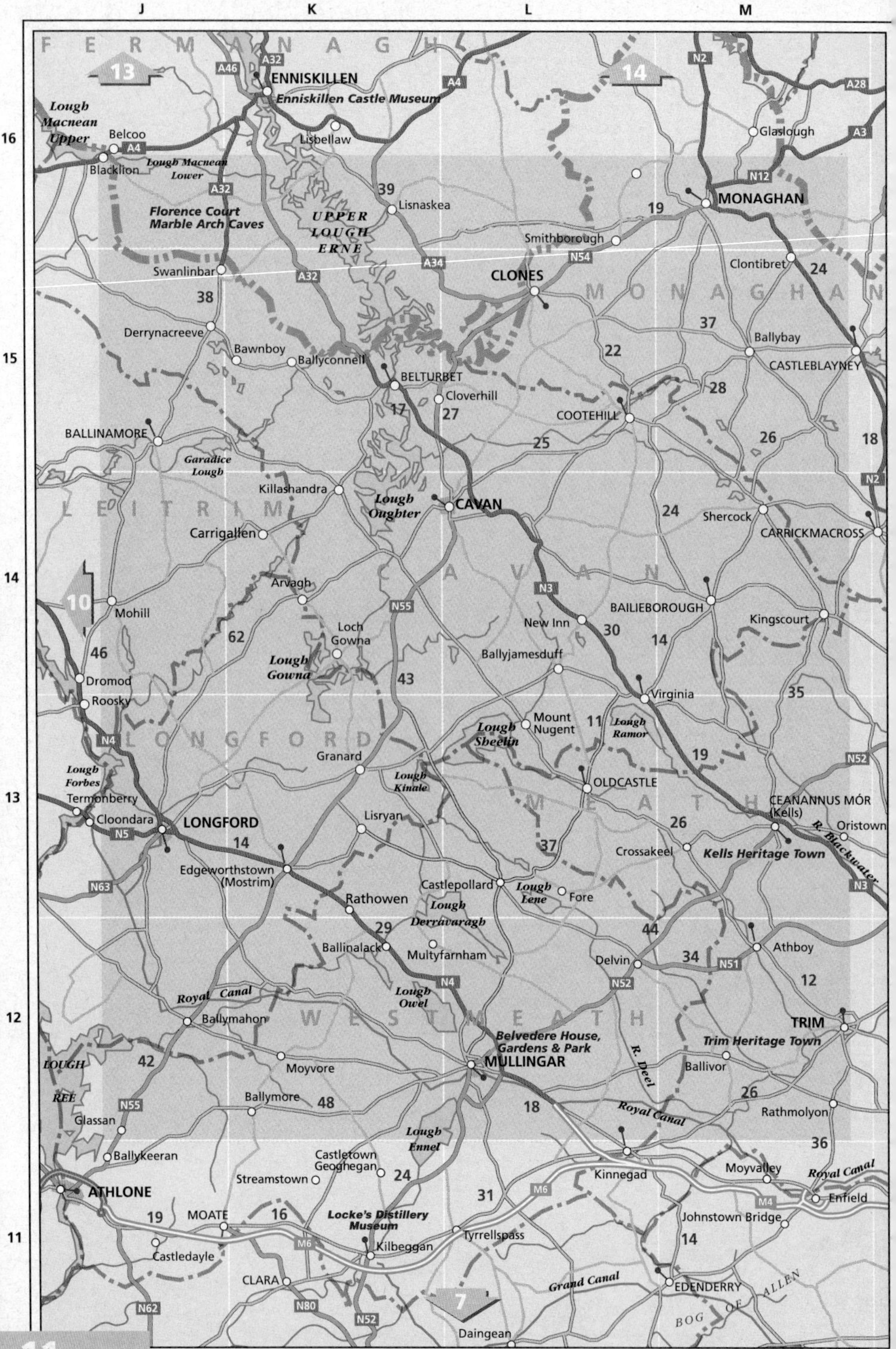
J
K
L
M
16
15
14
13
12
11
FERMANAGH
MONAGHAN
LEITRIM
CAVAN
LONGFORD
MEATH
WESTMEATH
13
14
10
7
ENNISKILLEN
Enniskillen Castle Museum
Lough Macnean Upper
Lough Macnean Lower
Belcoo
Blacklion
Lisbellaw
Florence Court
Marble Arch Caves
UPPER LOUGH ERNE
Lisnaskea
Swanlinbar
Derrynacreeve
Bawnboy
Ballyconnell
BELTURBET
Cloverhill
Glaslough
MONAGHAN
Smithborough
CLONES
Clontibret
Ballybay
CASTLEBLAYNEY
COOTEHILL
BALLINAMORE
Garadice Lough
Killashandra
Lough Oughter
CAVAN
Carrigallen
Shercock
CARRICKMACROSS
Arvagh
Mohill
Loch Gowna
Lough Gowna
New Inn
BAILIEBOROUGH
Kingscourt
Ballyjamesduff
Dromod
Roosky
Virginia
Mount Nugent
Lough Sheelin
Lough Ramor
Granard
Lough Kinale
OLDCASTLE
Lough Forbes
Termonberry
Cloondara
LONGFORD
Lisryan
CEANANNUS MÓR (Kells)
Oristown
R. Blackwater
Crossakeel
Kells Heritage Town
Edgeworthstown (Mostrim)
Castlepollard
Lough Lene
Fore
Rathowen
Lough Derravaragh
Ballinalack
Multyfarnham
Delvin
Athboy
Lough Owel
Royal Canal
Ballymahon
TRIM
Belvedere House, Gardens & Park
Trim Heritage Town
MULLINGAR
R. Deel
Ballivor
LOUGH REE
Moyvore
Ballymore
Rathmolyon
Glassan
Lough Ennel
Ballykeeran
Castletown Geoghegan
Kinnegad
Moyvalley
ATHLONE
Streamstown
Enfield
MOATE
Locke's Distillery Museum
Johnstown Bridge
Castledayle
Kilbeggan
Tyrrellspass
CLARA
Grand Canal
EDENDERRY
BOG OF ALLEN
Daingean
A46
A32
A4
A34
A28
A3
N2
N12
N54
N55
N3
N4
N5
N63
N52
N51
M6
M4
N62
N80

11

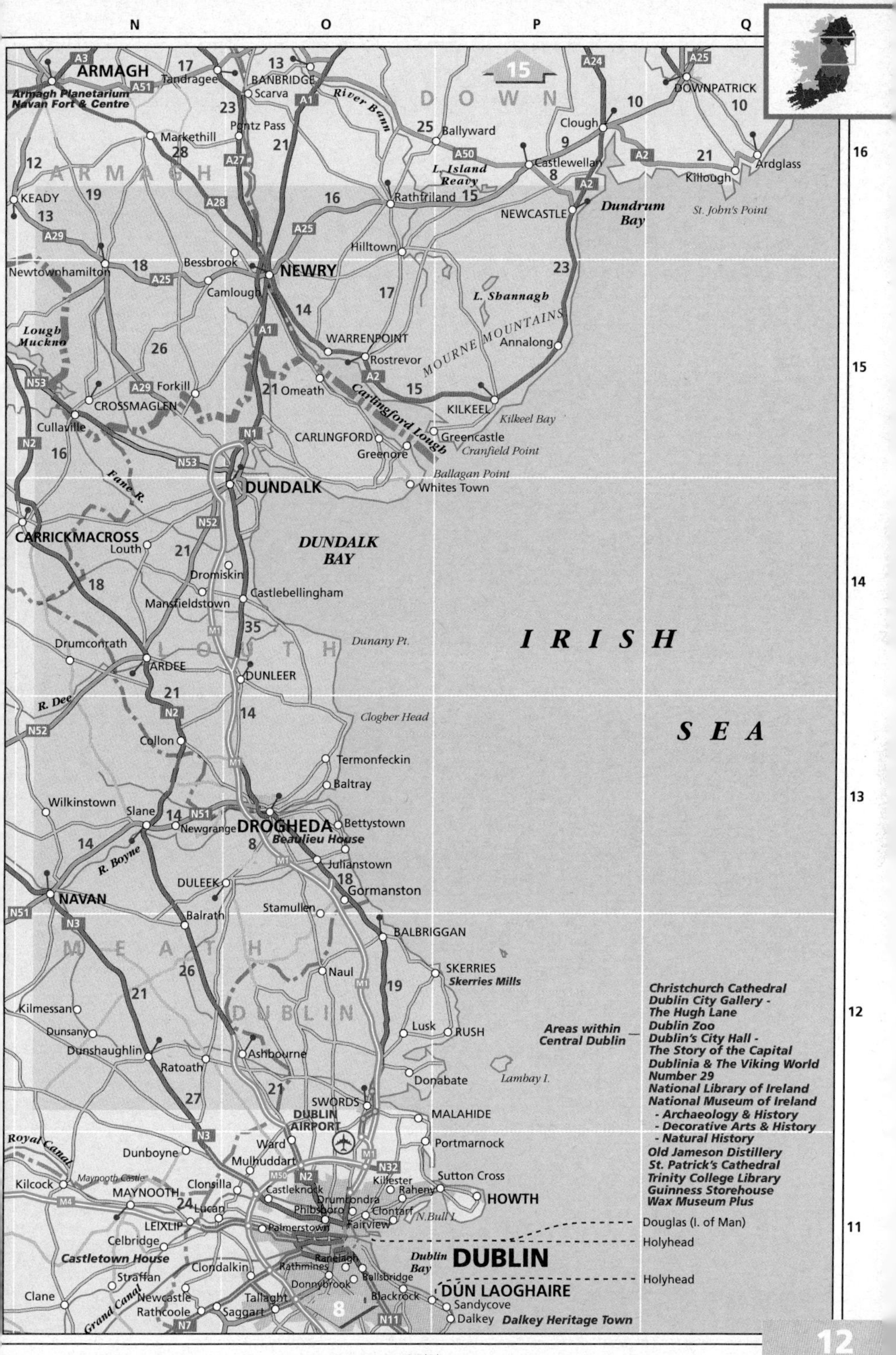
N
O
P
Q
ARMAGH
Armagh Planetarium
Navan Fort & Centre
Tandragee
BANBRIDGE
Scarva
River Bann
DOWN
DOWNPATRICK
Poyntz Pass
Markethill
Ballyward
Clough
Castlewellan
Ardglass
Killough
ARMAGH
KEADY
L. Island Reavy
Rathfriland
NEWCASTLE
Dundrum Bay
St. John's Point
Hilltown
Bessbrook
Newtownhamilton
NEWRY
Camlough
L. Shannagh
MOURNE MOUNTAINS
Lough Muckno
WARRENPOINT
Rostrevor
Annalong
Forkill
CROSSMAGLEN
Omeath
Carlingford Lough
KILKEEL
Kilkeel Bay
Cullaville
CARLINGFORD
Greenore
Greencastle
Cranfield Point
Fane R.
DUNDALK
Ballagan Point
Whites Town
CARRICKMACROSS
Louth
DUNDALK BAY
Dromiskin
Castlebellingham
Mansfieldstown
Drumconrath
LOUTH
Dunany Pt.
IRISH SEA
ARDEE
DUNLEER
R. Dee
Clogher Head
Collon
Termonfeckin
Baltray
Wilkinstown
Slane
Newgrange
DROGHEDA
Bettystown
Beaulieu House
R. Boyne
Julianstown
DULEEK
Gormanston
NAVAN
Balrath
Stamullen
BALBRIGGAN
MEATH
Naul
SKERRIES
Skerries Mills
Kilmessan
DUBLIN
Lusk
RUSH
Dunsany
Dunshaughlin
Ratoath
Ashbourne
Donabate
Lambay I.
SWORDS
DUBLIN AIRPORT
MALAHIDE
Royal Canal
Dunboyne
Ward
Portmarnock
Mulhuddart
Kilcock
Maynooth Castle
Clonsilla
Killester
Sutton Cross
MAYNOOTH
Castleknock
Raheny
HOWTH
Drumcondra
Lucan
Phibsboro
Clontarf
N.Bull I.
LEIXLIP
Fairview
Palmerstown
Celbridge
Castletown House
Ranelagh
Rathmines
Dublin Bay
DUBLIN
Clondalkin
Straffan
Donnybrook
Ballsbridge
Clane
Grand Canal
Newcastle
Tallaght
Blackrock
DÚN LAOGHAIRE
Rathcoole
Saggart
Sandycove
Dalkey
Dalkey Heritage Town
Areas within Central Dublin
Christchurch Cathedral
Dublin City Gallery - The Hugh Lane
Dublin Zoo
Dublin's City Hall - The Story of the Capital
Dublinia & The Viking World
Number 29
National Library of Ireland
National Museum of Ireland
- Archaeology & History
- Decorative Arts & History
- Natural History
Old Jameson Distillery
St. Patrick's Cathedral
Trinity College Library
Guinness Storehouse
Wax Museum Plus
Douglas (I. of Man)
Holyhead
Holyhead
15
8
16
15
14
13
12
11
12

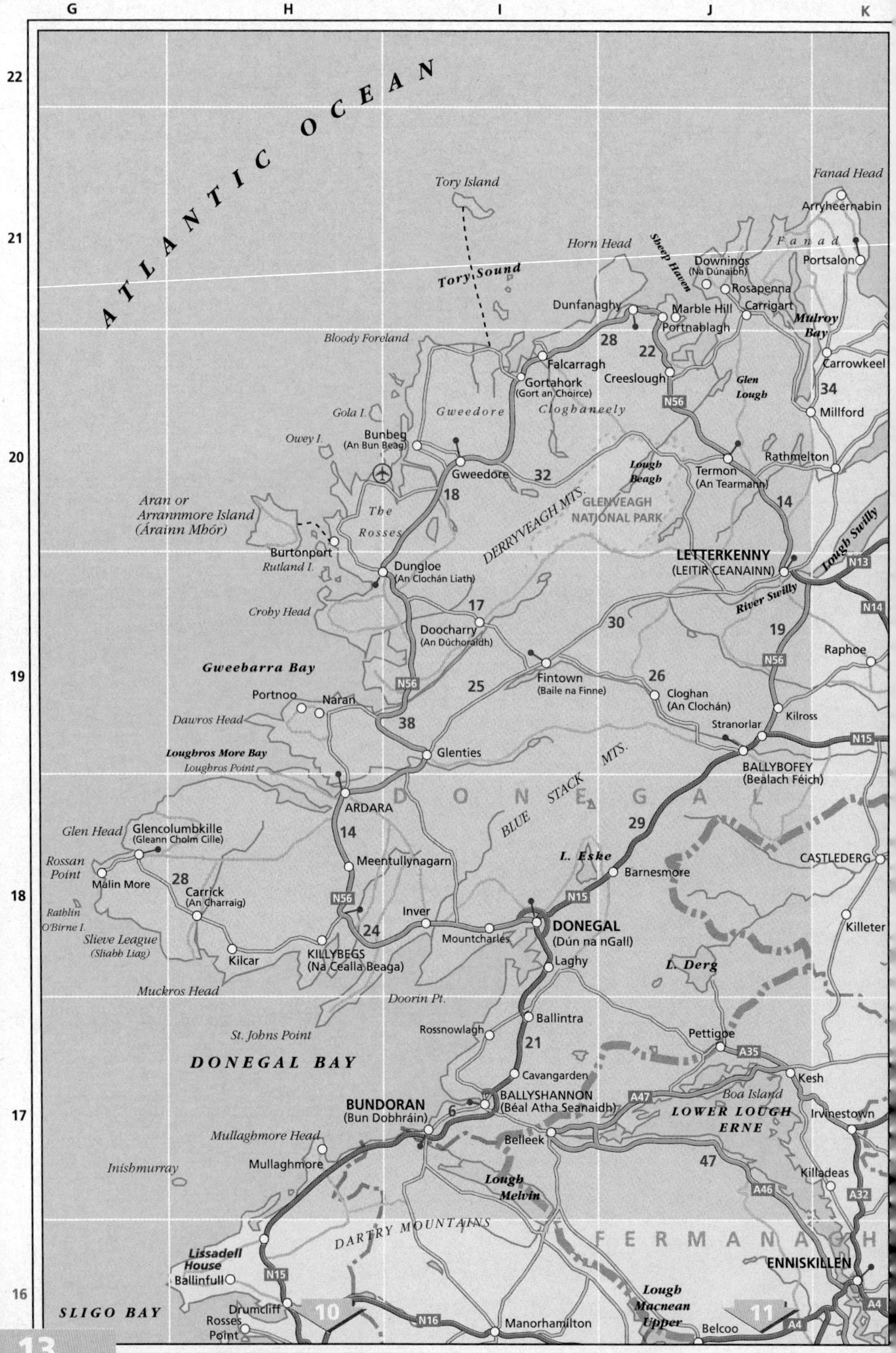
G
H
I
J
K
22
21
20
19
18
17
16
ATLANTIC OCEAN
Tory Island
Tory Sound
Fanad Head
Arryheernabin
Fanad
Portsalon
Horn Head
Sheep Haven
Downings
(Na Dúnaibh)
Rosapenna
Carrigart
Mulroy Bay
Dunfanaghy
Marble Hill
Portnablagh
Bloody Foreland
Falcarragh
Gortahork
(Gort an Choirce)
Creeslough
Carrowkeel
Glen Lough
Millford
Gola I.
Gweedore
Cloghaneely
Bunbeg
(An Bun Beag)
Owey I.
Gweedore
Lough Beagh
Termon
(An Tearmann)
Rathmelton
Aran or
Arannmore Island
(Árainn Mhór)
The Rosses
DERRYVEAGH MTS.
GLENVEAGH NATIONAL PARK
Burtonport
Rutland I.
Dungloe
(An Clochán Liath)
LETTERKENNY
(LEITIR CEANAINN)
Lough Swilly
River Swilly
Croby Head
Doocharry
(An Dúchoraidh)
Raphoe
Gweebarra Bay
Fintown
(Baile na Finne)
Cloghan
(An Clochán)
Portnoo
Naran
Kilross
Dawros Head
Stranorlar
Lough bros More Bay
Loughbros Point
Glenties
BALLYBOFEY
(Bealach Féich)
BLUE STACK MTS.
ARDARA
DONEGAL
Glen Head
Glencolumbkille
(Gleann Cholm Cille)
Rossan Point
Malin More
Meentullynagarn
L. Eske
Barnesmore
CASTLEDERG
Rathlin O'Birne I.
Carrick
(An Charraig)
Inver
DONEGAL
(Dún na nGall)
Killeter
Slieve League
(Sliabh Liag)
Kilcar
KILLYBEGS
(Na Ceala Beaga)
Mountcharles
Laghy
L. Derg
Muckros Head
Doorin Pt.
Ballintra
St. Johns Point
Rossnowlagh
Pettigoe
DONEGAL BAY
Cavangarden
Kesh
BUNDORAN
(Bun Dobhráin)
BALLYSHANNON
(Béal Atha Seanaidh)
Boa Island
LOWER LOUGH ERNE
Irvinestown
Mullaghmore Head
Belleek
Inishmurray
Mullaghmore
Lough Melvin
Killadeas
DARTRY MOUNTAINS
FERMANAGH
Lissadell House
Ballinfull
ENNISKILLEN
SLIGO BAY
Drumcliff
Rosses Point
Manorhamilton
Lough Macnean Upper
Belcoo
N56
N13
N14
N15
N16
A35
A47
A46
A32
A4
10
11
28
22
34
32
18
14
17
30
19
25
26
38
29
24
21
6
47

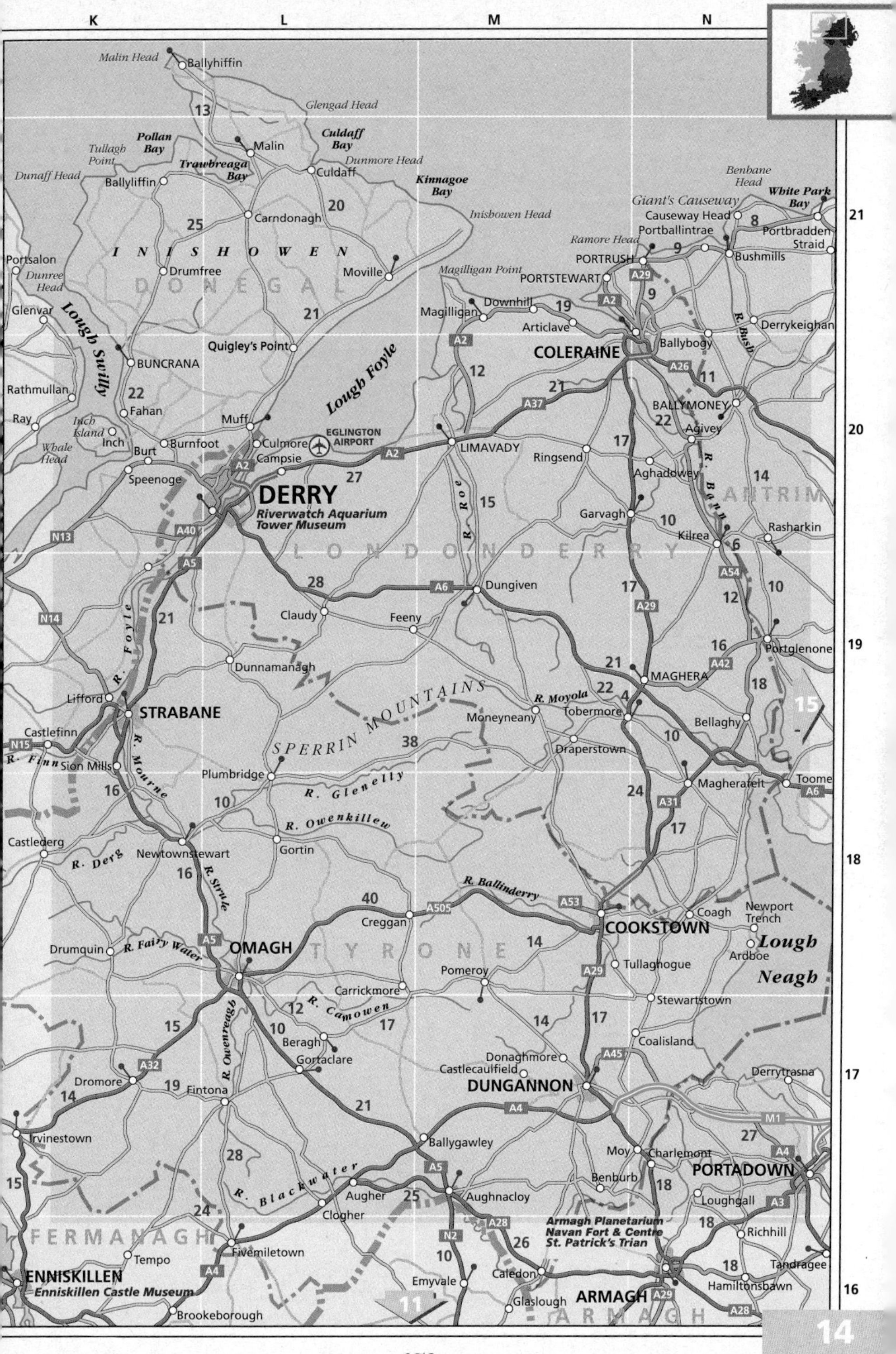
K
L
M
N
21
20
19
18
17
16
14
Malin Head
Ballyhiffin
Glengad Head
Pollan Bay
Tullagh Point
Culdaff Bay
Malin
Trawbreaga Bay
Dunmore Head
Culdaff
Dunaff Head
Ballyliffin
Kinnagoe Bay
Carndonagh
Inishowen Head
INISHOWEN
DONEGAL
Portsalon
Dunree Head
Drumfree
Moville
Magilligan Point
Glenvar
Lough Swilly
Quigley's Point
BUNCRANA
Lough Foyle
Rathmullan
Fahan
Ray
Inch Island
Muff
Inch
Whale Head
Burnfoot
Burt
Culmore
EGLINTON AIRPORT
Campsie
Speenoge
DERRY
Riverwatch Aquarium
Tower Museum
LONDONDERRY
Benbane Head
Giant's Causeway
White Park Bay
Causeway Head
Portballintrae
Portbradden
Straid
Ramore Head
PORTRUSH
Bushmills
PORTSTEWART
Magilligan
Downhill
Articlave
Derrykeighan
R. Bush
COLERAINE
Ballybogy
BALLYMONEY
Agivey
LIMAVADY
Ringsend
Aghadowey
R. Bann
ANTRIM
R. Roe
Garvagh
Kilrea
Rasharkin
Dungiven
Claudy
Feeny
Portglenone
Dunnamanagh
MAGHERA
R. Foyle
Lifford
STRABANE
SPERRIN MOUNTAINS
R. Moyola
Tobermore
Moneyneany
Bellaghy
Castlefinn
R. Finn
Sion Mills
Draperstown
R. Mourne
Plumbridge
R. Glenelly
Magherafelt
Toome
R. Owenkillew
Castlederg
Newtownstewart
Gortin
R. Derg
R. Strule
R. Ballinderry
COOKSTOWN
Coagh
Newport Trench
Creggan
Drumquin
R. Fairy Water
OMAGH
TYRONE
Lough Neagh
Ardboe
Tullaghogue
Pomeroy
Carrickmore
Stewartstown
R. Camowen
R. Owenreagh
Beragh
Coalisland
Gortaclare
Donaghmore
Castlecaulfield
DUNGANNON
Derrytrasna
Dromore
Fintona
Irvinestown
Ballygawley
Moy
Charlemont
PORTADOWN
R. Blackwater
Augher
Benburb
Aughnacloy
Loughgall
Clogher
Armagh Planetarium
Navan Fort & Centre
St. Patrick's Trian
Richhill
FERMANAGH
Fivemiletown
Tempo
Caledon
Tandragee
ENNISKILLEN
Enniskillen Castle Museum
Emyvale
Hamiltonsbawn
Glaslough
ARMAGH
Brookeborough

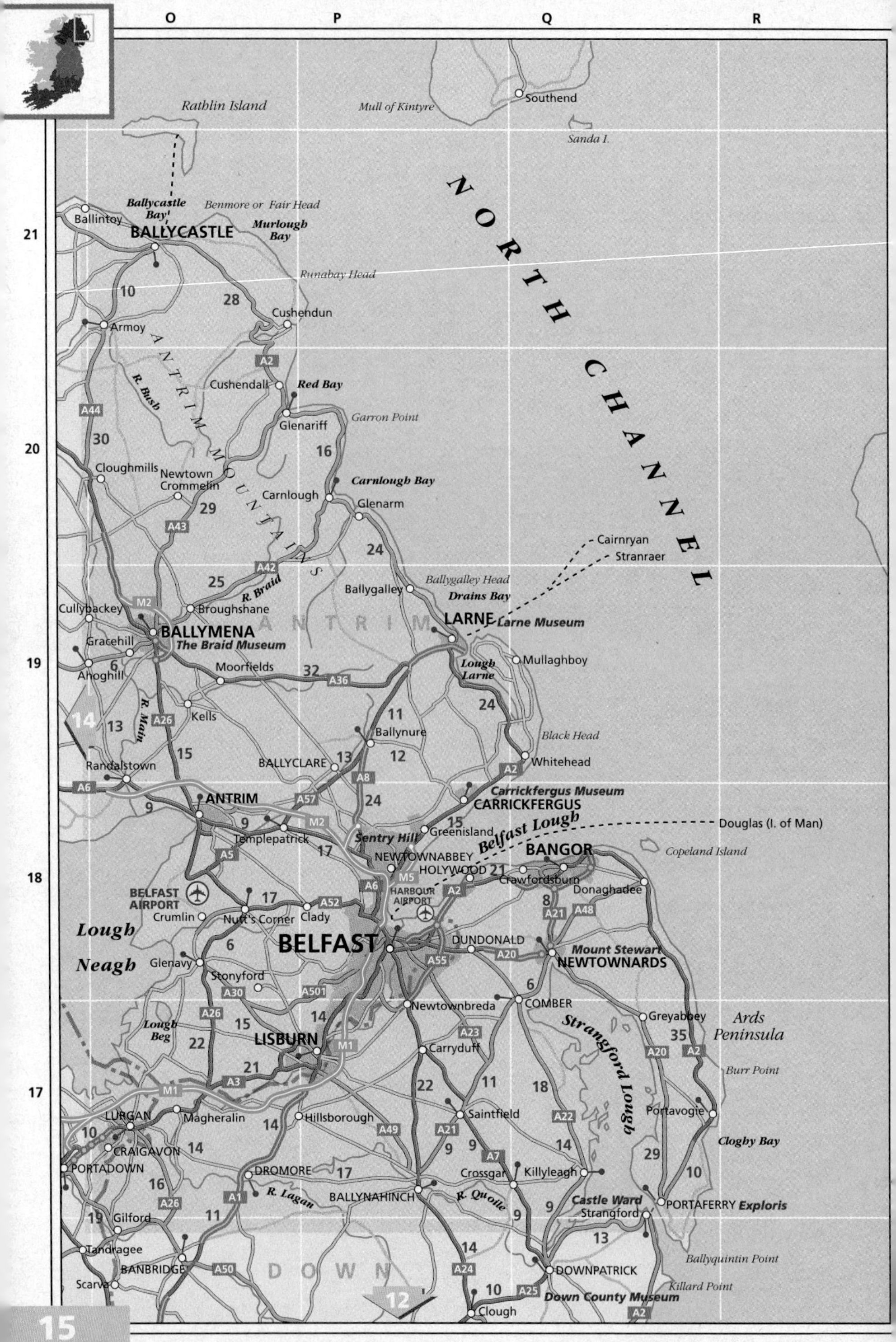
O
P
Q
R
21
20
19
18
17
Rathlin Island
Mull of Kintyre
Southend
Sanda I.
NORTH CHANNEL
Ballycastle Bay
Benmore or Fair Head
Ballintoy
BALLYCASTLE
Murlough Bay
Runabay Head
Cushendun
Armoy
ANTRIM MOUNTAINS
R. Bush
Cushendall
Red Bay
Glenariff
Garron Point
Cloughmills
Newtown Crommelin
Carnlough
Carnlough Bay
Glenarm
Cairnryan
Stranraer
Ballygalley
Ballygalley Head
Drains Bay
R. Braid
Cullybackey
Broughshane
BALLYMENA
The Braid Museum
ANTRIM
LARNE
Larne Museum
Gracehill
Ahoghill
Moorfields
Lough Larne
Mullaghboy
R. Main
Kells
Ballynure
Black Head
Randalstown
BALLYCLARE
Whitehead
ANTRIM
Carrickfergus Museum
CARRICKFERGUS
Templepatrick
Sentry Hill
Greenisland
Belfast Lough
Douglas (I. of Man)
NEWTOWNABBEY
BANGOR
Copeland Island
HOLYWOOD
Crawfordsburn
Donaghadee
BELFAST AIRPORT
HARBOUR AIRPORT
Crumlin
Nutt's Corner
Clady
Lough Neagh
BELFAST
DUNDONALD
Mount Stewart
NEWTOWNARDS
Glenavy
Stonyford
Newtownbreda
COMBER
Greyabbey
Ards Peninsula
Strangford Lough
Lough Beg
LISBURN
Carryduff
Burr Point
LURGAN
Magheralin
Hillsborough
Saintfield
Portavogie
Clogby Bay
CRAIGAVON
PORTADOWN
DROMORE
Crossgar
Killyleagh
R. Lagan
BALLYNAHINCH
R. Quoile
Castle Ward
Strangford
PORTAFERRY
Exploris
Gilford
Tandragee
BANBRIDGE
DOWN
DOWNPATRICK
Ballyquintin Point
Scarva
Killard Point
Down County Museum
Clough
A2
A44
A43
A42
M2
A36
A26
A8
A6
A57
A5
A52
A6
M5
A21
A48
A20
A55
A30
A501
A23
A20
M1
A3
A49
A21
A22
A7
A1
A26
A50
A24
A25
14
12
15

A

An Crúiscín Lán Hotel
Spiddal, Co. Galway 186
☎ 091-553148

An Glen Guesthouse
Dublin City, Co. Dublin 237
☎ 01-855 1374

An Portán
Dingle (An Daingean), Co. Kerry............66
☎ 066-915 6212

Anglers Rest Hotel
Headford, Co. Galway 181
☎ 093-35528

Annaly Hotel
Longford Town, Co. Longford 282
☎ 043-334 2058

Annebrook House
Mullingar, Co. Westmeath 299
☎ 044-935 3300

Anner Hotel & Leisure Centre
Thurles, Co. Tipperary 110
☎ 0504-21799

Anno Santo Hotel
Galway City, Co. Galway 171
☎ 091-523011

Aran View House Hotel & Restaurant
Doolin, Co. Clare......................140
☎ 065-707 4061

Arbutus Hotel
Killarney, Co. Kerry....................76
☎ 064-663 1037

Ard Einne Guesthouse
Aran Islands, Co. Galway..........163
☎ 099-61126

Ard Na Breátha
Donegal Town, Co. Donegal 156
☎ 074-972 2288

Ardagh Hotel & Restaurant
Clifden, Co. Galway.................167
☎ 095-21384

Ardagh House
Dublin City, Co. Dublin 237
☎ 01-497 7068

Ardboyne Hotel
Navan, Co. Meath....................290
☎ 046-902 3119

Ardilaun Guesthouse
Ennis, Co. Clare........................144
☎ 065-682 2311

Ardilaun Hotel, Conference Centre & Leisure Club
Galway City, Co. Galway 171
☎ 091-521433

Ardmore Country House Hotel and Restaurant
Westport, Co. Mayo 202
☎ 098-25994

Ard-Na-Sidhe Country House
Caragh Lake, Co. Kerry 64
☎ 066-976 9105

Ariel House
Dublin City, Co. Dublin 238
☎ 01-668 5512

Arklow Bay Conference, Leisure & Spa Hotel
Arklow, Co. Wicklow................303
☎ 0402-32309

Arlington Hotel O'Connell Bridge
Dublin City, Co. Dublin 238
☎ 01-804 9100

Arlington Hotel Temple Bar
Dublin City, Co. Dublin 238
☎ 01-670 8777

Arlington Lodge Town House & Restaurant
Waterford City, Co. Waterford 119
☎ 051-878584

Arnolds Hotel
Dunfanaghy, Co. Donegal........158
☎ 074-913 6208

Ashbourne Marriott Hotel
Ashbourne, Co. Meath 286
☎ 01-835 6800

Ashdown Park Hotel Conference & Leisure Centre
Gorey, Co. Wexford..................127
☎ 053-948 0500

 SEE ALSO INDEX TO LOCATIONS PAGES 14-15

Bambury's Guest House
Dingle (An Daingean), Co. Kerry ..67
☎ 066-915 1244

Bank House Hotel
Dungannon, Co. Tyrone 225
☎ 028-8772 8080

Barnawee Bridge Guesthouse
Dungarvan, Co. Waterford........113
☎ 058-42074

Barr na Sraide Inn
Dingle (An Daingean), Co. Kerry ..67
☎ 066-915 1331

Barrowville Town House
Carlow Town, Co. Carlow 35
☎ 059-914 3324

Bay View Hotel & Leisure Centre
Killybegs, Co. Donegal 159
☎ 074-973 1950

Bayview Hotel
Ballycotton, Co. Cork 37
☎ 021-464 6746

Beach Guest House
Dunmore East, Co. Waterford ..115
☎ 051-383316

Beach Haven House
Tramore, Co. Waterford............117
☎ 051-390208

Beaufort House
Carlingford, Co. Louth 283
☎ 042-937 3879

Beech Hill Country House Hotel
Derry City, Co. Derry 221
☎ 028-7134 9279

Bel-Air Hotel
Ashford, Co. Wicklow 304
☎ 0404-40109

Belfry Hotel
Waterford City, Co. Waterford ..119
☎ 051-844800

Belleek Castle
Ballina, Co. Mayo 196
☎ 096-22400

Bellinter House
Navan, Co. Meath....................290
☎ 046-903 0900

Belvedere Hotel Parnell Square
Dublin City, Co. Dublin 239
☎ 01-873 7700

Ben View House
Clifden, Co. Galway..................168
☎ 095-21256

Berkeley House
Kilkenny City, Co. Kilkenny........99
☎ 056-776 4848

Best Western Esplanade Hotel
Bray, Co. Wicklow....................305
☎ 01-286 2056

Best Western Eviston House Hotel
Killarney, Co. Kerry....................77
☎ 064-663 1640

Best Western Flannery's Hotel
Galway City, Co. Galway 172
☎ 091-755111

Best Western Hotel Rosslare
Rosslare Harbour, Co. Wexford....129
☎ 053-913 3110

Best Western Milford Inn Hotel
Milford, Co. Donegal................162
☎ 074-915 3313

Best Western Pery's Hotel
Limerick City, Co. Limerick........191
☎ 061-413822

Best Western Premier Academy Plaza Hotel
Dublin City, Co. Dublin 240
☎ 01-817 4141

Bettystown Court Conference & Leisure Hotel
Bettystown, Co. Meath............287
☎ 041-981 2900

SEE ALSO INDEX TO LOCATIONS PAGES 14-15

Bewley's Hotel Ballsbridge
Dublin City, Co. Dublin 240
☎ *01-668 1111*

Bewley's Hotel Dublin Airport
Dublin Airport, Co. Dublin........234
☎ *01-871 1000*

Bewley's Hotel Leopardstown
Dublin City, Co. Dublin 240
☎ *01-293 5000*

Bewley's Hotel Newlands Cross
Dublin City, Co. Dublin 242
☎ *01-464 0140*

Bianconi
Killorglin, Co. Kerry....................92
☎ *066-976 1146*

Blakes Hotel & Spa
Dublin City, Co. Dublin 242
☎ *01-668 8324*

Blarney Castle Hotel
Blarney, Co. Cork 40
☎ *021-438 5116*

Blarney Golf Resort
Blarney, Co. Cork 40
☎ *021-438 4477*

Blarney Stone
Cork City, Co. Cork 47
☎ *021-427 0083*

Blarney Woollen Mills Hotel
Blarney, Co. Cork 41
☎ *021-438 5011*

Bloomfield House Hotel
Mullingar, Co. Westmeath 300
☎ *044-934 0894*

Blue Haven Kinsale (The)
Kinsale, Co. Cork 56
☎ *021-477 2209*

Boffin Lodge
Westport, Co. Mayo 202
☎ *098-26092*

Boland's Guesthouse
Dingle (An Daingean), Co. Kerry ..67
☎ *066-915 1426*

Bracken Court Hotel
Balbriggan, Co. Dublin 233
☎ *01-841 3333*

Brandon House Hotel & Solas Croí Eco Spa
New Ross, Co. Wexford 128
☎ *051-421703*

Breffni Arms Hotel
Arvagh, Co. Cavan....................231
☎ *049-433 5127*

Brehon (The)
Killarney, Co. Kerry....................77
☎ *064-663 0700*

Bridge Court House
Kilkenny City, Co. Kilkenny........99
☎ *056-776 2998*

Bridge Hotel
Arklow, Co. Wicklow................303
☎ *0402-31666*

Bridge House Hotel
Tullamore, Co. Offaly 295
☎ *057-932 5600*

Brighton House
Clonmel, Co. Tipperary 108
☎ *052-612 3665*

Brogan's
Trim, Co. Meath 291
☎ *046-943 1237*

Brook Lodge Hotel
Killarney, Co. Kerry....................78
☎ *064-663 1800*

Brook Manor Lodge
Tralee, Co. Kerry........................95
☎ *066-712 0406*

Brookhaven Country House
Waterville, Co. Kerry..................97
☎ *066-947 4431*

Brooks Hotel
Dublin City, Co. Dublin 242
☎ *01-670 4000*

Brown Trout Golf & Country Inn
Aghadowey, Co. Derry..............221
☎ *028-7086 8209*

Bunratty Castle Hotel & Angsana Spa
Bunratty, Co. Clare 140
☎ *061-478700*

GUINNESS

C

 SEE ALSO INDEX TO LOCATIONS PAGES 14-15

GUINNESS

Charlemont Arms Hotel
Armagh City, Co. Armagh 218
☎ 028-3752 2028

Charleville Lodge
Dublin City, Co. Dublin 246
☎ 01-838 6633

Charleville Park Hotel & Leisure Club
Charleville, Co. Cork 43
☎ 063-33700

Chester Beatty Inn
Ashford, Co. Wicklow 304
☎ 0404-40206

City North Hotel
Gormanston, Co. Meath 288
☎ 01-690 6666

Ciúin House
Carrick-on-Shannon, Co. Leitrim..188
☎ 071-967 1488

Clanard Court Hotel
Athy, Co. Kildare......................274
☎ 059-864 0666

Claregalway Hotel
Galway City, Co. Galway 172
☎ 091-738300

Clarence (The)
Dublin City, Co. Dublin 246
☎ 01-407 0800

Clayton Hotel Galway
Galway City, Co. Galway 173
☎ 091-721900

Clew Bay Hotel
Westport, Co. Mayo 204
☎ 098-28088

Clifden Guesthouse
Dublin City, Co. Dublin 246
☎ 01-874 6364

Clifden Station House Hotel
Clifden, Co. Galway 168
☎ 095-21699

Cliff House Hotel
Ardmore, Co. Waterford...........112
☎ 024-87800

Clifton House
Limerick City, Co. Limerick 192
☎ 061-451166

Clonea Strand Hotel, Golf & Leisure
Dungarvan, Co. Waterford........114
☎ 058-45555

Clonmel Park Conference Leisure & Spa Hotel
Clonmel, Co. Tipperary 108
☎ 052-618 8700

Clontarf Castle Hotel
Dublin City, Co. Dublin 247
☎ 01-833 2321

Club House Hotel
Kilkenny City, Co. Kilkenny 100
☎ 056-772 1994

Coach House
Waterford City, Co. Waterford ..120
☎ 051-384656

Coachmans Townhouse
Kenmare, Co. Kerry....................72
☎ 064-664 1311

Coastline Guesthouse
Dingle (An Daingean), Co. Kerry ..68
☎ 066-915 2494

Commercial & Tourist Hotel
Ballinamore, Co. Leitrim 187
☎ 071-964 4675

Commodore Hotel
Cobh, Co. Cork 45
☎ 021-481 1277

Commons Inn
Cork City, Co. Cork 48
☎ 021-421 0300

Connemara Coast Hotel
Furbo, Co. Galway....................170
☎ 091-592108

Connemara Country Lodge
Clifden, Co. Galway..................169
☎ 095-22122

Conrad Dublin
Dublin City, Co. Dublin 247
☎ 01-602 8900

Coolcower House
Macroom, Co. Cork....................59
☎ 026-41695

SEE ALSO INDEX TO LOCATIONS PAGES 14-15

Corick House Hotel
Clogher, Co. Tyrone 224
☎ 028-8554 8216

Cork International Airport Hotel
Cork Airport, Co. Cork 46
☎ 021-454 9800

Corralea Court
Tuam, Co. Galway 187
☎ 093-24188

Corrib Haven Guest House
Galway City, Co. Galway 173
☎ 091-524171

Corrib Wave Guest House
Oughterard, Co. Galway 184
☎ 091-552147

Corthna-Lodge Guesthouse
Schull, Co. Cork..........................61
☎ 028-28517

County Arms Hotel & Leisure Club
Birr, Co. Offaly 294
☎ 057-912 0791

Courtenay Lodge Hotel
Newcastle West, Co. Limerick ..195
☎ 069-62244

Courthouse (The)
Ballyhaunis, Co. Mayo 198
☎ 094-963 0068

Courtmacsherry Hotel & Costal Cottages
Courtmacsherry, Co. Cork 53
☎ 023-884 6198

Courtown Hotel
Courtown Harbour, Co. Wexford..125
☎ 053-942 5210

Courtyard Hotel Leixlip
Leixlip, Co. Kildare 276
☎ 01-629 5100

Courtyard Marriott Galway
Galway City, Co. Galway 173
☎ 091-513200

Crawford Guesthouse
Cork City, Co. Cork 48
☎ 021-427 9000

Creevy Pier Hotel (The)
Ballyshannon, Co. Donegal......153
☎ 071-985 8355

Creggan Court Hotel
Athlone, Co. Westmeath..........296
☎ 090-647 7777

Crofton Bray Head Inn
Bray, Co. Wicklow....................305
☎ 01-286 7182

Croke Park Hotel (The)
Dublin City, Co. Dublin 247
☎ 01-871 4444

Crowne Plaza Dublin Northwood
Dublin Airport, Co. Dublin........235
☎ 01-862 8888

Crystal Springs
Killarney, Co. Kerry....................79
☎ 064-663 3272

Cuan (The)
Strangford, Co. Down..............223
☎ 028-4488 1222

Cullinan's Seafood Restaurant & Guesthouse
Doolin, Co. Clare......................142
☎ 065-707 4183

D

d (The)
Drogheda, Co. Louth 284
☎ 041-987 7700

D4 Berkeley
Dublin City, Co. Dublin 248
☎ 01-668 4468

Danby Lodge Hotel
Rosslare, Co. Wexford..............129
☎ 053-915 8191

Darby O'Gill's Country House Hotel
Killarney, Co. Kerry....................80
☎ 064-663 4168

Days Hotel Castlebar
Castlebar, Co. Mayo 198
☎ 094-928 6200

Deebert House Hotel
Kilmallock, Co. Limerick............191
☎ 063-31200

Deer Park Hotel Golf & Spa
Howth, Co. Dublin 269
☎ 01-832 2624

Delphi Mountain Resort
Leenane, Co. Galway................182
☎ 095-42208

Derby House Hotel
Kildare Town, Co. Kildare 275
☎ 045-522144

Dergvale Hotel
Dublin City, Co. Dublin 248
☎ 01-874 4753

Diamond Coast Hotel
Enniscrone, Co. Sligo 208
☎ 096-26000

Diamond Hill Country House
Waterford City, Co. Waterford ..120
☎ 051-832855

Dingle Bay Hotel
Dingle (An Daingean), Co. Kerry ..68
☎ 066-915 1231

Dingle Benners Hotel
Dingle (An Daingean), Co. Kerry ..69
☎ 066-915 1638

Dingle Skellig Hotel & Peninsula Spa
Dingle (An Daingean), Co. Kerry ..69
☎ 066-915 0200

Donegal Manor
Donegal Town, Co. Donegal 157
☎ 074-972 5222

Dooley's Hotel
Waterford City, Co. Waterford ..120
☎ 051-873531

Doonmore Hotel
Inishbofin Island, Co. Galway ..181
☎ 095-45814

Dorrians Imperial Hotel
Ballyshannon, Co. Donegal......154
☎ 071-985 1147

Dough Mor Lodge
Lahinch, Co. Clare 148
☎ 065-708 2063

Downhill House Hotel & Eagles Leisure Club
Ballina, Co. Mayo 197
☎ 096-21033

Downhill Inn
Ballina, Co. Mayo 197
☎ 096-73444

Downings Bay Hotel
Downings, Co. Donegal 158
☎ 074-915 5586

Drinagh Court Hotel
Wexford Town, Co. Wexford 131
☎ 053-914 3295

Dromhall Hotel
Killarney, Co. Kerry....................80
☎ 064-663 9300

Dromoland Castle
Newmarket-on-Fergus, Co. Clare..151
☎ 061-368144

Drury Court Hotel
Dublin City, Co. Dublin 248
☎ 01-475 1988

Dublin Citi Hotel
Dublin City, Co. Dublin 249
☎ 01-679 4455

Dublin Skylon Hotel
Dublin City, Co. Dublin 249
☎ 01-884 3900

Dun Ri Guesthouse
Clifden, Co. Galway 169
☎ 095-21625

Dunboyne Castle Hotel & Spa
Dunboyne, Co. Meath.............287
☎ 01-801 3500

Dundrum House Hotel, Golf & Leisure Resort
Cashel, Co. Tipperary 107
☎ 062-71116

Dunmore House Hotel
Clonakilty, Co. Cork 43
☎ 023-883 3352

Dunraven Arms Hotel
Adare, Co. Limerick..................190
☎ 061-605900

 SEE ALSO INDEX TO LOCATIONS PAGES 14-15

Dunsilly Hotel
Antrim, Co. Antrim 215
☎ 028-9446 2929

Dylan Hotel
Dublin City, Co. Dublin 249
☎ 01-660 3000

E

Eagle Lodge
Ballybunion, Co. Kerry 64
☎ 068-27224

Earls Court House
Killarney, Co. Kerry....................80
☎ 064-663 4009

Egan's Guesthouse
Dublin City, Co. Dublin 250
☎ 01-830 3611

Europe Hotel Resort (The)
Killarney, Co. Kerry 81
☎ 064-667 1300

Eyre Square Hotel
Galway City, Co. Galway 174
☎ 091-569633

F

Failte Hotel
Killarney, Co. Kerry 81
☎ 064-663 3404

Fairhill House Hotel
Clonbur (An Fháirche), Co. Galway ..170
☎ 094-954 6176

Fairview Guesthouse
Killarney, Co. Kerry....................82
☎ 064-663 4164

Faithlegg House Hotel
Faithlegg, Co. Waterford 116
☎ 051-382000

Falls Hotel & Spa
Ennistymon, Co. Clare..............146
☎ 065-707 1004

Fanad House
Kilkenny City, Co. Kilkenny 100
☎ 056-776 4126

Faythe Guest House
Wexford Town, Co. Wexford 131
☎ 053-912 2249

Feerick's Hotel
Rathowen, Co. Westmeath 302
☎ 043-667 6025

Fels Point Hotel
Tralee, Co. Kerry........................96
☎ 066-719 9100

Fennessy's Hotel
Clonmel, Co. Tipperary 108
☎ 052-612 3680

Fernhill Hotel
Carrigaline, Co. Cork..................42
☎ 021-437 2226

Fernhill House Hotel
Clonakilty, Co. Cork 44
☎ 023-883 3258

Ferrycarrig Hotel
Wexford Town, Co. Wexford 131
☎ 053-912 0999

Ferryport House
Rosslare Harbour, Co. Wexford....130
☎ 053-913 3933

Ferryview House
Dublin City, Co. Dublin 250
☎ 01-833 5893

Finnstown Country House Hotel
Lucan, Co. Dublin 270
☎ 01-601 0700

Fir Grove Hotel
Mitchelstown, Co. Cork..............60
☎ 025-24111

Fitzgeralds Vienna Woods Hotel Cork
Cork City, Co. Cork 48
☎ 021-455 6800

Fitzgeralds Woodlands House Hotel & Spa
Adare, Co. Limerick 190
☎ 061-605100

Fitzpatrick Castle Dublin
Killiney, Co. Dublin 270
☎ 01-230 5400

Fitzsimons Hotel
Dublin City, Co. Dublin 250
☎ 01-677 9315

Fitzwilton Hotel
Waterford City, Co. Waterford ..121
☎ 051-846900

Foleys Townhouse
Kenmare, Co. Kerry....................72
☎ 064-664 2162

Foley's Townhouse & Restaurant
Killarney, Co. Kerry....................82
☎ 064-663 1217

Forge Guesthouse (The)
Saggart, Co. Dublin..................271
☎ 01-458 9226

Forster Court Hotel
Galway City, Co. Galway 174
☎ 091-564111

Fort Royal Country House
Rathmullan, Co. Donegal 163
☎ 074-915 8100

Fota Island Hotel & Spa
Fota Island, Co. Cork 54
☎ 021-467 3000

Four Seasons Hotel Dublin
Dublin City, Co. Dublin 251
☎ 01-665 4000

Foyles Hotel
Clifden, Co. Galway..................169
☎ 095-21801

Friars Glen
Killarney, Co. Kerry....................82
☎ 064-663 7500

Friar's Lodge
Kinsale, Co. Cork 57
☎ 021-477 7384

Fuchsia House
Killarney, Co. Kerry....................83
☎ 064-663 3743

G

g Hotel (The)
Galway City, Co. Galway 174
☎ 091-865200

Gables Guesthouse & Leisure Centre
Newbridge, Co. Kildare............278
☎ 045-435330

Galgorm Resort & Spa
Ballymena, Co. Antrim 215
☎ 028-2588 1001

Galway Bay Hotel, Conference & Leisure Centre
Galway City, Co. Galway 175
☎ 091-520520

Garnish House
Cork City, Co. Cork 49
☎ 021-427 5111

Garryvoe Hotel
Shanagarry, Co. Cork 62
☎ 021-464 6718

Glasson Hotel & Golf Club
Athlone, Co. Westmeath..........296
☎ 090-648 5120

Gleann Fia Country House
Killarney, Co. Kerry....................83
☎ 064-663 5035

Gleesons Townhouse & Restaurant
Roscommon Town, Co. Roscommon ..207
☎ 090-662 6954

Glendalough Hotel
Glendalough, Co. Wicklow 307
☎ 0404-45135

Glendine Inn
Kilkenny City, Co. Kilkenny 100
☎ 056-772 1069

Gleneagle Hotel
Killarney, Co. Kerry....................84
☎ 064-663 6000

Gleneany House
Letterkenny, Co. Donegal 160
☎ 074-912 6088

Glengarriff Eccles Hotel
Glengarriff, Co. Cork..................54
☎ 027-63003

Glengarriff Park Hotel
Glengarriff, Co. Cork..................55
☎ 027-63000

Glenlo Abbey Hotel
Galway City, Co. Galway 175
☎ 091-526666

Glenogra House
Dublin City, Co. Dublin 251
☎ 01-668 3661

SEE ALSO INDEX TO LOCATIONS PAGES 14-15

Glenroyal Hotel (The)
Maynooth, Co. Kildare 276
☎ 01-629 0909

Glenside Hotel
Drogheda, Co. Louth 284
☎ 041-982 9185

Glenview Hotel & Leisure Cub
Glen-O-The-Downs, Co. Wicklow ..308
☎ 01-287 3399

Glenwood House
Carrigaline, Co. Cork..................42
☎ 021-437 3878

Gorman's Clifftop House and Restaurant
Dingle (An Daingean), Co. Kerry ..69
☎ 066-915 5162

Gougane Barra Hotel
Gougane Barra, Co. Cork 55
☎ 026-47069

Grafton Capital Hotel
Dublin City, Co. Dublin 252
☎ 01-648 1100

Grand Central Hotel
Bundoran, Co. Donegal............155
☎ 071-984 2722

Grand Hotel
Wicklow Town, Co. Wicklow 309
☎ 0404-67337

Grand Hotel
Malahide, Co. Dublin 271
☎ 01-845 0000

Grand Hotel
Tralee, Co. Kerry........................96
☎ 066-712 1499

Granville Hotel
Waterford City, Co. Waterford ..122
☎ 051-305555

Great Northern Hotel
Bundoran, Co. Donegal............155
☎ 071-984 1204

Green Isle Conference & Leisure Hotel
Dublin City, Co. Dublin 252
☎ 01-459 3406

Greenbrier Inn Guesthouse
Lahinch, Co. Clare 148
☎ 065-708 1242

Greenmount House
Dingle (An Daingean), Co. Kerry ..70
☎ 066-915 1414

Gregans Castle Hotel
Ballyvaughan, Co. Clare 139
☎ 065-707 7005

Grennans Country House & Cottages
Tullamore, Co. Offaly 295
☎ 057-935 5893

Gresham (The)
Dublin City, Co. Dublin 252
☎ 01-874 6881

Gresham Metropole
Cork City, Co. Cork 49
☎ 021-464 3700

Greville Arms Hotel
Mullingar, Co. Westmeath 300
☎ 044-934 8563

Grovemount House
Ennistymon, Co. Clare..............146
☎ 065-707 1431

H

Halpin's Townhouse Hotel
Kilkee, Co. Clare 147
☎ 065-905 6032

Hamlet Court Hotel
Johnstownbridge, Co. Meath ..288
☎ 046-954 1200

Hampton Hotel
Dublin City, Co. Dublin 253
☎ 01-668 0995

Hanoras Cottage
Ballymacarbry, Co. Waterford ..113
☎ 052-613 6134

Harbour Hotel & Restaurant
Naas, Co. Kildare 277
☎ 045-879145

Harbour House & Leisure Centre
Castlegregory, Co. Kerry............65
☎ 066-713 9292

Harbour View Hotel
Rosslare Harbour, Co. Wexford....130
☎ 053-916 1450

Harbour View Hotel
Schull, Co. Cork..........................61
☎ 028-28101

Harcourt Hotel
Dublin City, Co. Dublin 253
☎ 01-478 3677

Harding Hotel
Dublin City, Co. Dublin 253
☎ 01-679 6500

Harrington Hall
Dublin City, Co. Dublin 254
☎ 01-475 3497

Harvey's Guest House
Dublin City, Co. Dublin 254
☎ 01-874 8384

Harvey's Point Hotel
Donegal Town, Co. Donegal 157
☎ 074-972 2208

Hayfield Manor Hotel
Cork City, Co. Cork 50
☎ 021-484 5900

Hazel Hotel
Monasterevin, Co. Kildare 276
☎ 045-525373

Headfort Arms
Kells, Co. Meath 288
☎ 0818-222 800

Healys Restaurant & Fishing Lodge
Pontoon, Co. Mayo 201
☎ 094-925 6443

Heaton's Guesthouse
Dingle (An Daingean), Co. Kerry ..70
☎ 066-915 2288

Heights Hotel - Killarney (The)
Killarney, Co. Kerry....................84
☎ 064-663 1158

Heritage Golf & Spa Resort (The)
Killenard, Co. Laois..................280
☎ 057-864 5500

Heron's Cove
Ballyshannon, Co. Donegal......154
☎ 071-982 2070

Highlands Hotel
Glenties, Co. Donegal 159
☎ 074-955 1111

Hillgrove (The)
Dingle (An Daingean), Co. Kerry ..70
☎ 066-915 1131

Hillgrove Hotel Leisure & Spa
Monaghan Town, Co. Monaghan....294
☎ 047-81288

Hillville Manor
Dingle (An Daingean), Co. Kerry....71
☎ 066-713 8118

Hilton Belfast
Belfast City, Belfast City 219
☎ 028-9027 7000

Hilton Dublin
Dublin City, Co. Dublin 254
☎ 01-402 9988

Hilton Dublin Airport
Dublin Airport, Co. Dublin........235
☎ 01-866 1800

Hilton Templepatrick
Templepatrick, Co. Antrim........218
☎ 028-9443 5500

Hodson Bay Hotel
Athlone, Co. Westmeath..........297
☎ 090-644 2000

Holiday Inn Killarney
Killarney, Co. Kerry....................84
☎ 064-663 3000

Hopper Inn
Tralee, Co. Kerry........................96
☎ 066-7148 641

Horse and Hound Hotel
Foulksmills, Co. Wexford..........126
☎ 051-428323

Horse and Jockey Hotel
Horse and Jockey, Co. Tipperary..109
☎ 0504-44192

SEE ALSO INDEX TO LOCATIONS PAGES 14-15

GUINNESS

Keadeen Hotel
Newbridge, Co. Kildare............278
☎ 045-431666

Keepers Arms
Ballyconnell, Co. Cavan............231
☎ 049-952 3318

Kee's Hotel & Leisure Club
Ballybofey, Co. Donegal 153
☎ 074-913 1018

Kelly's Resort Hotel & Spa
Rosslare, Co. Wexford.............129
☎ 053-913 2114

Kennys Guest House
Castlebar, Co. Mayo 199
☎ 094-902 3091

Kettles Country House Hotel
Swords, Co. Dublin..................273
☎ 01-813 8511

Kilcaw Guesthouse
Kinsale, Co. Cork 57
☎ 021-477 4155

Kilcoran Lodge Hotel, Lodges & Leisure Centre
Cahir, Co. Tipperary 106
☎ 052-744 1288

Kildare Hotel, Spa and Country Club - The K Club
Straffan, Co. Kildare 278
☎ 01-601 7200

Kilford Arms Hotel
Kilkenny City, Co. Kilkenny 101
☎ 056-776 1018

Kilkee Thalassotherapy Centre & Guesthouse
Kilkee, Co. Clare 147
☎ 065-905 6742

Kilkenny House Hotel
Kilkenny City, Co. Kilkenny 101
☎ 056-777 0711

Kilkenny Ormonde Hotel
Kilkenny City, Co. Kilkenny 102
☎ 056-772 3900

Kilkenny River Court
Kilkenny City, Co. Kilkenny 102
☎ 056-772 3388

Killarney Avenue Hotel
Killarney, Co. Kerry....................86
☎ 064-663 2522

Killarney Guest House
Cork City, Co. Cork 51
☎ 021-427 0290

Killarney Lodge
Killarney, Co. Kerry....................87
☎ 064-663 6499

Killarney Park Hotel
Killarney, Co. Kerry....................87
☎ 064-663 5555

Killarney Plaza Hotel & Spa
Killarney, Co. Kerry....................87
☎ 064-662 1100

Killarney Royal Hotel
Killarney, Co. Kerry....................88
☎ 064-663 1853

Killarney Towers Hotel & Leisure Centre
Killarney, Co. Kerry....................88
☎ 064-663 1038

Killeen House Hotel
Killarney, Co. Kerry....................88
☎ 064-663 1711

Killeshin (The)
Portlaoise, Co. Laois...............280
☎ 057-863 1200

Killyhevlin Hotel
Enniskillen, Co. Fermanagh 223
☎ 028-6632 3481

Kilmurry Lodge Hotel
Limerick City, Co. Limerick 192
☎ 061-331133

Kilmurvey House
Aran Islands, Co. Galway..........164
☎ 099-61218

Kilronan Castle Estate & Spa
Ballyfarnon, Co. Roscommon ..207
☎ 071-961 8000

Kilronan Guesthouse
Dublin City, Co. Dublin 255
☎ 01-475 5266

SEE ALSO INDEX TO LOCATIONS PAGES 14-15

Kingfisher Lodge Guesthouse
Killarney, Co. Kerry....................89
☎ 064-663 7131

Kirby's Lanterns Hotel
Tarbert, Co. Kerry......................94
☎ 068-36210

Knightsbrook Hotel Spa & Golf Resort
Trim, Co. Meath 292
☎ 046-948 2100

Knock House Hotel
Knock, Co. Mayo......................200
☎ 094-938 8088

Knockranny House Hotel & Spa
Westport, Co. Mayo 204
☎ 098-28600

Kylemore Pass Hotel
Kylemore, Co. Galway..............182
☎ 095-41141

L

La Mon Hotel & Country Club
Belfast City, Belfast City 219
☎ 028-9044 8631

La Stampa Hotel
Dublin City, Co. Dublin 256
☎ 01-677 4444

Lady Gregory Hotel, Conference & Leisure Club
Gort, Co. Galway 180
☎ 091-632333

Lahinch Golf & Leisure Hotel
Lahinch, Co. Clare 148
☎ 065-708 1100

Lake Hotel
Killarney, Co. Kerry....................89
☎ 064-663 1035

Lake House Hotel
Portnoo, Co. Donegal 162
☎ 074-954 5123

Lakeside Manor Hotel
Virginia, Co. Cavan 233
☎ 049-854 8200

Landmark Hotel
Carrick-on-Shannon, Co. Leitrim ..188
☎ 071-962 2222

Langton House Hotel
Kilkenny City, Co. Kilkenny 102
☎ 056-776 5133

Lansdowne Arms Hotel
Kenmare, Co. Kerry....................73
☎ 064-664 1368

Lansdowne Hotel
Dublin City, Co. Dublin 256
☎ 01-668 2522

Laragh Guest House
Kilkenny City, Co. Kilkenny 103
☎ 056-776 4674

Laurels
Kilkenny City, Co. Kilkenny 103
☎ 056-776 1501

Lawlors Hotel
Dungarvan, Co. Waterford........114
☎ 058-41122

Leenane Hotel
Leenane, Co. Galway................182
☎ 095-42249

Leeson Inn Downtown
Dublin City, Co. Dublin 256
☎ 01-662 2002

Lemongrove House
Enniscorthy, Co. Wexford 125
☎ 053-923 6115

Lisdonagh House
Caherlistrane, Co. Galway 166
☎ 093-31163

Lismar Guesthouse & Serviced Apartments
Dundalk, Co. Louth..................285
☎ 042-935 7246

Lismore House Hotel
Lismore, Co. Waterford 116
☎ 058-72966

Loch Lein Country House
Killarney, Co. Kerry....................89
☎ 064-663 1260

SEE ALSO INDEX TO LOCATIONS PAGES 14-15

Moorland Guesthouse
Laghey, Co. Donegal................160
☎ 074-973 4319

Mount Herbert Hotel
Dublin City, Co. Dublin 261
☎ 01-614 2000

Mount Juliet
Thomastown, Co. Kilkenny 105
☎ 056-777 3000

Mount Wolseley Hotel Spa & Country Club
Tullow, Co. Carlow 36
☎ 059-918 0100

Mountain View Guest House
Oughterard, Co. Galway 184
☎ 091-550306

Moy House
Lahinch, Co. Clare....................149
☎ 065-708 2800

Muckross Park Hotel & Cloisters Spa
Killarney, Co. Kerry....................90
☎ 064-662 3400

Mullingar Park Hotel
Mullingar, Co. Westmeath 302
☎ 044-933 7500

Mulranny Park Hotel
Mulranny, Co. Mayo 201
☎ 098-36000

Munster Arms Hotel
Bandon, Co. Cork 39
☎ 023-884 1562

Murphys of Killarney
Killarney, Co. Kerry....................90
☎ 064-663 1294

Muskerry Arms
Blarney, Co. Cork 41
☎ 021-438 5200

N

Newbay Country House
Wexford Town, Co. Wexford 132
☎ 053-914 2779

Newbury Hotel
Mullingar, Co. Westmeath 302
☎ 044-934 2888

Newgrange Hotel
Navan, Co. Meath 291
☎ 046-907 4100

Newpark Hotel
Kilkenny City, Co. Kilkenny 104
☎ 056-776 0500

Newtown Farm Guesthouse
Ardmore, Co. Waterford............112
☎ 024-94143

No 1 Pery Square, Hotel & Spa
Limerick City, Co. Limerick 193
☎ 061-402 402

North Star Hotel & Premier Club Suites
Dublin City, Co. Dublin 261
☎ 01-836 3136

Number 31
Dublin City, Co. Dublin 261
☎ 01-676 5011

Nuremore Hotel & Country Club
Carrickmacross, Co. Monaghan ..292
☎ 042-966 1438

O

Oakwood Arms Hotel
Shannon Airport, Co. Clare 151
☎ 061-361500

Ocean Hotel
Dunmore East, Co. Waterford ..116
☎ 051-383136

O'Connors Guesthouse
Doolin, Co. Clare......................142
☎ 065-707 4498

O'Connor's Guesthouse
Cloghane, Co. Kerry 65
☎ 066-713 8113

O'Donnabhain's
Kenmare, Co. Kerry....................73
☎ 064-664 2106

O'Donovan's Hotel
Clonakilty, Co. Cork 44
☎ 023-883 3250

 SEE ALSO INDEX TO LOCATIONS PAGES 14-15

 SEE ALSO INDEX TO LOCATIONS PAGES 14-15

S

 SEE ALSO INDEX TO LOCATIONS PAGES 14-15

GUINNESS

GUINNESS

SEE ALSO INDEX TO LOCATIONS PAGES 14-15